Essential Writings in Violence Risk Assessment and Management

Essential Writings in Violence Risk Assessment and Management

Edited by Hy Bloom and Christopher D. Webster

Centre for Addiction and Mental Health
Centre de toxicomanie et de santé mentale

Library and Archives Canada Cataloguing in Publication

Essential writings in violence risk assessment and management / edited by
Hy Bloom and Christopher D. Webster.

Issued also in PDF and HTML formats.
Includes bibliographical references.
ISBN 978-0-88868-589-6

1. Violence—Forecasting. 2. Risk assessment. 3. Forensic psychiatry.
4. Recidivism. 5. Violent offenders. I. Bloom, Hy II. Webster, Christopher D.
III. Centre for Addiction and Mental Health

RC569.5.V55E88 2007   616.85'82   C2007-902356-8

ISBN: 978-0-88868-589-6 (PRINT)
ISBN: 978-0-88868-590-2 (PDF)
ISBN: 978-0-88868-591-9 (HTML)
Product code PG125
Printed in Canada

For information on other CAMH publications or to place an order, please contact:

Publication Services
Tel.: 1 800 661-1111 or 416 595-6059 in Toronto
E-mail: publications@camh.net

Website: www.camh.net

This book was produced by:
Development: Andrew Johnson, Diana Ballon, CAMH
Editorial: Diana Ballon, Nick Gamble, Jacquelyn Waller-Vintar, CAMH; Deborah Viets,
Marguerite Martindale, Robert Maurin
Design: Mara Korkola, CAMH
Print production: Christine Harris, CAMH
Typesetting: Costa Leclerc Design Inc.

An Important Note
Essential Writings in Violence Risk Assessment and Management **is a collection of reprinted
journal articles and book chapters selected because they provide the best overview of the field.
Because they are reprinted material, CAMH is not responsible for the accuracy of these writings.
Please contact the original publisher if you have any questions or concerns about a particular
article or chapter.**

PG125/3188/05-07

In Memory

The Honourable Justice Thomas P. Callon (1918–2006). Justice Callon was a member of the Supreme Court of Ontario, Chair of the Lieutenant Governor's Board of Review (1986–92) and Chair of the Ontario Review Board (1992–93).

Dr. Edward Turner (1926–2006). Dr. Turner was Professor of Forensic Psychiatry at the University of Toronto, Psychiatrist-in-Charge and Director of the Metropolitan Toronto Forensic Service (METFORS) (1977–87) and Chief of Forensic Services (1967–69) at the former Clarke Institute of Psychiatry, now part of CAMH.

In Appreciation

From Hy Bloom

To Resa, an idea-a-minute spouse, friend and co-worker who has always taken the time to vet my many and sometimes half-baked notions, and then to guide me to my senses; to Sammy, who has the uncanny ability to quickly convert a dour moment of creative inertia at the computer into an uplifting Elmo-fest; and to Wilbur and Nellie-Belle, who happily dispense my much-needed daily dose of pet therapy. My heartfelt love and appreciation to Resa for recognizing my need to undertake yet another project, even when it makes me less available, and for having faith in the hoped-for value of my work.

Finally, I am deeply grateful to my friend and co-editor, Chris Webster, for his guidance, enthusiasm and willingness to share his considerable experience and vast knowledge in the field of violence risk assessment and management.

From Chris Webster

To Dianne, a wonderful support, now for more than 20 years, in all my professional and personal endeavours. Her logical way of thinking and her willingness to read and improve even book-length manuscripts are greatly appreciated. I'm thankful that she assists me in my undertakings even when it cuts into time we could be spending together.

I have greatly enjoyed the many projects completed with Hy Bloom and Resa this past decade and more.

Acknowledgments

In a 1995 article, which is included in this collection, we described the historical development of forensic psychiatry in Toronto. Although before our time, we acknowledge the pioneering interdisciplinary work of the late Kenneth Gray, who brought the specialty to prominence in Ontario and who understood the importance of working closely with the judiciary on a day-to-day basis. This tradition was then carried forward not only by Dr. Edward Turner, to whom this book is jointly dedicated, but also by the late Dr. Kenneth McKnight, who was well known to Chris. Subsequently, both of us were colleagues of the late Dr. Donald Atcheson. We are grateful to him for his leadership, scholarship and clinical acumen.

We are also grateful, of course, to the authors who generously agreed to have their writings reproduced and to their publishers, who granted permission to include them in this collection.

Saena Cha organized the mass of paperwork, entered the text we wrote and kept the project on course through many revisions. Her patience, dedication and attention to detail are much appreciated, as are her positive spirit and preparedness to go the extra mile to get the job done.

The Ontario Review Board encouraged and supported the project. We especially appreciate the help provided by the Board's chair, the Honourable Douglas H. Carruthers.

Sincere thanks are due to the staff of Publication Services at CAMH. Andrew Johnson helped inspire the undertaking and offered his helpful opinion in shaping its content. While he was on temporary leave, Diana Ballon guided *Essential Writings* toward publication. We benefited greatly not only from her attention to detail in its editing, but from her valuable suggestions about how the material should be ordered and introduced. Nick Gamble and Jacquelyn Waller-Vintar provided copy editing expertise, while Mara Korkola skilfully designed the book, dexterously creating a publication that is both aesthetically pleasing and easy to navigate.

Contents

I The Historical Shift from "Dangerousness" to Violence Risk Assessment

II The Emergence of Actuarial Violence Prediction

III Clinical Prediction and Assessment

IV The Actuarial versus Clinical Controversy

V Decision Making

VI Treatments, Security and Program Planning

Appendices

A Message from the
Honourable Douglas H. Carruthers, QC

Safeguarding the public from the most dangerous mentally disordered persons, while not restricting their freedom any more than is necessary and at the same time promoting their rehabilitation, is no simple juggling act. As Chair of Canada's largest quasijudicial tribunal charged with this responsibility, I have come to hold the deepest respect for the developing scientific and clinical disciplines of violence risk assessment and management as the core expertise and knowledge that inform this decision-making process.

Knowledge is a continuous and evolving process that involves integrating didactic learning, reading, study and personal reflection on our experiences. Our efforts to provide board members—a cross-section of judges, lawyers, psychiatrists, psychologists and members of the public—with the required education about dangerousness and violence risk assessment begins with the training of newly appointed members, and is ongoing. We offer our members annual educational days, each focused on a central theme, and special seminars for the different disciplines over the course of a member's tenure on the board. As enjoyable as these sessions are, and as worthwhile as the knowledge to be gained from them is, it can be difficult to retain this information over the long term.

It is for this reason that Drs. Bloom and Webster decided to draw together some substantive papers that have already passed the peer-review hurdle in the area of risk assessment and management. By doing this, they provide a "permanent" set of readings that all members can consult at leisure. Since the standard of examination of individual cases at board hearings is likely directly linked to board members' expertise, it behooves us to ensure that the best and most relevant thinking is on hand.

In supporting this book, the Ontario Review Board recognized its value to our members, as well as members of other tribunals and courts who—when confronted with the task of releasing or derestricting dangerous individuals—face the same difficulty in having members be *au courant* with the rapidly expanding and changing scientific and professional literatures. Violence risk assessment and management principles cross divisions between forensic, civil and correctional systems, and they apply both to people who have been placed in institutional care and to those granted permission to live under supervised conditions in the community. The challenge is to provide the best available knowledge in order to protect the public while ensuring that accused persons, hospitalized patients and parolees are not subjected to any more constraints than are absolutely necessary.

THE HONOURABLE DOUGLAS H. CARRUTHERS, QC
CHAIR, ONTARIO REVIEW BOARD
CHAIR, NUNAVUT REVIEW BOARD

Foreword

I am delighted to write a foreword to a volume that will improve our understanding of the prediction and management of violent behaviour. Recent events have again underlined the importance of advancing knowledge on these topics.

The first step in managing violent behaviour is to accurately assess the risk that such behaviour will occur and the factors that increase and decrease risk for a particular individual. Mental health professionals require knowledge of how best to assess risk: they need the tool(s) that provide the most accurate predictions for different populations, knowledge of the optimal intervals for re-assessing risk, and the organizational structure that insists on accurate assessments conducted by multidisciplinary teams, rather than by one individual. Further, mental health professionals need to know how to use the information obtained in regular risk assessments to modify the risk factors that *can* be changed. This will help to ensure that violent behavior does not occur.

In some situations, such as in general psychiatric services, mental health professionals make decisions about risk with little involvement of lawyers and judges. However, in other situations, once a criminal offence has occurred, judges make decisions based on opposing arguments from legal counsel. These decisions are more likely to succeed in protecting the public, while restricting the accused person's liberty as little as possible, if judges understand the reasoning and evidence underpinning the mental health professionals' recommendations.

As I write this foreword, two documents are sitting on the table in my office. Both report on tragic events, and remind me of the importance of accurate risk assessment and effective management of violent behaviour, and the current limits to our knowledge of how to best achieve these goals. One is a notice that appeared in the *New England Journal of Medicine* on November 16, 2006, reporting the death, at the hands of a patient with schizophrenia, of a well-known clinical-academic whose work has contributed to improving our understanding of the causes and effective treatment of schizophrenia. The second report, 2.5 centimetres thick, double-sided, was recently published by the Department of Health in the United Kingdom and is entitled "Report of the Independent Inquiry into the Care and Treatment of John Barrett." As its title implies, it is a lengthy investigation of the care received by Mr. Barrett, a patient with schizophrenia who had been convicted of serious assaults, and later killed a man and was convicted of manslaughter. The report led to an editorial in *The Times* on November 17, 2006, which included the following: "It is clear that John Barrett, a paranoid schizophrenic, should never have been free to kill Denis Finnegan in Richmond Park in 2004. The question is why no one has ever been disciplined for this lapse and why the secure unit involved has been allowed to blunder on." The editorial continues, "The Barrett inquiry describes a culture that values 'engaging' with dangerous patients over protecting the public—despite clear Home Office guidance to the contrary. It describes an almost willful lack of communication and supervision by professionals . . . ."

Encouragingly, there are other documents on my table describing positive outcomes achieved when risk is assessed and managed. One is a manuscript that reports a study I completed with numerous colleagues in four countries. It provides descriptive evidence of successful treatment by forensic systems of severely mentally ill patients with long histories of antisocial and violent behaviour. Another manuscript recently completed with colleagues from the United States circumscribes the types of violent crimes committed by severely mentally ill persons and, while highlighting new treatment targets, shows that certain forms of violence by certain types of patients occur very rarely or not at all. Another ever-growing folder includes papers on effective treatments (medications and cognitive-behavioural therapy) and management strategies (community treatment orders plus medication) that have been shown to reduce violent behaviour among severely mental ill persons. A huge set of folders describes effective cognitive-behavioural programs for non–mentally ill offenders—in fact, offenders who have personality disorders—that reduce criminal recidivism.

Not only is there an ever-growing amount of evidence documenting progress in managing violent behaviour and in understanding its origins, current investigations focus on how to *prevent* violent behaviour. Prospective, longitudinal investigations of children who present characteristics that put them at high risk for engaging in violent behaviour later in life are being undertaken in several centres. Findings from these investigations are being used to improve the effectiveness of parent training programs for children with conduct problems. One day, the findings from such research will be used to establish early childhood intervention programs that could effectively eliminate the precursors of violent behaviour, and perhaps, just perhaps, make violence risk assessment and management in adults obsolete.

In the meantime, this one-volume compendium provides mental health professionals, students, lawyers and judges with a historical understanding of the development of thinking and research on assessing the risk of violent behaviour. It includes articles previously published in a wide range of journals over the past 30 years, and reviews major conceptual issues and significant empirical findings. The editors have written introductions to each section, and a preface, to help highlight important issues for the reader. The reprinted journal articles and book chapters provide readers with the thoughts and findings of insightful and skilful clinician-scientists attempting to extend knowledge and thereby improve clinical practice. The volume provides a solid basis of understanding of the field of risk assessment and management for both mental health and legal professionals. Further, it offers a conceptual framework into which new findings can be integrated and understood. It is essential reading.

PROFESSOR SHEILAGH HODGINS, PHD
HEAD, DEPARTMENT OF FORENSIC MENTAL HEALTH SCIENCE
INSTITUTE OF PSYCHIATRY, KING'S COLLEGE LONDON

About the Editors

Hy Bloom, LLB, MD, FRCPC, is a forensic psychiatrist and lawyer who assesses individuals whose psychological and emotional state, motivation or behaviour are potentially relevant in criminal, civil, professional regulatory or employment matters. He is an associate of the central branch of the PSILEX Group, Consultants in Behavioural Sciences and the Law, and CEO of workplace.calm, inc., a multidisciplinary group of consultants who specialize in assessing and managing workplace conflict, behavioural difficulties and violence risk. He is also a part-time staff member in the Law and Mental Health Program at the Centre for Addiction and Mental Health, an assistant professor in the Department of Medicine at the University of Toronto, an assistant clinical professor in the Department of Psychiatry at McMaster University, and adjunct faculty at the University of Toronto's Law School, where he co-teaches a course called The Mentally Disordered Accused.

Hy is an alternate chairperson of the Ontario Review Board and a psychiatric member of the Nunavut Review Board. He was called to the Bar of Ontario in 1980. Hy has published extensively on numerous topics in psychiatry and the law. His most recent books include *Mental Disorder and the Law: A Primer for Legal and Mental Health Professionals* (2006), which he co-authored with Justice Richard D. Schneider and *Mental Health Courts: Decriminalizing the Mentally Ill* (2007), which he co-wrote with Justice Richard D. Schneider and Mark Hereema.

Christopher D. Webster, PhD, FRSC, is a psychologist and clinical criminologist who has been researching the assessment and management of violence and related risks for 30 years. During this time, he has also counselled people with substance use problems and people on probation and parole for committing sexual and domestic assaults. Chris has published several books and structured professional guides on these topics, including—most recently—*Violence Risk Assessment and Management* (2007), which he co-authored with Stephen Hucker. He is perhaps best known as one of the authors of the *HCR-20: Assessing Risk for Violence* (1997) and as one of the editors of *HCR-20 Violence Risk Management Companion Guide* (2001).

Chris has received a career achievement award from the American Psychological

Association. He is a fellow of the Canadian Psychological Association, the American Psychological Association and the Royal Society of Canada, and a member of the Ontario Review Board. Chris consults regularly with the National Parole Board, the Forensic Psychiatric Services Commission of British Columbia, the Child Development Institute in Toronto and international risk assessment projects funded and co-ordinated through Simon Fraser University. He is a professor emeritus of psychology at Simon Fraser University and professor emeritus of psychiatry at the University of Toronto.

Preface

Mental health clinicians now deal with a wider range of violence assessment tasks than they did a generation or two ago. At the same time, they likely conduct a greater number of evaluations. Laws in most jurisdictions worldwide are being continually amended to ensure that clinical assessments are conducted as competently and as diligently as possible. Professional organizations frequently publish new guidelines on various violence risks.[1] The clinical and research literature on "dangerousness" assessment and management is rapidly increasing. And articles are being published in an array of journals, some of which are not easy to locate, even in an electronic age.

The field of risk assessment and management continually crosses civil, forensic and correctional boundaries. It is moving in three interrelated directions. Firstly, clinicians, researchers and politicians have a continued interest in prediction accuracy. (They acknowledge that, even if complete precision is a chimera, establishing limits remains a vital scientific challenge.) Secondly, they recognize the need for evidence-based, best-practice clinical and research standards. (Even if there are limits to prediction accuracy, it is still important to ensure that best practices are being upheld.) And finally, there is a growing realization that more attention must be focused on risk management (i.e., that risk assessment and risk management are integrally related and that the latter often casts much-needed light on the former).

Essential Writings in Violence Risk Assessment and Management has been created to help mental health and correctional professionals—both those established in practice and those still in training—to navigate the growing body of literature in the field. The journal articles and book chapters in this collection were not chosen because they were the most arcane and obscure articles we could locate. On the contrary, we selected papers that provided the best overview of the field, so as to be relevant to a wide cross-section of people interested in the field, including clinicians, lawyers, judges, law enforcement officials, health and correctional administrators and journalists.

This collection aims to give readers practical information about how to undertake the tasks of violence risk assessment and management. The arguments presented in the reprinted papers remind readers that, while there has been progress in assessing and managing risk, there are still perplexing questions on how to assess and manage risk with both accuracy and due attention to ethical considerations, which have been increasingly recognized as an important aspect of the field. The articles also offer an overview of the central issues surrounding risk management and assessment, while the introductions to each section provide a synopsis of key issues in six main areas. We offer a historical perspective on violence risk assessment; a discussion of statistical or "actuarial" methods of predicting violence; clinical prediction and assessment approaches; a debate on the merits of actuarial versus clinical predictions; insights into issues around decision making; and an overview of treatment, security and program planning in the corrections and mental health systems. By simply reading each introduction, readers can gain an understanding of the field; those wanting a more detailed description of the arguments, in the voice of mental health and correctional professionals, can refer to the articles and chapters provided. We propose our collection as a curriculum for foundational knowledge in this burgeoning field.

NOTES

1. See, for example, the American Psychiatric Association's 2003 guidelines for assessing for suicide risk. See also Simon (2004), the U.K.'s National Institute for Clinical Excellence's 2005 guidelines for evaluating short-term violence risk, and the American Psychological Association's 2006 guidelines for evidence-based practice as listed in the References that follow.

REFERENCES

American Psychiatric Association. (2003). *Practice Guideline for the Assessment and Treatment of Patients with Suicidal Behaviors.* Washington, DC: American Psychological Association.
American Psychological Association Presidential Task Force on Evidence-Based Practice. (2006). Evidence-based practice in psychology. *American Psychologist, 61,* 271–285.
National Institute for Clinical Excellence. (2005). *Clinical Guideline 25. Violence: The Short-Term Management of Disturbed/Violent Behaviour in In-patient Psychiatric Settings and Emergency Departments.* London: National Institute for Clinical Excellence. Available: www.nice.org.uk/CG025NICEguideline. Accessed March 14, 2007. (See also *Clinical Guideline 25: Quick Reference Guide*).
Simon, R.I. (2004). *Assessing and Managing Suicide Risk: Guidelines for Clinically Based Risk Management.* Washington, DC: American Psychiatric Publishing.

The Historical Shift from "Dangerousness" to Violence Risk Assessment

Section I

Introduction

This section begins with an article by the late British forensic psychiatrist **Peter Scott**. (Published in 1977, his paper predates all others in this collection.) Scott reminds us that good clinical work in violence risk assessment and management rests more on patience, persistence and thoroughness than on intuitive brilliance or well-honed interviewing skills. He offers an "elementary practical guide" to assessing "dangerousness"—or violence risk, as it is currently termed. Scott advises clinicians to be level-headed and not to necessarily accept at face value the statements being made by the accused.

His approach to assessments involved drawing on multiple domains of information, such as police records, interviews with employers and psychological testing. This method has become the standard for medico-legal evaluations of violence risk. Scott's worldview is phenomenological: he insists that the patient's perspective be taken fully into account and that evaluators treat people being assessed with sympathy and respect. Scott is thoughtful, even humble. He concedes the difficulty in knowing how to weigh the various factors that apply to each person being assessed. And he recognizes that these factors interact differently, depending on the case. Well before the Hare Psychopathy Checklist—Revised was propounded (Hare, 1985, 1991, 2003), Scott pointed to the necessity of establishing an evaluee's capacity for compassion, for expressing remorse and for learning from experience.

In 1978, distinguished American psychologist **Saleem Shah** outlined 15 points in the civil mental health, forensic psychiatric and correctional practice systems in which clinicians and decision makers try to make accurate forecasts of potential violence. He stressed that evaluators need to exercise great care when making decisions about someone's risk for future "dangerousness." While underprediction of a person's future violence can sometimes have serious consequences for friends, relatives and society at large, overprediction carries its own serious repercussions. People erroneously deemed to represent a risk for violence and other harms to the public can be unnecessarily detained in institutions or needlessly over-restricted in society (i.e., through probation, parole, community supervision orders).

Contemporary mental health clinicians are being held to increasingly high standards to protect the public from being unnecessarily exposed to violence risks. (In October 2006, for instance, the Ontario Court of Appeal ordered a psychiatrist to provide substantial financial compensation to a family for her decision to release a patient from hospital, after the patient—six weeks following his release—killed his sister. As our contributor Peter Scott says, "Wrong guesses about a patient's potential for violence can have a devastating effect on the patient, the victim (often a family member or acquaintance of the patient) and the psychiatrist's emotional well-being."

Shah's contribution was significant in drawing attention to the ubiquitousness of assessing, predicting and managing risk across the mental health, forensic and correctional systems. His original 15-point list, later expanded to 16 points in his 1981 article (Chapter 2), pointed to parole decision making, legally designating people as habitual or dangerous offenders, and admitting people to civil psychiatric hospitals as just some of the "decision points" when considering a person's dangerousness. This list has greatly expanded over the years. It now covers risks and conditions that were underacknowledged or even unknown at the time. These include violence at school or in the workplace, posttraumatic stress disorder, Internet crimes, knowingly exposing people to HIV through unprotected sex, and irresponsible driving while intoxicated.

Shah helped turn the field in the late 1970s and early '80s from decided pessimism about the ability of clinicians to predict violence to guarded optimism. His perspective stands in marked contrast to the views propounded by the influential American psychiatrist Allan Stone in the 1985 collection *Dangerousness: Probability and Prediction, Psychiatry and Public Policy.* Stone reiterated what he had said in his earlier writings; namely, that, given that mental health and correctional professionals had not demonstrated an ability to predict violence in people with a major mental disorder or personality disorder, they should not even try. Shah strongly disagreed with this iconoclastic view. He believed that some people who purport to be able to predict violence can likely meet this challenge, at least to some degree, while others cannot.

The idea that individual clinicians vary markedly in their ability to predict risk was novel in the late 1970s and early '80s. It is remarkable that the capacity of individual clinicians and researchers to predict violence has been studied so little. The professional abilities required will likely only be revealed through highly organized research studies. Under ordinary work pressures, clinicians complete one violence assessment after another but seldom, if ever, learn how accurate their predictions have been.

Shah highlights the importance of addressing the contextual or situational factors that must be taken into account in conducting risk assessments. Clinicians have tended to place too much emphasis on the intrapsychic workings of personality and too little on the physical and social circumstances that likely trigger a person's violence. He believed strongly that detailed research was needed to find out who, if anyone, is clinically skilled enough to predict violence. He helped set in motion several long-term prediction-outcome studies, some of which are mentioned in this book. Undoubtedly, Shah's opinions deeply influenced John Monahan's 1981 writing of *Predicting Violent Behavior: An Assessment of Clinical Techniques.* Monahan's text set the course for research and practice in violence risk assessment this past quarter century. Like Scott's "elementary practical guide," *Predicting Violent Behavior* contains a wealth of theoretical, methodological and research information. It helped shift the focus of violence prediction from assessing "dangerousness" as an entity inherent within the individual, to looking at "risks" as influenced not only by the individual, but also by situational, sociological and cultural factors.

In 1996, **Randy Borum** wrote what was to become a highly influential article about how violence risk assessment might be improved (Chapter 3). He carefully reviewed the few violence risk assessment devices that had become available since Monahan's book was published. Borum felt that it was time for researchers and clinicians to draw collaboratively on what was known about violence risk assessment and for clinicians to apply this knowledge to their practice. Without promising new and unattainable standards of predictive accuracy, Borum believed it was possible to set some basic standards for clinical and research practice. Clinicians, he argued, could likely improve their efficiency and their competence by adhering to some self-imposed definitions and procedures.

Borum's article undoubtedly inspired a group of mainly Canadian researchers to persist with what has come to be known as the "structured professional judgment" (SPJ) approach to violence risk assessment. The principle of this approach is that evaluations should be guided by reasonably precise definitions of violence and by considering the specific individual factors that may be linked to subsequent violence.

Chapter 4, by **Hy Bloom**, **Christopher Webster**, **Stephen Hucker** and **Karen De Freitas**, explains in some detail how the SPJ movement has strengthened since the mid- to late 1990s. It describes the importance of Robert Hare's 20-item Psychopathy Checklist—Revised (1991, 2003)[1,2] and shows how this approach to measurement was pivotal in the evolution of the Historical/Clinical/Risk-20 system (HCR-20; Webster et al., 1997). The HCR-20 relies on 20 defined factors. Ten of these factors refer to the assessee's history, five deal with his or her current clinical status and five invite the evaluator to forecast the individual's potential to be violent in the future. All of these items, like the Hare PCL-R, are scored 0 (not present), 1 (possibly present) or 2 (definitely present). Since the initial 1995 publication of the HCR-20 and its revision in 1997, various other SPJ schemes have evolved to cover different groups, such as children, adolescents, sex offenders, people who have assaulted a spouse and those who have attempted suicide. The chapter by Bloom et al. gives an overview of how the SPJ violence risk evaluation approach has evolved so far.

NOTES

1. A good grasp of the concept of psychopathy can be obtained by reading Hare's *Without Conscience (1998)* and *Babiak and Hare's Snakes in Suits: When Psychopaths Go to Work* (2006). Readers are also directed to a new book on the topic, edited by Patrick (2006).
2. The Hare PCL-R items are as follows: 1. Glibness/superficial charm; 2. Grandiose sense of self-worth; 3. Need for stimulation/proneness to boredom; 4. Pathological lying; 5. Conning/manipulative; 6. Lack of remorse or guilt; 7. Shallow affect; 8. Callous/lack of empathy; 9. Parasitic lifestyle; 10. Poor behavioural controls; 11. Promiscuous sexual behaviour; 12. Early behavioural problems; 13. Lack of realistic, long-term goals; 14. Impulsivity; 15. Irresponsibility; 16. Failure to accept responsibility for own actions; 17. Many short-term marital relationships; 18. Juvenile delinquency; 19. Revocation of conditional release; 20. Criminal versatility. Generally, Hare and others have amassed statistical evidence to show that psychopathy can be considered to have two main factors: 1. Interpersonal/affective (Facet 1: Interpersonal; Facet 2: Affective); 2. Social deviance (Facet 3: Lifestyle; Facet 4: Antisocial). The factor structure of the PCL–R is explained in the 2003 manual (pp. 77–86).

REFERENCES

Babiak, P. & Hare, R.D. (2006). *Snakes in Suits: When Psychopaths Go to Work.* New York: HarperCollins.

Hare, R.D. (1985). A checklist for the assessment of psychopathy in criminal populations. In M.H. Ben-Aron, S.J. Hucker & C.D. Webster (Eds.), *Clinical Criminology: The Assessment and Treatment of Criminal Behaviour.* Toronto: M and M Graphics.

Hare, R.D. (1991). *Manual for the Hare Psychopathy Checklist—Revised.* Toronto: Multi-Health Systems.

Hare, R.D. (1998). *Without Conscience: The Disturbing World of the Psychopaths among Us.* New York: Guilford.

Hare, R.D. (2003). *The Psychopathy Checklist—Revised* (2nd ed.). Toronto: Multi-Health Systems.

Megargee, E. (1976). The prediction of dangerous behavior. *Criminal Justice and Behavior, 3,* 3–22.

Menzies, R.J., Webster, C.D. & Sepejak, D.S. (1985). The dimension of dangerousness: Evaluating the accuracy of psychometric predictions of violence among forensic patients. *Law and Human Behavior, 9,* 35–36.

Monahan, J. (1981). *Predicting Violent Behavior: An Assessment of Clinical Techniques.* Beverly Hills, CA: Sage.

Patrick, C.J. (Ed.). (2006). *Handbook of Psychopathy.* New York: Guildford.

Quinsey, V.L. (1980). The base rate problem and the prediction of dangerousness: A reappraisal. *Journal of Psychiatry and Law, 8,* 329–340.

Shah, S.A. (1978). Dangerousness: A paradigm for exploring some issues in law and psychology. *American Psychologist, 33,* 224–238.

Stone, A.A. (1985). The new legal standard of dangerousness. Fair in theory, unfair in practice. In C.D. Webster, M.H. Ben-Aron & S.J. Hucker (Eds.), *Dangerousness: Probability and Prediction, Psychiatry and Public Policy* (pp. 13–24). New York: Cambridge University Press.

Webster, C.D., Douglas, K.S., Eaves, D. & Hart, S.D. (1997). *HCR-20: Assessing Risk for Violence.* Burnaby, B.C.: Mental Health Law and Policy Institute, Simon Fraser University.

1

Assessing Dangerousness in Criminals

P.D. SCOTT

ABSTRACT: *This article formulates a definition of the term dangerousness, indicates why the commission of dangerous offences cannot be reliably predicted, and then reviews the several factors which have been or might be used by those who have to make decisions about dangerousness in criminals. It suggests that these factors are useful insofar as they help to illuminate the individual's capacity to feel sympathy and to learn by experience. Since the accuracy of prediction varies inversely with time, the maintenance of personal relationships and good communication seems the inescapable requirement in the management of potentially dangerous criminals.*

INTRODUCTION

Dangerousness is a dangerous concept (Shaw, 1973). It is difficult to define, yet very important decisions are based upon it; there is as yet little reliable research in relation to it; it is a term which raises anxiety and which is therefore peculiarly open to abuse, especially to over-response of a punitive, restrictive or dissociative nature. Because we have all experienced dangerous emotions there is the risk of projection and scapegoating. The label, which is easy to attach but difficult to remove, may contribute to its own

Reprinted with permission. British Journal of Psychiatry, 131, *127–142.* © *1977 Royal College of Psychiatrists.*

continuance, or may become a convention for evading responsibility or for jumping treatment queues. To legislate for treatment (which, in the absence of transportation and judicial elimination, usually implies incarceration) before the nature and effect of that treatment is known, is very expensive in terms of liberty as well as services and often falls into disuse; there is a risk that the response will repeat the causes and thus lead to a vicious circle.

DEFINITION OF DANGEROUSNESS IN CRIMINALS

It is easier to say what dangerousness is not than what it is. It is not simply that which is noxious or evil, and it is not necessarily a violent, explosive trait of an individual; the man who smokes on a tanker is dangerous by reason of the explosive potential outside him. Similarly, in social animals, much dangerousness depends upon disturbing the often precarious adjustment of other individuals, especially within a group; hence the importance of behavioural conventions or what are now called good manners, which in effect announce the individual's self-control and his concern for the feelings of others. The media of mass communication besides modifying attitudes to, and expectations of, violence, also change the boundaries of groups. In this sense the dangerous individual is simply one who engenders too much anxiety. Dangerous degrees of anxiety are raised not so much by a single breach of convention as by the failure of the offender to respond to the counter-measures of society, and this is likely to indicate, or to be interpreted as, defiance. If our smoker on the tanker immediately responds to the angry order to "douse that glim" dangerousness will not be implied, but if he does it again it is likely to be assumed that he is motivated, not by the gentle faults of fecklessness, foolishness or forgetfulness, but by dangerous intentions. Thus perception of a lack of response, or adaptiveness resulting in a tendency to repetition and incorrigibility, are likely to lead to a label of dangerousness in any person who has once demonstrated or threatened destructiveness. The context, nature and degree of this aggression or destructiveness will be important. As to context, aggression will be most alarming in two situations, when society is totally unprepared for it, i.e. the appearance of a new form of attack; and when, having been painfully bitten, or nearly defeated, in this way on previous occasions, it is over-prepared, and likely to respond with a volley instead of a gesture. The nature of the behaviour which society is likely to label dangerous is that which is violent. Violence is aggression concentrated into brief time, and is not necessarily more destructive than continued aggression of lesser intensity. Possibly among many other reasons for the relative tolerance of this extensive aggression is the feeling that there is time to organize resistance, to call for help, or to take evasive action. The distance of the aggression from the body image is an important criterion of perceived dangerousness. In this sense attacks range between assault on the person on the one hand and destruction of public or unowned objects on the other. Offences in certain areas: burglary of the home, especially invasion of the bedroom, and damage to clothing and motor cars, are inclined to cause very marked distress or anger in the owners. Offences such as these, together with blackmail, are on the borderline of dangerousness and likely to raise impassioned debate when attempts to define the concept are made. Other factors, notably permanence of damage, may be helpful in reaching a conclusion. The question is often posed "should psychological damage be included as well as personal or material damage and destruction"? Clearly psychological damage is very real and is frequently noted as a result of aggression. The Butler Committee's report (1975) includes "lasting psychological harm" as well as serious physical injury. Psychological harm, especially that which is lasting, is so very difficult to distinguish from preexisting idiosyncratic vulnerability, so intangible and so easy to claim or simulate, that it will offer, at present, insuperable difficulties.

A still more difficult problem is the point at which individually non-dangerous offences, if repeated sufficiently often, achieve dangerousness by their threat to the rule of law.

The criteria of degree and permanence of damage are obvious, but nonetheless difficult to quantify unless there is actual loss of function or of life. Walker (1959), in considering sentencing, asks "How difficult would it be to undo the harm if it happened?" More difficult still is that factor which in a medical analogy would be called infectious-ness, and which indicates the belief that others will be inclined to follow suit, to use this loophole in the law, to join the insurrection, to practise this clever form of deceit, or to gain ascendancy or preference in this new way.

The medical analogy is also inescapable in relation to the further criteria of treata-bility and predictability. If an "attack" of dangerous violence can be anticipated and aborted, or treated, then it ceases to be dangerous. This emphasizes the further complex inter-relationship of the threatening organism with the responses or defences of the body of society. Society may deal with dangerousness by eradicating its causes, isolating its carriers, or acquiring immunity to its effects.

Dangerousness, then, is an unpredictable and untreatable tendency to inflict or risk serious, irreversible injury or destruction, or to induce others to do so. Dangerousness can, of course, be directed against the self.

This definition may be thought to be so unsatisfactory that it would be better for most purposes to substitute a probability figure of this or that sort of damaging behaviour occurring in this or that expected environment.

PREDICTION

Prediction of dangerousness is particularly difficult because: dangerousness is the resultant of a number of processes which occasionally may be synergistic amounting to more than the sum of their parts, some within the individual and some in society; it is not static; key factors are the individual's adaptiveness, resistance to change, and his intention (which Emile Durkheim said in 1897 is "too intimate a thing to be interpreted by another person"): a common mistake is to confuse recidivism with dangerousness, they are not necessarily the same and may be combined in various patterns. Dangerous behaviour lies at the extreme of the aggression parameter, and most standardized tests tend to become unreliable at both their extremities, yet it is in just these areas that the most important decisions lie. Existing predictive scales tend to be over-inclusive; their results may be very useful for administrative purposes but are clinically unreliable; they are an encouragement to attempt treatment and a negation of nihilism, but give little help in the commonly posed distinction, not so much between nuisance and danger as between danger and extreme danger. The prognosis for dangerousness may be independent of the prognosis of coexisting conditions, for example the presence of a florid mental illness; such prognoses may even be reciprocal.

Steadman and Cocozza (1974), from their follow-up of nearly 1,000 supposedly dangerous Baxstrom patients, who had perforce been transferred to civil mental hospitals, wrote: "If we attempt to distinguish the potentially dangerous patient, we double our error by identifying as dangerous all of a group of patients when only one third of them will live up to their expectations." This was neatly capped by the medical superintendent of one of our own Special Hospitals who said he was sure half of his patients were not dangerous and could be safely released, but he wasn't sure which half.

Prediction studies should aim not to replace but to complement the clinical approach, and *vice versa*. This is well seen in our parole system, where the prediction score, made for every male candidate, is useful but not central in decision making.

We cannot at present hope, by taking infinitely careful aim, to direct our dangerous patient to safety like an arrow to its target; rather, through effective supervision, we must accompany him, being prepared to adapt to his varying needs, whether encouraging independence, moderating activity or recalling him to start again from the beginning.

PRACTICAL ISSUES

We have to rely on a combination of acumen, prediction and after-care. While this cannot be said to be reliable, it is pragmatic and certainly avoids or abbreviates many long terms of segregation, even though there may be occasional mistakes. If it is done it can be done better. What are the factors that can be looked for and fed to the diagnostic procedure, and from what different aspects should the problem be viewed? The following is an elementary practical guide to the more rational use of intuition.

The plan is to consider a series of factors seriatim, but realizing with Kozol (1972) that there are no direct indicators of dangerousness and that each factor may become important in the presence of other factors or may be neutralized by yet others. For some factors, especially personality traits, their correlation with dangerousness will only be of a high order if their definitions are nearly tautological. A good deal of confusion will be avoided if it is acknowledged that some factors may have positive (or negative) correlations with dangerousness at both ends of their scale (too much or too little). The extremes of some factors which in lesser degree predispose to dangerousness may in fact prevent it, e.g. a mild tendency to incest may permit restoration of the offender to his family and consequent repetition, whereas the children of an offender who showed a grosser tendency are likely to be removed permanently; similarly the severely subnormal person is likely to be under permanent supervision, while the subnormal is free to re-offend.

Before factors can be considered they must be gathered. It is patience, thoroughness and persistence in this process, rather than any diagnostic or interviewing brilliance, that produces results. In this sense the telephone, the written request for past records, and the checking of information against other informants, are the important diagnostic devices.

Having collected the facts under the headings: (1) the offence; (2) past behaviour; (3) personal data; (4) social circumstances it is useful then to scan them from a number of different directions with a view to answering certain key questions relating to dangerousness. The most important of these are concerned with the subject's capacity to feel sympathy with others, and his capacity to learn by experience.

(1) The Offence

The legal category, even murder, arson and rape, is not very useful in determining dangerousness. It is axiomatic that all behaviour can be reached by different paths, each of which has different implications for the future. To put it another way, offence entities all tend to comprise a majority of benign cases which have made a single and temporary crossing of the threshold, and a malignant minority which are firmly entrenched across that threshold. Just as some of the major offences do not qualify for dangerousness, some of the lesser offences (theft, drunkenness) may.

The detail of the behaviour, on the other hand, is so valuable that opinions should not be stated until the fullest possible information, including at least the witnesses' statements and the depositions, has been obtained. Such detail helps very much in the essential reconstruction of the equation: offender+victim+circumstance = the offence; each element of the equation is equally important.

It is very difficult to generalize about the significance of offences committed in a group or alone. It will depend on whether the group is a loosely structured one (as occurs in youthful affrays and pack rapes) or a highly organized group of professional criminals. Members of organized groups using fire arms, sometimes re-offend in this way even after a long prison sentence and therefore have to be regarded as dangerous, whereas the youthful group members will very probably mature satisfactorily. Members of a structured gang are very much less likely to have any form of mental illness or any personality disorder, sufficient to prevent them relating to the other members, or sufficient to make their behaviour unreliable or unpredictable, for such qualities would be an embarassment and danger to the other members.

Much behaviour which at first sight seems insane, unadaptive, or inexplicable is seen to be rational when the longitudinal development of the incident is studied—the small steps by which it was reached, encouragement by a partner, the basic anxiety which the behaviour sought to allay (often very much greater than the fear of detection and punishment), the resonance of the provocation with previous, perhaps infantile experience. The impact of a breaking marriage may be very different in a man whose mother deserted when he was five.

It is sometimes difficult to accept that the provision of a rational understanding of behaviour may indicate greater, not less, dangerousness; rational behaviour may be exceedingly difficult to treat and very likely to recur. Explanation of behaviour does not eliminate its dangerousness, nor ensure treatability; it only poses further questions which must be answered before a conclusion can be reached.

Offence detail is informative in relation to the "impulsive or prepared," "provoked or spontaneous" questions. These two scales are identical, for a person is not impelled without provocation; provocation is no more than strong or persistent stimulation. The legal concept of provocation is a concession to human frailty and therefore must be strictly limited in its application (English, 1970; White, 1970; Brett, 1970), whereas, psychologically, provocation is a common or even usual element in violent behaviour. The principal differences between legal and lay concepts of provocation depend upon the failure of the law to recognize two sorts of provocation: displacement of aggression from a highly provoking source to an area which may be scarcely provoking at all; e.g. the situation in which the rejected wife kills her baby, saying to her husband (as Medea did) "that will stab thy heart," and also the extremely common and potent provocation offered by a state of continued uncertainty; e.g. when a reluctant or frightened wife rejects but as it were leaves the door open and permits occasional contact; it is the vacillating rather than the abusing or aggressive wife who is most at risk. To the psychologist a degree of contemplation or even preparation and planning, or the use of apparently disproportionate force does not invalidate provocation as an operative factor in the assessment of dangerousness. But once again, such provocation only raises the further questions: will this situation arise again, are the offender, the victim (if still alive), and the environment open to significant modification?

Where the victim is no longer alive, the reasoning is sometimes heard: "he has killed his mother and will never have another," or "she has no further babies"; but, as Dr McGrath of Broadmoor has remarked "Mothers have surrogates"; and battering mothers are fertile and seem to need babies. It is even more essential to recognize that most killings are domestic and therefore much involved with the quality of the marital relationship; there is much to suggest that assortative mating can lead to the repeated selection of an unsatisfactory or provoking spouse; some individuals may be regarded as life-long injustice or provocation collectors.

"Compulsive" has misleading implications in describing offenders. Unless the offender really feels that the behaviour is foreign to him, unless he resists it, and at no stage gives himself up to enjoying it (however much he regrets it afterwards), then it should be called impulsive, not compulsive. Compulsive offending is a myth.

Many dangerous offenders, believing that they cannot control their impulses, seek help from the police or from doctors. They must be taken seriously, for rejection of their angry dependency seems to facilitate the threatened crime. Some offenders, notably paedophiles, have a tendency to use psychiatric clinics as a sort of insurance policy against the next offence; their responsibility, if they wish to be at large, has to be made clear to them.

The degree of violence used in the current offence is often cited as a factor in predicting dangerousness and is thus used in sentencing. Multiplicity of stabs, blows or shots, as well as combinations of methods of killing have been variously attributed to:

(1) the degree of emotional involvement (Berg and Fox, 1947);

(2) the presence of mental illness (Reichard and Tillman, 1950);

(3) victim resistance (Wolfgang, 1958);

(4) youthfulness of the offender (Wertham, 1941, suggests 15–25 years);

(5) lack of motivation (Satten et al, 1960);

(6) intoxication (Wolfgang, 1958).

The present author studied 218 cases of male murderers and amongst them found 38 minimum-violence cases who had killed with a single blow, shot or stab (coup), and 52 who had killed with excessive violence (8 or more coups, range 8–124). Each group was further divided into wife killing and non-wife killing, wife being defined as the woman with whom the subject lived. The excessive violence group contained 19 wife killings, the minimum violence only 2. It was concluded that wife-killers favour use of excessive violence. Since the average ages of the two groups of men were 30.8 years (excessive group) and 27.3 (minimum group) age is not the significant factor. The excessive violence men were more likely to involve multiple killings (15.3 per cent as against 2.6 per cent of the minimum group). There was no significant difference on an impulsive-deliberate scale; more than half of both groups were deliberate. Within the excessive violence group the average number of coups in the wife-killers and non-wife killers was the same (15.7 and 15.6 respectively), which suggests that emotional involvement is not the important factor. All the murdered women (whether wives, prostitutes, or old ladies interrupting robberies) were killed with excessive violence. Low intelligence was rare in both groups but twice as common (5.7 per cent) in the excessive group as in the minimum group (2.6 per cent). Twenty-one per cent of the excessive group and 5.2 per cent of the minimum group were mentally ill or had a history of mental illness, and this was nearly all schizophrenia. Strong men capable of resistance, if they get murdered do not often receive multiple coups, and where the motive for the murder contains an element of fear, then excessive violence becomes rare (1.9 per cent in the excessive group, 18.4 per cent in the minimum violence group). Alcohol intoxication seems important (30.7 per cent excessive and 13.1 per cent minimum). There is a strong indication that defencelessness is an invitation to violence, and that once violence is unleashed it tends to continue to the point of satiation or exhaustion, unless controlled by fear of retaliation.

Excessive violence very doubtfully warrants the importance assigned to it by judges and others who assess dangerousness as a guide to sentencing. We forget that most murderers are amateurs and most victims healthy people with a firm hold on life, so that the killer is often horrified at the difficulty of killing and the awful sight and sounds involved, so that he strives in desperation or panic, to end the process quickly.

Separate from the quantity of violence is *the quality of violence*. Some murders, nearly all by excessive violence, involve bizarre desecration of the body, pushing things into body orifices or slitting them open; cutting off or biting nose, ears, breasts; urinating or masturbating upon the body. Such behaviour indicates either mental illness (Satten et al, 1960) or more commonly severe degrees of personality disorder associated with high degrees of deprivation of care or companionship in infancy. Quality of violence is a better indicator of dangerousness than quantity.

Disinhibiting factors, if likely to continue or recur, will contribute to dangerousness. The three major varieties are the depressive drugs (i.e. alcohol and the barbiturates rather than lysergic acid or amphetamine), the presence of companions, and fatigue. Groups of immature offenders, once embarked upon aggressive activity can stimulate one another in circular fashion so that very great and quite unexpected and inappropriate degrees of destruction can be achieved within seconds. Common examples are the activities of 10- or 12-year-olds who have broken into a factory, or adolescents who indulge in the so-called pack-rapes. Fatigue, sleeplessness, low blood sugar, can all lead to irritability and a reduced tolerance to long continued stresses which are so commonly the background of violence.

The detail of the offence should also include information as to the offender's *behaviour after the offence*. There are two areas to be considered. The presence of humane feelings—whether or not he tried to repair the damage, seek help, relieve suffering, or whether egocentric needs for escape or concealment were dominant, but this aspect will be considered later. The subsequent behaviour also sheds light on the state of mind at the time of the offence. Stress is sufficiently great or continued, causes an often quite sudden and dramatic "breakdown" or change in behaviour, this is loosely called regression. It implies emotion and behaviour which is unrestrained, excessive, out of character and senseless, in that, though directed towards immediate relief (running away, self-injury, total denial in the presence of incontrovertible evidence), it is not realistically adaptive. Such behaviour inevitably invites the comparison with infantile behaviour, and this has been used in some ingenious classifications (Sullivan, Grant and Grant, 1957). Individuals vary greatly in the ease and depth of such regression. At one end of the scale, a few primitive personalities may be said to be more often regressed than not, whereas some resilient and resourceful persons retain their adaptiveness under high degrees of stress, and, when they break down, quickly recover (Lifton, 1957).

Study of murderers shows that 90 per cent of those who use excessive violence and 68 per cent of those who use minimum violence are regressed at the time of the killing. It is very useful to study the susceptibility, circumstances, specificity of stress, depth and duration of, this regression. It is often possible to trace the stages, of induction and recovery, much as one does in administering an anaesthetic. The study of regression is one of the most useful modes of approaching the assessment of dangerousness. As ever rules of thumb are not possible; some denials in the face of incontrovertible evidence are adaptive, e.g. the paedophile who fears, not the judicial process, but hostility from other prisoners; or behaviour which is dictated by subcultural loyalties.

(2) Criminal Record and Past Behaviour

All agree that the best indication of future behaviour is past behaviour, and it has long been known that it is the offender against property rather than against the person who has the highest tendency to repeat his offence. Neithercutt (1972) reviews the evidence for this paradox: that the most serious crimes, if you lump them together, have the best statistical predictions. Once a person has broken through the barrier between wish and action in a violent manner (even against himself) he could do so again. If to this is added the factor of age, the prediction becomes even more successful. Steadman and Cocozza (1974) constructed a scale for predicting repetition of dangerous offences, using juvenile record, number of previous arrests, convictions for violence, and severity of the last offence, all these factors being in effect refinements of past criminal behaviour.

If aggression appears early and is widely distributed—at home, at school and in the neighbourhood, and if it is present also in siblings and father, then it is likely to persist (Robins, 1966).

The exceptions to these general conclusions are unfortunately common. Some of the most devastating violence is produced by quiet, inoffensive persons with no previous criminal record, who have been under great stress for a long time and finally explode into a single brief but perhaps very dangerous act. Megargee (1966), Blackburn (1970) and Neustatter (1965) have described this phenomenon. A man of 47 asked the female stores keeper at his place of work for an item; she failed to produce it and treated him with scant respect. He picked up a spanner and beat her about the head in a manner which very nearly killed her. When examined he was not mentally ill, not depressed, not paranoid, and was distressed and perplexed by his behaviour. There was no previous crime of any sort. He was an excellent worker, employed beneath his capacity but had never pressed for advancement. He was married to a dominant lady who nagged him and frequently expressed her dissatisfaction with his wages. He had not had a holiday away from home for 20 years. In the last few weeks he had had bronchitis, which kept him awake. He was tired and not feeling well, and he was taking a prescribed medication containing codeine. The stores keeper, he had hoped, would treat him with respect; she was an attractive and popular middle-aged women whom he liked but had never tried to make a relationship with. When she behaved like his wife he reacted in a way which could be interpreted as venting all his suppressed resentment of his wife upon her.

Another exception to the general rule is the so-called aggressive psychopath who on follow-up (Gibbens, 1970), is shown to have been much less aggressive than expected. Aggressive psychopaths are of many different varieties; one of the commoner types is the man of tender self-regard who relieves his fears of being deflated, by actual or threatened aggression; such men do not enjoy being violent, they do not attack non-threatening persons (children, hospital staff) and they improve with ageing. This type probably contributes largely to the observed fact that many psychopathic states resolve at about 35–40 years. It is equally striking that aggressive psychopaths with a strong paranoid component, and those showing recurrent bouts of tension, agitation, often with hypochondriacal features together with violent and destructive behaviour, do not resolve; the latter group often commit suicide in their 50s.

A previous record of non-violent crime is less predictive of dangerousness. Stereotyped non-violent crime is unlikely to switch or evolve into violence, but there are plenty of exceptions, as when the career takes a new turn into drug or alcohol abuse, exploitation by others, or some new frustration or alienation arises. If, however, non-violent crimes are interspersed with violent ones the outlook is very poor, particularly if penal or other treatments have been tried and failed.

(3) Personal Data

Sex

Women are less likely to seek violent solutions to their difficulties, and this is probably because they are, or have been conditioned to believe that they are physically weaker. Support for this argument lies in the fact that mothers are as likely to batter their babies as are men, and when they kill them post mortem examination shows just the same excessive violence (Scott, 1973). The general clinical experience is that women more rarely cross the threshold into dangerousness, but when they do, perhaps by substituting stealth for strength, they offer the same difficulties of prediction and treatment as do men. The battering of babies has been regarded as a syndrome, or a specific variety of violence, but in fact it is more a microcosm of violent crime, demonstrating the same broad factors as crime and delinquency in general. There is the same difficulty in determining causative factors, the same constellation with other inadequacies or insufficiencies, the same wide variety of types with a small intractable hard core, and a large penumbra of cases which are easily helped and unlikely to repeat. Important differences depend upon the family setting, the captive victim, the impact of the spouse, and the domestic secrecy which is possible and which adds to the difficulties of supervision.

Age

This has already been touched upon. It is a difficult area for those who sentence or who serve on parole boards; youth is intolerant of incarceration which, on its own, appears to have little or no reformative function (Cornish and Clarke, 1975), yet it is precisely this age group which is most likely to recidivate. In this respect it is very important not to fall into the common error of failing to differentiate between violent and non-violent offenders in respect of recidivism. Heilbrun and his colleagues (1976), using a new and reliable method of assessing the degree of self-control in crimes, found that paroled convicts who committed violent crimes had a better chance of remaining free from further convictions (as judged by a six-month follow-up) than non-violent convicts. They emphasized that the crimes of violent criminals were less controlled than those of non-violent criminals, and that this was true of young criminals as well. They therefore arrived at the conclusion that "offenders demonstrated less self-control in crimes of violence than in non-violent crimes"; and that "offenders committing less self-controlled crimes of violence were more successful on parole than offenders committing more self-controlled crimes of violence." This they found to be true with young offenders also. Once again we are prevented from making any simple rules such as "youthfulness is always equated with a tendency to repeat," or "display of uncontrolled violence is of bad prognosis." Still less can we put these two predictions together and say "young, violent offenders must be a very poor risk." Perhaps what Heilbrun is saying is that violent crimes, even though poorly self-controlled, are mostly once and for all. That is an important message but does not obscure the danger of the repeated, poorly self-controlled individual.

Some of the most difficult problems for the forensic psychiatrist occur in the late adolescent range, when a youth of previously "good character" (as the lawyers, but perhaps not the psychiatrists, would say) has committed an entirely unprovoked violent assault upon a girl; these attacks have no manifest sexual features but seem to be an expression of the following sequence: strong sexual attraction, total inability to effect contact, consequent frustration and anger, which is then expressed on the object which disturbs him. The usual finding in the youth is a combination of weak control, high sexual inhibition with normal sexual drive. The sexual inhibition (usually shared with the family) prevents any frank discussion either with the youth himself (who is by now thoroughly scared of his own impulses) or with his parents, whose only object is to maintain the myth of family "normality." Is this a single incident of adolescence or is the blocking of sexual expression more permanent? Will he be able to share his problems when the storm has died down, and thus alleviate his situation, or will the denial persist? And always there is the awareness that if a pessimistic or cautious view is expressed, this will probably result in a lengthy incarceration in a closed institution which, whatever else it does, will effectively prevent the natural solution of finding a suitable girl friend. Provided there is no gross family history of psychiatric disorder, and provided the youth's personality is not too seriously damaged, experience shows that calculated risks are justified, particularly if initial impressions can be checked through a short period of close observation in a hospital, hostel or Borstal institution.

Do sexual offences cease at the male climacteric? The nearest approximation to an answer in the present state of knowledge is that if the offence is directed towards orgasm it will cease, but if not it can continue with little or no abatement far into the senium. Examples of some sexual offences which are not directed towards orgasm are some indecent exhibitionism (sometimes to children, and sometimes of quite a frightening character), some paedophilic offences, including those with a sadistic element, some retaliations against women, especially prostitutes. The resort to violence does in general diminish with age even though offences continue, and of course the violence becomes increasingly easy to resist, and access to children and other potential victims may become a little less easy. But many sexual perverts are incredibly persuasive and successful in getting their unsuspecting victims to co-operate at least in the initial stages.

Marital Status

An offender's marital status gives a valuable insight into whether a close relationship can be or was ever achieved and maintained, and if there are children as well then their adjustment too offers a very useful barometer of parental competence. Once adolescence is passed, persistent failure to achieve a sexual partnership, despite attempts, with a history of at least one violent assault upon a female, is usually ominous.

It has to be accepted that if a sexually active man has never managed a mutually acceptable sexual relationship and has tried to force one violently, he may do so again; despite good intelligence, absence of any psychiatric abnormality (including any other evidence of personality disorder); despite a previously clear record and excellent behaviour during a perhaps long prison sentence; despite the opinion of a psychotherapist that he has cooperated well, gained good insight into his psychopathology and is ready for release; and despite the offender's own expressed confidence that he is cured. This is not to say that recurrence is inevitable, but experience shows that it is frequent.

Personality Traits

There is no characteristic profile, either of dangerous violence or of specific patterns of violence so that psychological test results from personality inventories and other sources take their place amongst all the other factors which must be scanned. It may be useful to note a high score on the lie scale or the hostility scale, but such findings must be checked against all the other information. Owing to secondary learning effects and changes in motivation, test results are particularly unreliable (as are all other modes of assessment) in trying to decide on fitness to end indeterminate detention. There is no magic about a standardized test. Bartholomew (1975) reaches similar conclusions: "Even testing by the psychologist is likely to produce misleading results, as it is not so very difficult for the intellectually able person to recognize the type of answer that should not be given if an early release is hoped for."

No doubt the contribution of new forms of standardized test is potentially great, but to date they are not clinically very helpful in this field. One of the possible reasons for this may be that the clinicians are not yet able to tell the psychometrists what it is that they wish to be measured. Another barrier is that the objective of a test must be clear and simple, and if this is so the purpose of the test will quickly be apparent to the subject who has good reason to defeat it.

Space permits only a few considerations of special features.

Deceptiveness and transparency. Deceptiveness may be the response of an intelligent individual bent upon release from a situation, but as a personality trait it often stems from a parent-child learning situation in which there was mutual lack of trust. Perhaps mother and child conspired together in keeping a powerful father-figure "sweet" (the "as-if" character of Greenacre, 1945); more commonly untrusting and inquisitorial, punitive parents almost compel their children to lie. If together with this the child emerges into adult life with antagonistic and aggressive impulses, then, when he offends it will be difficult to gain his confidence and difficult for the after-care officer to help him. This antagonism and antisociability will hinder attempts to alleviate the offender's situation. Such individuals tend to have poor relationships with prison staff, so that distrust can progressively develop and bind the offender to the least helpful prison subculture. Slightly different is the factor of transparency. Some individuals, either because they need support and reassurance or because of a sort of verbal incontinence, readily reveal their thoughts and feelings, so that their actions are easily anticipated.

This is particularly important in those who suffer periodic psychosis, perhaps of a depressive-suicidal or paranoid-homicidal nature. Some are very skilled at concealing such states, but others readily reveal them. Such factors are, of course, of great importance to the after-care agent. Much greater risks in liberating dangerous subjects are justified if they are transparent and not deceptive.

Jealousy, as Shepherd (1961) has said, "is a notoriously dangerous passion and constitutes a well recognized motive for crimes of violence. . . ." A mild degree of jealousy is useful in preserving family life and is often a matter of pride to the wife. Higher degrees of jealousy are associated with less and less justification and are ultimately destructive. Jealousy is difficult to differentiate from, and may be combined with an intolerance of rejection, a fear of being deserted, a constant (probably narcissistic) need for admiration and reassurance; unlike these, jealousy is independent of how the spouse is treating the subject. Jealousy is sometimes frankly delusional or may be part of a psychosis, but pathological degrees of jealousy are not dependent upon delusion (i.e. they are compatible with good insight). Pathological jealousy is often (especially in Continental psychiatry) linked with alcoholism, but the relationship is probably in parallel, for each may be quite independent of the other.

In the present context it is essential to grasp certain features of the natural history of pathological jealousy, otherwise very dramatic and serious errors will be made.

Pathological jealousy is exceptionally difficult to treat. Very intensive and long treatment has been observed to achieve control, through the voluntary return for further help of one or both parties, but the basic pathological tendency is not eradicated. The really essential point is that the most gross and dangerous forms may quickly and dramatically clear up in response to such measures as divorce or enforced separation, but will almost inevitably recur, even after years of apparent well-being, when this or a different relationship is resumed. Very many second murders are due to pathological jealousy.

Other dangerous traits. The personality traits of pathological (paranoid) suspicion, and sado-masochism often have to be considered *inter alia* in problems of dangerousness. While both tend to arise very early and to remain throughout life, it is important to recognize that intercurrent states of anxiety and depression can exaggerate minor degrees of these traits which may then be mistaken for fully-fledged features of the personality and lead to over-pessimistic prediction. This is particularly to be observed in children and adolescents who possibly try to dispel depression by giving themselves up to sadistic or masochistic phantasy which will not be and has not been acted out. In such cases it is unwise to attach the rather emotive label of paranoid or sadistic without taking a very close longitudinal view, if possible with a period of hospital observation.

The sadistic tendency is often revealed through the subject's fascination with dictators, Nazi insignia, horror films (especially if the same film is seen repeatedly). Some sadistic individuals collect, or have collected, weapons and cannot pass a gunsmith's shop. Children's drawings and prisoners choice and use of pornographic magazines are worth inquiry. The prisoner's "pinups" are often informative, but his fetish drawings and pictures may be carefully hidden at the back of the lowest drawer. The occupational preference will sometimes give a hint (butchering and work in abattoirs). Sadistic children often want to be veterinary surgeons, and show a morbid interest in sick and damaged animals which quickly die in their care, as do their pets. A combination of sadistic phantasy with actual violence is an ominous finding, especially if the violence is discussed in a dispassionate, guilt-free manner, and if there is no manipulative endeavour to impress the examiner. Part of the differential diagnosis of active sadism concerns the person who, knowing that he is going to be incarcerated for a long time, manipulates his way into psychiatric care by claiming abnormal impulses, or perhaps by untruthfully inflating phantasy into reality. Some children find relief from their own anxieties by making others anxious and discover that relating horrific, violent or cruel stories will effect this; these children do not have the same prognosis as those who actually seek relief through such actions.

(4) Historical Data

Childhood, "deprivation," very unsatisfactory parent-child relationships, beatings in childhood, alcoholic fathers, dominant mothers are all features which have often been found to correlate with later violence. Duncan and Duncan (1971) find that "a history of parental violence remains a significant consideration in evaluating homicidal risk." Palmer (1960) found that the incidence of childhood frustration was significantly higher among murderers than in their next older brothers. The so-called neurotic traits of childhood are not indicators of violence (nor apparently of anything else), though several authors find that a combination of enuresis, firesetting and cruelty to animals may predict later violence (Hellman, 1966). Battering parents are held, particularly in the American literature, to have experienced physical violence in their own childhoods, but there are many exceptions; clinical and ethological data suggest that other deprivations (of access to mother or to play-fellows) may be equally important.

Jessen and Roosenburg (1971), in assessing recidivism (not necessarily through dangerous violence), found only one factor which effectively distinguished between recidivists and non-recidivists, and that was running away from home after the age of 17 years.

Severe head injuries before the age of 10 are not usually associated with adult violence (Climent and Ervin, 1972), though psychopaths with a history of head injury have worse criminal records than those without head injury (Gibbens, 1955).

A host of genetic and biological factors have been supposed to indicate dangerousness: minimal brain damage, temporal lobe disorder, anomalies of the Y chromosome, testosterone overproduction; but as Rubin (1972) says ". . . the presence of these defects in known criminals has no predictive value in their possible future violence . . . ."

Relationship with Mental Illness

Some studies, for instance that of Giovannoni and Gurel (1967) find that released psychiatric patients are much more likely to commit homicide, and rather more likely to commit aggravated assault than members of the general public. But most studies make it quite clear that the link between both crime and violent crime on the one hand and mental illness on the other is very slender indeed.

A recent study by Guze (1976) of 223 men and 65 women convicted of serious crimes, mainly of violence and theft, finds very high rates of sociopathy and alcoholism but very low rates of psychiatric illness. Sociopathy, alcoholism, and drug dependence are associated with serious crime; "Schizophrenia, primary affective disorders, anxiety neurosis, obsessional neurosis, phobic neurosis and brain syndromes, are not." Schizophrenia was diagnosed in only two of the males and one of the females.

Hafner and Boker (1973), in a very large-scale German study find that mental patients and defectives together show no higher an incidence of violence than do mentally sound persons. Schizophrenics, they say, are by far the most likely among psychiatric patients to commit acts of violence, but even so the rate is extremely low (5 in 10,000). The corresponding rate for affective psychoses and subnormals together is 6 in 100,000. The age and sex distribution in mentally disturbed violent offenders is similar to that of mentally sound violent offenders. A stay in hospital is followed by a high risk of violence over a period of six months, and marital partners, lovers and children are most at risk particularly from patients with affective psychoses and delusions.

The incidence of violence amongst hospital patients or prisoners must not be too readily attributed to any psychiatric condition rather than to those grave frustrations which are common to closed institutions (Folkard, 1957).

Of all illnesses, epilepsy, in view of its traditional links with explosive aggression, might be expected to correlate with violence. But in general no such correlation exists either with quantity or quality of violence. It seems that, despite the early textbooks, epilepsy is not especially linked with arson, rape or murder. This field has been well reviewed by Gunn (1969 and 1971). Although the crimes of epileptics can only be directly attributed to the epileptic process extremely rarely, yet when an epileptic acts violently in, or immediately after his fit, then he may do the same in subsequent fits. Two second murders, in my experience, have certainly been of this nature. The degree of violence sometimes shown in these "ictal" crimes is sometimes extremely great.

(5) Progress in Custody

This can be prognostically useful, but also misleading.

The outlook for youthful rebellion which has perhaps involved some violence as part of a well directed and understandable retaliation is nearly always excellent, even if within the institution the subject has had many conflicts with authority and has made a great nuisance of himself or herself. In general, aggressive behaviour which stems from strength and determination resolves itself, especially in the young.

Also hopeful (and of course gratifying) are inmates or patients who are at first rebellious and difficult but later conform; the task then will be to determine whether they have made genuine progress towards self-control, have learnt how to manipulate the system (not necessarily an unfavourable feature), or have deteriorated into institutional dependence.

Less hopeful are those whose violence seems to be based on a weakness. These will be particularly difficult to assess if the expression of their violence involved alcohol, drugs, women, children, possession of money, or access to gambling, because these are not openly available in most secure hospitals and prison establishments.

Consideration also has to be given to the things which *are* present in institutions but not outside: the presence of authority to supplement conscience, to protect, control and make decisions.

A single interview near the time of release by a stranger is not a good basis, on its own, for assessing dangerousness. As already stated most help is to be got from plodding through records, nurses' notes and trial transcripts, and talking to the staff who are in daily contact with the patient. It also helps to know the idiosyncrasies of staff. It is sometimes worrying if a certain staff member does *not* produce his usual unfavourable report. Dr Stürup (1968) of Herstedvester indicates the usefulness of staff of both sexes: "If several of the women have the same (intuitive) feeling I am inclined to take it very seriously." The reactions of other patients or inmates can be very useful, as are those of the victim or the victim's family. In serious cases the English parole board habitually makes inquiry about the probable local response before conditionally releasing the offender. The institution cat or dog, particularly in assessing young people, can prove a useful staff member, revealing either carefully hidden capacities for affection or cruelty; animals are not so easily deceived as humans.

(6) After-Care

The subject's plans for his life outside (or lack of them) are of course important and may reflect his realism and aspirations. Brown and his colleagues (1972) have shown that schizophrenics are more likely to relapse after discharge from hospital if they are returned to the bosom of their families. Very many dangerous offences are based upon the individual's inability to solve ordinary problems of human relationship, which are, of course, most intense within the family. Thus it is often unwise to return offenders to the very setting in which their problem arose.

After-care, and intermediate placements between secure hospital or prison, together with indeterminacy of detention, or partial indeterminacy offered by borstal sentences and various forms of parole and conditional discharge provide our only means of compensating for our inability to make accurate predictions of dangerousness. The after-care officer's onerous task is relieved if he is introduced to the offender at an early stage; if he is well briefed on his charge's characteristics, if his supervision is supplemented by periodic reassessments of the offender and discussion with the responsible medical officer, and if recall is undertaken quickly when the danger signals appear.

Favourable response to after-care is seen when there is movement towards improvement rather than achievement; and, conversely, complete stasis, with consequent frustration, in any important area of life (especially the ability to love or relate to people) is ominous, the more so if there is a well tried perverse solution at hand.

CONSIDERATION OF THE DATA

Every single factor, however promising, fails as an indicator of dangerousness, so that the factors can only be used in answering a number of further questions which may be hoped to approach an answer.

For a start, it is healthy for the investigator to review his own role: has he been strictly neutral in his approach? Has every reasonable attempt been made to collect the necessary information? To what extent did the subject suppress or actively distort the facts? Particularly if the offender emerges as a thoroughly attractive person who ought to be summarily released, or if a complex and fully explanatory psychopathology is instantly apparent, then the chances of some form of deception are high, for those who have committed a violent crime (even with provocation) usually have very marked weaknesses of one sort or another.

Consider the subject's life longitudinally, his existential manner of being in the world, what roles he sought or was pushed into, and by whom. Is the sum of the information consistent? High degrees of consistency or of inconsistency should lead to reappraisal, for most individuals' life stories are in the mid position.

Consider the behaviour from the point of view of as many theoretical standpoints as possible. Learning theory can be particularly helpful where the behaviour has been stereotyped: was it well learnt, but to antisocial standards; was it reparative behaviour to circumvent some basic prohibition; was it a conditioned avoidance response to a specific anxiety, or a non-adaptive response to an insoluble and inescapable problem of discrimination? Each of these quite different responses can lead, if the lesson was implanted sufficiently early, repeatedly and in the requisite emotional turmoil, to the most obstinate repetitiveness, and each should be treated in a different manner.

If the dangerous behaviour was not stereotyped but varied and perhaps mixed with non-violent offences, then we are dealing with incorrigibility of a different nature, probably not mainly due to faulty social learning. Very early, constitutional, perhaps organic or psychotic factors may have prevented or destroyed lessons; and there is a variety of indiscriminate offending seen in children who, coming from chaotic homes, have had no consistent social lessons and are without discernible conscience. Many such cases improve when a stable environment has been experienced, but this disorganized group of people, if dangerous violence has appeared more than once, are likely to continue to be dangerous.

It is useful also to consider whether the repeated dangerous behaviour is directed towards satisfying some (perhaps perverse) appetite, which, like any appetite, will certainly recur, or if it is an attempt to evade or cope with a specific problem, which may not recur.

Motive

This leads to the vexed consideration of motive; a difficult area because it is usually over-determined, is vulnerable to unconscious or deliberate falsification, and especially because, on its own, it gives no indication of choice of behaviour. All our motivations have components at all the levels of our being. In well adjusted persons only the socially approved part of the motivation will appear, and the selected solution will be correspondingly polite. In someone who has been "driven to distraction" by long exposure to a strong motive and an equally strong set of prohibitions, or in someone whose social adjustment has been destroyed by some process or intoxication, the primitive response to the same motivation may appear. Sending a bunch of red roses, and committing a savage rape, may have the same motive operating at different levels of the personality. The single motive is likely to be labelled differently according to the level at which the personality is operating; at a fairly high level a robbery will be called an urgent need for money; at a lower level it will be admitted that the act relieves intolerable tension; at a lower level it may be ritual retaliation against a parsimonious mother; and at a still lower level there may be no words to express it because at that age the offender could not talk. Motive, therefore, always has to be considered alongside other factors, especially the current level of personality integration and the ease with which regression under stress occurs.

Sarabin (1967) says that there are three ways of meeting a crisis: the autistic, the social and explosive violence. Either one withdraws and does without, suffering the consequent symptoms, or one copes on a realistic basis of new adjustment; or one goes like a bull in a china shop for the simple solution. It is useful to study the way in which the offender made his selection. Did he cast about for practical solutions, and with what degree of resourcefulness; did he try to absorb the problem autistically and how much could he stand, or did he go straight for, or almost straight for the violent solution; in which case he is quite likely to do the same next time? A non-commissioned officer had suffered long conflict with his wife; he went through a period of alcoholism (autistic); tried to get a divorce (social), got himself posted to Ireland and volunteered for dangerous duty (the beginnings of the violent solution, but against himself), he then deserted his post, hoping to be dismissed the service (a variety of suicide), and finally shot his wife with a high velocity rifle in the kitchen (the final violent solution). As Menninger (1938) has observed, every murder includes a wish to kill, a wish to die and a wish to survive. It is perhaps the inability to make a choice between these simultaneous motives which compels a violent solution.

Linking Concepts

Are there any key areas in which these protean factors have a common bearing? Again a simple answer eludes us, but most of the factors are best utilized in trying to answer two very basic questions, both concerned more with the future than with the current offence. First, is this person capable of compassionate feelings; is he able to feel sympathy with the sort of persons who may become his victims, or is he so ego-centric or so indoctrinated or influenced or damaged that such feelings are absent or lastingly obscured? Unless there is some recognizable sympathy for others, and revulsion at causing suffering, there is always a vulnerability to situational aggressive impulses which are bound to recur. This must be assessed by looking deeply into the subject's life pattern and relationships. The common practice of looking for "signs of remorse" in relation to the current offence is not a good criterion, for after a horrifying deed there are so many protective mechanisms which may be mistaken for callous indifference.

Second, is this person's capacity to learn by experience still intact? Perhaps this comes close to begging the main question, "is he going to do it again?", but the question forms a central peg on which many other considerations hang, especially the manner in which the antisocial tendency was acquired, the resources which oppose it, the maturity of the personality, and the ease with which regression occurs under stress of various sorts, or on the other hand the obstinacy or lack of adaptiveness which some people show when passions are aroused.

CONCLUSION

We strive after accurate prediction of dangerousness because this would quell our anxieties, enable us to draw clear lines between the dangerous and non-dangerous, and avoid the necessity of continuing contact with and concern for them. But no such magical process will be possible.

Our disappointment may be alleviated if we accept that short-term assessment (which permits the scanning of the subject's present environment and associates, and his reactions to these) is likely to be much more reliable than long-term assessment, which, especially in the present setting of a mobile and changeable society, is likely to be totally beyond our reach. The point is illustrated by the introduction into an institution, many years ago, of a pencil and paper test to indicate propensity to abscond (I believe it was called the Chernukin test). At first we were very pleased with it, but we soon realized that it only indicated how the individual was feeling at that moment; tomorrow after a letter from home or an altercation with the staff he might feel and act quite differently; the test, to be useful, would have to be given every day, and anyway could achieve no more than would a friendly conversation. Further, the knowledge that absconding may be imminent is useless unless there is a means of dealing with the problem; to lock the subject up (which only delays, whilst amplifying, his need to abscond), or to reduce the tension through personal contact. It was realized that it is an economy to aim straight for the personal contact, which has the advantage of serving a host of other useful functions simultaneously; it has the further advantage that it can be achieved by non-medical personnel provided they are well supported by a good system of communications. Involvement on a long-term basis and good communications are therefore the inescapable bases for assessment of dangerousness.

REFERENCES

Berg, I. & Fox, V. (1947) Factors in homicides committed by 200 males. *Journal of Social Psychology,* 26, 109–10.

Blackburn, R. (1970) Personality types among abnormal homicides. Special Hospitals Research Report. No. I.

Brett, P. (1970) The physiology of provocation. *Criminal Law Reform,* 634–40.

Brown, G. W., Wing, J.K. & Birley, J. L. T. (1972) *British Journal of Psychiatry,* 121, 241.

Butler Committee (1975) Report of the Committee on Mentally Abnormal Offenders. Cmnd 6244. London: HMSO.

Climent, C. E. & Ervin, F. R. (1972) Historical data in the evaluation of violent subjects. *Archives of General Psychiatry,* 27, 621–4.

Cornish, D. B. & Clarke, R. V. G. (1975) Residential treatment and its effects on delinquency. *Home Office Research Studies;* No. 32. London: HMSO.

Duncan, J. W. & Duncan, G. M. (1971) Murder in the family: a study of some homicidal adolescents. *American Journal of Psychiatry,* 127, 1498–501.

English, P. (1970) What did Section 3 do to the law of provocation? *Criminal Law Reform,* 249–67.

Folkard, M. S. (1957) A sociological contribution to the understanding of aggression and its treatment. *Netherne Monographs, I.* Coulsdon, Surrey: Netherne Hospital.

Gibbens, T .C. N. (1970) How should we treat violent offenders. *New Society,* 3 September, 408–10.

—— Pond, D. A. & Stafford-Clark, D. (1955) A follow-up study of criminal psychopaths. *British Journal of Delinquency,* 6, 1–11. See also *Journal of Mental Science* (1959) 105, 108–15.

Giovannoni, J. & Gurel, L. (1967) Socially disruptive behavior of ex-mental patients. *Archives of General Psychiatry,* 17, 146–53.

Greenacre, Phyllis (1945) Conscience and the psychopath. *American Journal of Orthopsychiatry,* 15, 495.

Gunn, J. C. (1973) *Violence.* Newton Abbott: David and Charles.

—— (1969) The prevalence of epilepsy among prisoners. *Proceedings of the Royal Society of Medicine,* 62, 60–3.

—— & Bonn, J. (1971) Criminality and violence in epileptic prisoners. *British Journal of Psychiatry,* 118, 332-43.

Guze, S. (1976) *Criminality and Psychiatric Disorders.* London: Oxford University Press.

Hafner, H. & Boker, W. (1973) Mentally disordered violent offenders. *Social Psychiatry,* 8 (4), 220–9.

Heilbrun, A. B., Knopf, I. J. & Bruner, P. (1976) Criminal impulsivity and violence and subsequent parole outcome. *British Journal of Criminology,* 16, 4.

Hellman, D. S. & Blackburn, M. (1966) Enuresis, firesetting and cruelty to animals: a triad predictive of adult crime. *American Journal of Psychiatry,* 122, 1431–5.

Jessen, J. L. & Roosenburg, A. M. (1971) Treatment results at the Dr Henri van der Hoeven Clinic, Nirecht. *Proceedings of the Fifth World Congress of Psychiatry.* Amsterdam: Excerpta Medica.

Kozol, H. L., Boucher, R. F. & Garofolo, R. F. (1972) The diagnosis and treatment of dangerousness. *Journal of Crime and Delinquency,* 18, 371–92.

Lifton, R. J. (1957) Chinese communist thought reform. In *Group Processes. Transactions of the Third Conference,* pp 219-312. New York: Josiah Macy Jr Foundation.

MacDonald, J. M. (1968) *Homicidal Threats.* Illinois: Thomas.

—— (1963) The threat to kill. *American Journal of Psychiatry,* 120, 125–30.

Megargee, E. S. (1966) Undercontrolled and overcontrolled personality types in extreme antisocial aggression. *Psychological Monograph,* 80, no. 611.

Menninger. K. A. (1938) *Man Against Himself.* New York: Harcourt Bruce.

Michaels, J. J. & Steinberg, A. (1952) Persistent enuresis and juvenile delinquency. *British Journal of Delinquency,* 3, 114–23.

Neithercutt, M. G. (1972) Parole violation patterns and commitment of offence. *Journal of Research in Crime and Delinquency,* 9, 87–98.

Neustatter, L. (1965) The state of mind in murder. *Lancet, i,* 861–3.

Palmer, S. (1960) *A Study of Murder.* New York: Thomas Y. Crowell.

Rappoport, J. R. (1967) *The Clinical Evaluation of Dangerousness of the Mentally Ill.* Springfield, Illinois: Charles C. Thomas.

Reichard, S. & Tillman, C. (1950) Murder and suicide as defences against schizophrenic psychosis. *Clinical Psychopathology,* 11, 149–63.

Robins, L. (1966) *Deviant Children Grown Up*. London: Livingstone.

Rubin, B. (1972) Prediction of dangerousness in mentally ill criminals. *Archives of General Psychiatry*, 27, 397.

Sarabin, T. R. (1967) The dangerous individual. *British Journal of Criminology*, 7, 285–95.

Satten, J., Menninger, K., Rosen, I. & Mayman, M. (1960) Murder without apparent motive. *American Journal of Psychiatry*, 117, 48–53.

Scott, P. D. (1973) Parents who kill their children. *Medicine Science and Law*, 13, 120–6.

—— (1973) Fatal battered baby cases. *Medicine Science and Law*, 13, 197–206.

Shaw, S. H. (1973) The dangerousness of dangerousness. *Medicine Science and Law*, 13, 269–71.

Shepherd, M. (1961) Morbid jealousy: some clinical and social aspects. *Journal of Mental Science*, 107, 687–753.

Stanton, J. M. (1969) Murderers on parole. *Crime and Delinquency*, 15, 149–55.

Steadman, H. J. & Cocozza, J. J. (1975) We can't predict who is dangerous. *Psychology Today*, 8 (8), 22–35 and 84.

—— —— (1974) Some refinements in the measurement and prediction of dangerous behaviour. *American Journal of Psychiatry*, 131 (9), 1012–14.

Stürup, G. K. (1968) *Treating the Untreatable*. Baltimore: The Johns Hopkins Press.

—— (1968) Will this man be dangerous? *The Mentally Abnormal Offender*, Ciba symposium (eds A. V.S. de Reuk & R. Porter), pp 5–18. London: J. & A. Churchill.

Sullivan, C., Grant, M. Q. & Grant, J. D. (1957) The development of interpersonal maturity: application in delinquency. *Psychiatry*, 20, 373.

Tennent, G. (1971) Dangerousness. *British Journal of Hospital Medicine*, 6, 269.

Walker, N. (1969) *Sentencing in a Rational Society*. London: Allen Lane, Penguin Press.

Wertham, F. (1941) *Dark Legend*. New York: Duell, Sloan & Pearce.

White, S. (1970) A note on provocation. *Criminal Law Reform*, 446–52.

Wolfgang, M. E. (1958) Patterns in Criminal Homicide. Philadelphia: University of Pennsylvania.

2

Dangerousness: Conceptual, Prediction and Public Policy Issues

SALEEM A. SHAH

My concern here is with some issues pertaining to the phenomena of dangerous behaviors. And, although such behaviors may be directed at oneself as well as at others, this discussion will deal only with behaviors that are dangerous to others.

Acts that threaten and actually inflict serious harm on the lives and physical welfare of other members of a community have been of long-standing concern to all societies. Clearly, the criminal justice system is not the only system in our society concerned with the regulation and control of dangerous behaviors; the mental health, health, social welfare, and other systems are also involved in various ways and to varying degrees. This discussion will focus upon a number of issues and problems as they pertain to and have major implications for criminal justice and mental health systems, as well as for other social agencies and institutions.

After defining the term "dangerousness," I shall focus on some important considerations about how behavior should be conceptualized. This will lead to a discussion of controversies and dilemmas dealing with the prediction of dangerousness. Finally, I will address some questions and problems pertaining to public policies concerned with the handling of dangerous and violent behaviors in our society.

The topic of "dangerousness" seems often to be associated with strong beliefs and ideologies and, understandably, such feelings and explicit or implicit value systems

Reprinted with kind permission of Springer Science and Business Media. J.R. Hays, T.K. Roberts & K.S. Solway (Eds.), Violence and the Violent Individual. *New York: SP Medical and Scientific Books. © 1981 Springer Science and Business Media.*

tend very much to influence how we define and study such phenomena and also how we wish to deal with them. It seems desirable, at least initially, to distinguish certain essentially empirical and technical questions from the normative, ideological, and policy concerns that also have to be considered.

I am using the word dangerousness despite my awareness of certain problems associated with the term. Certainly it is a rather vague term and one which is often used with numerous different meanings. Another problem is that the term seems to imply that there is a trait of dangerousness that constitutes a relatively enduring and stable characteristic of persons so designated. But, as I will indicate later in discussing some conceptual issues, this particular connotation of the term (as necessarily suggesting an enduring characteristic) requires clarification and correction. Despite such problems, however, there are two main reasons why I still prefer to use the term "dangerousness." First, the term is widely used in both criminal and civil law and thus has broad reference and recognition. Second, "dangerousness" serves better to illustrate a broad range of programmatic and policy concerns than do terms like aggression and violence.

DEFINITION

As used here, *dangerousness* refers to a propensity, i.e., an increased probability as compared to others, to engage in dangerous behavior. *Dangerous behaviors* refer to acts that are characterized by the application or overt threat of force and are likely to result in injury to other persons. This definition also applies to the term violent behaviors. Thus, as used here, dangerous behaviors are considered to be synonymous with violent behaviors.

Acts that commonly are defined as *crimes of violence* exemplify the behaviors of major concern; the core offenses of concern to the criminal law are probably represented in the Uniform Crime Reports (UCR) of the FBI (Webster, 1978). The category of violent crimes includes murder, aggravated assault, rape, and robbery. Along with these major offense categories would also be included the so-called inchoate crimes or attempts.

Of course, one could go well beyond this category of violent crimes and include such other criminal acts as assault and battery, arson, kidnapping, extortion, and other offenses (Goldstein and Katz, 1960). The range of dangerous acts to be included under formal legal and other societal responses is basically a matter of public policy that is determined by the political processes of a society. And, as I shall discuss later, considerations of values and power are inextricably involved in the political process and in matters affecting public policy.

An individual's dangerousness is considered at many decision points in the criminal justice and mental health systems. Indeed, with respect to the mental health system, there has been a marked increase in the past few years in the number of jurisdictions that have begun to use the criterion of dangerousness (and/or the closely related notion of "likelihood of serious harm") for purposes of involuntary commitment of the mentally ill. A survey of civil commitment statutes published in the *Harvard Law*

Review (1974) indicated that only four state laws were explicitly phrased in terms of "dangerousness" as a commitment criterion, and ten laws used the criterion of "likelihood of serious harm." A survey done as of September, 1977 (Schwitzgebel, 1978), indicates, however, that fully 20 commitment laws included the "dangerousness" criterion, either alone or in conjunction with other criteria, and the phrase "likelihood of serious harm" was used in 28.

Following is a list of some decision points that involve considerations of an individual's dangerousness:

1. Decisions concerning the granting of bail (or release on personal recognizance) to persons accused of crimes, and the level at which bail is to be set.
2. Decisions concerning the waiver of juveniles charged with serious crimes to adult courts.
3. Sentencing decisions following criminal convictions, including those about release on conditions of probation.
4. Decisions pertaining to work-release and furlough programs for incarcerated offenders.
5. Parole and other conditional release decisions for offenders.
6. Decisions pertaining to removal of a child from the home in cases of child abuse or battery.
7. Decisions pertaining to the commitment and release of persons handled via a number of quasicriminal statutes concerned with "sexual psychopaths," "sexually dangerous persons," "mentally disordered sex offenders," and the like.
8. For criminal defendants who have been civilly committed after adjudication as incompetent to stand trial or as not guilty by reason of insanity and who have been sent to maximum security hospitals or units, a transfer to a nonsecurity unit is based on a determination that the individuals are not "manifestly dangerous."[1]
9. Decisions regarding the special handling (including transfer to special prisons) of offenders who are disruptive and dangerous in regular penal settings.
10. Decisions regarding the transfer to security hospitals of mental patients found to be too difficult or dangerous to be handled in regular civil hospitals.
11. Commitment of drug addicts because of fears that they will commit violent crimes to support their drug habits.
12. Decisions concerning the emergency and longer-term involuntary commitment of mentally ill persons considered to pose a "danger to self or others."
13. Decisions concerning the "conditional" and "unconditional" release of involuntarily confined mental patients.
14. Decisions concerning the hospitalization (on grounds of continuing mental disorder and dangerousness) of criminal defendants acquitted by reason of insanity.
15. Decisions concerning the invocation of special legal proceedings or sentencing provisions for "habitual" and "dangerous" offenders.
16. Decisions concerning the likelihood of continued dangerousness of persons convicted of capital crimes as a basis for determinations regarding the imposition of the death penalty.[2]

Despite the serious consequences that may follow for persons officially designated as dangerous, it is astonishing to note the frequent absence of clear and specific definitions and criteria as bases for the key terms in relevant laws. Moreover, even though "dangerousness" as used in various laws and regulations is clearly a *legal* term that requires determinations by courts and other designated triers of fact, often such crucial determinations actually tend to be made by various mental health experts. This situation has been criticized with regard to the apparent arrogation by psychiatrists and other mental health professionals of roles and determinations that are fundamentally legal. In fairness it must be noted, however, that the problem is much more a reflection of judicial default than of the arrogance of mental health experts (Shah, 1974).

SOME CONCEPTUAL ISSUES

A major consideration in efforts to assess, predict, prevent, and change dangerous behavior pertains to the manner in which behavior is conceptualized. Behavior—whether defined as dangerous, friendly, constructive, or antisocial—is often viewed as stemming largely if not entirely from within the person, that is, as being a stable and fairly consistent characteristic of the person. In a traditional trait perspective, behavior is viewed as being determined largely by the individual's personality.

The trait model of behavior seems to have been a dominant force in personality research, theory, and clinical practice. According to the classic personality-trait model, traits were considered to be the prime determinants of behavior and helped to explain the apparent consistencies of behavior over time and in different situations. And, even though the trait model recognizes the impact of situational factors, there has tended to be an assumption that persons described as "friendly," or "dependable," or "honest," or "aggressive" tend to display such behaviors across a variety of situations. That is, such personality traits are believed to reflect fairly general and enduring personality and behavioral characteristics (Endler and Magnusson, 1976). In contrast to such notions of personality traits, more recent uses of the trait concept indicate only that there are indeed individual differences in certain personality and behavioral characteristics, that such differences are often quite stable over time and across settings, that individuals do have certain stylistic consistencies in interpersonal behaviors, and also discernibly different probabilities of displaying certain behaviors (Gough, 1969; Hogan et al., 1977).

Psychodynamic theories of personality are much like the trait model in that they also assume a basic personality core which is believed to serve as a predispositional base for behavior in various situations. In the stress upon person-related factors as major determinants of behavior, the psychodynamic model is analogous to the traditional trait model (Endler and Magnusson, 1976).

In contrast, a *situation-focused* model places much emphasis on external stimuli and variables in the setting and situation as the basic determinants of individual behavior. Although recognizing individual differences, situationism is basically a stimulus-response (S-R) approach that focuses major attention on the stimulus factors that influence subsequent responses (Endler and Magnusson, 1976). The weakness of this model is that it tends to ignore, or at least underemphasize, person-related consistencies in interpersonal behaviors.

Much theoretical and empirical work has been done in recent years with respect to an *interactional* model of behavior. This model emphasizes the importance of person-situation interactions in efforts to understand both personality and behavior. The view is that behavior involves an indispensable and continuous interaction between individuals and the various situations they encounter (Shah, 1966). As Endler and Magnusson (1976) recently noted:

> Not only is the individual's behavior influenced by significant features
> of the situations he or she encounters, but the person also selects the
> situations in which he or she performs, and subsequently affects the
> character of these situations (p. 958).

During the past decade the interactionist perspective has gained many followers in the field of personality and social psychology. After some earlier debates among those emphasizing person-related and others emphasizing situation-related factors, the accumulating empirical evidence has demonstrated rather clearly that individual-situation interactions are much more helpful in understanding and predicting behavior than either set of variables alone (Endler and Magnusson, 1976). Thus, the field has moved ahead and there is now general recognition that questions about the relative importance of one or the other set of factors are futile—both are unquestionably important, especially the particular ways in which they interact (Bowers, 1973; Bem and Allen, 1974; Ekehammer, 1974; Mischel, 1973, 1977; Moos, 1969, 1973).

The available evidence does not imply, however, that different persons will not indeed act differently and also with some degree of consistency across situations and with some stability over time. Rather, the evidence strongly indicates that particular classes of settings and situations must be taken into account far more carefully than they have in the past (Mischel, 1973). Just as individuals vary in range and types of behaviors likely in particular situations and also across situations, social settings of life also vary in the degree to which they prescribe and limit the range of expected and acceptable behaviors for persons in particular roles and situations. Mischel (1973), for example, described a number of cognitive social-learning person-related variables that help in understanding how the individual will tend to perceive, construct, and respond to various environmental situations. Similarly, Bowers (1973) points out that ". . . situations are as much a function of the person as the person's behavior is a function of the situation" (p. 327). Pervin (1977) notes that personality is coming to be seen as expressing both stability and change, and that it is the *pattern* of stability and change in relation to specific situations that needs to be better understood.

The point was demonstrated by J. Douglas Grant and Hans Toch (Toch, 1969) in a study of violence-prone men. The study involved 128 men (police officers, men who had assaulted police officers, prison inmates, and parolees) who had shown patterns of repeated violent encounters. Attention was focused on the chain of interactions between aggressors and victims and on the sequential developments as the encounters resulting in violence unfolded. As Toch points out: ". . . consistencies in a person's approach to others can produce situations in which violence always results— sometimes without the person being aware of the fact that he is the instigator of destructive (or self-destructive) games" (p. 6).

From detailed interviews with aggressors and their victims, as well as intensive study of relevant reports of the violent incidents, Toch developed a ten-category typology of violence-prone men. These categories were given rather descriptive titles such as "rep defending," "'norm' enforcing," "self-image defending," and "self-image promoting."

> The *rep defending* . . . person commits violence because his social position, physical size, or group status obligates him to do so—a matter of "noblesse oblige," so to speak. This sort of person is expected to have violent involvements, and he has therefore come to expect the same himself; he is aware of his role and of the need to defend it or to sustain it or to live by it (Toch, 1969: p. 149).

> A *self-image promoter* is a man who works hard at manufacturing the impression that he is not to be trifled with—that he is formidable and fearless. He goes out of his way to make sure that people under-stand how important he is and how important it is to him that he is important (p. 137).

Toch's study of violence-prone men provides a vivid illustration of the point that some individuals have rather consistent interpersonal orientations and styles which enable them to perceive, construct, and respond to a variety of interpersonal situations in a manner that produces high probabilities of violent interactions. These individuals respond aggressively to certain interpersonal stimuli which arouse no such response from other individuals. In a very real sense, therefore, such "violence-prone" individuals manage to *create* their own situations with minimal external cues or provocation.

The foregoing conceptual issues with regard to personality and behavior have been discussed at some length because the implicit or explicit conceptualization that one uses has implications for the manner in which the tasks of assessment, prediction, and han-dling of dangerous behaviors will be approached. Thus, traditional practice (following trait and psychodynamic perspectives) is to focus attention primarily on the individual's major personality and behavioral traits and inferred psychodynamics. Relatively little attention seems to be focused on the particular setting and situational factors, and on the pattern of individual-specific interactions which may differentially affect the occurrence of certain behaviors of concern. It is essential, however, that greater attention be focused on the particular setting and situational conditions which have in the past and are likely in the future to elicit, provoke, and maintain certain violent, criminal, and other related behaviors. More attention also needs to be paid to social settings and contexts in the community in which the person will live; similarly, assessments of likely functioning and problems must consider the availability and nature of supportive, stressful, and other relevant factors likely to affect the person's functioning in the community. It has been shown, for example, that accurate predictions of posthospital adjustment of mental patients in the community hinged on knowledge of the environment in which the ex-patients would be living, the availability of jobs, family and related support systems—rather than on any measured characteristic of the individual's personality or his in-hospital behavior (Fairweather, 1967; Fairweather et al., 1974).

SOME ISSUES PERTAINING TO PREDICTIONS OF DANGEROUSNESS

Earlier in this chapter the term dangerousness was defined as referring to a propensity (i.e., an *increased probability* as compared to others) to engage in dangerous or violent behavior. The words emphasized above indicate that what is to be predicted is the *probability* that certain persons are likely to engage in violent behaviors. Such predictions need to be distinguished from those in which some specific dangerous or violent behavior is to be predicted, for example, that Mr. Smith is very likely in the next 12 months to commit an armed robbery or a rape.

Given the admittedly vague and overly broad uses-and-misuses-of the term "dangerousness," it has often been suggested that what should be predicted is the specific dangerous behavior and not some vague propensity. Such a view is common and understandable. To require mental health professionals and others to make definite predictions of some specific behaviors reduces the opportunity for them to encompass their own particularistic notions of what constitute harmful and violent acts under the term "dangerousness." There is much evidence that for a variety of reasons, and especially when dealing with behaviors that have very low frequency of occurrence (i.e., low base rates), mental health professionals display poor predictive accuracy and tend to markedly overpredict dangerousness (Steadman and Cocozza, 1974; Monahan, 1975; Cocozza and Steadman, 1974, 1976).

However, to require a yes/no type of prediction of a specific act that has a low base rate poses a number of problems. Yes/no type predictions do not reflect the considerable range of variability and probability that are actually involved and that will be reflected in the predictions. Such predictions are also expected to ignore the aleatory factors commonly involved in determining whether or not a criminal act will actually take place. A variety of factors, such as those pertaining to situational events, targets of opportunity, and presence or absence of pressure from companions, will typically be involved.

Thus, the predictions to be made should refer to the *probability* that certain individuals with particular characteristics (as reflected mainly in past behavioral patterns), and functioning in particular social settings, may engage in certain types of behaviors (e.g., serious criminal acts) over a given period of time such as 12 or 24 months. Given the many problems associated with the clinical predictions typically provided to courts and other related agencies (Monahan, 1978b; Shah, 1978a, b; Steadman and Cocozza, 1978b) and in order that the probabilities may be determined reliably and precisely, actuarial and statistical approaches should be relied on in predicting dangerousness. The use of such statistical approaches (e.g., base expectancy tables and other related devices) combined with more systematically derived and periodically tested clinical indicators, would markedly reduce the problems inherent in relying on the vague clinical judgments, hunches, and intuitions of mental health professionals. Moreover, although some clinicians may well have good predictive skills, quite typically the predictive expertise of mental health professionals is assumed or ascribed—it has *not* been tested and demonstrated empirically. Thus, it is understandable when clinicians cite their clinical experiences as the basis for their predictive judgments and still come to widely differing conclusions. It is difficult to make systematic assessments to predictive validity (accuracy) when the reliability (consistency) of such judgments varies markedly across cases and is generally poor.

In essence, then, I suggest that what is very much needed are predictions that are more systematically and empirically related to probability statements. Various actuarial and statistical methods may be used to develop such probability estimates. Reliable and relevant clinical information about the individual could be used to modify the actuarially derived probabilities within some specified range. The reliability and validity of the clinical information should be determined empirically. Such an approach would, I believe, make it easier to separate the essentially empirical and technical questions pertaining to predictive accuracy from the normative, legal, and public policy decisions that must eventually be made. It might be stated, for example, that Mr. Smith seems to have a 75-percent probability of engaging in further serious criminal behavior within a 12-month period; however, were his drinking problem to be controlled and other community supports provided, this probability might be markedly lowered. It would then be the responsibility of the sentencing judge to determine whether (given the nature and seriousness of the instant offense, the past criminal record, the likelihood of adequate probation supervision, and other pertinent factors) the above probability estimate justifies probation, probation with a variety of specific conditions, or some period of incarceration. In short, predictions of dangerousness will seldom point *directly* to the ultimate legal or policy decision. Such predictions constitute only one of the many considerations that must be weighed and balanced by the ultimate decision-makers.

Can Dangerousness Be Predicted?

Given the considerable literature that has developed on the topic, many, if not most, persons may well respond to such a question with a flat, No! Such a response to the general question may be accompanied by a comment like, We know from social science research that dangerous or violent behavior cannot be predicted. This seems to have become the common wisdom, and several empirical studies (of varying relevance to the specific predictive situation) could be cited in support of such a view (Wenk et al., 1972; Steadman and Cocozza, 1974, 1978b; Monahan, 1975; Cocozza and Steadman,

1976). It must be noted, however, that the answer to the question as it was posed in the heading of this section cannot be given in any clear or definite fashion.

The question was posed in a very general and vague fashion. No reference was made to particular groups or subgroups for whom future dangerousness was to be predicted, nor was there any mention of the prediction methods to be used (clinical or actuarial) or the level of accuracy to be expected or even desired in such predictions. In view of these considerations, we might wonder whether a flat response to such a question would have been made had the reference been to another aspect of behavior. Suppose, for example, the question were, Can generosity be predicted? Can friendliness be predicted? Can trustworthiness be predicted? Or, to turn the issue around completely, Can public safety be predicted?

The point is simply that such questions cannot be answered with a flat yes or no. To say that something is difficult to do (namely, to achieve high levels of accuracy in predicting events with very low base rates) is *not* the same as asserting that the task is impossible and simply cannot be done. As Monahan (1978a) recently noted, ". . . a careful reading of the prediction research to date does not support the unqualified conclusion that the accurate prediction of violence is impossible under all circumstances or that psychiatrists, psychologists, and others will invariably overpredict its occurrence by several orders of magnitude" (p. 198).

Of course, as a matter of public policy, certain levels of predictive accuracy may well be needed—even required—before particular decisions could be based upon such predictions. The basic issue, therefore, is the degree of reliability and accuracy that should be expected before a variety of important legal, social, and public-policy decisions can properly be made.

Events that have low base rates are very difficult to predict with high levels of accuracy. Moreover, even the accuracy that is achieved comes at the cost of high rates of "false positives," that is, persons who are predicted to be dangerous but who will not actually display such behavior. The relevant literature on this point goes back more than 20 years (Meehl, 1954; Meehl and Rosen, 1955), but many of the "experts" who appear regularly in courts to testify on the issue of "dangerousness" seem not to be familiar with this work and its implications for their clinical predictions.

It must also be noted, however, that the level of reliability and accuracy that is needed is not absolute. It will vary with the nature and importance of the decisions to be made. Likewise, the specific decision situation will involve differing sets of competing objectives and trade-offs; thus, differing rates of "error" will be acceptable as long as certain other objectives can be met. For example, different rates of "false positive" errors will be accepted depending on whether we are dealing with discretionary release decisions for an offender with several previous felony convictions, with protecting the president from certain would-be assassins, or with a probation-versus-incarceration decision involving a check passer. In short, the fundamental public-policy decision will not hinge simply or only on the empirical or technical state of the predictive information.

PREDICTIONS INVOLVING RECIDIVISTIC OFFENDERS

In situations related to events with very low base rates, there are typically rather high rates of "false positive" errors. When dealing with a group that has much higher base rates for dangerous behaviors (e.g., offenders with three or more previous convictions for serious misdemeanors and felonies), however, the predictive task is easier. Nevertheless, since one is still predicting "dangerousness" (the *probability* of engaging in further serious and violent crimes), higher levels of accuracy, but not absolute accuracy, will be obtained. Much recent research evidence points clearly to certain groups of delinquents and criminals who have high rates of committing serious and violent offenses.

Wolfgang et al. (1972), for example, in a birth cohort study involving almost 10,000 boys born in Philadelphia, found that about one-third (3,475) of the boys had had at least one officially recorded police contact; but almost half of these youngsters showed no further police contacts. A very small proportion of the total cohort (6 percent), however, and a small proportion of those who had had a single police contact (18 percent), had been charged with five or more offenses. This group of 627 chronic offenders accounted for fully *71 percent* of all the homicides committed by the cohort, *77 percent* of the rapes, *70 percent* of the robberies, and *69 percent* of the aggravated assaults. Wolfgang and his associates have followed a 10-percent random sample of the original cohort since 1968, and official and self-reported offenses through age 26 and arrests and dispositions to age 30 have been analyzed further (Wolfgang, 1977). The followup shows that while 18 percent of all the offenders in the cohort were chronic offenders (with five or more crimes) by age 18, by age 30 fully 31.4 percent were chronic offenders. Using the birth cohort data up to age 30, Wolfgang found that, after the fourth offense, the probability that the offender will recidivate was about 0.80, and the likelihood that the next offense would be an index crime averaged 0.426 (ranging from 0.300 to 0.722).

Similarly, a study in New York City (Shinnar and Shinnar, 1975) found that while only two percent of all persons arrested had been previously arrested for homicide, 40 percent of all those arrested for homicide had previous arrests for a violent crime and 30.5 percent for felonious assaults.

The Rand Corporation has conducted a series of studies of career criminals. One of these (Petersilia et al., 1977; Petersilia, 1978) involved 49 felons in a medium-security prison who had at least one conviction of armed robbery, and who had served at least one previous prison term. In contrast to research that uses official police statistics or relies on victimization surveys, the data in this study were derived from detailed personal interviews with the felons and from checks of official criminal justice records. Obviously, given the selected nature of this sample, no broad generalizations can be made, but some interesting and potentially useful information was obtained by these investigators.

The 49 offenders reported a total of 10,500 crimes, or an average of 214 per offender. In a criminal career averaging about 20 years (with about half the time spent in prison), each offender committed an average of about 20 major felonies per year (about 4 violent and 16 property crimes). When the self-reported crimes were compared with the official data, *only 12 percent* of the reported crimes were found to have resulted in a recorded arrest. (These and similar findings have obvious implications with respect to relying only on officially recorded arrests, let alone criminal convictions, for accurate estimations of the nature and extent of an individual's actual criminal behavior.)

Petersilia (1978) reports that criminal careers typically had begun as early as age 14, had tended to peak in the early twenties, and then begun to decline around and after age 30. For instance, in the age group of 14 to 21 years, the offense rates averaged between 20 to 40 crimes per year; for those 22 to 25 years old, the rate was about 12 crimes per year; and by the time the offenders were 26 to 30 years old, the number of offenses had dropped to 7 per year.

In addition, two broad categories of offenders emerged from this study sample: the intensives, who saw themselves as criminals and went about their crimes in a rather purposeful manner, and the *intermittents*, who were less likely to see themselves as criminals and whose crimes were less frequently but more recklessly committed. The *intensives* tended to commit several crimes a month but were arrested for only about 5 percent of their crimes. In contrast, even though the *intermittents* had generally lower rates of crimes, they were much more likely to be arrested (Petersilia et al., 1977).

As interesting and informative as these findings are with respect to career offenders and the pattern of their offensive behavior, there are limitations to the wider generalization of the findings in view of the small size and selected nature of the sample. Similar findings, however, have been obtained by the Institute for Law and Social Research (INSLAW) in Washington, D. C., based on information from PROMIS (Prosecutor's Management Information System) Research Project. PROMIS (1977a, b) analyzed data pertaining to all arrests for nonfederal crimes in the District of Columbia between January 1, 1971 and August 31, 1975. Information was available on 72,610 arrests which involved 45,575 defendants; the data file provided information about the frequency with which individuals were rearrested, reprosecuted, and reconvicted during the 56-month period of the study.

This major study found that persons who were repeatedly arrested, prosecuted, and convicted accounted for a disproportionately large share of street crime. For example, persons who had been arrested four or more times in the 56-month period represented only 7 percent of the arrestees but they accounted for fully 24 percent of all the arrests. Thus, the extensiveness of the criminal history (regardless of whether it is expressed in terms of arrests, prosecutions, or convictions) seems to be a good predictor of future criminality. In essence, the PROMIS project found that if a defendant had 5 or more arrests before the current arrest, the probability of subsequent arrest approached certainty. It was also found that a significant percentage of these repeat offenders switched between felonies and misdemeanors: today's petty larceny defendant may have been involved in a past robbery and might possibly be involved in a future aggravated assault or even homicide. Similarly, 30 percent of defendants who had been arrested at least twice during the 56-month period accounted for the majority of arrests (felonies and serious misdemeanors) during this period. With respect to crimes of violence, it was found that 18 percent of the persons arrested for crimes of violence accounted for 35 percent of the arrests. Moreover, fully 26 percent of all felony cases—

31 percent of robbery cases and 28 percent of the murder cases—involved defendants who had been arrested while on conditional release (pretrial release or probation or parole).

Given this type of empirical data about career and recidivistic criminals, especially the findings from the PROMIS project that involved 45,575 defendants and Wolfgang's longitudinal study of a birth cohort, is it really accurate to say that dangerousness cannot be predicted? Although there will certainly be public policy and moral dilemmas pertaining to the actual uses of such predictive judgments, the technical predictive task is not as difficult for groups who have high base rates for serious and violent criminal behavior.

Improving Clinical Predictions

Elsewhere (Shah, 1978a, b) I have discussed some systematic sources of error in clinical assessments and predictions, namely, errors associated with illusory correlations and those caused by ignoring certain statistical rules in making predictive judgments. Some of these were not simply the result of careless clinical practices but appeared to be inherent in the nature and social context of the judgmental tasks. Moreover, the errors were very much influenced by powerful social contingencies which, in particular situations, implicitly or even explicitly direct that "false positive" errors are much to be preferred to "false negative" errors. Nevertheless, as I noted, greater awareness of and sensitivity to these systematic errors, and related training efforts, should help to distinguish the technical difficulties of the predictive task from certain social and political pressures and to develop procedures that make more effective use of normative statistical principles in efforts to reduce errors in predictions.

Another problem associated with the use of clinical predictions is that we have not developed effective means for evaluating their reliability and accuracy. The usual error-rate method (whether the particular prediction was right or wrong) is simple, but not very useful. It is insensitive to some important aspects of the predictive task. For example, the error-rate method does not take into account the magnitude of the error; it fails to distinguish a decision from the particular evidence on which the decision was based; and it does not penalize the judge who chooses to forecast dire outcomes (i.e., overpredicts dangerousness) rather than to attempt accurate predictions. Thus, as noted earlier, while case outcome decisions can be considered right or wrong, probabilities are not. They are best considered as being more or less accurate.

These aspects of evaluating clinical predictions have been demonstrated by Shapiro (1977) in his effort to evaluate the predictive skills of physicians in managing particular medical cases and problems. The error-rate method failed to detect meaningful differences between faculty and students, since the range was between 23 and 27. In contrast, when an accuracy coefficient was used, these measures ranged from 0.039 to 0.323, and they not only revealed important differences among the physicians with respect to predictive accuracy, but the method helped to pinpoint various sources of inaccurate judgments.

The work by Shapiro (1977) has not been cited to suggest that predictions of dangerousness are much like the medical predictions he studied. Rather, this work points to the critical importance of developing more systematic and meaningful methods for evaluating the reliability and the accuracy of clinical predictions of dangerousness. Only when such assessments have been undertaken can meaningful distinctions be made between clinicians who tend to be fairly good predictors and those lacking such skills. Such systematic assessments of clinical predictions could also allow clinical indicators to be combined with various actuarial data in efforts to further improve the accuracy of predictions of dangerousness.

SOME PUBLIC POLICY CONCERNS

In any pluralistic society there are numerous values, ideologies, goals and interests, as well as proponents and advocates of these interests who seek to influence public policies. Rarely is there a single value or societal goal involved with respect to issues of broad public concern, and seldom are such issues simple or clear-cut. Typically, the decisions regarding formulation and implementation of policies involve the weighing and balancing of several competing, and at times even conflicting, values and objectives. The primary responsibility for balancing competing claims and interests rests with specially designated decision-makers who are expected to be aware of a broad range of perspectives relevant to public concerns. In arriving at determinations of public policy, legislatures, courts, and other policymakers attempt to weigh competing interests, to consider their respective social value, and to articulate a balance that is compatible with the perceived interests and welfare of society at large. Following are a few of the many public policy concerns that pertain to the definition, assessment, prediction, and handling of dangerousness.

Societal Values and Dangerous Behaviors

There are markedly different societal and governmental responses to various types and sources of danger to the community. Clearly, societies are not equally concerned about all forms of behaviors, social conditions and practices that are likely to result in serious injury and/or loss of life. The basic problem is not simply whether or not a person is viewed as dangerous; much appears to depend upon *who* the person is, in *what ways* he is dangerous, the *social contexts* in which the behavior occurs, and the *value judgments* of influential and powerful groups in society with respect to the perceived harms that are officially to be designated as "dangerous." In essence, the defining, labeling, and handling of dangerous behaviors and situations are very much influenced by the dominant values, power structures, and associated political processes that exist in a society. For example, social deviants labeled as mentally ill have for several hundred years in the Anglo-American experience aroused much societal apprehension and have been major targets for preventive confinement (Dershowitz, 1974a, b). Yet many other categories of persons and groups who have quite glaringly demonstrated their dangerousness to society (e.g., repeatedly drunken drivers and offenders with 3 or more convictions for serious and violent crimes) do not seem to evoke similar concerns, nor are they as readily subjected to preventive confinement as are the mentally ill (Shah, 1974).

It is also ironic that our society tends to focus attention more readily on the dangerous acts of particular individuals but appears less concerned about certain social conditions and practices that pose serious hazards to the health, safety, and physical well-being of literally millions of citizens each year. For example, the *President's Report on Occupational Safety and Health* (1972) estimated that total deaths annually from job-related injuries amounted to over 14,000, with an estimated 2.2 million disabling injuries. The incidence of occupational diseases is less well-known, but estimates have pointed to "at least 390,000 new cases of disabling occupational diseases each year" (*President's Report on Occupational Safety and Health*, 1972, p. 111). It was also estimated in this report that there may be as many as 100,000 deaths per year from occupationally caused diseases (see also Hunter, 1970; Greene, 1974; Schanche, 1974).

Obviously, not all nor perhaps even the majority of these industrial and occupation-related deaths, diseases, and disabling injuries can be avoided. It is important to note, however, the remarkably different societal and governmental response to different types and sources of danger to the community. It seems very difficult for lawmakers and other governmental agencies to establish effective controls when powerful groups are involved. And even when regulations and established standards do exist for occupational safety and health, enforcement practices and sanctions reflect marked tolerance and "kid-glove" treatment of these powerful interests (Franklin, 1969; Page and O'Brien, 1973; Brodeur, 1974; Scott, 1974).

Thus in testifying before the House Select Subcommittee on Labor, Paul Brodeur (author of *Expendable Americans,* 1974) said:

> I submit that if a million people in the so-called middle class or professional class were dying each decade of preventable occupational disease, and if nearly four million were being disabled, there would long ago have been such a hue and cry for remedial action that if the Congress had not heeded it vast numbers of its members would have been turned out of office (Brodeur, 1974, p. 274).

Why Does "Dangerousness" Get Linked with Mental Illness?

One troublesome aspect of involuntary civil commitment of the mentally ill pertains to general beliefs and presumptions about the dangerousness of such persons. The concept of dangerousness (or the related notion of "likelihood of serious harm") is considered both in reference to danger to oneself and danger to others. I have argued (Shah, 1977) that many problems are created when the *parens patriae* responsibilities of the state (the benevolent functions of providing care for persons who are unable to care for themselves) are confused and confounded with the state's duty to protect the community from danger and harm (the police-power functions). As noted at the beginning of this discussion, the major concern here is with dangerous acts that are directed toward others.

The police-power concerns of the state involve the social control of criminal behavior and also the control of dangerous acts by persons considered to be mentally ill. With respect to the use of preventive confinement measures designed to protect the community, however, our society seems primarily to have singled out the mentally ill. There is the implicit, sometimes even explicit, assumption that by virtue of being mentally ill a person is more likely to engage in dangerous and violent behaviors. Yet, despite the presence of extensive and serious criminal records and the possibility of fairly accurate predictions of further criminal recidivism, in our criminal justice system such considerations are not the bases for continued incarceration once a prisoner's sentence has expired. In short, commitment laws for the mentally ill seem to be premised on the assumption (actually a belief) that, as a group, the mentally ill constitute one of the most dangerous groups in our society. Yet there is no sound or convincing empirical evidence to support such belief.

Many empirical studies over the past several decades have compared the arrest rates of hospitalized mental patients after their release with the arrest rates for the general population. The earlier studies indicated fairly consistently that released mental patients had lower arrest rates than the general population (Ashley, 1922; Pollock, 1938; Cohen and Freeman, 1945; Brill and Malzberg, 1954) while more recent studies rather consistently found higher arrest rates for the mental patients (Rappeport and Lassen, 1965, 1966; Giovannoni and Gurel, 1967; Zitrin et al., 1976; Durbin et al., 1977). Given the different jurisdictions and time periods involved, as well as methodological variations among these studies, it is not possible to make precise comparisons. There are clear suggestions however, about variations over time with respect to policies and practices for the hospitalization and release of mental patients. The studies, by and large, did not undertake more refined analyses to ascertain the reasons for the variations in arrest rates among mental patients. Moreover, all the comparisons were between released mental patients and the general population. Oddly, no comparisons were done with a sample of offenders released from penal institutions—if in fact one of the concerns was to determine the dangerousness of certain population groups.

Steadman and his associates (Steadman et al., 1978a, b) have recently undertaken some research that provides a much-needed clarification and explication of the basic policy-relevant questions. These investigators also have compared, in a New York jurisdiction, the arrest rates of released mental patients and the general population with similar rates for released criminal offenders. Two samples were used, patients released (during a 12-month period) in 1968, and another sample released in 1975. Summarized briefly, Steadman et al. (1978a) indicate that it is patients with arrest records before their hospitalization who account for the subsequently higher arrest rates for the released mental patients. Hospitalized mental patients without previous arrest records had later arrest rates generally *lower* than those of the general population. What seems to account for the higher arrest rates of the mental patients (as compared with the general population) in more recent years (namely, the 1975 sample), is the fact that there were more persons in state mental hospitals who had previous arrest records.

More importantly, when comparisons were made between patients released from state mental hospitals and offenders released from penal institutions in the same jurisdiction and during the same period of time, it was glaringly evident that the ex-prisoners had subsequent arrest rates *three to six times higher* than those of the patients. And, with respect to *violent crimes* the arrest rates (per 1000) for the 1968 sample for the general population, the ex-patients, and the ex-prisoners were 2.2, 2.05, and 22.63, respectively. Similarly, the arrest rates for *violent crimes* for the 1975 group, and in the same sequence, were 3.62, 12.35, and 87.50, respectively (Steadman et al., 1978b).

These findings support what is well-known to criminologists. For both the 1968 and the 1975 groups, those persons (mental patients and offenders) who had one arrest before their confinement were rearrested substantially more often than the general population, and those with multiple prior arrests had exceedingly high rates for arrests following their release. The ex-offenders had rearrest rates for violent crimes that were *six to ten times higher* than those of the mental patients.

As is evident from the research cited earlier (PROMIS Research Project, 1977a, b; Wolfgang et al., 1972; Wolfgang, 1977) persons who have displayed repeated and serious criminal conduct constitute one of the most dangerous groups in our society. Yet the mentally ill have been the group most affected by preventive confinement measures. This situation may be explained, perhaps in large measure, by the considerable research that has shown that strongly negative and rejecting public attitudes typify societal reactions to the mentally ill (Nunnally, 1961; Phillips, 1963, 1964; Bord, 1971; Rabkin, 1972). Selective reporting by the media of criminal and violent acts by mental patients may also have helped to foster and maintain public attitudes and policies that are discriminatory and stigmatizing (Steadman and Cocozza, 1978a).

In recent years there has been much reform in laws and practices concerning the commitment and release of mental patients, and a wide range of procedural due process protections has been extended to these citizens. Nevertheless, there continues to be a noteworthy absence of judicial scrutiny of the more basic *substantive* due process problems inherent in such policies. Stated simply, one aspect of substantive due process demands that all state actions be reasonably related to a reasonable and valid goal. Further, when such actions involve infringements of other "fundamental interests," e.g., depriving citizens of their right to liberty, these actions must be shown to promote not only a reasonable or valid but a *compelling* state goal. Although one would not dispute the validity of the state's interest in protecting the community from harm, very serious constitutional problems pertaining to equal protection and fundamental fairness are raised by the fact that the mentally ill have in large measure been singled out for preventive confinement, even though recidivistic offenders are clearly and demonstrably a far more dangerous group (Note, 1974; Shah, 1977).

The Rule of Law and the Role of "Experts"

When such key terms as "mental illness" and "dangerous" appear in various laws, they are meant to have precise legal meaning and should be defined carefully in the statutes. When these terms are used in such legal contexts they have a legal, and not a medical, psychiatric or psychological meaning. And, since these statutory definitions pertain to broad public policy concerns and objectives, the definition and interpretation of such key terms should not devolve exclusively, nor even primarily, upon mental health experts. However, as a result of vagueness in statutory language, the lack of clear definitions, and also because of judicial default, in practice the "experts" often seem to end up making such crucial public policy determinations (Shah, 1974, 1977).

The Texas Code of Criminal Procedure provides, for example, that criminal defendants who have been committed following adjudication, as incompetent to stand trial and as not guilty by reason of insanity, to a maximum security hospital or unit, cannot be transferred to nonsecurity units *unless* they are determined not to be "manifestly dangerous" (see note 1). It seems, however, that when the legislature revised this statute in 1975 and mandated the establishment of a review board, it failed to define "manifestly dangerous" (Dudley, 1978). Thus, even though the Texas Department of Mental Health and Mental Retardation set about establishing criteria and standards for the review board to determine manifest dangerousness, it must obviously be difficult to determine something that the legislature did not see fit to define.

Situations of this type place mental health experts in roles that are specifically designated for legislative and judicial policymakers, since the relevant decisions involve not only narrow technical questions but ultimate legal and public policy determinations. The blurring and confusing of such roles and responsibilities means that experts may be placed in positions of bringing their own particularistic and personal views to the determination of issues that involve normative judgments and require careful balancing of competing societal objectives, for example, the rights of the individual and the protection of the community.

Legislative and judicial bodies as well as mental health and related experts may need to consider Freidson's admonition on the role of professionals in making essentially normative and policy decisions:

> (T)he profession's role in a free society should be limited to contributing the technical information men need to make their own decisions on the basis of their own values. When he preempts the authority to direct, even constrain men's decisions on the basis of his own values, the professional is no longer an expert but rather a member of a new privileged class disguised as expert (Freidson, 1970: p. 382).

Death-Penalty Decisions and the Role of Mental Health Professionals

The foregoing discussion about the role of "experts" is relevant to some recent developments in the use of mental health expertise in decisions on the imposition of the death penalty. The relevant law in Texas illustrates the manner in which the use of mental health professionals may blur fundamentally legal and moral judgments with considerations of technical expertise.

After finding a defendant guilty of a capital offense, courts in Texas· are required to conduct a separate sentencing proceeding to determine whether the defendant shall be sentenced to death or to life imprisonment. Article 37.071 of the Texas Code of Criminal Procedure (note 2) spells out the sentencing procedures and decision criteria to be used in capital cases. At the conclusion of the presentation of the evidence, the court submits the following three issues to the jury:

> (1) whether the conduct of the defendant that caused the death of the deceased was committed deliberately and with the reasonable expectation that the death of the deceased or another would result;

> (2) whether there is a probability that the defendant would commit criminal acts of violence that would constitute a continuing threat to society; and

> (3) if raised by the evidence, whether the conduct of the defendant in killing the deceased was unreasonable in response to the provocation, if any, by the deceased (Art. 37.071).

If the jury returns an affirmative finding on each of these three questions, the court is required to impose the death penalty. If a negative finding is returned on any one of the issues, the court is required to give a sentence of confinement for life by the Texas Department of Corrections.

Expert testimony by mental health professionals has been used in reference to the second issue. Hence, it is this particular issue that will be the subject of this brief discussion. (Readers interested in a more detailed discussion of the legal questions and problems raised by Texas procedure in capital cases should see Dix, 1977a, b.)

As noted, mental health professionals who appear as expert witnesses in various legal and related proceedings should be knowledgeable about and sensitive to the relevant legal issues and questions: Moreover, when testifying as experts they should also reflect good awareness and understanding of the existing scientific and professional literature, and particularly of the empirical research evidence that points to the limitations associated with various technical tasks, for example, the prediction of events with low base rates. Indeed, it has been urged that since the statements and recommendations of the experts may well be accepted with undue deference, and since such statements can have very serious consequences for the persons affected, being knowledgeable about the specific legal and technical issue should be viewed as a professional and ethical obligation by mental health professionals (Shah, 1969).

Yet, in light of some of the published reports concerning the expert testimony given by mental health professionals in capital sentencing procedures in Texas (Dix, 1977a, 1978), serious questions arise about the role and function of the expert witnesses. Questions are also raised about the level and nature of the expertise that seems to have been displayed in some of these cases.

My particular concern here, however, relates to the broader implications of the role of mental health professionals with regard to the second issue cited above, "whether there is a probability that the defendant would commit criminal acts of violence that would constitute a continuing threat to society." Clearly, in these sentencing decisions, the alternative to imposition of the death penalty after conviction of a capital offense is penal confinement for life.[3] Thus, it seems that two major questions are raised by the concern about the defendant's posing a "continuing threat to society": whether the person is likely to display violent behavior toward other inmates and staff while serving a life sentence; and whether, following release to the community *after* serving a life sentence, the person would engage in further "criminal acts of violence."

It would typically be difficult to answer the first question without knowing about the specific penal setting in which the defendant is likely to be confined and the particular situations in which opportunities for violent behavior may be available. Penal authorities could address this concern by providing the necessary degrees of security and supervision during the confinement—as they doubtless do in the case of other inmates who pose such threats during their incarceration. As for the second question, given the numerous problems associated with even shorter-range predictions of behavior (e.g., for periods of 12 and 24 months), the prospects of reliable and accurate predictions *following* completion of a life sentence in prison boggle the mind. If the defendant is a young male with an extensive and serious record of criminal violence, and if a life sentence may in fact allow release on parole in 10 to 15 years, it may be that such a defendant released in his late twenties or early thirties could still pose some risk of further dangerousness. However, even though an individual might reasonably be considered to pose a "continuing threat" at the time of sentencing, the so-called burning-out phenomenon as a function of aging makes it rather unlikely that a person returned to the community in his late forties or early fifties will still pose a "continuing threat to society."

In light of what has been discussed about the problems associated with clinical predictions and the relative advantages of actuarial and statistical approaches, the most relevant and reliable information about future dangerousness could be obtained by triers of fact, weighing the nature and extensiveness of the defendant's previous criminal behavior. Since predictions of dangerousness always involve probabilities, even a very high probability (e.g., 90 percent) of further dangerous behavior would reduce—but not eliminate—the likelihood of error. The defendant could still be in that 10 percent that is *not* likely to present a continuing threat of violence either during or following a life sentence in prison. Thus, the ultimate decision-makers must still face awesome legal and moral judgments. If imposition of the death penalty serves primarily to express society's sense of condemnation, revulsion, and retribution for crimes regarded as especially brutal and horrifying, then the question arises whether there is *any* role for mental health professionals making such decisions.

In essence, it seems that mental health expertise may possibly be used, or even misused, in these situations to cloak and launder the vexing moral judgments that must be made by the triers of fact.

CONCLUSION

This discussion has noted several decision points in the criminal justice and mental health systems where the issues of an individual's dangerousness and of various dispositional options are considered. Yet, despite the extensive uses of the notion of dangerousness and the serious consequences that may follow such determinations, clear and precise definitions are overdue, and much clarification and improvement are needed. The vagueness of a concept that is so critical for a variety of decisions can and indeed does lead to many problems because the notion can be pulled and stretched to fit dispositional and ideological preferences. Similarly, the manner in which behavior is commonly conceptualized and various predictive assessments made gives insufficient attention to the setting and situational variables that influence behavior. It has been suggested that an interactional perspective, one which considers both individual and situational variables, offers many improvements over traditional personality-trait, psychodynamic, and situationistic approaches.

Even though major decisions about people are based on assessments and predictions about their future dangerousness, there are many technical difficulties inherent in predicting events with very low base rates. Although such predictive tasks remain difficult, greater use of actuarial and statistical approaches could lead to several improvements. Predictive accuracy may be increased only modestly and false-positive errors reduced to some degree, but the major gain would be in markedly improved consistency and reliability of such assessments. Improvements in consistency should enhance the equity and fairness of the decisions.

The manner in which therapeutic and social-control objectives tend to become confused and confounded, to the detriment of the individual affected, was noted. Even though the value placed on individual liberty leads to the use of demanding rules in the criminal process before conviction and incarceration can result, the values associated with coercive confinement undergo a major shift when the person is labeled as mentally ill and the purpose of the confinement is couched in the idiom of remediation and treatment. The application of the label mentally ill and the invocation of therapeutic objectives have long had the effect of neutralizing the values and decision rules that would otherwise require our society to let nine guilty persons go free rather than risk the erroneous confinement of a single individual. Although courts have in recent years given much attention to these sources of unfairness and significant improvements have been made, constitutional issues of substantive due process (namely, in singling out the mentally ill for preventive confinement) still remain to be addressed. The discriminatory practices vis-à-vis the mentally ill tend to reinforce and maintain longstanding social prejudices. Thus, to the extent that policy-makers concentrate their concerns with "dangerous" behaviors largely on the mentally ill, they help to perpetuate the myth that the mentally ill, as a group, are the most dangerous persons in our society. Yet there is abundant empirical evidence to demonstrate that certain other groups (e.g., drunken drivers and serious recidivistic criminals) are clearly and convincingly more dangerous to the community.

Mental health professionals who function as experts in interactions with the criminal justice and legal systems must be knowledgeable about and sensitive to the relevant legal issues and questions. If indeed such professionals are to function as experts, they should also be knowledgeable about the relevant professional and scientific literature— especially the empirical research that points to the limitations of assessment, predictive, and therapeutic skills. Indeed, when the lives and welfare of people are seriously to be affected, the acquisition of this knowledge and understanding should be viewed as a professional and ethical obligation.

Finally, mental health professionals and others who interact with the legal system should take care to ensure that their limited technical contributions and expertise are not blurred and confounded with the ultimate legal, moral, and public policy judgments that are the proper responsibility of other societal decision makers.

NOTES

1. Texas Code of Criminal Procedure (1975), Art. 46.02, Sec. 608; Art. 46.03, Sec. 8.
2. Texas Code of Criminal Procedure (1975), Art. 37.071, "Procedure in capital case." Section (b) refers to three issues that the jury has to address; subsection 2 requires a determination "whether there is a probability that the defendant would commit criminal acts of violence that would constitute a continuing threat to society."
3. The Texas Code of Criminal Procedure (1975), Art. 12.32, provides that an individual adjudged guilty of a first degree felony "shall be punished by confinement in the Texas Department of Corrections for life or for any term of not more than 99 years or less than 5 years" (p. 410).

REFERENCES

Ashley, M. C. Outcome of 1000 cases paroled from the Middletown State Homeopathic Hospital. *State Hospital Quarterly* 8:64–70, 1922.

Bem, D., and Allen, A. On predicting some of the people some of the time: the search for cross-situational consistencies in behavior. *Psychol. Rev.* 81:50–520, 1974.

Bord, R. J. Rejection of the mentally ill: continuities and further developments. *Social Problems* 18:496–509, 1971.

Bowers, K. S. Situationism in psychology: an analysis and critique. *Psychol. Rev.* 80:307–336, 1973.

Brill, H., and Malzberg, B. Statistical Report of the Arrest Record of Male Ex-Patients, Age 16 and Over, Released from New York State Mental Hospitals During the Period 1946–48. Albany: New York State Department of Mental Hygiene, Albany, 1954. (American Psychiatric Association, Mental Hospital Service Supplementary Mailing 153. August 1962).

Brodeur, P. *Expendable Americans*. Viking Press, New York, 1974.

Cohen, L. H., and Freeman, H. How dangerous to the community are state hospital patients? *Connecticut State Medicine Journal* 9:697–700, 1945.

Cocozza, J. J., and Steadman, H. J. Some refinements in the measurement and prediction of dangerous behavior. *Am. J. Psychiatry* 131:1012–1020, 1974.

Cocozza, J. J., and Steadman, H. J. The failure of psychiatric predictions of dangerousness: clear and convincing evidence. *Rutgers Law Review* 29:1084–1101, 1976.

Dershowitz, A. M. The origins of preventive confinement in Anglo-American law. Part l. *University of Cincinnati Law Review* 43:1–60, 1974a.

Dershowitz, A. M. The origins of preventive confinement in Anglo-American law. Part II. *University of Cincinnati Law Review* 43:781–846, 1974b.

Dix, G. E. The death penalty, "dangerousness," psychiatric testimony, and professional ethics. *American Journal of Criminal Law* 5:151–214, 1977a.

Dix, G. E. Administration of the Texas death penalty statute: constitutional infirmities related to the prediction of dangerousness. *Texas Law Review* 55:1343–1414, 1977b.

Dix, G. E. Participation by mental health professionals in capital murder sentencing. *International Journal of Law and Psychiatry* 1:283–308, 1978.

Dudley, H. K. A review board for determining the dangerousness of mentally ill offenders. *Hosp. Community Psychiatry* 29:453–456, 1978.

Durbin, J. R., Pasewark, R. A., and albers, D. Criminality and mental illness: a study of arrest rates in a rural state. *Am. J. Psychiatry* 134:80–83, 1977.

Ekehammer, B. Interactionism in personality from a historical perspective. *Psychol. Bull.* 81:1026–1048, 1974.

Endler, N. S., and Magnusson, D. Toward an interactional psychology of personality. *Psychol. Bull.* 83:956–974, 1976.

Fairweather, G. W. *Methods in Experimental Social Innovation*. Wiley, New York, 1967.

Fairweather, G. W., Sanders, D., and Tornatzky, L. *Creating Change in Mental Health Organizations*. Pergamon Press, New York, 1974.

Franklin, B. A. The scandal of death and injury in the mines. *N.Y. Times Magazine*, March 30, 1969.

Freidson, E. *Profession of Medicine*. Dodd, Mead, New York, 1970.

Giovannoni, J. M., and Gurel, L. Socially disruptive behavior of ex-mental patients. *Arch. Gen. Psychiatry* 17:146–153, 1967.

Goldstein, J., and KATZ, J. Dangerousness and mental illness. *Yale Law Journal* 70:225–239, 1960.

Gough, H. G. *Manual for the California Psychological Inventory* (rev. Ed.). Consulting Psychologists Press, Palo Alto, California, 1969.

Greene, W. Life vs. livelihood. *N.Y. Times Magazine*, Nov. 24, 1974, pp. 95–98, 104–105.

Hogan, R., Desoto, C. B., and Solano, C. Traits, tests, and personality research. *Am. Psychol.* 32:255–264, 1977.

Hunter, D. *The Diseases of Occupation*. English Universities Press, London, 1970.

Meehl, P. E. *Clinical vs. Statistical Prediction*. University of Minnesota Press, Minneapolis, 1954.

Meehl, P. E., and Rosen, A. Antecedent probability and the efficiency of psychometric signs, patterns, or cutting scores. *Psychol. Bull.* 52:194–216, 1955.

Mischel, W. Toward a cognitive social learning reconceptualization of personality. *Psychol. Rev.* 80:252–283, 1973.

Mischel, W. On the future of personality measurement. *Am. Psychol.* 32:246–254, 1977.

Monahan, J. The prediction of violence, in *Violence and Criminal Justice*. D. Chappell and J. Monahan, eds. Lexington Books, Lexington, Mass., 1975, pp. 15–35.

Monahan, J. The prevention of violence, in *Community Mental Health and the Criminal Justice System*. J. Monahan, ed. Pergamon Press, New York, 1976, pp. 13–34.

Monahan, J. Prediction research and the emergency commitment of dangerous mentally ill persons: a reconsideration. *Am. J. Psychiat.* 135:198–201, 1978a.

Monahan, J. The prediction of violent criminal behavior: a methodological critique and prospectus, in *Deterrence and Incapacitation: Estimating the Effects of Criminal Sanctions on Crime Rates*. A. Blumstein, J. Cohen, and D. Nagin, eds. National Academy of Science, Washington, D.C., 1978b, pp. 244–269.

Moos, R. H. Sources of variance in responses to questionnaire and in behavior. *J. Abnorm. Psychol.* 74:405–412, 1969.

Moos, R. H. Conceptualizations of human environments. *Am. Psychol.* 28:652–665, 1973.

Note. Developments in the law—civil commitment of the mentally ill. *Harvard Law Review* 87:1190–1406, 1974.

Note. Mental illness: a suspect classification. *Yale Law Journal* 83:1237–1270, 1974.

Nunnally, J. D. *Popular Conceptions of Mental Health.* Holt, Rinehart & Winston, New York, 1961.

Pace, J. A., and O'Brien, M. *Bitter Wages.* Grossman, New York, 1973.

Pervin, L. The representative design of person-situation research, in *Personality at the Crossroads: Current Issues in International Psychology.* D. Magnusson and N. S. Endler, eds. Erlbaum, Hillsdale, N. J., 1977.

PetersiliA, J. Career criminal prosecution: an idea whose time has come. *Prosecutor's Brief, July-August,* 24–27, 1978.

Petersilia, J., Greenwood, P. W., and Lavin, M. *Criminal Careers of Habitual Offenders.* Rand Corp., Santa Monica, California, 1977.

Phillips, D. L. Rejection: a possible consequence of seeking help for mental disorders. *Am. Sociol. Rev.* 28:963–972, 1963.

Phillips, D. L. Rejection of the mentally ill: the influence of behavior and sex. *Am. Sociol. Rev.* 29:679–687, 1964.

Pollock, H. M. Is the paroled patient a menace to the community? *Psychiat. Quart.* 12:236–244, 1938.

President's Report on Occupational Safety and Health. U.S. Govt. Printing Office, Washington, D.C., 1972.

Promis Research Project. *Highlights of Interim Findings and Implications.* (Publ. 1) Institute for Law and Social Research, Washington, D.C., 1977a.

Promis Research Project. *Curbing the Repeat Offender: A Strategy for Prosecutors.* (Publ. 3) Institute for Law and Social Research, Washington, D.C., 1977b.

Rabkin, J. G. Opinions about mental illness: a review of the literature. *Psychol. Bull.* 77:153–171, 1972.

Rappeport, J. R., and LASSEN, G. Dangerousness—arrest rate comparisons of discharged mental patients and the general population. *Am. J. Psychiatry* 121:776–783, 1965.

Rappeport, J. R., and Lassen, G. The dangerousness of female patients: a comparison of arrest rates of discharged psychiatric patients and the general population. *Am. J. Psychiatry* 123:413–419, 1966.

Schanche, D. A. Vinyl chloride: time bomb on the production line. *Today's Health* 52:16–19, 70–72, 1974.

Schwitzgebel, R. K. Survey of state civil commitment statutes, in *Civil Commitment and Social Policy.* A. L. McGarry, R. K. Schwitzgebel, P. D. Lipsett, and D. Lelos, eds. (Final Report on NIMH grant MH25955) Laboratory of Community Psychiatry, Harvard Medical School, Boston, Massachusetts, 1978, pp. 70–104.

Scott, R. *Muscle and Blood.* Dutton, New York, 1974.

Shah, S. A. Treatment of offenders: some behavioral concepts, principles, and approaches. *Federal Probation* 30:1–9, 1966.

Shah, S. A. Crime and mental illness: some problems in defining and labeling deviant behavior. *Mental Hygiene* 53:21–33, 1969.

Shah, S. A. Some interactions of law and mental health in the handling of social deviance. *Catholic Univ. Law Rev.* 23:674–719, 1974.

Shah, S. A. Dangerousness: some definitional, conceptual, and public policy issues, in *Perspectives in Law and Psychology*, vol. 1. B. D. Sales, ed. Plenum, New York, 1977, pp. 91–119.

Shah, S. A. Dangerousness: a paradigm for exploring some issues in law and psychology. *Am. Psychol.* 33:224–238, 1978a.

Shah, S. A. Dangerousness and mental illness: some conceptual, prediction, and policy dilemmas, in *Dangerous Behavior: A Problem in Law and Mental Health.* C. J. Frederick, ed. U.S. Govt. Printing Office, Washington, D.C., 1978b, pp. 153–191.

ShapirO, A. R. The evaluation of clinical predictions. *N. Engl. J. Med.* 296:1509–1514, 1977.

Shinnar, R., and Shinnar, S. The effects of the criminal justice system on the control of crime: a quantitative approach. *Law & Society Rev.* 9:581–611, 1975.

Steadman, H. J., and Cocozza, J. J. *Careers of the Criminally Insane.* Lexington Books, Lexington, Massachusetts, 1974.

Steadman, H. J., and Cocozza, J. J. Selective reporting and the public's misconceptions of the criminally insane. *The Public Opinion Quarterly* 41:523–533, 1978a.

Steadman, H. J., and Cocozza, J. J. Psychiatry, dangerousness and the repetitively violent offender. *J. Criminal Law & Criminology*, 69:226–231, 1978b.

Steadman, H. J., Cocozza, J. J., and MELICK, M. E. Explaining the increased arrest rate among mental patients: the changing clientele of state hospitals. *Am. J. Psychiatry* 135:816–820, 1978a.

Steadman, H. J., Vanderwyst, D., and Ribner, S. Comparing arrest rates of mental patients and criminal offenders. *Am. J. Psychiatry* 135:1218–1220, 1978b.

Toch, H. *Violent Men: An Inquiry into the Psychology of Violence.* Aldine, Chicago, 1969.

Webster, W. H. *Crime in the United States—1977.* (Uniform Crime Reports) U.S. Govt. Printing Office, Washington, D.C. 1978.

Wenk, E. A., Robison, J. O., and Smith, G. W. Can violence be predicted? *Crime and Delinquency* 18:393–402, 1972.

Wolfgang, M. E. From boy to man—from delinquency to crime. Paper delivered at the National Symposium on the Serious Juvenile Offender, Dept. of Corrections, State of Minn., Minneapolis, Sept., 1977.

Wolfgang, M. E., Figlio, R. M., and Sellin, T. *Delinquency in a Birth Cohort.* University of Chicago Press, Chicago, 1972.

Zitrin, A., Hardesty, A. S., and Burdock, E. T. Crime and violence among mental patients. *Am. J. Psychiatry* 133:142–149, 1976.

3

Improving the Clinical Practice of Violence Risk Assessment: Technology, Guidelines, and Training

RANDY BORUM

ABSTRACT: *Despite a long history of interest in, and criticism of, the ability of mental health professionals to assess and predict violence, there have been few efforts to develop or evaluate interventions to improve decision making in this area. This article provides a brief overview of recent research developments on violence risk. Drawing on these advances, 3 recommendations are outlined for improving the clinical practice of risk assessment: (a) to improve assessment technology, (b) to develop clinical practice guidelines, and (c) to develop training programs and curricula.*

The prediction of violence is one of the most complex and controversial issues in behavioral science and law (Grisso & Appelbaum, 1992, 1993; Litwack, 1993; Poythress, 1992). Nevertheless, courts have continued to rely on mental health professionals for assistance in civil and criminal cases when determining facts involving potential dangerousness or risk for future violence (Melton, Petrila, Poythress, & Slobogin, 1987).

The importance of violence as a clinical issue, however, is not limited to mental health professionals who practice in the forensic arena, or even to those who work primarily with high-risk clients (Borum, Swartz, & Swanson, 1996). As public and private mental health systems are increasingly penetrated by various forms of managed care, patients' risk for committing violent behavior has become a critical balancing factor in attempts to contain costs and limit service utilization. Patients who are assessed as dangerous inevitably utilize high-cost services (e.g., inpatient hospitalization) and are vulnerable to system attempts at cost shifting (Petrila, 1995). In these circumstances, patients' risk for violence can become an issue in their ultimate exclusion from a benefit plan (e.g., because they rapidly exceed the benefit limit) or a ticket into an alternate public system.

Perhaps the most familiar reminders of violence in clinical practice have come from the sequelae of the California Supreme Court's decision in *Tarasoff v. Regents of the University of California* (1976), which created a duty for mental health professionals to protect third parties against patient violence. According to the court, this duty obtains "once a therapist does in fact determine, or *under applicable professional standards* [italics added] reasonably should have determined that a patient poses a serious danger of violence to others" (*Tarasoff*, 1976, p. 345).

One of the key obstacles for clinicians who must fulfill this duty, and for mental health and managed care systems that must assess, manage, and communicate about persons at risk for violent behavior, is that no explicit national professional standards exist in psychology or other mental health disciplines for assessment and management of violence risk. Nor have there been many substantial attempts in this field to develop systematic training programs in risk assessment; to integrate this training into graduate education in professional psychology; or to evaluate how, or even whether, such training can improve clinicians' assessments and judgments. Furthermore, despite a long history of clinical and research interest in, and criticism of, clinicians' ability to predict violence, there have been few efforts to develop or evaluate interventions to improve decision making in this area.

This article covers two major domains relating to these issues. The first section provides a brief overview of recent research progress in risk assessment. This section includes an overview of studies on predictive ability (How accurate are mental health professionals' predictions of violent behavior among people with mental disorder?); the relationship between violence and mental disorder (Are people with mental disorder more likely to be violent than people without mental disorder?); base rates of violent behavior (What is the prevalence of violent behavior among people with and without mental disorder?); and risk factors for violent behavior (Which individual, historical, clinical, and contextual factors are associated with, or statistically increase, the risk of violent behavior?). Advancing knowledge in these areas provides the foundation for improving clinical risk assessment practice.

The second section outlines three recommendations for improving the clinical practice of risk assessment among persons with mental disorder. These recommendations are (a) to improve assessment technology, (b) to develop clinical practice guidelines, and (c) to develop training programs and curricula. It is argued that professionals in psychology and other mental health disciplines should apply what they have learned from two generations of research (as discussed in the first section) in order (a) to develop and research new assessment tools and methods, (b) to establish clinical guidelines for their application, and (c) to train clinicians to practice according to these guidelines.

RESEARCH PROGRESS

Research on Predictive Ability

Early research on the ability of mental health professionals to assess dangerousness in people with mental disorder produced less than encouraging results. In 1981, John Monahan did a comprehensive review of the few existing studies and concluded that

> the "best" clinical research currently in existence indicates that *psychiatrists and psychologists are accurate in no more than one out of three predictions of violent behavior over a several-year period among institutionalized populations that had both committed violence in the past (and thus had a high base rate for it) and who were diagnosed as mentally ill.* (pp. 47, 49)

On the basis of a second generation of studies within the past 15 years, the current tenor of researchers in this area is somewhat more optimistic. Most suggest that mental health professionals have at least a modest ability to predict violence and that their predictions are significantly more accurate than chance (Lidz, Mulvey, & Gardner, 1993; Monahan & Steadman, 1994; Mossman, 1994; Otto, 1992; cf. Menzies & Webster, 1995). In a comprehensive review of the second-generation research, Otto (1992) concluded that "changing conceptions of dangerousness and advances in predictive techniques suggest that, rather than one in three predictions of long-term dangerousness being accurate, at least one in two short-term predictions are accurate" (p. 130). However, he also cautioned that "even under the best circumstances . . . mental health professionals will still make a considerable number of incorrect predictions with false positives being the most common type of error" (p. 128). Likewise, Mossman, in his reanalysis of 58 existing data sets on prediction of violence from the past two decades (including both first- and second-generation studies), concluded (a) that clinicians were able to distinguish violent from nonviolent patients with a "modest, better-than-chance level of accuracy"; (b) that predictive ability in the second-generation studies appeared better than that in the first-generation studies; (c) that the accuracy of short-term predictions was not significantly different than the accuracy of long-term predictions; and (d) that past behavior was a robust predictor of future behavior (in some cases even better than clinical judgments or cross-validated actuarial techniques).

In part, the level of predictive accuracy improved as a result of advances in research methodology. For example, if a person is predicted to be violent and subsequently engages in violent behavior, but that behavior is not detected by researchers, the prediction erroneously appears to be a false-positive one. However, by using self-reports and collateral reports, and not relying solely on arrest records as a criterion for violent behavior, more violent events are identified, thereby reducing artifactual false-positive predictions and improving overall rates of accuracy (Mulvey, Shaw, & Lidz, 1994). In addition, two key assumptions that previously were seen as causative of limited predictive accuracy have been challenged by recent research: (a) that there is no significant relationship between mental disorder and violence and (b) that base rates (prevalence) of violence are so low that it is almost impossible to predict.

Relationship between Mental Disorder and Violence

For many years, the conventional wisdom among social scientists maintained that no significant relationship existed between violence and mental illness, when other variables such as drug abuse, poverty, gender, age, and victimization were taken into account. Thus, by extension,

> mental health professionals generally have been considered incapable of accurate predictions of future violence by the mentally ill—at least in part because there was assumed to be no relationship between that which mental health professionals knew (namely, how to diagnose mental disorder) and the predictions they were being asked to make (whether a person would be violent). (Appelbaum, 1994, p. 78)

However, recent research efforts, including two large-scale community epidemiologic surveys (Link, Andrews, & Cullen, 1992; Swanson, Holzer, Ganju, & Jono, 1990), and a second generation of studies that improved on the limitations of earlier research now suggest that "mental disorder may be a robust and significant risk factor for the occurrence of violence" (Monahan, 1992, p. 519; for reviews, see Appelbaum, 1994; Link & Stueve, 1995; Monahan, 1992, in press; Monahan & Steadman, 1994; Mulvey, 1994; Taylor, 1995).

Base Rates of Violence

In the assessment of violence risk, the term *base rate* refers to the known prevalence of a specified type of violent behavior within a given population over a given time period. Because low base-rate (infrequent) conditions, by their very nature, are difficult to predict, much of the early research suggested that predictions of violence were doomed to high rates of error because violent behavior was a rare event, even among persons with mental illness. However, current research has shown that base rates for violence are considerably higher than was previously believed.[1]

Early studies estimated base rates by examining rates of arrest for violent crime among people who had been discharged from psychiatric hospitals and found that these rates were fairly low, typically ranging from 2% to 5% over a one-year follow-up period (Hiday, 1992; Monahan & Steadman, 1994; Steadman, Cocozza, & Melick,

1978). However, more recently, investigators have expanded their research criterion measures and sources of information on violence. For example, a series of studies by Klassen and O'Connor (1988a, 1988b, 1988c, 1989) included in the criteria for violence, not only arrest but also rehospitalization for an act that would have resulted in arrest for a violent crime and found that approximately 25–30% of patients released into the community met this criterion within a one-year follow-up period. Similarly, pilot data from the MacArthur Risk Assessment Study (Steadman et al., 1994) showed that across three study sites, 27% of participants reported at least one violent event within a follow-up period of up to six months. The one site where the follow-up extended the full six months had a reported violence rate of 33%. It is also worth noting that these rates were calculated before data from official records were available, so the rates could actually be somewhat higher (Steadman et al., 1994).

Lidz et al. (1993) studied 714 patients who presented to a psychiatric emergency room and followed them in the community for six months. In that period, violence was reported in approximately 45% of the cases (53% in the cases predicted to be violent and 36% in the comparison group). The same trend also appears to hold for violent behavior in inpatient settings, where approximately 15–28% of people engage in some type of physically assaultive behavior, whereas as many as 40–50% engage in some type of broadly defined dangerous behavior, including threats and other physical acts (Otto, 1992).

Finally, although in the general population men have much higher rates of violent offending (higher base rates) than do women (Federal Bureau of Investigation, 1993; Maccoby & Jacklin, 1974; Wilson & Herrnstein, 1985), among people with mental disorder, men and women do not significantly differ in their base rates of violent behavior. Indeed, the rates are remarkably similar and in some cases are slightly higher for women (Lidz et al., 1993; Newhill, Mulvey, & Lidz, 1995; Steadman et al., 1994; Swanson, 1994), suggesting that similar levels of predictive accuracy could be attained across gender.

Research on Risk Factors for Violence

In addition to advances in research on predictive accuracy, the base of scientific knowledge about risk factors for violent behavior has also grown tremendously over the past 15 years (Monahan & Steadman, 1994). Whereas studies of predictive ability focus on clinicians' rates of accuracy in predicting violence, studies of risk factors focus on identifying the individual, historical, clinical, and contextual variables that are empirically associated with violent behavior.

As noted above, several features of this recent research contradict the findings of the early research, including findings on the relationships between violence and mental disorder and between violence and demographic variables. In addition, there is a critical body of research evolving on situational-environmental variables that influence aggression (Estroff & Zimmer, 1994; Estroff, Zimmer, Lachicotte, & Benoit, 1994; Goldstein, 1994). Substantial contributions along these lines are also expected to emerge from a third generation of studies arising from the MacArthur Risk Assessment Study, a large-scale, multisite, longitudinal study of approximately 1,000 people admitted to civil psychiatric hospitals (Steadman et al., 1994). This study is examining a wide range of risk factors within four domains: dispositional (e.g., demographic, personality, and cognitive variables); historical (e.g., social history, prior hospitalization and treatment compliance, and history of crime and violence); contextual (e.g., perceived stress, social support, and means for violence); and clinical (e.g., diagnosis, symptom patterns, functioning, and substance abuse). To the extent that such studies identify more accurate risk factors, this information should be used by clinicians to make more accurate, empirically based predictions of violence risk.

IMPROVING RISK ASSESSMENT IN CLINICAL PRACTICE

Despite substantive advances in knowledge about the risk for violent behavior among people with mental disorder, there have been virtually no systematic efforts to incorporate this information into a useful, empirically based framework for clinical assessment. Nor have many investigators focused on developing interventions to improve the accuracy (or the validity) of violence predictions or examining the ability of mental health professionals to reliably make such assessments. Because mental health professionals must continually make such determinations in the context of *Tarasoff* situations, level of care decisions, civil commitment, forensic evaluations, and so forth, these topics seem worthy of attention. As Webster, Eaves, Douglas, and Wintrup (1995) noted, "The great challenge in what remains of the 1990s is to integrate the almost separate worlds of research on the prediction of violence and the clinical practice of assessment. At present the two domains scarcely intersect" (p. v).

In seeking to advance and improve clinical decision making about people's risk for violent behavior, at least three areas seem worthy of attention: (a) advancing risk assessment technology, (b) defining clinical practice guidelines, and (c) developing training programs and curricula. As professional advances are made in these areas, they will form a foundation for a research agenda to improve decision making in violence risk assessment.

Improving Risk Assessment Technology

The use of standardized assessment instruments is an important element in efforts to improve the reliability and the validity of risk judgments and to enhance the clarity of risk communication. At a minimum, these devices can serve as a checklist for clinicians to ensure that essential areas of inquiry are recalled and evaluated. At best, they may be able to provide hard actuarial data on the probability of violence among people (and environments) with a given set of characteristics, circumstances, or both. As Schopp (1996) notes,

> To the extent that developments in this research allow more precise statements of the probability of harmful conduct of specified types or severity in specified conditions, these probability statements provide decision makers with more useful information while remaining within the descriptive and explanatory expertise of psychologists. (p. 940)

Webster et al. (1995) outlined several requirements for an assessment instrument or scheme to be useful: accessibility (organized around a few important ideas commonly understood across disciplines), scientific integrity (rooted in what is already known), testability (defined precisely enough to permit testing of items), administrative feasibility (linked to established policies and practices), and efficiency (designed with time constraints in mind; p. vi).

The current medical literature suggests that using structured data-gathering methods can lead to a more comprehensive and a potentially less selective examination. For example, Houziaux and Lefebvre (1986) reviewed much of the literature on computer-assisted medical history taking, or computer-assisted anamnesis (CAA). They noted that "accuracy and reliability seem to have reached a very high level in all experiments" (Houziaux & Lefebvre, 1986, p. 138). They also found strong evidence to suggest that CAA produces more comprehensive and systematic data collection than that typically taken by physicians. Grossman, Barnett, and McGuire (1971) commented on the prevalence of confirmatory bias in medical decision making (selectively collecting and recording data that support initial hypotheses) and pointed to the advantages of CAA in eliminating this type of error.

Quaak, Westerman, and van Bemmel (1987) compared computerized and traditional written patient histories. They found 40% more information in the computerized history, and the participating doctors found the diagnostic hypotheses from the computer history were more certain than those from the written interview. However, the doctors believed that the written interview better expressed the main complaints. In another study by Lawrence, Clifford, and Taylor (1987), physicians' diagnostic accuracy rose from 51% to 69% with the use of a structured history form. Overall, the medical literature suggests that structured data-gathering methods facilitate more accurate and reliable judgments.

There have been several attempts to apply traditional psychological tests, such as the Minnesota Multiphasic Personality Inventory (e.g., Fraboni, Cooper, Reed, & Saltstone, 1990; Sloore, 1988) and the Rorschach (e.g., Hughes, Deville, Chalhoub, & Romboletti, 1992; Maitra, 1985), to the prediction of violence, and a few studies have attempted to construct brief self-report measures for this purpose (e.g., Dutton, 1995; Feinstein & Plutchik, 1990: Korn et al. 1992; Plutchik & van Praag, 1990). However, until recently, there have been few empirically based instruments designed to help structure the collection and the evaluation of relevant data as part of a comprehensive professional risk assessment (e.g., including information from interviews, records. and third parties). A few of these instruments with standardized scoring systems based on clinicians' ratings have been developed very recently, and a sample of them are briefly discussed below, not as an exhaustive review or critique but to raise awareness about some of the emerging attempts to improve risk assessment technology and to stimulate further research.

Dangerous Behavior Rating Scheme

The Dangerous Behavior Rating Scheme (DBRS; Webster & Menzies, 1993) represented perhaps the first systematic attempt to develop an instrument with known psychometric properties that could be used in clinical assessments of dangerousness. Twenty-two items (later reduced to 11), each rated on a seven-point Likert scale, were derived from Megargee's (1976) theoretical framework for assessing dangerousness and included such factors as anger, rage, tolerance, and guilt. Four global assessment measures of dangerousness to self and others at present and in the future were also added. Although after some preliminary work, the raters were able to achieve acceptable levels of interrater agreement on the items, the two-year follow-up validation yielded only modest correlations between DBRS items and ratings of subsequent dangerousness. Individual item correlations ranged from .06 to .32, and the aggregate factor score yielded a correlation of only .34 with dangerousness outcome measures. Even when optimal measures from the DBRS were used, the results of this semistructured instrument could account for only about 12% of the variance in follow-up dangerous behavior (Webster & Menzies. 1993).

In another study with longer longitudinal follow-up, the predictive ability of the DBRS appeared even weaker. Again, using optimal measures (aggregate factor scores) from the raters with the highest levels of validity, the instruments correlated with subsequent violence at only .16 after one year, .18 after three years, and .15 after six years (Menzies & Webster, 1995; Menzies, Webster, McMain, Staley, & Scaglione, 1994).

A number of factors may have limited the validity of this instrument, including the lack of a clear operational definition for each item and the inclusion of items that intuitively and conceptually would appear to be relevant but that were not, in fact, empirically associated with violent behavior. Nevertheless, the idea of having a theoretically driven, reliably rated, semistructured interview for dangerousness assessment marked a conceptual advance for assessment technology.

Violence Prediction Scheme

The Violence Prediction Scheme combines clinical and actuarial factors in a comprehensive scheme for assessing dangerousness and risk (Webster, Harris, Rice, Cormier, & Quinsey, 1994). The actuarial component is based on the Violence Risk Assessment Guide (VRAG), a 12-item tool that was empirically derived by using information gathered in comprehensive record reviews of a sample of 618 patients from a maximum security psychiatric hospital in Ontario, Canada (Harris, Rice, & Quinsey, 1993). The 12 variables include psychopathy; separation from parents by age 16 or younger; victim injury in index offense (negatively related); schizophrenia (diagnosed on the basis of criteria in the *Diagnostic and Statistical Manual of Mental Disorders*, 3rd ed. [*DSM-III*], American

Psychiatric Association [APA], 1980; negatively related);[2] never married; elementary school maladjustment; female victim-index offense (negatively related); failure on prior conditional release; property offense history age at index offense (negatively related); alcohol abuse history; and *DSM-III* personality disorder. With an average follow-up period of 81.5 months, the VRAG had a classification accuracy rate of about 75%.

To form the Violence Prediction Scheme, the VRAG was combined with a 10-item clinical scheme called the ASSESS-LIST (Webster & Polvi, 1995). This acronym stands for antecedent history, self-presentation, social and psychosocial adjustment, expectations and plans, symptoms, supervision, life factors, institutional management, sexual adjustment, and treatment progress.

It should be noted, however, that the VRAG actuarial formula was developed using a sample of persons with a prior history of significant violence, including at least one documented serious offense. Although Harris et al. (1993) anticipated that their "results will generalize both to mentally disordered offenders from other jurisdictions *and* to serious offenders in prison populations" (p. 331), at this time any generalization of their findings to other populations should be approached with caution.

HCR-20

The HCR-20 is an instrument–guide

> designed for use in the assessment of risk for future violent behavior
> in criminal and psychiatric populations. Briefly, the first 10 items of
> the HCR-20 pertain to the *historical* [italics added], or static, variables
> of the individual being assessed (H Scale), the next five items reflect
> the current *clinical* [italics added], status and personality characteristics
> of the individual (C Scale), and the remaining five pertain to future
> *risk* [italics added] of violent behavior (R Scale). (Webster et al., 1995)

The items were chosen on the basis of a comprehensive review of the literature and the clinical wisdom of some experienced forensic clinicians.

Although it has a fairly clearly defined three-level scoring system for each item, similar to that of the Psychopathy Checklist-Revised (Hare, 1991), it currently cannot be considered a test in the formal sense. Data on its reliability and validity are very preliminary, so its primary value is as a checklist to prompt the examiner to cover or consider the major relevant areas of inquiry. It currently should be viewed as a research instrument.

The instrument is based on the HCR-20 Scheme (Webster et al., 1995), so it is grounded in a systematic model for assessing risk. In this model, the historical variables are accorded the greatest weight because they are actuarial factors that have empirically demonstrated importance in assessments of dangerousness and violence risk. The historical variables include previous violence, age at first violent offense, relationship stability, employment stability, alcohol or drug abuse, mental disorder, psychopathy, early maladjustment (at home and school), personality disorder, and prior release or detention failure. The items are clearly defined so that data on these variables can easily be collected and compiled by a trained assistant and would not necessarily require clinician time for the comprehensive record review. It is expected that these historical variables will be retrospectively coded primarily from medical, psychological, and legal files and records.

The second phase consists of data collection on five clinical variables: insight, attitude, symptomatology, stability, and treatability. Although for research purposes this information could be compiled by trained assistants, in a clinical evaluation these data on current mental status would need to be evaluated and rated by a qualified mental health professional on the basis of interviews, progress notes, psychological assessments, or similar sources.

The final phase includes an assessment of five risk variables: plan feasibility, access, support and supervision, compliance, and stress, each of which "pertain to existing circumstances in the community or to future situations that the individual may encounter upon release from institutionalization" (Webster et al., 1995, p. 60). Like the historical variables, these data can be coded primarily from other assessments, such as social work, presentencing, or prerelease parole reports.

Webster and colleagues (Douglas, Webster, Eaves, Wintrup, & Hart, 1996) have recently begun three projects to investigate the psychometric properties of the HCR-20. Preliminary data, although limited, appear promising. In a retrospective study of 72 Canadian maximum security federal inmates, significant correlations were found between both the H and C Scales of the HCR-20 and scores on the VRAG (Harris et al., 1993), the Psychopathy Checklist—Revised (Hare, 1991), and the number of previous charges for violent offenses.[3] It also appears likely that the items can be reliably coded (Douglas et al., 1996).[4]

The promise of this instrument lies in its foundation on a conceptual model or scheme for assessing dangerousness and risk; its basis in the empirical literature; its operationally defined coding system allowing for increased reliability; and its practical use, as evidenced in its brevity and allowance for time-consuming data collection to be done by trained assistants. The field eagerly awaits new data on this instrument as well as other instruments that it may inspire.

Spousal Assault Risk Assessment Guide

The Spousal Assault Risk Assessment Guide (SARA) is a 20-item clinical checklist of risk factors for spousal assault (Kropp, Hart, Webster, & Eaves, 1994). In contrast to the HCR-20, it is designed for a more narrowly specified population and type of violence. However, like the HCR-20, it is brief, based in the empirical literature, and has an operationally defined three-level scoring scheme. Scoring criteria for each item are prefaced by an explicit rationale for its inclusion in the instrument, with references to the professional literature that support its relevance. The SARA was not designed to be a formal test; rather, it was constructed to be used as a clinical guide for assessing the risk of future violence in men arrested for spousal assault. In this way, it may enhance the comprehensiveness of the evaluation and ensure that the proper (empirically established) and relevant factors are considered and assessed.

The SARA has four main sections. The criminal history section includes items relating to past assault of family members, past assault of strangers or acquaintances, and past violation of conditional release or community supervision. The section on psychosocial adjustment includes items relating to recent relationship problems; recent employment problems; victim of and/or witness to family violence as a child or adolescent: recent substance abuse/dependence; recent suicidal or homicidal ideation/intent; recent psychotic and/or manic symptoms; and personality disorder with anger, impulsivity, or behavioral instability. The section covering spousal assault history includes the following items: past physical assault; past sexual assault/sexual jealousy; past use of weapons, and/or credible threats of death; recent escalation in frequency or severity of assault: past violation of "no contact" orders; extreme minimization or denial of spousal assault history; and attitudes that support or condone spousal assault. The final section consists of three items relating to the alleged (current) offense: severe and/or sexual assault; use of weapons, and/or credible threats of death; and violation of "no contact" order. After all four sections are completed, the clinician is prompted to make a "summary risk rating" (low, moderate, or high) of imminent risk of violence toward a partner and imminent risk of violence toward others.

The preliminary data for the SARA are encouraging. In a retrospective study of 50 court-referred spousal assaulters (25 reoffenders and 25 nonreoffenders), the interrater reliability for the sum of items was .92, and the reliability for the SARA-informed risk rating was .80. Concerning the potential validity of the SARA, it is interesting to note that neither the sum of items nor the number of positive items was related to reoffending. The therapists' clinical risk ratings (not based on the SARA) were also not related to reoffending outcomes; however, the SARA-informed summary risk ratings were strongly related to reoffending. Indeed, spousal assaulters with SARA ratings of high risk were five and one-half times more likely to reoffend than were those with ratings of low or moderate risk (Kropp, Whittemore, Hart, Webster, & Eaves. 1996).

Kropp et al. (1994) recommend that for clinical or forensic decision-making purposes, persons who use the SARA should, at a minimum, have expertise in individual assessment and in the area of spousal assault. However, other individuals may use the SARA for education, consultation (e.g., use by a lawyer in cross-examination), or evaluative research.

Future research on each of these instruments should assess their psychometric characteristics, including internal consistency, factor structure, temporal stability of items, interrater reliability of scoring or coding by trained assistants and by professionals, length of time required for a protocol to be scored, concurrent validity (i.e., relationships between individual items and other existing scales that measure similar constructs), and predictive validity (e.g., relationships between individual items or total scores and measures of subsequent violent behavior).

Actuarial Methods in Risk Assessment

In addition to the first generation of assessment instruments currently emerging, efforts are underway to develop actuarial decision tools for specified populations. Actuarial methods or formulas are based exclusively on empirically established relationships between the variables and the criterion, and a substantial body of research has suggested that in almost all tasks actuarial formulas predict as well as or better than clinical judgments (Borum, Otto, & Golding, 1993; Dawes, Faust, & Meehl, 1989; Garb, 1994; Meehl, 1970). Thus, their application to the assessment of dangerousness and risk appears to hold substantial promise for improving predictive accuracy (Brizer & Crowner, 1989; Monahan, 1981, 1988, 1996).

During the past several years, a number of researchers have attempted to develop actuarial aids for assessing the risk of violence using multivariable statistical methods such as logistic regression and discriminant function analysis (e.g., Convit. Jaeger, Lin, Meisner, & Volavka, 1988; Klassen & O'Connor, 1989: McNiel, Binder, & Greenfield, 1988). On the basis of the research conducted to date, actuarial methods for predicting violence appear to result in predictions whose accuracy exceeds chance (see Otto, 1992, for a review) and that are slightly more accurate than clinical predictions exceeding a one-year time frame (Mossman, 1994).

Despite the advantages of actuarial methods, they often are not used in clinical practice because their complexity makes them impractical (Gardner, Lidz, Mulvey, & Shaw, 1996). A few recent investigations have attempted to develop actuarial aids that can be more easily applied and that might be clinically useful. Three studies illustrate these more recent efforts.

Sexual Offenders

Quinsey, Rice, and Harris, 1995 reanalyzed follow-up data on 178 known sex offenders (rapists and child molesters) who were assessed at a maximum security psychiatric facility. The offenders were followed for an average of 59 months. Using findings from previous research, Quinsey et al. selected a series of variables related to demographic, psychiatric, criminal history, sexual misbehavior, and sexual preference characteristics that were entered into a series of regression analyses to predict sexual reconviction or violence recidivism. Because such multiple regression formulas are known to predict much less accurately when applied on a cross-validation sample (due to shrinkage), they used a statistical method developed by Nuffield (1982) to reduce this attenuation.

> By this technique, predictor variables are selected according to their univariate relationship with the outcome variable. In the prediction equation, each variable is assigned a positive or negative integer value that depends both upon the subject's score on that variable and on the overall magnitude between that predictor variable and the outcome. (Quinsey et al., 1995, p. 97)

Through this strategy, they developed the Recidivism Prediction Instrument. Scores from this scale correlated .45 with reconviction for a sexual offense and .46 with violence recidivism. When Nuffield's method was applied using all variables that were significant in the multivariate models, the results yielded a 72% rate of accurate classification (with 42% relative improvement over chance) for violence failure and a 77% rate of accurate classification (with 44% relative improvement over chance) for sexual reconvictions. Quinsey et al. (1995) advised that the strategy they proposed for use of such information is not simply to use it as another piece of information in a clinical appraisal of risk but rather to use it "to anchor clinical judgment by having the clinician start with an actuarial estimate of risk and then to alter it by examining dynamic variables, such as treatment outcome, treatment intensity, and supervision quality" (p. 100).

Psychiatric Inpatients

Recognizing that most previously developed actuarial formulas were impractical for use in routine clinical practice, McNiel and Binder (1994) developed a brief actuarial screening tool to aid in the assessment of patients' potential for violence upon admission to an inpatient unit. The screening checklist consists of five items: (a) history of physical attacks or fear-inducing behavior in the two weeks prior to admission; (b) absence of suicidal behavior (attempts, gestures, or threats) in the two weeks prior to admission; (c) diagnosis of schizophrenia or mania; (d) male gender; and (e) currently married or living together. Each positive item is assigned a one-point value. Receiver operating characteristic analysis was applied to a calibration sample of 238 patients who had been committed to derive an optimal cutting score of three points. A score of three or higher was considered high risk, whereas a score of two or lower was deemed to be low risk. These cutting scores were used to apply the checklist to a validation sample of 338 patients, resulting in a total predictive value (overall correct classification) of 65%, with a 28% relative improvement over chance in distinguishing which patients would display any type of aggressive behavior (e.g., attacks or fear-inducing behavior) on the ward. Although to some these results may appear modest, McNiel and Binder (1994) noted that the checklist performed better than most studies of clinical judgment in assessing violence risk (p. 585). Theoretically, of course, actuarial tools predict with perfect reliability when there is no measurement error and when the cutting scores are consistently applied. Perhaps the greatest contribution of this checklist is that it demonstrates the potential for developing brief, simple, easy-to-use actuarial methods that have utility in evaluating patients' risk of violence.

Community Violence by Persons with Mental Disorders

Gardner et al. (1996) used sophisticated statistical methodology to produce a simple, user-friendly actuarial tool to identify persons with mental disorder who are at risk for frequent incidents of physically violent behavior (laying hands on another with intent to harm, using a weapon, or threatening with a weapon) in the community.

On the basis of an actuarial method (classification and regression-tree algorithm),

Gardner et al. (1996) constructed a hierarchical decision tree with four yes-no questions that classify the patient into one of five categories; each category has a predicted rate of violence reported in units of incidents per month. The four questions are as follows: (a) Is the Brief Symptom Inventory-Hostility Scale score greater than two? (b) Are there more than three prior violent acts? (c) Is age less than 18?, and (d) Is the patient a heavy drug user?

This regression tree generally performed as well as (similar sensitivity and specificity) a negative binomial regression model using an almost identical array of variables. Although the area under the receiver operating curve could not be plotted to assess the quality of the regression tree, the negative binomial regression model enclosed 70.8% of the area under the curve, which is very consistent with Mossman's (1994) report of 71.3% for previous actuarial predictors of patient violence. Thus, this simple regression tree was able to classify patients about as well as more complex actuarial formulas based on multivariable statistical models. However, in light of its current limitations, Gardner et al. (1996) "do not recommend these procedures for routine clinical use" (p. 47).

Nevertheless, the regression-tree approach does represent another methodological advance in developing actuarial methods for use in clinical settings. And, like McNiel and Binder's (1994) screening checklist, the empirically based decision-tree method is brief, practical, and easily understood and applied in clinical practice.

Defining Clinical Practice Guidelines

There has been a recent trend in the medical profession to develop clinical practice guidelines to aid practitioners in the diagnosis and treatment of several common but significant medical problems. These diverse guidelines have come from insurers, managed care organizations, regulatory agencies, scientific groups, and professional associations. The Agency for Health Care Policy and Research has developed a series of these guidelines as part of a systematic effort to enhance the quality, the appropriateness, and the effectiveness of health care services. In the mental health arena, APA has assembled a steering committee on practice guidelines and has already issued guidelines for substance abuse (APA, 1995b), psychiatric evaluation of adults (APA, 1995a), bipolar disorder (APA, 1994), major depressive disorder in adults (APA, 1993b), and eating disorders (APA, 1993a).

In general, these guidelines are developed by panels of experts from diverse disciplines on the basis of systematic reviews of the relevant literature, with some also soliciting input from professional and consumer organizations and individuals. Drafts of the proposed guidelines are subjected to peer review and are circulated among practitioners in the field to gauge their conceptual and operational utility. Typically, the guidelines explicitly acknowledge that they provide only a basic guide for assessment and management of the condition and that even the few fundamental principles outlined will not apply to or be appropriate for every patient or case. It is also expected that they will be revised over time on the basis of new empirical knowledge, evaluations, and critiques. Nevertheless, these practice guidelines represent a significant attempt to operationalize some scientifically grounded principles for the assessment and treatment of certain conditions based on professional consensus (Clinton, McCormick, & Bestemun, 1994).

It should be noted that most of these practice policies being proposed are guidelines rather than standards. In summarizing the distinction made by Eddy (1990), Appelbaum (1992) noted that "standards define procedures that must be followed in all cases; they can be formulated only when indications for evaluation or treatment are unambiguous. Guidelines, used when greater flexibility is needed, allow modification to meet the needs of individual patients" (p. 341).

Of course, to consider applying this technology to the assessment and management of violence risk is a somewhat different matter. On the one hand, although some people with mental disorders do engage in violent behavior, violence per se is not a psychological or a medical condition. On the other hand, mental health professionals are routinely required to assess and manage violence risk in clinical practice (e.g., *Tarasoff*-like situations) and must make these judgments in accord with applicable professional standards, despite the fact that no explicit national standards exist. It seems that the emerging body of scientific knowledge on violence risk assessment has advanced sufficiently to allow professional consensus on some core issues that could lead to some clearly articulated practice guidelines for assessing and managing people with mental disorder who may be at risk for violence (see Webster et al., 1995, for an example of some general principles for violence prediction).

According to principles of tort liability, clinicians are not held accountable for the accuracy (or the inaccuracy) of the decision per se; rather, they are judged by whether the decision was reasonably made. That is, did the clinician gather the information that most clinicians would consider relevant to assessing violence risk, and on the basis of that information, would most clinicians have arrived at a similar conclusion? Appelbaum (1985) noted that in *Tarasoff*-like cases,

> the requirement that therapists protect victims not only when they know of potential dangerousness but when, according to professional standards, they *should know* of it is probably too stringent, given the limits of current abilities to predict dangerousness and the absence of professional standards for this task. (p. 429)

Thus, developing explicit practice guidelines would seem to be directly relevant to help clinicians answer these questions, fulfill their duty to protect, and practice more effectively.

Petrila (1995) recently recommended that

> providers who become or anticipate becoming responsible for the care of individuals who may be at risk for civil commitment or who may present a risk to self or others should consider adopting formal risk-assessment protocols so that the risk-assessment process is standard and consistent for all patients and clinicians. . . . Standardized protocols

may provide some protection from malpractice claims alleging that a practitioner negligently discharged a patient committed as dangerous by enabling the practitioner to argue that the risk assessment decision was made in accordance with the best available professional knowledge. . . . Such a protocol may be useful in treatment as well; the best available research on risk assessment suggests that situational and environmental factors are as relevant to dangerous behaviors as they are to treatment. (pp. 1047–1048)

However, if any guidelines are to be successful, it is essential that they reflect "*the minimal standards necessary for competent professional practice* and not the ideals to which an organization [or clinician] would aspire if it had unlimited resources" (Monahan, 1993, p. 247). Setting excessively high standards would serve only to increase, rather than decrease, clinicians' liability.

Poythress (1990) and Monahan (1993) have advocated for clinical guidelines, in the form of clearly defined policies and procedures, for making decisions to release individuals from institutional settings. Poythress even suggested that prerelease records should include a specific form or document that addresses the patient's potential for violence. These policies and guidelines direct the clinician to conduct a systematic inquiry and analysis about violence risk and help to structure and standardize the clinical risk assessment process.

Appelbaum (1985) proposed a three-stage model for dealing with potentially violent patients in *Tarasoff*-like situations. He suggested that clinicians must (a) gather relevant data and make a determination of dangerousness of risk, (b) select a course of action that has a reasonable likelihood of protecting potential victims, and (c) implement the selected course of action. These three stages also form a conceptual framework for the development of clinical guidelines. First, on the basis of the current research literature, it seems likely that substantial consensus could be reached about the core data that clinicians should reasonably attempt to gather and consider to make a professionally adequate determination of risk (Appelbaum, 1985; Borum et al., 1996; Givelber, Bowers, & Blitch, 1984; Monahan, 1981, 1993; Monahan & Steadman, 1994; Mulvey & Lidz, 1984; Tardiff, 1991). The use of clinical checklists or specialized assessment instruments such as those described above could also be helpful in this regard.

Obviously, operationalizing the decisional tasks is somewhat more difficult. There is less empirical guidance about how to systematically integrate relevant information to arrive at a probabilistic decision about risk or about which interventions (courses of action) have proven most effective for persons determined to be dangerous. Most decision-making models are clinically or conceptually based (Appelbaum & Gutheil, 1991; Monahan, 1981; Mulvey & Lidz, 1995; Truscott, Evans, & Mansell, 1995). Nevertheless, the general acceptance of a model, or of certain principles for decision making, would be useful to clinicians in guiding their judgments of dangerousness. The decisional model may be modified as future research emerges showing how these judgments can be made most reliably as well as the impact of varying interventions designed to protect potential victims.

A more general approach has been suggested by those attempting to define a standard of care for managing people at risk for suicide in inpatient settings (Bongar, Maris, Herman, Litman, & Silverman, 1993; Silverman, Berman, Bongar, Litman, & Maris, 1994). Recognizing the diversity in contexts and clinical situations, as well as the need for guiding principles not to be overly specific and hence restrictive, these experts have proposed that standards of care be based on broad categories of action to which a clinician must attend. "Hence, standards are categories of actions that must be performed in order to provide the minimum standard of care in the assessment, treatment and management [of the patient]" (Silverman et al., 1994, p. 154). They have constructed these broad categories around two key tort principles used to establish negligence: forseeability (reasonable anticipation that harm or injury is likely to result from certain acts or omissions) and causation (the act by which an effect is produced: Black, 1991).

It may be that these categories of action could be integrated with categories of risk, such as those proposed by Monahan and Steadman (1996). For the purpose of developing clinical practice guidelines, these categories might correspond to specific "critical action thresholds" (Monahan & Steadman, 1996; Wernly, 1994). Reaching these thresholds would indicate that consideration of various inquisitive prescriptions (i.e., the need to gather additional information) or therapeutic prescriptions (i.e., therapeutic interventions designed to reduce the risk of harm) may be warranted (Monahan & Steadman, 1996; Schopp, 1996).

Regardless of the approach chosen, there will be many obstacles to developing clinical guidelines for risk assessment practice. Clinicians must routinely assess violence potential and make related management decisions in psychiatric emergency services, civil psychiatric hospitals, forensic evaluation and treatment settings, and even outpatient private practice offices. There is tremendous diversity among the varying circumstances in which such judgments may be required, and there are notable logistic limitations in making these judgments within a clinical or an organizational context. Different settings may require information about different types of risk, or they may have varying time frames for prediction of the relevant behavior. Different risk assessment tasks require different types of decisions and vary in their critical action thresholds. Although expert consensus may be reached about optimal assessment practices, the exigency in certain clinical situations may require decisions to be made with a degree of immediacy that would limit the comprehensiveness of an examination. Thus, it may be that separate (or more specified) guidelines need to be developed for different settings or assessment tasks.

Developing Training Programs and Curricula

Despite the fact that most mental health professionals encounter situations requiring them to make decisions about the risk of violence posed by their clients, it is currently unclear whether their professions are adequately training them to handle these situations. Although there are no existing studies examining the extent of graduate training in assessment and management of violence risk, one survey found that only 40% of all graduate programs in clinical psychology offered any formal training in the study of suicide—a high-risk area that is even more clearly defined in the purview of mental health (Bongar & Harmatz, 1989).

Monahan (1993) suggested that

> four tasks form the basis of any professionally adequate risk assessment: The clinician must be educated about what information to gather regarding risk, must gather it, must use this information to estimate risk, and, if the clinician is not the ultimate decision maker, must communicate the information and estimate to those who are responsible for making clinical decisions. (p. 242)

One of Monahan's primary guidelines for "risk containment" is to be sure that clinicians are educated about the basic concepts and current findings in risk assessment research. He even recommended that larger facilities designate a "risk educator" to keep track of current research in this area and to conduct periodic training updates.

Education and training are certainly sensible recommendations: however, there are currently few clearly articulated training models or curricula for violence risk assessment and management in psychology, and there are no requirements in professional accreditation that these issues be addressed. It might be worthwhile for psychology to take the lead in this effort by assembling multidisciplinary teams or panels to work on models for training mental health practitioners in the study of violence and applications to clinical practice. Comprehensive models would need to account for core content areas of knowledge, frameworks for clinical decision making, and guidelines for supervision and consultation. Lomax (1986) proposed one such comprehensive model for training psychiatric residents in key aspects of suicide. He emphasized the need for presentation of relevant didactic material early in the training, with the development of clinical skills occurring primarily in the course of supervised experience. This attention to developing knowledge as well as skills seems particularly well-founded, given that there is evidence to suggest that mere knowledge of relevant risk factors may not be sufficient to allow a clinician to respond appropriately and effectively to high-risk patients in actual practice (Inman, Bascue, Kahn, & Shaw, 1984). A final recommendation from Lomax is that training programs should build in requirements for minimal practice competencies and develop ways to assess them.

Different models may be developed for various mental health disciplines or for varying levels of mental health training. For psychology, one option would be to define the assessment and management of violence risk as a proficiency area in accord with the American Psychological Association's emerging efforts to define specialty areas of competence in professional psychology. A broader and potentially more useful approach would be to develop a recommended curriculum for graduate training programs to incorporate into existing courses or to develop as a separate seminar. The didactic part of the curriculum could flow easily from the clinical care guidelines outlined above, with core components consisting of education about risk factors, decision making, management strategies, and approaches to handling the categories of action. Beginning training at this level would probably allow for the best integration of didactic material with supervised experience. In addition, as Monahan (1993) suggested, because the body of research knowledge is developing so rapidly, continuing-education programs are also important to maintaining competence, particularly for clinicians working with high-risk populations (e.g., forensic settings, acute psychiatric facilities, and substance abuse populations). Future research efforts could also be directed toward evaluating the efficacy of such training programs by examining their impact on the reliability and the accuracy of clinicians' assessments of violence risk.

CONCLUSION

The assessment and the management of violence risk are critical issues, not just for psychologists and psychiatrists in forensic settings but for all practicing clinicians. Despite a long-standing controversy about the ability of mental health professionals to predict violence, the courts continue to rely on them for advice on these issues and in many cases have imposed on them a legal duty to take action when they know or should know that a patient poses a risk of serious danger to others.

Given the ethical and legal obligations to appropriately assess and manage persons at risk for violence, more attention in each of the mental health disciplines needs to be given to improving technology and instrumentation to aid in these assessments, defining clinical practice guidelines, and training professionals in these critical tasks. Recent advances in research have laid the foundation for progress in each of these areas and have set the stage for an important research and policy agenda, contributing to the goal of improving clinical care and enhancing the validity of risk assessment in clinical practice.

This article is based, in part, on the Saleem Shah Award Address that was presented at the 104th Annual Convention of the American Psychological Association, Toronto, Ontario, Canada, August 1996.

NOTES

1. It should he noted that most of the rates cited below were drawn from samples of persons who either were treated or seeking treatment. Although in many ways this is the most relevant comparison group for clinical risk assessment tasks, people may be "selected" into these groups because of the severity of their disorder or dangerous behavior. Thus, their rates of violent behavior may be higher than those for persons with mental disorder, generally.
2. The reader may note that in this model, a diagnosis of schizophrenia is negatively related to violence, whereas in McNiel and Binder's (1994) model, schizophrenia is positively related to violence. One explanation for this discrepancy (which also appears in other studies) lies in the difference between the sample populations. Specifically, the sample in Harris et al.'s (1993) study consisted of patients in a maximum security psychiatric hospital who had a documented history of serious violence, current criminal charges, and a high rate of personality disorders. In contrast, the sample in McNiel and Binder's study consisted of civil psychiatric patients in a university-based inpatient setting. The relative risk for schizophrenia operates differently in these two samples. When compared with a group of civil psychiatric patients, persons with schizophrenia may

have a somewhat higher risk for violence. However, when compared with a group of incarcerated persons with a history of violence, criminal charges, and personality disorders, persons with schizophrenia may have a somewhat lower risk for violence. In that case, the lower risk would have nothing to do with schizophrenia per se but with the pre-ponderance of positive risk factors in the comparison group,

3. HCR-20 items pertaining to psychopathy and previous violence were removed from each of the two latter analyses, respectively, to avoid artificially inflating correlations.

4. On a random subset of 10 files, the average correlation between two raters for the H and C Scales was .795.

REFERENCES

American Psychiatric Association. (1980). *Diagnostic and statistical manual of mental disorders* (3rd ed.). Washington, DC: Author.

American Psychiatric Association. (1993a). Practice guidelines for eating disorders. *American Journal of Psychiatry, 150*, 212–228.

American Psychiatric Association. (1993b). Practice guidelines for major depressive disorder in adults. *American Journal of Psychiatry, 150* (Suppl. 4), 1–26.

American Psychiatric Association. (1994). Practice guidelines for the treatment of patients with bipolar disorder. *American Journal of Psychiatry, 151* (Suppl. 12), 1–36.

American Psychiatric Association. (l995a). Practice guidelines for psychiatric evaluation of adults. *American Journal of Psychiatry, 152* (Suppl. 11), 63–80.

American Psychiatric Association. (1995b). Practice guidelines for the treatment of patients with substance use disorders: Alcohol, cocaine. opioids. *American Journal of Psychiatry, 152* (Suppl. 11), 1–59.

Appelbaum, P. S. (1985). *Tarasoff* and the clinician: Problems in fulfilling the duty to protect. *American Journal of Psychiatry, 142*, 425–429.

Appelbaum, P. S. (1992). Practice guidelines in psychiatry and their implications for malpractice. *Hospital and Community Psychiatry, 43*, 341–342.

Appelbaum, P. S. (1994). New directions in the assessment of dangerousness of the mentally ill. *The Japanese Journal of Psychiatry and Neurology, 48*, 77–83.

Appelbaum, P. S., & Gutheil, T. G. (1991). *Clinical handbook of psychiatry and the law.* Baltimore: Williams & Wilkins.

Black, H. C. (1991). *Black's law dictionary.* St. Paul, MN: West.

Bongar, B., & Harmatz, M. (1989). Graduate training in clinical psychology and the study of suicide. *Professional Psychology: Research and Practice, 20*, 209–213.

Bongar, B., Maris, R. W., Berman, A. L., Litman, R. E., & Silverman, M. M. (1993). Inpatient standards of care and the suicidal patient. Part I: General clinical formulations and legal considerations. *Suicide and Life-Threatening Behavior, 23*, 245–256.

Borum, R., Otto, R., & Golding, S. (1993). Improving clinical judgment and decision making in forensic evaluation. *Journal of Psychiatry and Law, 21*, 35–76.

Borum, R., Swartz, M., & Swanson, J. (1996). Assessing and managing violence risk in clinical practice. *Journal of Practical Psychiatry and Behavioral Health, 4*, 205–215.

Brizer, D. A., & Crowner, M. L. (Eds.). (1989). *Current approaches to the prediction of violence.* Washington, DC: American Psychiatric Press.

Clinton, J. J., McCormick, K., & Besteman, J. (1994). Enhancing clinical practice: The role of practice guidelines. *American Psychologist, 49*, 30–33.

Convit, A., Jaeger, J., Lin, S. P., Meisner, M., & Volavka, J. (1988). Predicting assaultiveness in psychiatric inpatients: A pilot study. *Hospital and Community Psychiatry, 39*, 429–434.

Dawes, R., Faust, D., & Meehl, P. (1989, March 31). Clinical versus actuarial judgment. *Science, 243*, 1668–1674.

Douglas, K. S., Webster, C. D., Eaves, D., Wintrup, A., & Hart, S. D. (1996, March). *A new scheme for the assessment of dangerousness and the prediction of violence.* Paper presented at the biennial meeting of the American Psychology-Law Society. Hilton Head, SC.

Dutton, D. G. (1995). A scale for measuring propensity for abusiveness. *Journal of Family Violence, 10*, 203–221.

Eddy, D. M. (1990). Designing a practice policy: Standards, guidelines, and options. *Journal of the American Medical Association, 263,* 3077–3084.

Estroff, S. E., & Zimmer, C. (1994). Social networks, social support, and violence among persons with severe, persistent mental illness. In J. Monahan & H. Steadman (Eds.), *Violence and mental disorder* (pp. 259–295). Chicago: University of Chicago Press.

Estroff, S. E., Zimmer, C., Lachicotte, W. S., & Benoit, J. (1994). The influence of social networks and social support on violence by persons with serious mental illness. *Hospital and Community Psychiatry, 45,* 669–679.

Federal Bureau of Investigation. (1993). *Crime in the United States: The uniform crime reports.* Washington. DC: Author.

Feinstein, R., & Plutchik, R. (1990). Violence and suicide risk assessment in the psychiatric emergency room. *Comprehensive Psychiatry, 31,* 337–343.

Fraboni, M., Cooper, D., Reed, T. L., & Saltstone, R. (1990). Offense type and two-point MMPI code profiles: Discriminating between violent and nonviolent offenders. *Journal of Clinical Psychology, 46,* 774–777.

Garb, H. N. (1994). Toward a second generation of statistical prediction rules in psychodiagnosis and personality assessment. *Computers in Human Behavior, 10,* 377–394.

Gardner, W., Lidz, C. W., Mulvey, E. P., & Shaw, E. C. (1996). A comparison of actuarial methods for identifying repetitively-violent patients. *Law and Human Behavior, 20,* 35–48.

Givelber, D., Bowers, W., & Blitch, C. (1984. March/April). *Tarasoff,* myth and reality: An empirical study of private law in action. *Wisconsin Law Review,* 443–497.

Goldstein, A. P. (1994). *The ecology of aggression.* New York: Plenum.

Grisso, T., & Appelbaum, P. S. (1992). Is it unethical to offer predictions of future violence? *Law and Human Behavior, 16,* 621–633.

Grisso, T., & Appelbaum, P. S. (1993). Structuring the debate about ethical predictions of future violence. *Law and Human Behavior, 17,* 482–485.

Grossman, J. H., Barnett, G. O., & McGuire, M. T. (1971). Evaluation of computer-acquired patient histories. *Journal of the American Medical Association, 215,* 1286–1291.

Hare, R. D. (1991). *The Hare Psychopathy Checklist-Revised.* Toronto, Ontario. Canada: Multi-Health Systems.

Harris, G. T., Rice, M. E., & Quinsey, V. L. (1993). Violent recidivism of mentally disordered offenders: The development of a statistical prediction instrument. *Criminal Justice and Behavior, 20,* 315–335.

Hiday, V. A. (1992). Civil commitment and arrests: An investigation of the criminalization thesis. *Journal of Nervous and Mental Disease, 180,* 184–191.

Houziaux, M., & Lefebvre, P. J. (1986). Historical methodological aspects of computer-assisted medical history taking. *Medical Informatics, 11,* 129–143.

Hughes, S. A., Deville, C., Chalhoub, M., & Romboletti, R. (1992). The Rorschach human anatomy responses: Predicting sexual offending behavior in juveniles. *Journal of Psychiatry and Law, 20,* 313–333.

Inman, D., Bascue, J., Kahn, W., & Shaw, P. (1984). The relationship between suicide knowledge and suicide interviewing skills. *Death Education, 8,* 179–184.

Klassen, D., & O'Connor, W. A. (1988a). Crime, inpatient admissions, and violence among male mental patients. *International Journal of Law and Psychiatry, 11,* 305–312.

Klassen, D., & O'Connor, W. A. (1988b). Predicting violence in schizophrenic and non-schizophrenic patients: A prospective study. *Journal of Community Psychology, 16,* 217–227.

Klassen, D., & O'Connor, W. A. (1988c). A prospective study of predictors of violence in adult male mental health admissions. *Law and Human Behavior, 12,* 143–158.

Klassen, D., & O'Connor, W. A. (1989). Assessing the risk of violence in released mental patients: A cross-validation study. *Psychological Assessment: A Journal of Consulting and Clinical Psychology, I,* 75–81.

Korn, M. L., Botsis, A. J., Kotler, M., Plutchik, R., Conte, H. R., Finkelstein, G., Grosz, D., Kay, S., Brown, S., & van Praag, H. M. (1992). The Suicide and Aggression Survey: A semistructured instrument for the measurement of suicidality and aggression. *Comprehensive Psychiatry, 33,* 359–365.

Kropp, P. R., Hart, S. D., Webster, C. D., & Eaves, D. (1994). *Manual for the Spousal Assault Risk Assessment Guide.* Vancouver, British Columbia, Canada: The British Columbia Institute on Family Violence.

Kropp, P. R., Whittemore, K., Hart, S. D., Webster, C. D., & Eaves, D. (1996, March). *The development of the Spousal Assault Risk Assessment Guide.* Paper presented at the biennial meeting of the American Psychology-Law Society. Hilton Head, SC.

Lawrence, P. C., Clifford, P. C., & Taylor, I. F. (1987). Acute abdominal pain: Computer-aided diagnosis by non-medically qualified staff. *Annals for the Royal College of Surgeons of England, 69,* 233–234.

Lidz, C. W., Mulvey, E. P., & Gardner, W. (1993). The accuracy of predictions of violence to others. *Journal of the American Medical Association, 269,* 1007–1011.

Link, B. G., Andrews, H., & Cullen, F. T. (1992). The violent and illegal behavior of mental patients reconsidered. *American Sociological Review, 57,* 275–292.

Link, B. G., & Stueve, A. (1995). Evidence bearing on mental illness as a possible cause of violent behavior. *Epidemiologic Reviews, 17,* 1–10.

Litwack, T. R. (1993). On the ethics of dangerousness assessments. *Law and Human Behavior, 17,* 479–482.

Lomax, J. W. (1986). A proposed curriculum on suicide for psychiatric residency. *Suicide and Life-Threatening Behavior, 16,* 56–64.

Maccoby, E., & Jacklin, C. (1974). *The psychology of sex differences.* Stanford. CA: Stanford University Press.

Maitra, A. K. (1985). Rorschach signs of aggression, sadism and hostility. *Psychological Research Journal, 9,* 17–23.

McNiel, D. E., & Binder, R. L. (1994). Screening for risk of inpatient violence: Validation of an actuarial tool. *Law and Human Behavior, 18,* 579–586.

McNiel, D. E., Binder, R. L., & Greenfield, T. K. (1988). Predictors of violence in civilly committed acute psychiatric patients. *American Journal of Psychiatry, 145,* 965–970.

Meehl, P. (1970). Psychology and criminal law. *University of Richmond Law Review, 5,* 1–30.

Megargee, E. J. (1976). The prediction of dangerous behavior. *Criminal Justice and Behavior, 3,* 3–22.

Melton, G., Petrila, I., Poythress, N. G., & Slobogin, C. (1987). *Psychological evaluations for the courts: A handbook for mental health professionals and lawyers.* New York: Guilford Press.

Menzies, R., & Webster, C. D. (1995). Construction and validation of risk assessments in a six-year follow-up of forensic patients: A tridimensional analysis. *Journal of Consulting and Clinical Psychology, 63,* 766–778.

Menzies, R., Webster, C. D., McMain, S., Staley, S., & Scaglione, R. (1994). The dimensions of dangerousness revisited. *Law and Human Behavior, 18,* 1–28.

Monahan, I. (1981). *The clinical prediction of violent behavior.* Rockville. MD: National Institute of Mental Health.

Monahan, J. (1988). Risk assessment of violence among the mentally disordered: Generating useful knowledge. *International Journal of Law and Psychiatry, 11,* 249–257.

Monahan, J. (1992). Mental disorder and violent behavior: Perceptions and evidence. *American Psychologist, 47,* 511–521.

Monahan, J. (1993). Limiting therapist exposure to *Tarasoff* liability: Guidelines for risk containment. *American Psychologist, 48,* 242–250.

Monahan, J. (1996). Violence prediction: The last 20 years and the next 20 years. *Criminal Justice and Behavior, 23,* 107–120.

Monahan, J. (1997). Major mental disorders and violence to others. In D. Stoff, J. Breiling, & J. Maser (Eds.), *Handbook of antisocial behavior* (pp. 92–100). New York: Wiley.

Monahan, I., & Steadman, H. (Eds.). (1994). *Violence and mental disorder: Developments in risk assessment.* Chicago: University of Chicago Press.

Monahan, J., & Steadman, H. J. (1996). Violent storms and violent people: How meteorology can inform risk communication in mental health law. *American Psychologist, 51,* 931–938.

Mossman, D. (1994). Assessing predictions of violence: Being accurate about accuracy. *Journal of Consulting and Clinical Psychology, 62,* 783–792.

Mulvey, E. P. (1994). Assessing the evidence of a link between mental illness and violence. *Hospital and Community Psychiatry, 45,* 663–668.

Mulvey, E. P., & Lidz, C. W. (1984). Clinical considerations in the prediction of dangerousness in mental patients. *Clinical Psychology Review, 4,* 379–401.

Mulvey, E. P., & Lidz, C. W. (1995). Conditional prediction: A model for research on dangerousness to others in a new era. *International Journal of Law and Psychiatry, 18,* 129–143.

Mulvey, E. P., Shaw, E., & Lidz, C. W. (1994). Editorial: Why use multiple sources in research on patient violence in the community? *Criminal and Mental Health, 4,* 253–258.

Newhill, C. E., Mulvey, E. P., & Lidz, C. W. (1995). Characteristics of violence in the community by female patients seen in a psychiatric emergency service. *Psychiatric Services, 46,* 785–795.

Nuffield, J. (1982). *Parole-decision making in Canada: Research towards decision guidelines.* Ottawa, Ontario, Canada: Supply and Services Canada.

Otto, R. (1992). The prediction of dangerous behavior: A review and analysis of "second generation" research. *Forensic Reports, 5,* 103–133.

Petrila, J. (1995). Who will pay for involuntary civil commitment under capitated managed care? An emerging dilemma. *Psychiatric Service, 46,* 1045–1048.

Plutchik, R., & van Praag, H. M. (1990). A self-report measure of violence risk, II. *Comprehensive Psychiatry, 31,* 450–456.

Poythress, N. G. (1990). Avoiding negligent release: Contemporary clinical and risk management strategies. *American Journal of Psychiatry, 147,* 994–997.

Poythress, N. G. (1992). Expert testimony on violence and dangerousness: Roles for mental health professionals. *Forensic Reports, 5,* 135–150.

Quaak, M. J., Westerman, R. F., & van Bemmel, J. H. (1987). Comparisons between written and computerised patient histories. *British Medical Journal, 295,* 184–190.

Quinsey, V. L., Rice, M. E., & Harris, G. T. (1995). Actuarial prediction of sexual recidivism. *Journal of Interpersonal Violence, 10,* 85–105.

Schopp, R. F. (1996). Communicating risk assessments: Accuracy, efficacy, and responsibility. *American Psychologist, 51,* 939–944.

Silverman, M. M., Berman, A. L., Bongar, B., Litman, R. E., & Maris, R. W. (1994). Inpatient standards of care and the suicidal patient. Part II: An integration with clinical risk management. *Suicide and Life-Threatening Behavior, 24,* 152–169.

Sloore, H. (1988). Use of the MMPI in the prediction of dangerous behavior. *Acta Psychiatrica Belgica, 88,* 42–51.

Steadman, H. J., Cocozza, J. J., & Melick, M. E. (1978). Explaining the increased arrest rate among mental patients: The changing clientele of state hospitals. *American Journal of Psychiatry, 135,* 816–820.

Steadman, H. J., Monahan, I., Appelbaum, P. S., Grisso, T., Mulvey, E. P., Roth, L. H., Robbins, P. C., & Klassen, D. (1994). Designing a new generation of risk assessment research. In J. Monahan & H. Steadman (Eds.), *Violence and mental disorder: Developments in risk assessment* (pp. 297–318). Chicago: University of Chicago Press.

Swanson, J. W. (1994). Mental disorder, substance abuse, and community violence: An epidemiological approach. In J. Monahan & H. Steadman (Eds.), *Violence and mental disorder: Developments in risk assessment* (pp. 101–136). Chicago: University of Chicago Press.

Swanson, J. W., Holzer, C. E., Ganju, V. K., & Jono, R. T. (1990). Violence and psychiatric disorder in the community: Evidence from the Epidemiologic Catchment Area Surveys. *Hospital and Community Psychiatry, 41,* 761–770.

Tarasoff v. Regents of the University of California. 131 Cal. Rptr. 14, 551 P.2d 334 (1976).

Tardiff, K. (1991). Violence by psychiatric patients. In R. I. Simon (Ed.). *Review of clinical psychiatry and the law* (pp. 175–233). Washington, DC: American Psychiatric Press.

Taylor, P. J. (1995). Schizophrenia and the risk of violence. In S. R. Hirsch & D. R. Weinberger (Eds.), *Schizophrenia* (pp. 163–183). London: Blackwell Science.

Truscott, D., Evans, J., & Mansell, S. (1995). Outpatient psychotherapy with dangerous clients: A model for clinical decision making. *Professional Psychology: Research and Practice, 26,* 484–490.

Webster, C. D., Eaves, D., Douglas, K., & Wintrup, A. (1995). *The HCR-10 Scheme: The assessment of dangerousness and risk.* Burnaby. British Columbia, Canada: Simon Fraser University and Forensic Psychiatric Services Commission of British Columbia.

Webster, C. D., Harris, G. T., Rice., M. E., Cormier, C., & Quinsey, V. L. (1994). *The Violence Prediction Scheme: Assessing dangerousness in high risk men.* Toronto, Ontario, Canada: Centre of Criminology, University of Toronto.

Webster, C. D., & Menzies, R. J. (1993). Supervision in the deinstitutionalized community. In S. Hodgins (Ed.), *Mental disorder and crime* (pp. 22–38). Newbury Park: Sage.

Webster, C. D., & Polvi, N. H. (1995). Challenging assessments of dangerousness and risk. In J. Ziskin (Ed.), *Coping with psychiatric and psychological testimony* (pp. 221–240). Marina del Rey, CA: Law and Psychology Press.

Wernly, D. (1994). *The roles of meteorologists and hydrologists in disaster preparedness* (World Meteorological Organization Technical Document No. 598). Geneva, Switzerland: World Meteorological Association.

Wilson, J. Q., & Herrnstein, R. J. (1985). *Crime and human nature.* New York: Simon & Schuster.

4

The Canadian Contribution to Violence Risk Assessment: History and Implications for Current Psychiatric Practice

HY BLOOM, CHRISTOPHER WEBSTER, STEPHEN HUCKER
AND KAREN DE FREITAS

ABSTRACT: *Over the past quarter-century, Canadian researchers, clinical practitioners, and policy specialists have made several notable contributions to the broad field of violence risk assessment and management. In part, these contributions have been fostered by major changes in law over this period; in part, they have been spurred by findings from large-scale Canadian prediction–outcome studies. This paper offers references for a range of Canadian-inspired assessment schemes designed to evaluate psychopathy and potential for violence against others.*

KEYWORDS: *risk assessment, violence, Hare Psychopathy Checklist—Revised, PCL-R, Violence Risk Appraisal Guide, VRAG, Historical/Clinical/Risk Management-20, HCR-20*

Introducing a book that he described as placing considerable emphasis on the topic of assessing and predicting violence, the distinguished American psychologist John Monahan drew attention not long ago to the "remarkably strong international presence of Canada in forensic psychology and psychiatry, a presence out of all proportion to relative population size, not to mention relative crime rate" (1). Canadian researchers and mental health practitioners indeed exert a notably disproportionate

Reprinted with permission. Canadian Journal of Psychiatry, 50 *(1), 3–11.* © 2005 Canadian Psychiatric Association.

Clinical Implications

- Mental health professionals who are called on to evaluate individuals thought to be at risk for violence against others should draw upon Hare's definition of the construct of psychopathy.
- Professionals should appreciate the contribution of actuarial approaches to the prediction of violence. The extent to which it is possible to attenuate risks assessed as high on such measures remains unknown.
- Professionals should also take note of an emerging literature on structured clinical approaches to risk assessment.
- That there are appreciable limitations to any approaches to risk assessment must be accepted. This being so, a gradual approach to the release of accused persons and offenders with mental disorders is usually the safest.

Limitations

- This review is largely restricted to Canadian contributions to this area of research and practice.
- This paper deals only with assessing general risk of violence against others, not violence toward self or suicide. It does not consider nonviolent recidivism or specific types of violence, such as sex offending or spousal assault.
- This paper does not cover studies of the reliability and validity of various actuarial and structured clinical guides or current assessment schemes.

---

influence on the world's risk assessment literature. Although it may be comforting to receive such accolades from afar, it is important to consider how recent developments in violence risk assessment actually affect daily practice at home. What may seem at first glance to be a nationally aggrandizing approach to the present topic can be more aptly justified on the ground that Canadian clinicians conducting risk assessments must inevitably frame them within the context of the Criminal Code of Canada, the Corrections and Conditional Release Act, the Dangerous and Long-Term Offender Act (2), the new Youth Criminal Justice Act, and the various provincial and territorial mental health acts (3). This paper is divided into 3 sections. The first is included to remind readers why assessing the risk of violence against others is such an important clinical, research, and policy topic. The second explicates the Canadian contribution to the subject from a historical perspective. The third draws on the first 2 to outline a set of broad principles that may help psychiatrists as they undertake violence risk assessments in emergency, civil, forensic, and correctional psychiatry. Another purpose is to mention the seemingly bewildering array of structured risk assessment devices now evolving, with which clinicians and researchers are increasingly expected to have at least a passing acquaintance.

THE IMPORTANCE OF ASSESSING RISK
OF VIOLENCE AGAINST OTHERS

Evaluating violence risk in various people and places is an inherent dimension of psychiatric practice. It is not a responsibility that can be abrogated or set aside. The duty is not solely confined to the domain of tertiary level consultants, although it will almost invariably fall to the latter to assess violence and recidivism risk in a criminal context, as follows:

- to determine the risk an accused would present to public safety, if released on bail.
- to advise the courts when called upon to do so about how future risk considerations should figure into the rehabilitative and incapacitation aspects of sentences being imposed by trial judges.
- to give expert opinion as to whether the accused poses a risk of physical or psychological harm to the public so substantial that he or she should be designated a long-term offender, or so great and seemingly immutable that he or she merits the designation of dangerous offender.
- to assess whether an inmate can be safely managed in the community on parole.
- to inform derestriction and release decisions in regard to accused persons' being held under the jurisdiction of a provincial review board following a finding of not criminally responsible by reason of mental disorder (NCRMD) or unfit to stand trial (UST).

Civil commitment under provincial or territorial mental health acts is undoubtedly the most essential and onerous risk decision-making area for psychiatrists in hospital and other day-to-day clinical settings; it is a responsibility that most clinicians cannot avoid. Decisions about involuntary detention are almost always predicated on a dangerousness standard, which requires that risk assessments be informed and focused.

On the one hand, false negatives can result in serious harm or death and, potentially, subsequent legal liability. Conversely, false positives can result in temporary or even more permanent abrogation of a patient's right to move about freely in society (4). Not only may the victim of a clinician's inaccurate risk appraisal be traumatized, such penalizing can also lead to legal challenges against the professional. Occasionally, forensic psychiatrists are expected to use civil commitment procedures to continue the post-sentence detention of supposedly dangerous mentally ill offenders. The appropriateness of using civil commitment proceedings for what has been referred to as "psychiatric gating" is currently a contentious issue (5).

Several kinds of risk assessment skills are required in daily clinical practice. One of these is the ability to characterize the types of problematic conduct that patients are capable of. Such estimates have implications for diagnosis and management. Psychiatrists must help guide colleagues in their own and associated disciplines toward defensible, professionally sound judgments about risk—judgments that are relevant and based on well-established principles. Clinicians may be found liable for failing to assess competently the degree of risk for violence that persons represent toward third parties, as well as the degree of risk for suicide or self-harm: clinical pronouncements, no matter how apparently weighty, do not suffice when professional and civil liberty issues are at stake. Clinicians must also be able to respond effectively and with alacrity in high-risk situations wherein the ordinary doctor–patient relationship must be set aside and wherein they are obliged to alert authorities to the risk of impending violence by the client toward a third party (6,7). Disclosure of clinical information to protect the public is permissible, or even required, when there is a clear and imminent risk to an identifiable person or group (that is, risk of serious bodily harm or death).

HISTORICAL BACKGROUND

In the Canadian context, any consideration of dangerousness or, as it has evolved over time, risk assessment begins with the foundational work of Dr Kenneth Gray. Writing in 1947, Gray was acutely aware of the risks faced by nursing and other staff members working in the psychiatric hospitals of the day (8), a time long before psychotropic medications were added to the violence management armamentarium. He and his nursing colleagues offered sensible and practical advice to mental hospital staff and drew attention to the idea that interdisciplinary cooperation is vital for the safe management of aggressive and violent conduct. Under his direction, forensic psychiatry gained its foothold in the Toronto Psychiatric Hospital. Subsequently, Mohr, Turner, and Jerry showed how particular problems such as pedophilia, voyeurism, and exhibitionism could be researched and understood (9). This early groundwork laid the basis for the subsequent Clarke Institute of Psychiatry research and practice in the field of sexual offending. In due course, sexology was strengthened and expanded by the inspired theoretical and practical contributions of Kurt Freund (10) and Ron Langevin (11,12). It continues today in the sex offender assessment and treatment research of Blanchard (13) and Barbaree (14).

The Oak Ridge Division of the Mental Health Centre, Penetanguishene

Oak Ridge, a free-standing, maximum-secure building on the grounds of the Mental Health Centre at Penetanguishene, Ontario, has long been the facility for detaining the most severely ill male patients found NCRMD. It came to international prominence in the 1960s with the reporting of the Oak Ridge staff's determined efforts to treat patients suffering from severe mental and personality disorders. Inspired by Dr Elliot Barker and others, including former patients (15), Oak Ridge came to be seen as a place where positive changes could be wrought, even under difficult circumstances. Such was the influence of this pioneering work that it actually began to alter the courts' interpretation of the Canadian insanity defence (16).

In 1975 the hospital administration appointed Vernon Quinsey, a psychologist, to create a research department at Oak Ridge. Under his leadership, the small unit expanded and soon showed itself capable of attracting external research funds. Some of the new projects concentrated on phallometric testing and so complemented work occurring in Toronto (17); some dealt with the practicalities of managing highly violent behaviours of the kind especially apt to occur in maximum security units (18); and some dealt with assessing risk for violence (19).

Quinsey and colleagues conducted studies that revealed the then awkward-seeming findings that clinicians' assessments of risk are no more valid than those of nonprofessionals (20) and that clinicians in interdisciplinary teams tend not to agree with one another in their judgments about the kinds of treatments most beneficial for individual patients (21). At the same time, members of this group were beginning to question the US experience (22) that it is wholly impossible to predict the future violent behaviour of persons institutionalized for having committed serious acts of violence while suffering from mental illness (23).

In 1993, a key paper to emanate from Oak Ridge on the topic of general violence risk assessment was published (24). This introduced the now well-known Violence Risk Appraisal Guide (VRAG). The paper's authors, Harris and colleagues, linked file information from some 600 persons assessed at Oak Ridge with actual outcome 7 years later. About one-half of those assessed were treated at the institution for at least 2 years; the rest were channelled through the correctional system. Two separate sets of research assistants were employed: one set to extract pertinent pieces of information from the voluminous Oak Ridge files and one set to collect actual outcome data (that is, new violent offences or returns to hospital for aggressive acts). Harris and his group then integrated the 2 sets of data statistically. By doing this they were able to achieve prediction –outcome correlations of around 0.50 in some of their computations. This was above a threshold or "sound barrier" purported to exist by Toronto-based researchers working on similar projects at about the same time (25, see following section).

The VRAG scheme is built on 12 items. Some items are loaded more heavily than others. The most strongly weighted is the Hare Psychopathy Checklist—Revised (PCL-R, see below). Other heavily weighted items are "early childhood maladjustment" and "employability." A history of mental illness is weighted negatively (that is, it serves a protective function in the scheme). The VRAG is an example of an actuarial device in that its pooled data offer a likelihood figure regarding possible future violent offending. On a probabilistic basis, those with a high VRAG score have an increased risk of offending violently, and those with a low score are likely to be relatively insulated from future offending. The VRAG has now been contextualized with the publication in 1998 of a book on the topic (26); it has also been reinforced through subsequent research (27). In this research, the authors provide data for their study group at 10 years' follow-up, give detailed VRAG scoring instructions, and include an expanded version specifically geared toward sex offenders—the Sex Offender Risk Assessment Guide (SORAG). Generally speaking, Quinsey and his colleagues argue strongly for the superiority of actuarial prediction over clinical judgments about risk.

The Metropolitan Forensic Service

The Metropolitan Forensic Service (METFORS) was established in Toronto in 1977. Administered by the then Clarke Institute of Psychiatry, situated at the then Queen Street Mental Health Centre, and funded by the Ontario Ministry of the Attorney General, METFORS was created to facilitate interdisciplinary fitness-to-stand-trial assessments of persons being held in the 3 Toronto-area correctional remand centres. Though fitness was the major issue, "dangerousness" soon emerged as a second researchable line in forensic psychiatry and psychology (28). Clinicians worked with researchers to create assessment schemes. One of these was a 23-item device called the Dangerous Behaviour Rating Scheme (DBRS). Its strength as a predictor was gauged against follow-up via hospital and police records, first, after 2 years (29) and later, after 6 years (30). The authors concluded that, although possessing some power to predict in specific contexts, the sizes of correlations between DBRS scores and actual outcome did indeed fail to cross the 0.40 "sound barrier" they themselves had posited. One of the METFORS research group, Robert Menzies, offered a penetrating analysis of possible iatrogenic effects inherent in some multidisciplinary risk assessments—a contribution of considerable importance in this line of research. Menzies was able to show from his data that, unless they are on guard, clinicians may unwittingly "construct dangerousness" in the course of completing evaluations and that evaluations can also be subject to sex and other biases (31).

Changes in the Law Concerning Mentally Disordered Offenders

In the 1970s, the Law Reform Commission of Canada reviewed the status of mentally disordered offenders in Canada. At that time, the Criminal Code of Canada required trial judges to order that accused persons acquitted by reason of insanity be "kept in strict custody . . . until the pleasure of the Lieutenant Governor is known"(32). Similar provisions dealt with those found UST. This system had several shortcomings, among which was the fact that length of time spent in custody was indeterminate. As a result, many individuals spent far longer under the restrictions of a Lieutenant Governor's Warrant than they would have if they had been found guilty of the offence and sent to prison. Detention was also automatic. The law assumed that all offenders suffering from mental illness were dangerous and had to be detained to protect the public. There was no codified requirement to differentiate between offenders who were dangerous and those who were not. The standard (or test) justifying continuing detention in fact had seemingly little to do with dangerousness or risk and was instead predicated on whether the accused had "recovered."

In its 1976 report, the Law Reform Commission recommended the abolition of the Lieutenant Governor's Warrant. It also recommended that "the present verdict of 'not guilty by reason of insanity' become a real acquittal, subject only to a post-acquittal hearing to determine if the individual is civilly committable" (33). This hearing to determine whether the individual was civilly committable included assessing the level of risk to self and to the public. With this report released, the federal government of the day established the Mental Disorder Project. This gave the researchers at Penetanguishene, METFORS, and the Institut Pinel de Montréal, as well as those in provincial and federal corrections, a chance to meet with bureaucrats, administrators, and clinicians. Canadian social scientists had access to persons responsible for making changes to policy and law, and the resulting report of the Mental Disorder Project reflected their expertise and opinions. The report's recommendations were incorporated into a 1986 draft bill, which, however, languished until a decision by the Supreme Court of Canada forced the government to make some of the recommended legislative changes. In R v Swain, the Supreme Court of Canada found that the requirement to order the accused into strict custody to await the pleasure of the Lieutenant Governor was contrary to the Charter of Rights and Freedoms because it was an arbitrary rule that did not take into account the circumstances of the particular case (34). The Supreme Court gave the government 6 months to change the law. As a result, the proposed amendments, known as Bill C-30, were passed and proclaimed into effect on February 4, 1992.

The changes wrought by the new law were too many and too complicated to discuss in detail here (35). However, one major alteration was that persons acquitted by reason of insanity were no longer automatically detained. Rather, they could be held only as long as they posed a "significant threat" to public safety (36). In effect, automatic detention was deemed to be contrary to the Charter, and provisions for it were replaced with clauses that allowed detention only when an individual posed a risk to the public. This made risk assessment a crucial and indispensable part of the approach to offenders suffering from mental illness.

Ontario's Reaction to the Bill C-30 Changes

Bill C-30 brought together those with key interests in public protection and the accused's rehabilitation by naming the accused, the hospital, and the attorney general of the province (and potentially any designated interested person) as parties to the proceeding. The new law made it quite apparent that the quality of clinical evidence brought before review boards would have to improve. In anticipation of the proclamation, Mr Justice Thomas Callon, then chair of the Ontario Lieutenant Governor's Review Board, established a small committee to suggest how risk assessments should ideally be conducted. This committee comprised representatives from several interested sectors, including experienced clinicians, administrators, and researchers. In due course, the research members of the committee published a short text on the topic of risk assessment (37). The lynchpin of this publication was the VRAG, and the publication also included a chapter on clinical (that is, dynamic) considerations organized according to a mnemonic device called ASSESS-LIST. The authors suggested that predictions of future violence be based on VRAG scores but that the scores could be modified upward or downward if circumstances warranted, provided that the adjustment did not vary by more than 10%. This notion—that actuarial scores should be open to modification based on clinical opinion—was later, and emphatically, set aside by Quinsey and colleagues (26). They argued that the actuarial prediction is what it says it is, no less and no more, and that, if dynamic clinical considerations are to enter the overall calculus in a risk assessment, they must do so in a different way.

Psychopathy

It will be recalled that psychopathy is the prime predictor of the 12 employed in the VRAG, or to be more precise, the Hare PCL-R score (38). As many readers will know, Hare's inventive work began with a consideration of the American psychiatrist Hervey Cleckley's 1941 text, *The Mask of Sanity* (39). In rich literary style, Cleckley describes several cases of persons who seem to skate over the surface of life, lack conscience, act deceitfully, do not form meaningful connections with others, and have a marked propensity for early and continuous entanglements with the law. Hare consolidated these observations, guided by his own emerging clinical experience in Canadian correctional facilities. This early version of the checklist had 22 items (40); its subsequent forms had 20 (38,41). The Hare PCL-R is an example of a structured clinical judgment device. It is remarkable for its 2 main characteristics: first, it is supported by a manual that gives full item descriptions along with precise scoring instructions; second, it includes standardization data (now, with the 2003 version, for women as well as men). Each item in the Hare PCL-R is scored either 0 (not present), 1 (may be present), or 2 (definitely present). With 20 items, the total possible score is therefore 40. A score of 30 is the normal cut-off for an ascription of psychopathy.

The MacArthur study on the fate of some 1000 patients released to the community (42) inspired the development of a 12-item Screening Version (PCL:SV, 43) that is particularly suited to community samples. A version specifically adapted and standardized on adolescent populations has now been published (PCL:YV, 44).

British Columbia's Reaction to the Bill C-30 Changes: Structured Approach to Risk Assessment

In the 1980s and 1990s, Dr Derek Eaves was the lead forensic psychiatrist and administrator on the Forensic Psychiatric Services Commission of British Columbia. Faced with implementing Bill C-30 in 1992, Dr Eaves, like his colleagues in Ontario and across the country, began to realize that advances were needed in the area of risk assessment. Although aware of the VRAG research, he opted for a different strategy, namely, to engage in detailed consultations with British Columbia's forensic and other clinicians in the various mental health disciplines. The eventual project was hosted by the Mental Health, Law and Policy Institute of Simon Fraser University and entailed individual interviews with some 20 professionals across various settings, including forensic, civil, and psychiatric emergency services. The idea was to isolate and define the important variables to consider when undertaking risk assessments for courts, review boards, and other tribunals. Influenced by the outcome of these individual consultations and the basic structure of the Hare PCL-R, he and others produced a first version of a violence risk assessment device in 1995, called the Historical/Clinical/Risk Management-20 (HCR-20, 45). As the HCR-20 evolved, its authors came to realize that, aside from accurately predicting risk, evaluators are absolutely required to base their reports and opinions on processes that are well informed and available to close legal examination.

The HCR-20 scheme employs the same basic idea of 20 items (each scored 0, 1, or 2) as is used in Hare's device. Ten of the items are historical, or "static," (that is, largely obtainable from the record and not apt to change much over time). One of the 10 is the Hare PCL-R score; some of the others are loosely similar to the VRAG. Five of the clinical items are allotted to current conditions dealing with insightfulness, severity of psychiatric symptoms, impulsivity, treatability, and attitudinal issues. The remaining 5 are future-directed and take into account the extent to which the subject has the ability to create and follow a rehabilitation plan, avail himself or herself of support, cope with anticipated stressors, comply with prescribed medications and rules, and avoid becoming destabilized by external influences. The scheme was reviewed in an influential 1996 US publication (46) and attracted the attention of Swedish and German colleagues. It was modified with their help in 1997 (47). Since then, it has been considerably researched (for example, 48), and it has found a place in various forensic, civil, and correctional services. Of some note, too, is the 2001 publication of a separate *Companion Guide* (HCR-20CG, 49), which, being remediative in orientation, shows how clinicians ought to be able to help patients and parolees gain insight, become treatable, and create plans. The idea is to use the basic HCR-20 to index change following the interventions suggested in the HCR-20CG.

The basic format (20 or so defined items, each scored 0, 1, or 2) has been extended to the creation of specific-to-purpose devices to assess assaultive spouses (Spousal Assault Risk Assessment, 50) and sex offenders (Sexual Violence Risk-20, 51; Risk of Sexual Violence Protocol, 52).

Mirroring the publication of the PCL:YV for assessing psychopathy in youth is the Structured Assessment for Violence Risk in Youth (SAVRY, 53), which actually followed the publication of 2 structured schemes—one for assessing violence risk in boys aged under 12 years (the Early Assessment and Risk List for Boys [EARL-20B], 554) and the other a similar but separate version for girls (EARL-21G, 55). The most recent development in this series has been the publication of a manual designed specifically to focus on short-term violence risks (including self-harm and suicide) in adult forensic, correctional, and civil populations. Titled the Short Term Assessment of Risk and Treatability (START, 56), the scheme presumes the prior completion of a historical analysis (as with the 10 historical items of the HCR-20 or the VRAG). It defines 20 dynamic variables cast both as risk markers and as possible protective factors. It is as yet untested. Table 1 summarizes the gradual evolution of these "decision support tools" (57).

TABLE 1

Contemporary Structured Guides for Assessing Psychopathy and Violence Risk: A Listing

YEAR OF PUBLICATION	ABBREVIATION	NUMBER OF ITEMS	SCOPE	FIRST AUTHOR
PSYCHOPATHY				
1985 (prelim)	PCL-R	22	Psychopathy	Hare
1991		20	Adults	
2003 (V2)		20		
1995	PCL:SV	12	Psychopathy Adults	Hart
2003	PCL:YV 20		Psychopathy Youth	Forth
VIOLENCE RISK—ADULTS				
1995	HCR-20	20	Violence Adults	Webster
1997 (V2)	HCR-20	20	Violence Adults	Webster
2001	HCR-20 CG	10 (Dynamic)	Violence Adults	Douglas
2003	START	20 (+ 20 protective)	Violence Adults	Webster
VIOLENCE RISK—CHILDREN AND ADOLESCENTS				
2000 2001 (V2)	EARL 20B	20	Violence Boys	Augimeri
2001	EARL 21G	21	Violence Girls	Levene
2002 2003 (V1.1)	SAVRY	24 (+ 6 protective)	Violence Youth	Borum

PCL-R = Psychopathy Checklist—Revised; PCL:SV = Psychopathy Checklist: Screening Version; PCL:YV = Psychopathy Checklist:Youth Version; HCR-20 = Historical/Clinical/Risk Management-20; HCR-20 CG = Historical/Clinical/Risk Management-20 Companion Guide; START = Short Term Assessment of Risk and Treatability; EARL 20B = Early Assessment Risk List for Boys; EARL 21G = Early Assessment Risk List for Girls

A 20-item guide for evaluating adolescent sex offenders, the Estimate of Risk of Adolescent Sexual Offence Recidivism (ERASOR, 58), has been published. Attempts have also been made to deal with workplace violence, both with respect to employees (the Employee Risk Assessment-20 [ERA-20], 59) and with respect to the situational aspects that may contribute to the genesis of such violence (the Workplace Risk Assessment-20 [WRA-20], 60). These are at an early consultative stage of development. Figure 1 shows how these schemes have evolved over time.

FIGURE 1

Evolution of Structured Professional Judgment Guides for Violence Risk Assessment

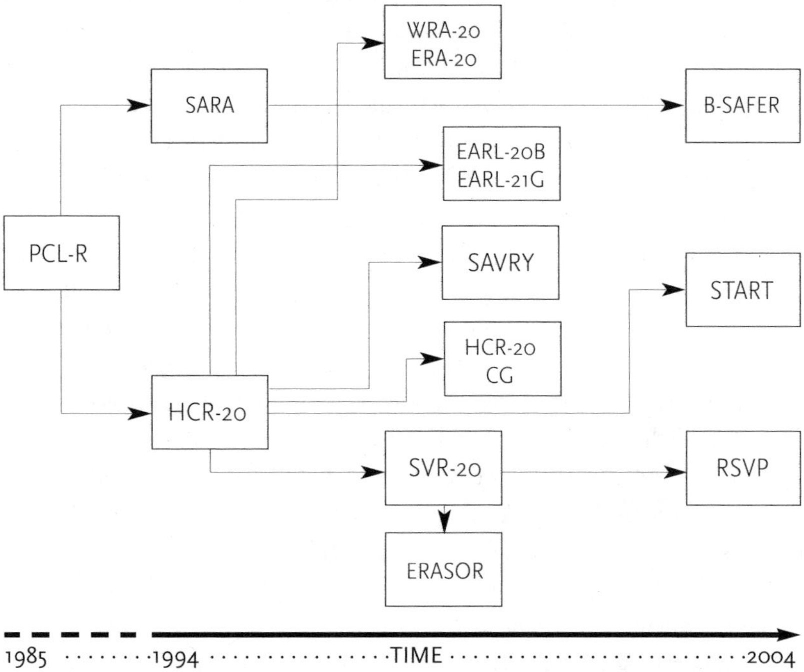

CONTEMPORARY RISK ASSESSMENT PRINCIPLES

Canadian psychiatrists might like to consider the following principles as they conduct risk evaluations in emergency, civil, forensic, and correctional psychiatry.

1. Assessments must accord with the pertinent legal test or professional standard. Decisions about violence risk are inevitably bounded by statute and case law. Psychiatrists and other mental health professionals need to review frequently the constantly evolving pertinent federal and provincial law. "Duty to protect" considerations must be weighed carefully and acted on if need be.

2. Assessment conditions must be satisfactory, and the evaluations themselves must be thorough. Dr Barry Boyd made this point many years ago, with respect to physical circumstances (61). With the accumulation over the last 2 decades of research evidence on the salience of actuarial risk predictors, an absolute requirement now exists for psychiatrists to obtain and review large amounts of historical information (62,63).

3. Assessments must be specific to the risk issue at hand. Opinions offered years earlier by other practitioners, on diverse issues that are only marginally related to current violence risk considerations, may be irrelevant and misleading. Predictions, when offered, should be specific. Of interest to courts, parole authorities, and the like is to know what type of violence might occur, under what sort of conditions, to whom, with

what effects, and in what space of time. Jackson has ably summarized this point (64). Conclusions about risk assessments should be expressed in clear and intelligible terms.

4. Assessing risk for violence is a broader task than predicting it. Psychiatrists and other mental health professionals may or may not be faulted for an erroneous prediction, but more certainly, they will be censured for producing assessments that do not meet accepted standards for completeness, thoroughness, accuracy, and objectivity (65). Second opinions, as in other areas of medicine, are indispensable in some cases.

5. Actuarial information obtained from records can focus and strengthen risk assessments. Prior violent behaviour is a predictor of future violent behaviour (66). Helpful information in clinical reports often comes to light in the course of completing the VRAG and other such schemes (for example, the Offender Group Reconviction Scale, 67; see 68). When these devices form part of the evaluation, they must be completed fully and accurately. Prompted by the case at hand, it is also incumbent on practitioners to search out relevant baseline statistical recurrence data. This would apply even where the published data are somewhat impressionistic (69).

6. Reports, whether based on published structured schemes or not, should identify key risk factors and offer a plausible theory as to how such factors conspired or intersected in a particular instance. The courts expect psychiatrists to offer explanations that transcend common sense (70). It is increasingly recognized that convincing psychological theories have to invoke intersecting factors operating in concert; more or less static conceptualizations are insufficient (3). It needs to be clear what factors in what combinations increase risk and how stipulated interventions may be expected to reduce defined risk.

7. Over the past quarter-century, the Hare PCL-R has emerged as a lead variable in risk prediction (71). The psychopathy construct provides a platform on which to build risk assessments (71,72).

8. The use of structured violence risk assessment guides can improve practice. It is often mistakenly thought that schemes like the HCR-20 rob psychiatrists of their clinical individuality and prowess. This is not so. These various schemes depended heavily upon clinical consultation during their development and ensuing testing. They act as aides-mémoire, helping to ensure that crucial items are not overlooked. They also improve consistency in communication among colleagues. Certainly, it is recognized that, because all items have equal weight (being limited to ratings of 0, 1, or at maximum, 2), some persons with low overall scores (out of, say, 40) will nonetheless have a high risk of harming others (see 73 for some recent clear individual case examples in the Canadian context). If structured guides are used, they should be used properly (74).

9. Risk assessments should link directly to risk management practices. This is implied in the HCR-20CG. Courts, review boards, and other tribunals are interested in what concrete steps should follow from a risk assessment. They need to know not only what the risk is but how it can likely be attenuated so that the individual can be reintegrated into society. Psychiatrists need to be aware of the rapidly growing literature on community treatment (75).

10. Attempts to establish risk factors in individual cases need to be matched with efforts to find particular strengths or "promotive" factors (76). Especially important is

the idea that patients' goals mesh with those proposed by psychiatrists and other mental health professionals.

CONCLUSIONS AND NEW DIRECTIONS

It is to be hoped that this paper will give readers unfamiliar with the emerging specialty of risk assessment a clearer idea of the purpose of recently evolved assessment schemes like the Hare PCL-R, VRAG, HCR-20, HCR-20CG, SAVRY, EARL-20B, EARL-21G, and START. Not particularly stressed in the paper was the debate about the validity and usefulness of actuarial, compared with clinical, prediction. Like others (66), our view is that this distinction is unhelpful because, in the end, it not only pays to have as much knowledge about statistical base rates for particular subgroups as can be obtained but also to have as much thoughtful and well-reasoned scientific clinical opinion as possible about the case at hand. This is particularly so because many established actuarial variables are in fact ultimately based in clinical knowledge and expertise (for example, psychopathy, personality disorder, mental disorder, and substance abuse).

As explained above, the forces that propelled Canadian risk assessment research and practice to the fore internationally had some of their roots in the legal and policy debates that occurred in Canada during the 1970s and 1980s. These foundations need to be acknowledged, since research and clinical practices in risk assessment and management have been forged in part by these developments. They provide the general framework within which is decided what evidence is fair to consider in a particular case and what is not. In Canada, a partnership has recently emerged between research and clinical practice. The key roles of administrators and policymakers have also become evident. Needed now is the fuller inclusion of patients and incarcerated persons themselves as we continue to evolve the kinds of clinical protocols that play such a large role in determining their fates.

REFERENCES

1. Monahan J. Foreward. In: Webster CD, Jackson MA, editors. Impulsivity: theory, assessment, and treatment. New York: Guilford Press; 1997. p x.
2. Eaves D, Douglas KS, Webster CD, Ogloff JRP, Hart SD. Dangerous and long-term offenders: an assessment guide. Burnaby (BC): Mental Health, Law and Policy Institute, Simon Fraser University; 2000.
3. Webster CS, Hucker SJ. Release decision making. Hamilton (ON): St Joseph's Healthcare Hamilton; 2003. p 3–7.
4. Mossman D. Understanding prediction instruments. In: Simon RI, Gold LH, editors. Textbook of forensic psychiatry. Washington (DC): American Psychiatric Publishing, Inc; 2004. p 501–23.
5. Conacher N, Shaw J. The use of the Ontario Mental Health Act as a means of preventative detention for the dangerous mentally ill offender. Journal of Forensic Psychiatry 1993;4:441–9.
6. Smith v Jones [1999] I SCR. 455.
7. Felthous AR. Personal violence. In: Simon RI, Gold LH, editors. Textbook of forensic psychiatry. Washington (DC): American Psychiatric Publishing, Inc; 2004. p 490 –2.
8. Fidler ND, Gray KG. Law and the practice of nursing. Toronto (ON): Ryerson Press; 1947.

9. Mohr JW, Turner RE, Jerry MB. Pedophilia and exhibitionism: a handbook. Toronto (ON): University of Toronto Press; 1964.

10. Freund K. Erotic preference in pedophilia. Behav Res Ther 1967:5:339–48.

11. Langevin R. Sexual strands: understanding and treating sexual anomalies in men. Hillsdale (NJ); Lawrence Erlbaum Associates; 1983.

12. Langevin R, Curnoe S, Federoff P, Bennett R, Langevin, M, Peever C, and others. Lifetime sex offender recidivism: a 25-year follow-up study. Canadian Journal of Criminology and Criminal Justice 2004;46(5):531–52.

13. Blanchard R. Fraternal birth order and the maternal immune hypothesis of male homosexuality. Horm Behav 2001;40:105–14.

14. Barbaree HE, Seto MC, Langton CM, Peacock EJ. Evaluating the predictive accuracy of six risk assessment instruments for adult sex offenders. Crim Justice Behav 2001;28:490–521.

15. Barker ET, Mason MH. The insane criminal as therapist. Can Psychiatr Assoc J 1968;13:61–72.

16. Quinsey VL. The long term management of the mentally disordered offender. In: Hucker SJ, Webster CD, Ben-Aron MH, editors. Mental disorder and criminal responsibility. Toronto (ON): Butterworths; 1981. p 137–55.

17. Quinsey VL, Chaplin TC, Carrigan WF. Sexual preferences among incestuous and non-incestuous child molesters. Behav Ther 1979:10;562–5.

18. Rice ME. Violence in the maximum security hospital. In: Ben-Aron MH, Hucker SJ, Webster CD, editors. Clinical criminology: the assessment and treatment of criminal behaviour. Toronto (ON): M & M Graphics; 1985. p 57–79.

19. Quinsey VL. The base rate problem and the prediction of dangerousness: a reappraisal. Int J Psychiatry Law 1980;8:329–40.

20. Quinsey VL, Ambtman R. Variables affecting psychiatrists' and teachers' assessments of mentally ill offenders. J Consult Clin Psychol 1979;47:353–62.

21. Quinsey VL, Maguire A. Offenders remanded for a psychiatric examination: perceived treatability and disposition. Int J Law Psychiatry 1983;8:193–205.

22. Stone AA. The new legal standard of dangerousness: fair in theory, unfair in practice. In: Webster CD, Ben-Aron MH, Hucker SJ, editors. Dangerousness: probability and prediction, psychiatry and public policy. New York: Cambridge University Press; 1985. p 13–24.

23. Quinsey VL. Assessment of dangerousness of mental patients held in maximum security. Int J Law Psychiatry 1979;2:389–406.

24. Harris GT, Rice ME, Quinsey VL. Violent recidivism of mentally disordered offenders: the development of a statistical prediction instrument. Crim Justice Behav 1993;20:315–35.

25. Menzies RJ, Webster CD, Sepejak DS. Hitting the forensic sound barrier: predictions of dangerousness in a pre-trial psychiatric clinic. In: Webster CD, Ben-Aron MH, Hucker SJ, editors. Dangerousness: probability and prediction, psychiatry and public policy. New York: Cambridge University Press; 1985. p 115–43.

26. Quinsey VL, Harris GT, Rice ME, Cormier C. Violent offenders: appraising and managing risk. Washington (DC): American Psychological Association; 1998.

27. Harris GT, Rice ME, Cormier CA. Prospective replication of the Violence Risk Appraisal Guide in predicting violent recidivism among forensic patients. Law and Human Behaviour 2002;26:377–94.

28. Webster CD, Menzies RJ, Jackson MA. Clinical assessment before trial: legal issues and mental disorder. Toronto (ON): Butterworths; 1982.

29. Menzies RJ, Webster CD, Sepejak DS. The dimensions of dangerousness: evaluating the accuracy of psychometric predictions of violence among forensic patients. Law Hum Behav 1985;9:35–56.

30. Menzies RJ, Webster CD. The construction of validation of risk assessments in a six-year follow-up of forensic patients: a tridimensional analysis. J Consult Clin Psychol 1995;63:766–78.

31. Menzies RJ. Survival of the sanest: order and disorder in a pretrial psychiatric clinic. Toronto (ON): University of Toronto Press; 1989.

32. Criminal Code. S.542.

33. Law Reform Commission of Canada. Mental disorder in the criminal process. Ottawa: Law Reform Commission of Canada; 1976.

34. R v Swain [1991], SCR (4th) 253 (SCC).

35. Tollefson EA, Starkman B. Mental disorder in criminal proceedings. Scarborough (ON): Carswell; 1993.

36. Bloom H, Butler BT. Defending mentally disordered persons. Toronto (ON): Carswell; 1995.

37. Webster CD, Harris G, Rice M, Cormier C, Quinsey V. The violence prediction scheme: assessing dangerousness in high risk men. Toronto (ON): University of Toronto; 1994.

38. Hare R. Manual for Hare Psychopathy Checklist—Revised. Version 2. Toronto (ON): Multi-Health Systems; 2003.

39. Cleckley H. The mask of sanity. St Louis (MO): Mosby; 1941.

40. Hare R. A checklist for the assessment in criminal populations. In: Ben-Aron MH, Hucker SJ, Webster CD, editors. Clinical criminology: the assessment and treatment of criminal behaviour. Toronto (ON): M & M Graphics; 1985.

41. Hare R. Manual for the Hare Psychopathy Checklist—Revised. Toronto (ON): Multi-Health Systems; 1991.

42. Monahan J, Steadman HJ, Silver E, Appelbaum PS, Robbins PC, Mulvey EP, Roth L, Grisso T, Banks S. Rethinking risk assessment: the MacArthur study of mental disorder and violence. Oxford: Oxford University Press; 2001.

43. Hart SD, Cox D, Hare RD. The Hare Psychopathy Checklist: Screening Version (PCL:SV). Toronto (ON): Multi-Health Systems; 1995.

44. Forth AE, Kosson DS, Hare RD. Hare Psychopathy Checklist: Youth Version (PCL:YV). Toronto (ON): Multi-Health Systems; 2003.

45. Webster CD, Eaves D, Douglas KS, Wintrup A. The HCR-20 scheme: the assessment of dangerousness and risk–version 1. Burnaby (BC): Mental Health, Law and Policy Institute, Simon Fraser University; 1995.

46. Borum R. Improving the clinical practice of violence risk assessment. Am Psychol 1996;51:945–53.

47. Webster CD, Douglas KS, Eaves D, Hart SD. The HCR-20: assessing the risk for violence. Version 2. Burnaby (BC): Mental Health, Law and Policy Institute, Simon Fraser University; 1997.

48. Douglas KS, Ogloff JRP. Violence by psychiatric patients: the impact of archival measurement source on violence base rates and risk assessment accuracy. Can J Psychiatry 2003;48:734–40.

49. Douglas KS, Webster CD, Hart SD, Eaves D, Ogloff JRP, editors. HCR-20 CG (companion guide). Burnaby (BC): Mental Health Law and Policy Institute, Simon Fraser University; 2001.

50. Kropp PR, Hart SD, Webster CD Eaves D. Spousal Assault Risk Assessment: user's guide. Toronto (ON): Multi-Health Systems; 1999.

51. Boer DP, Hart SD, Kropp PR, Webster CD. Manual for Sexual Violence Risk-20: professional guidelines for assessing risk of sexual violence. Vancouver (BC): The British Columbia Institute Against Family Violence; 1998.

52. Hart SD, Kropp PR, Laws DR. The Risk for Sexual Violence Protocol: structured professional guidelines for assessment of sexual violence. Vancouver (BC): Mental Health, Law and Policy Institute, Simon Fraser University; 2003.

53. Borum R, Bartel P, Forth A. Manual for the structured assessment of violence risk in youth (SAVRY). Tampa (FL): University of South Florida; 2002.

54. Augimeri L, Koegl C, Webster CD, Levene K. The Early Assessment of Risk List for Boys (EARL-20B). Version 2. Toronto (ON): Earlscourt Child and Family Centre; 2001.

55. Levene KS, Augimeri LK, Pepler SJ, Walsh MM, Webster CD, Koegl CJ. Early Assessment Risk List for Girls (EARL-21G). Version 1. Consultation edition. Toronto (ON): Earlscourt Child and Family Centre; 2001.

56. Webster CD, Martin M-L, Brink J, Nicholls T, Middleton C. START: the Short Term Assessment of Risk and Treatability. Hamilton: St Joseph's Healthcare; 2004.

57. McNiel DE, Gregory AL, Lam JN, Binder RL, Sullivan GR. Utility of decision support tools for assessing acute risk of violence. J Consult Clin Psychol 2003;71:945–53.

58. Worling JR, Curwen T. The "ERASOR": Estimate of Risk of Adolescent Sexual Offence Recidivism. Version 2.0. Toronto (ON): Safe-T Program, Thistletown Regional Centre; 2001.

59. Bloom H, Webster CD, Eisen R. ERA-20, Employee Risk Assessment: a guide for evaluating potential workplace violence perpetrators. Toronto (ON): workplace.calm, inc; 2002.

60. Bloom H, Eisen RS, Pollock N, Webster CD. WRA-20, Workplace Risk Assessment: a guide for evaluating violence potential. Version 1. Toronto (ON): workplace.calm inc; 2000.

61. Boyd BA. Our jails and the psychiatric examination and treatment of the disturbed offender. Canadian Journal of Corrections 1994;6:477–9.

62. Elbogen EB, Tomkins AJ, Pothuloor AP, Scalora MJ. Documentation of violence risk in psychiatric hospital patient charts: an empirical investigation. J Am Acad Psychiatry Law 2003;31:58–64.

63. Dickey R. Assessing inmates for risk of future violence. CPA Bulletin 2000;32(6):168–170.

64. Jackson J. A conceptual model for the study of violence. In: Webster CD, Jackson MA, editors. Impulsivity: theory, assessment and treatment. New York: Guilford; 1997. p 223–47.

65. Weinstock R. Ethics in forensic psychiatry. In: Simon RI, Gold LH, editors. Textbook of forensic psychiatry. Washington (DC): American Psychiatric Publishing, Inc; 2004. p 91–115.

66. Blumenthal S, Lavender T. Violence and mental disorder: a critical aid to the assessment and management of risk. London (UK): Jessica Kingsley; 2001.

67. Copas J, Marshall P. The offender group reconviction scale: a statistical reconviction score for use by probation officers. Applied Statistics 1998;47:159–71.

68. Gray NS, Snowden RJ, MacCulloch S, Phillips H, Taylor J, MacCulloch MJ. Relative efficacy of criminological, clinical and personality measures of future risk of offending in mentally disordered offenders: a comparative study of HCR-20, PCL-SV, and OGRS. J Consult Clin Psychol 2004;72:523–30.

69. Hogg W. Mothers who murder their children: an impressionistic study. Am J Forensic Psychiatry 2004;25:45–54.

70. Foucault M. About the concept of the "dangerous individual" in 19th-century legal psychiatry. In: Weisstub DN, editor. Law and psychiatry. New York: Pergamon Press; 1978. p 1–18.

71. Hare RD, Clark D, Grann M, Thornton D. Psychopathy and the predictive validity of the PCL-R: an international perspective. Behav Sci Law 2000;18:623–45.

72. Wulach JS. The criminal personality as a DSM-III-R antisocial, narcissistic, borderline, and histrionic personality disorder. Int J Offender Ther Comp Criminol 1998;32:185–99.

73. Robertson RG, Yaren S, Globerman D. Assessing risk for violence: a retrospective analysis from a forensic service. Am J Forensic Psychiatry 2004;5:5–15.

74. Webster CD, Muller-Isberner R, Fransson G. Violence risk assessment: using structured clinical guides professionally. Int J Forensic Mental Health 2003;1:43–51.

74. Estroff SE, Zimmer C. Social networks, social support, and violence among persons with severe, persistent mental illness. In: Monahan J, Steadman JH, editors. Violence and mental disorder: developments in risk assessment. Chicago (IL): University of Chicago Press; 1994. p 259–95.

75. Stouthamer-Loeber M, Loeber R, Wei E, Farrington DP, Wikstrom P-OH. Risk and promotive effects in the explanations of persistent serious delinquency in boys. J Consult Clin Psychol 2002;70:111–23.

II

The Emergence
of Actuarial Violence
Prediction

Section II

Introduction

While an earlier notion of dangerousness implied that the propensity for violence lies almost exclusively within the individual, the modern shift to "risk analysis" recognizes that social and physical factors can also influence risk. Social and physical situations can be highly unpredictable, and it can be difficult to identify and measure the salient risk factors in "naturally occurring" social contexts, especially those located in communities. For this reason, predicting violence and related risks is now understood to be a more complex task than it was when risk was viewed as being related mainly to factors within the individual. Trying to make exact forecasts that account for both the particular characteristics of would-be perpetrators (to say nothing of possible victims) and the moment-to-moment state of prevailing circumstances is, not surprisingly, a challenge. While it is not impossible to make accurate predictions in particular cases, it is difficult, especially when the prediction expectation is made highly specific (i.e., that Mr. X will act violently in a particular way against another person or persons, under stipulated conditions, over a stated period of time). (See Jackson, 1997.)

Clinicians and researchers are increasingly considering how inherent predisposition intersects with a range of victimological, situational, environmental and protective variables. The resulting calculus may actualize or inhibit potentially violent outcomes. As Sherlock Holmes cunningly remarks in Sir Arthur Conan Doyle's 1890 novel *The Sign of Four*, the individual is an "unsolvable puzzle" (2001, p. 84). Yet when the individual is but one member of a group (and thus can be averaged as part of that group), the person achieves "mathematical certainty" (p. 84).

Any clinician, researcher or policy analyst with expertise in the violence risk assessment area must appreciate certain statistical realities. Research over the past 30 years has been spurred by the results of several major statistically based projects. The best example of an early study is Henry Steadman's and Joseph Cocozza's so-called "Operation Baxstrom" (1974). These researchers astutely took advantage of a set of unusual legal circumstances that afforded the opportunity to find out how well clinical and administrative opinion about violence risk associated with actual outcome. In 1961, a man named Johnnie Baxstrom—who had a history of violence—was being held in custody at a New York State correctional facility. When it was time for him to be released, Baxstrom's detention was continued under civil mental health legislation. He appealed this detention all the way to the Supreme Court of the United States. In 1966, the Court eventually decided in his favour and Baxstrom was let go. Not only was he freed, but the court also ruled that 966 other inmates were to be released or transferred to lower security conditions. As a result, it was possible to determine the real life outcome of people who ordinarily would have continued to be detained on the grounds of "dangerousness."

Steadman and Cocozza followed this group of almost a thousand people for four years. Using records obtained from various sources, they analyzed the data and found that, overall, the rate of recidivism was low, and especially low for violent reoffending. In other words, there was marked overprediction of violence. As indicated in the introductory remarks to Section I, there will always be errors—both in overpredicting and underpredicting violence (see Mossman's chapter in this section). In the Baxstrom study, as in most projects of its kind, the error of overprediction was found to be more common than underprediction.

Since violent offenders with a mental disorder can hardly be released by a process of random selection, only studies like Operation Baxstrom can make it possible to gauge the overall accuracy of prediction. People have to somehow be classified, measures of actual outcome have to be obtained after a set period, and there has to be a statistical way of relating predictions to outcomes. One of the incidental findings from the Baxstrom study, mentioned by Scott in Chapter 1, was that the chance of reoffending could have been fairly well predicted *on average* based on a few simple-to-gather pieces of information. For instance, researchers and clinician-researchers can find fairly strong statistical associations between simple, more-or-less demographic information (e.g., whether or not someone has ever been married, or whether or not the person was employed at the time of the offence). Though they have long recognized that previous violence is predictive of future violence, these demographic-type associations would not have been so fully anticipated prior to the Baxstrom study.

Douglas Mossman's piece (Chapter 5), originally published in a forensic psychiatry textbook, explains that there is still no test that can statistically predict someone's chance of reoffending. (Such a test would draw upon various clinical skills to measure factors that, for now, largely go unrecorded. These factors would then have to be integrated into complex programs and algorithms, accessing data pertinent to specific subpopulations.) Mossman concludes that errors in overpredicting and underpredicting violence cannot be avoided. (Overprediction errors result in so-called false positives, because the prediction is positive for violence but would prove false if the prediction were tested. Violence underprediction errors occur when, against expectation, a person is predicted to be negative for violence, but actually goes on to commit a violent act.

Mossman demonstrates, as have others before him, that it would be naive to expect that some newly developed prediction device could be powerful enough to enable courts, review boards and other tribunals to dispense with current methods. Present-day methods are largely ad hoc: they depend on the idiosyncratic views of key assessors, without any steps being made to measure their accuracy. Mossman is not suggesting that contemporary assessors and decision makers should discount "actuarial" information should it be available and pertinent to the case at hand. Rather, he emphasizes that successfully making a prediction is tied intricately to the frequency with which events occur. Predicting behaviours that occur at low rates is difficult and, although patients with mental disorders (a designation that includes people with personality disorders) have somewhat elevated rates of violence, both in institutions and the community, the overall rates nonetheless remain relatively low.

This difficulty of predicting uncommon behaviours has long been realized (e.g., by Quinsey, 1980). To an extent, this problem has been circumvented by using multiple violence outcome measures. (Some violent behaviours, such as verbal abuse, do of course occur with much greater frequency than do serious assaults.) Yet although we may know which variables in a given set of circumstances may predict minor violence, such as threats, there is always a question of how well these same predictors will forecast serious violence, such as murder.

Charles W. Lidz, **Edward P. Mulvey** and **William Gardner** (Chapter 6) aimed to find out if clinicians, as they form opinions about violence risk, can improve on chance. Their article flows well from Mossman's piece which, among other things, demonstrates that with relatively low-occurring violence, the best bet is to predict non-occurrence. The Lidz et al. study relied on a large sample of people assessed briefly by clinicians in a busy emergency psychiatric service. The results showed that the clinicians' predictions did exceed chance, if only modestly. What was surprising, though, was that the accuracy of predictions over the six-month follow-up period was strikingly weak for the women. The clinical assessors grossly underpredicted violence in the women (22%) relative to men (45%). Yet, in fact, the women committed *more* violent acts during follow-up (49%) than the men (42%). So prediction accuracy drops markedly if assessors underestimate or overestimate the baseline levels of violence in subgroups.

There is thus much to be gained from supplying clinical assessors with accurate, up-to-date data on recidivism rates and violent incidents for subpopulations. As well as teaching clinicians the "hands on" skills so ably described by Scott in Section I, merely providing actuarial data would likely help decrease the inaccuracy of risk prediction.[1]

In 1993, the same year that Charles Lidz and his colleagues published their paper, **Grant T. Harris**, **Marnie E. Rice** and **Vernon L. Quinsey** (Chapter 7) put forward the results of their seven-year follow-up of more than 600 men originally assessed in the maximum secure division of the Mental Health Centre Penetanguishene (MHCP) in

Ontario.[2] In the study, one set of research assistants searched the extensive MHCP records to isolate factors that might have a bearing on future violence risk. Another set of assistants searched for outcome data several years after individuals had been released into the community. The outcome data included violent incidents that occurred in both criminal justice and mental health systems. This meant that violent acts were taken into account even if no charges were laid because the person was admitted to a psychiatric facility.

Another feature of this study was that about half of the population was treated at MHCP (after having been found unfit to stand trial or found not criminally responsible by reason of mental disorder), while the other half was routed into the correctional system (i.e., they were found fit and criminally responsible for their acts). Had the study focused on either the mental health system or the criminal justice system alone, it would not have been as possible to generalize to the other set of circumstances.

As a result of painstaking work, the researchers were able to identify 12 risk factors that correlated appreciably with violent incidents that occurred over the next seven years. Although other factors were significantly associated with subsequent violence, they were not included in the instrument the authors developed, the Violence Risk Appraisal Guide (VRAG), as they were less powerful than the main 12.

The strongest correlations that the researchers found between prediction and outcome were achieved by the Hare PCL-R item (see Table 2 in Chapter 7). The Hare PCL-R, though never originally developed to be a risk assessment device, turns out—in study after study—to associate with subsequent violence as well as other outcomes, such as misconducts while in prison. Other variables strongly linked to violence outcome were separation from parents under age 16, elementary school maladjustment, failure on prior conditional release, a *DSM-III* diagnosis of personality disorder, and a property offence history. Some variables were found to have a protective role. Being relatively old was negatively correlated with future violence, as was lack of serious victim injury in the index offence that prompted the assessment at Pentaguishene. (In Chapter 1 Scott points out, in addition, that too much weight can be attributed to the "excessiveness" of violence in the offence under consideration[3]). Another protective factor against perpetrating future acts of violence was a *DSM-III* diagnosis of schizophrenia. This seemingly counterintuitive finding may be explained in part by the fact that about a quarter of the study's total population was deemed to have some kind of psychopathy, according to the Hare PCL-R. Relative to people with psychopathy, people with schizophrenia might have been at reduced risk for future violence (i.e., might have been more readily treated with medication and other interventions, and may have been more likely to be admitted to a psychiatric hospital to prevent violence.) This finding supports the often-made point that the links between major mental disorder and violence are relatively weak based on averaged data from statistical studies.[4]

Perhaps the most striking finding from the Harris et al. study is expressed visually (see Figure 1, page 145). This figure illustrates the relationship between the prediction scores, based on the 12 VRAG items (weighted statistically) and probability of violent recidivism. The predictor variable was the size of the VRAG score, ranging from very low to very high. These scores were divided into nine equal-sized "bins" with Bin 1 VRAG scores being the lowest and Bin 9 being the highest. Pitted against actual outcome, there is an increasing probability of violent offending from Bin 1 to Bin 2 to Bin 3, and so on. In light of the now well-established association between VRAG score and subsequent release, assessors should take the VRAG score into account (always assuming the individual being assessed possesses characteristics similar to those found in the Harris et al. standardization sample).

The actuarial approach espoused by Harris et al. is, of course, not unique. Much work had already been done with Canadian federal offenders using a device called the General Statistical Incidence of Recidivism (GSIR; Nuffield, 1982; Correctional Service Canada, 1997). Scores from the GSIR are used routinely to aid parole decision making in Canada. Similarly, a well-known device called the Offender Group Reconviction Scale (OGRS; Copas & Marshall, 1998) is used by some organizations in Great Britain. Very recently, Hickey et al. (in press) devised and tested a promising new actuarial device for use specifically with medium secure forensic populations (see the discussion in the final paragraphs of this introduction).

Gregg J. Gagliardi, **David Lovell**, **Paul D. Peterson** and **Ron Jemelka** (Chapter 8) show that most correctional systems, with the ready computerization of data, are capable of working out which variables in a certain population have predictive power. They demonstrate how, given a sample of 333 offenders with mental disorders, it is possible to find out which variables have predictive power and which do not. They examine nine variables in particular. What is especially striking from their results is that some of these variables proved not to be risk variables at all. Rather, the statistical analyses showed five of them to function protectively (e.g., being female, being a first-time sex offender, having a history of residential mental health treatment in prison).

Like other investigators, Gagliardi and colleagues found that a criminal history is linked strongly to recidivism. The authors are surprised that a few fairly straightforward pieces of background information, when cast against actual outcome, yield fairly robust associations. They point out that their "homemade" or "home-tailored" set of predictor variables did as well as or better than "state-of-the art" risk assessment instruments like the VRAG, the HCR-20, the Spousal Assault Risk Assessment Guide (SARA; Kropp, Hart, Webster and Eaves, 1995) and schemes specifically designed to evaluate violence risk in sex offenders. This home-made set of variables can be accomplished at low cost, as key predictive information is simply culled from existing correctional files.

This finding raises the question of what as-yet-undetermined (or underconsidered) atypical, non-criminogenic or protective factors could have as much, or more, predictive force than the traditional factors relied on by many current actuarial schemes. Given the tentative association between a history of mental illness and subsequent violence, Gagliardi et al. note that including mental illness as a risk factor "may not only unfairly prejudice mentally ill offenders but it may even degrade predictive accuracy" (page 168). As noted above, Hickey et al. (in press) have recently reported a study, using the study design by Gagliardi et al., based on about 900 offenders with schizophrenia and related disorders within British medium secure services. Their results achieved similar predictive accuracy to that of Gagliardi et al. and were more impressive than those found with the VRAG.

Hickey et al. built on the finding from Gagliardi's team that protective factors need to be fully considered when doing violence risk assessments. They point out that clinicians are at a disadvantage in the "clinical versus actuarial" debate (see Section IV), as it is difficult in actual mental health practice for clinicians to obtain reliable day-to-day, week-to-week information about dynamic, changeable variables—especially when services are being provided in the community, where variables are continuously changing. Without continuously gathered data, dynamic variables are forced to function as if they were static variables in predicting violence (Hickey et al., in press).

NOTES

1. This is the concluding point made by Gagliardi et al. in the final chapter in this section. They argue that most institutions have the capacity to provide their assessors with norms, created on site, based on the behaviour of people who actually pass through the violence risk assessment service and then into institutional care or the community. But generally, institutions lack the will to provide these norms. Particular organizations would likely be easily able to tailor the assessments of violence to local actualities and conditions. This would make assessments more accurate and fairer than using standardized assessment devices not tailored to a particular place or situation. Or, if ready-made devices are carefully selected and implemented by key clinicians, researchers and administrators, these schemes should be tested in situ (under the particular prevailing circumstance).

2. Since the publication of the original 1993 paper, the project has been extended, refined and published as a book, *Violent Offenders: Appraising and Managing Risk* (Quinsey et al., 1998, 2006).

3. Scott says, "Excessive violence very doubtfully warrants the importance assigned to it by judges and others who assess dangerousness as a guide to sentencing. We forget that most murderers are amateurs and most victims healthy people with a firm hold on life, so that the killer is often horrified at the difficulty of killing and the awful sight and sounds involved, so that he strives in desperation or panic, to end the process quickly" (p. 131). The results of modern studies are in agreement (e.g., Monahan et al., 2001).

4. It should be noted, as in the standardization sample, that most individuals tend to score in the mid-range (e.g., bins 4, 5 and 6 of the authors' nine "bins"). This can reduce the practical usefulness of the score. Review boards' tendencies to discount information that board members might view as extraneous (see Hilton and Simmons's article in Section V) can also reduce the score's usefulness.

REFERENCES

Copas, J.B. & Marshall, P. (1998). The offender group reconviction scale: The statistical reconvictions score for use by probation officers. *Journal of the Royal Statistical Society, 47*, 159–171.

Correctional Service Canada. (1997). *Case Management Manual, Annex J: Revised Statistical Information on Recidivism Scale*. Ottawa: Author.

Doyle, A.C. (2001). *The Sign of Four*. London: Penguin. (First published 1890)

Hickey, N., Yang, M. and Coid, J. (in press). The development of the Medium Secure Recidivism Risk Guide (MSRRG): An actuarial risk prediction instrument. *Journal of Forensic Psychiatry and Psychology*.

Jackson, J. (1997). A conceptual model for the study of violence. In C.D. Webster & M.A. Jackson (Eds.), *Impulsivity: Theory, Assessment and Treatment* (pp. 223–247). New York: Guilford.

Kropp, P.R., Hart, S.D., Webster, C.D. and Eaves, D. (1995). *Manual for the Spousal Assault Risk Assessment Guide*, 2nd ed. Vancouver: The British Columbia Institute Against Family Violence.

Monahan, J., Steadman, H.J., Silver, E., Appelbaum, P.S., Robbins, P.C, Mulvey, E.P., et al. (2001). *Rethinking Risk Assessment: The MacArthur Study of Mental Disorder and Violence.* Oxford, U.K.: Oxford University Press.

Nuffield, J. (1982). *Parole Decision-Making in Canada: Research Towards Decision Guidelines.* Ottawa: Ministry of Supply and Services Canada.

Quinsey, V.L. (1980). The base rate problem and the prediction of dangerousness: A reappraisal. *Journal of Psychiatry and Law, 8,* 329–340.

Quinsey, V.L., Harris, G.T., Rice, M.E. & Cormier, C. (1998). *Violent Offenders: Appraising and Managing Risk.* Washington, DC: American Psychological Association.

Quinsey, V.L., Harris, G.T., Rice, M.E. & Cormier, C. (2006). *Violent Offenders: Appraising and Managing Risk* (2nd ed.) Washington, DC: American Psychological Association.

Steadman, H.J. & Cocozza, J.J. (1974). *Careers of the Criminally Insane: Excessive Social Control of Deviance.* Lexington, MA: Lexington Books.

5

Understanding Prediction Instruments

DOUGLAS MOSSMAN

INTRODUCTION

Psychiatrists make predictions all the time, but usually without realizing it. Prescribing medication may not seem like a prediction, but a physician's deciding to use a drug in a patient's treatment entails a belief that the drug might help. That belief, in turn, rests on an implicit prediction about what the drug will do to alleviate the patient's distress. Making a psychotherapeutic interpretation involves an implicit prediction that formulating a patient's experience in a particular way will help the patient grasp connections among feelings, perceptions, events, and actions and will thereby let the patient function better.

Although psychiatrists learn to take these everyday clinical predictions in stride, being asked explicitly to make a prediction about what persons will do often makes psychiatrists uncomfortable. And probably no type of prediction generates more anxiety than one involving a person's future "dangerousness." One reason for this—the reason for the scare quotes in the previous sentence—is that "dangerousness" is an ambiguous term: it can refer to harm-causing acts, to acts with potential to cause harm, to behavior that seems threatening but does not itself cause harm, to having a high probability for acting violently, or to simply having any propensity to act violently. A second reason is

Reprinted with permission. R.I. Simon & L.H. Gold (Eds.), Textbook of Forensic Psychiatry, *pp. 501–523. Washington, DC: American Psychiatric Publishing. © 2004 American Psychiatric Publishing*

that since the 1970s, the *Tarasoff* decision (*Tarasoff v. Regents of the University of California* 1976) in California and related cases in other states have declared that society expects mental health professionals to try to identify patients who pose a threat to others, and that courts may hold mental health professionals accountable if they fail to do this. A third source of anxiety comes from the magnitude and gravity of the potential consequences of being wrong about dangerousness. Wrong guesses about medication rarely amount to more than a failed treatment effort or an intolerable side effect, problems that can easily be solved with another clinical intervention. Wrong guesses about a patient's potential for violence, however, can have a devastating effect on the patient, the victim (often a family member or acquaintance of the patient), and the psychiatrist's emotional well-being.

Few, if any, psychiatrists can avoid making predictions about dangerous behavior because dozens of common clinical actions require implicit judgments about the violence potential of a patient or evaluee. Twenty-five years ago, Shah (1978) identified 15 areas of forensic decision making that require mental health professionals to assess the risk of violence. More recently, Hall and Ebert (2002, pp. 167–768) noted 27 circumstances that require dangerousness assessments; their list includes activities common to most psychiatric practices, such as releasing patients from hospitals, treating potentially violent patients in psychotherapy, and initiating emergency hospitalization or civil commitment.

Depending on their work setting and clientele, psychiatrists may have to make many other kinds of assessments of dangerousness. Fitness-for-duty determinations, sentencing recommendations, custody assessments involving previously abusive parents, intervention recommendations concerning stalkers or their victims, and planning treatment for substance abusers who commit violent crimes to support their habit all require implicit estimates of the risk of violence. For some release decisions (e.g., discharging previously violent patients or allowing insanity acquittees to leave hospitals and return to the community), preventing or minimizing potential risk to the public dwarfs all other considerations in shaping a patient's clinical management. The frequency and popularity of continuing education seminars on "assessing dangerousness" attest to the concern and anxiety mental health practitioners experience when they have to make judgments about future violence.

Until recently, mental health professionals who made decisions about dangerousness had to rely primarily on what their "gut" told them. Expressed more formally, mental health professionals relied on their "clinical judgment" to make predictions about future violence risk and to plan treatment interventions to reduce that risk. In recent years, however, researchers have developed several instruments with demonstrated accuracy in predicting violent behavior. Psychologists describe these instruments as "actuarial" tools for making "risk assessments" about individuals. The term *actuarial* refers to a type of decision making in which a clinician gathers information about a (usually small) number of factors concerning an individual who is being evaluated. The clinician then categorizes the information by using an explicit scoring system and combines the scores into an overall numerical value that summarizes the individual's risk of violence. Published manuals for these instruments explain their development and rationale, and guide clinicians through the process of assembling the data needed to make actuarially based judgments.

It is easy to underestimate both the value of actuarial instruments and the advantages they afford over the old way of doing things. It also is easy to attribute more significance to results produced by actuarial measures than the developers of these measures intended. This chapter explains how actuarial prediction instruments can probably improve clinical judgments about violence; it also explains why even fairly accurate predictions may have limited practical importance. We shall begin by examining results from a hypothetical contest about the accuracy of violence prediction.

A VIOLENCE PREDICTION CONTEST

Once upon a time, two psychiatrists, Drs. Sybil Commitment and Lesley Faire, worked in a psychiatric emergency service at Gevalt Hospital. They respected each other's clinical talents but often disagreed about which patient needed to undergo hospitalization. Dr. Commitment hospitalized many patients because she worried about their violence potential; Dr. Faire hospitalized patients less frequently because she thought doctors should minimize the use of coercion. To see whose approach was best, the doctors had a contest. Each of them evaluated 1,000 patients whom a third colleague, Dr. Maven, had decided to admit to Gevalt Hospital. Drs. Commitment and Faire each rated these patients on a 5-point scale ("1" implying lowest risk, "5" implying highest); they also made yes-or-no predictions for each patient about whether he or she would become violent within 72 hours of admission. Because Gevalt Hospital carefully watched patients and kept good records about them, Drs. Commitment and Faire knew that any act of violence (which they carefully and unambiguously defined for purposes of their contest) would get noticed and recorded. The doctor whose predictions were most accurate would win the contest.

Several months later, Dr. Maven had admitted 1,000 patients, 100 of whom actually became violent, and Drs. Commitment and Faire were ready to learn who had been the best predictor. Some terminology (summarized in Table 1) will help us understand how Drs. Commitment and Faire tried to interpret the results of their contest. If a doctor predicted violence and the patient subsequently acted violently, the doctor's prediction was a *true positive* (TP) prediction. A *false negative* (FN) prediction was one in which the doctor did not predict violence for a patient who actually was violent. A *true negative* (TN) was a prediction of nonviolence that turned out to be correct, and a *false positive* (FP) was a prediction of violence that was incorrect. By examining a doctor's predictions and the patients' actual behavior, the doctors could calculate what fraction of predictions was correct in light of subsequent events. They also could calculate the ratio of TP to FP predictions to find the odds that a prediction of violence were correct.

TABLE 1

Definitions of Some Terms Used to Describe Prediction Accuracy

ACTUAL BEHAVIOR	PREDICTED VIOLENT	PREDICTED NOT VIOLENT
Violent	True positive (TP)	False negative (FN)
Not violent	False positive (FP)	True negative (TN)

Correct fraction (CF)=(TP+TN)/(TP+FP+FN+TN)
TP:FP ratio=TP/FP
True positive rate (TPR)=Sensitivity=TP/(TP+FN)
True negative rate (TNR)=Specificity=TN/(TN+FP)
False positive rate (FPR)=(1 − Specificity)=FP/(FP+TN)

Imagine the doctors' discussion of their results, which are shown in Table 2. Dr. Commitment was right only 36% of the time, while Dr. Faire was correct for about 86% of the patients. Yet Dr. Faire was wrong about 75% of the patients who acted violently, while Dr. Commitment missed just 10% of these patients. Dr. Commitment felt her performance reflected her concern about a psychiatrist's responsibility to protect the community. But Dr. Commitment made more than seven wrong predictions of violence for every correct one. Because Dr. Faire made fewer wrong predictions of violence, she believed that her performance vindicated her favoring decision making that preserved patients' freedom.

TABLE 2

Results of the Violence Prediction Contest

ACTUAL BEHAVIOR	DR. COMMITMENT'S PREDICTIONS		DR. FAIRE'S PREDICTIONS	
	VIOLENT	NOT VIOLENT	VIOLENT	NOT VIOLENT
Violent	90	10	25	75
Not violent	634	266	70	830
Correct fraction	0.356		0.855	
TP:FP ratio	1:7		1:2.8	
Sensitivity	0.900		0.250	
Specificity	0.296		0.922	

In fact, both psychiatrists did significantly better than chance at predicting violence, but you cannot tell this by looking at either the fraction of predictions that were correct or the ratio of TP to FP predictions. A doctor who simply had said *everybody* was not violent would have been correct 90% of the time. If half of the patients had been violent, a doctor who randomly predicted violence for half the patients would have a TP:FP ratio of about 1, despite no-better-than-chance performance.

The lower part of Table 1 includes accuracy indices that allow investigators to describe results in ways that do not conflate accuracy with the effects of base rates (Somoza and Mossman 1990). Medical publications often use the terms *sensitivity* and *specificity* to quantify diagnostic accuracy. If we interpret the psychiatrists' predictions as "diagnoses" of future violence, then sensitivity is the probability that a prediction of violence was made for an actually-violent patient, and specificity is the probability that a prediction of nonviolence was made for a nonviolent patient. The sensitivities and specificities for the doctors appear in Table 2. Notice, however, that these values still do not help much in deciding who did better.

In fact, as Table 3 shows, the psychiatrists made identical classifications of patients' risk of violence, but they used different decision thresholds when making the predictions. Dr. Commitment minimized false negative outcomes and avoided missing violent patients, and the result was high sensitivity but low specificity. Dr. Faire minimized false positive outcomes and predicted violence only when she had a very strong suspicion that a patient would become violent, and the result was high specificity but low sensitivity.

TABLE 3

Future Violence Ratings and Decision Thresholds

DOCTOR'S NAME	ACTUAL BEHAVIOR	RATINGS				
		1	2	3	4	5
Sybil Commitment	Violent	10	15	30	20	25
	Not violent	226	209	252	103	70
Lesley Faire	Violent	10	15	30	20	25
	Not violent	266	209	252	103	70
	True Positive rate	0.90	0.75	0.45	0.25	
	False positive rate	0.70	0.47	0.19	0.078	

Note: Vertical bars indicate doctor's decision threshold.

These observations suggest that we should measure diagnostic accuracy by using techniques that are not affected by base rates or clinicians' preferences for certain types of outcomes (Swets 1979). Single pairs of results from yes-or-no predictions will not tell the full picture about the accuracy of violence assessments. Ideally, we should describe accuracy in a way that reflects the trade-offs between sensitivity and specificity and that is independent of a clinician's actual cutoff or decision threshold.

As Table 3 shows, one can calculate four sensitivity-specificity pairs using the divisions between the clinicians' five rating categories as potential decision thresholds. At Dr. Faire's strict threshold, violence is predicted only for those patients rated 5. At this strictest threshold, the violence detection rate, or the *true positive rate* (TPR), is only 0.25, but the "false alarm" rate, or *false positive rate* (FPR), is just 0.08. (Note that TPR=sensitivity and FPR=1–specificity.) At the second strictest threshold, violence is predicted for patients rated 4 or 5; the FPR increases to 0.19 and the TPR increases to 0.45. One obtains the FPR and TPR for the two other thresholds in Table 3 similarly.

In the mid-1990s, several writers (Mossman 1994a, 1994b; Rice and Harris 1995; Gardner et al. 1996) recognized that adjustable thresholds are a feature of most violence prediction techniques and that the accuracy of violence prediction methods should therefore be described using *receiver operating characteristic* (ROC) analysis. This term, originally derived from radar applications (Lusted 1984), suggests that detection is characterized by the threshold at which the "receiver" (here, a clinician) operates. ROC analysis allows investigators to characterize the trade-offs between errors and correct identifications that arise from the intrinsic discrimination capacity of a detection method and to distinguish these features from the threshold or operating point that is used to make a decision (Mossman and Somoza 1991). ROC analyses typically utilize a ROC graph, which succinctly summarizes the results of a detection method as the threshold is moved throughout its range of possible values. A ROC graph customarily plots the TPR as a function of the FPR and depicts how the TPR increases as the FPR increases.

Figure 1 is an example of such a graph, based on the results shown in Table 3. Notice that the four possible thresholds lie along a ROC curve joining them. (To learn more about the mathematical assumptions used to fit ROC curves to data points, see Somoza and Mossman 1991 and Mossman 1994b.) The better a test or detection system, the greater the *area under the ROC curve* (AUC) that describes the performance of the test or detection system. The AUC of a test or detection system has a direct, practical interpretation (Hanley and McNeil 1982). In the context of quantifying the accuracy of violence prediction, AUC equals the probability that the detection method would rate a randomly selected, actually violent person as more likely to be violent than a randomly selected, nonviolent person. A prediction method that always rated violent and non-violent persons correctly would have an AUC of 1.0; a prediction method that gave no information would have an AUC of 0.5 and would be described by the diagonal line in Figure 1. For the hypothetical results from Table 3, AUC=0.701±0.028, implying an accuracy level that is significantly better than chance and is fairly typical of clinical judgments about future violence (Mossman 1994b).

These results can help us understand and lay to rest the often-voiced but mistaken (Mossman 2000) belief that predictions of violence—especially long-term predictions—are inaccurate. For the past two decades, many mental health professionals have thought that, as the LJ.S. Supreme Court put it, "[p]sychiatric predictions of future violent behavior by the mentally ill are inaccurate" (*Heller v. Doe* 1993, p. 324). The Court's view reflects conclusions in John Monahan's influential monograph *The Clinical Prediction of Violent Behavior* (1981), which summarized previously published studies of violence prediction in support of this conclusion. Looking at results such as those shown in Table 2 for Drs. Commitment and Faire, Professor Monahan correctly concluded "that psychiatrists and psychologists are accurate in no more than one out of three predictions of violent behavior" (Monahan 1981, p. 92). As we have seen, however, Drs. Commitment and Faire did much better than chance at categorizing patients according to their risk of violence. Their error pattern (the low TP:FP ratio) was a consequence of the low "base rate" of violence among the 1,000 subjects, only 10% of whom were violent during the follow-up.

FIGURE 1

ROC Graph Based on the Results Shown in Table 3

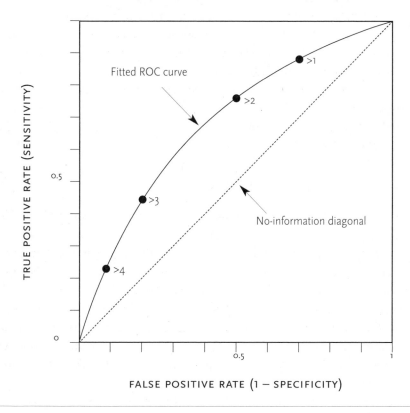

FALSE POSITIVE RATE (1 − SPECIFICITY)

The four possible thresholds are fit to ROC curve, the area under which is 0.701. The no-information diagonal (ROC area = 0.5) is also shown.

ROC methods keep low base rates from fooling us. Because neither FPR nor TPR is affected by base rates, ROC methods describe the accuracy of violence predictions in a way that separates properties of the detection process from the frequency of violence in the population being studied. As Mossman (1994b, 2000) and Buchanan and Leese (2001) have pointed out, reanalyses of previously published data (including those from the studies that Monahan described) show that short-, medium-, and long-term clinical predictions of violence all have a roughly similar, modestly-better-than-chance level of accuracy.

CLINICAL VERSUS ACTUARIAL PREDICTION METHODS

Our discussion of a make-believe contest looks at how well two hypothetical doctors used their "clinical judgment" to assess violence risk and make predictions about it. Most decisions about psychiatric care, and probably most decisions in medicine, are made this way. That is, doctors use facts they have gathered, their background knowledge, their specific knowledge about the person they are evaluating, their intuition, their "gut instincts," and/or whatever else they think is relevant to anticipate (predict) what will happen, and then intervene. Psychologists who study human decision making contrast predictions based on "clinical" judgments (also called "subjective" or "impressionistic" judgments) with "actuarial" predictions based on formulae, algorithms, or other "mechanical" means. As was stated earlier, actuarial tools direct the clinician's attention to specific "aspects, behavior, and other features" of the individuals they are evaluating. The clinician then uses these data to come up with a numerical value that summarizes the evaluee's risk of violence.

HCR-20

The HCR-20 (Webster et al. 1997) provides an easy-to-understand example of this process. This instrument, whose name is an acronym for its overall structure, directs the clinician's attention toward 20 factors—10 **H**istorical items, 5 **C**linical items, and 5 **R**isk management items—that are associated with increased risk of violence (Table 4). The manual for the HCR-20 succinctly describes published research that supports including each item as a risk factor. To use the HCR-20, a clinician gathers the information about each of the risk factor items and then, using the manual's instructions about coding information related to each risk factor, gives each item a score of 0, 1, or 2. An individual's score on the HCR-20 thus can range from 0 to 40, with higher scores implying higher probabilities of future violence.

A brief look at a few items on the HCR-20 will help readers appreciate how its creators have tried to identify a few salient risk factors for violence and have used these factors to produce a straightforward, reliable instrument for risk assessment.

An example of a historical item on the HCR-20 is H5, "Substance Use Problems." The authors justify including this item on the basis of several studies, including the finding by Swanson (1994), based on data originally obtained in the Epidemiologic Catchment Area study, that "having a substance abuse diagnosis yielded much stronger associations with violence than did having a mental disorder" (Webster et al. 1997, p. 36). One assigns a score of 0 on item H5 if the individual has "no substance use problems"; a score of 2 is assigned for "definite/serious substance use problems" that interfere with functioning; and a score of 1 is assigned for "possible/less serious substance use problems" (Webster et al. 1997, p. 37).

Item C3, "Active Symptoms of Major Mental Illness," serves as a good example of a clinical item in the HCR-20. Inclusion of this item gains support from research that associates active psychotic symptoms with violence (e.g., Swanson et al. 1996). A clinician codes this item 0 if an evaluee has "no active symptoms of major mental illness," 1 for "possible/less serious active symptoms," or 2 for "definite/serious active symptoms" (Webster et al. 1997, p. 55).

TABLE 4

Historical, Clinical, and Risk Management Items from the HCR-20

HISTORICAL ITEMS

H1.   Previous Violence
H2.   Young Age at First Incident
H3.   Relationship Instability
H4.   Employment Problems
H5.   Substance Use Problems
H6.   Major Mental Illness
H7.   Psychopathy
H8.   Early Maladjustment
H9.   Personality Disorder
H10. Prior Supervision Failure

CLINICAL ITEMS

C1.   Lack of Insight
C2.   Negative Attitudes
C3.   Active Symptoms of Major Mental Illness
C4.   Impulsivity
C5.   Unresponsive to Treatment

RISK MANAGEMENT ITEMS

R1.   Plans Lack Feasibility
R2.   Exposure to Destabilizers
R3.   Lack of Personal Support
R4.   Noncompliance With Remediation Attempts
R5.   Stress

Source: Reprinted from Webster CD, Douglas KS, Eaves E, et al.: *HCR-20: Assessing Risk for Violence*, Version 2. Burnaby, British Columbia, Mental Health, Law and Policy Institute, Simon Fraser University, 1997. Used with permission.

Item R4, "Noncompliance With Remediation Attempts," asks the evaluator to score the probability that a patient will not take medication or adhere to other therapeutic regimens. A score of 0 implies a "low probability of noncompliance"; 1, a "moderate probability"; and 2, a "high probability." Again, the authors cite research available in 1997 (e.g., Bartels et al. 1991; Haywood et al. 1995) to support inclusion of this risk factor. Subsequent studies (e.g., Swartz et al. 1998) have confirmed the importance of noncompliance as a predictor of posthospitalization violence.

Figure 2 is based on a study of the HCR-20 by Douglas and colleagues (1999) and is presented to help readers understand the relationship between patients' actual scores on an actuarial instrument, their future violence, and the ways that ROC techniques quantify the accuracy of predictions. In their study, Douglas and colleagues used the HCR-20 assessment scheme to code information about 193 former inpatients who had been civilly committed. Patients had subsequently been released to the community for an average of almost 2 years, during which time 73 of the patients became violent. Figure 2 contains histograms showing the patients' HCR-20 scores (which one can figure out from data presented by the authors in their original paper). Notice that the violent patients tended to score higher than did the nonviolent patients. Super-imposed on the histograms are two bell-shaped (Gaussian) curves that represent a best fit of the data (produced by using maximum likelihood estimation software available from Charles E. Metz, Ph.D., of the University of Chicago Department of Radiology). What one sees from examining the bell-shaped curves is that the effect of using the HCR-20 is to shift the distributions of violent and nonviolent patients about one standard deviation apart from each other.

FIGURE 2

Histograms Showing HCR-20 Scores of 73 Violent Patients and 120 Nonviolent Patients Studied by Douglas et al. (1999)

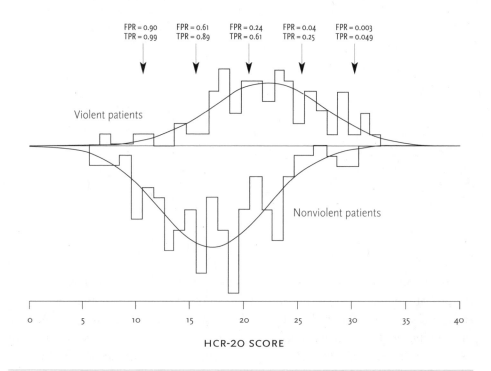

Superimposed on the histograms are two "bell-shaped" (Gaussian) curves that represent a best fit of the data. Also shown are the values of FPR and TPR associated with five possible cutoffs. The bell-shaped curves imply that the effect of using the HCR-20 is to shift the distributions of violent and nonviolent patients about one standard deviation apart from each other. This is equivalent to saying that about three-quarters of the time, the HCR-20 score of a randomly chosen violent patient will be higher than the score of a randomly chosen nonviolent patient.

Also shown in Figure 2 are arrows representing a few possible cutoffs, and the values of the FPR and TPR associated with those cutoffs. For example, a cutoff score of 20 (i.e., patients with scores above 20 are predicted violent, and those with scores of 20 or less are predicted nonviolent) can be expected to identify 61% of the violent patients and to mislabel 24% of the nonviolent patients (i.e., specificity is 76%). For the smooth ROC curve implied by the best-fit bell-shaped curves in Figure 2, AUC=0.758±0.035. In other words, Douglas et al.'s study suggests that about three-quarters of the time, the HCR-20 score of a randomly chosen violent patient will be higher than the score of a randomly chosen nonviolent patient.

When committing a violent crime was the outcome criterion, Douglas et al. (1999) found that the HCR-20 did even better—it had an AUC of 0.80. Other investigators have evaluated the HCR-20 in other countries and clinical contexts and have found that violent evaluees consistently get higher scores than nonviolent evaluees (Belfrage et al. 2000; Dernevik et al. 2002; Douglas and Webster 1999; Doyle et al. 2002; Grann et al. 2000; Tengström 2001). In other words, using the HCR-20 consistently helps an evaluator make a better-than-chance guess about who has been or will become violent.

Other Actuarial Methods

The HCR-20 is just one of several actuarial methods that have been developed recently and that are being actively evaluated by researchers. Examples of other methods are described below.

Violence Risk Appraisal Guide

The Violence Risk Appraisal Guide (VRAG; Quinsey et al. 1998) was developed by using data on mentally disordered offenders who were detained in a Canadian prison psychiatric facility between 1965 and 1980. Post-incarceration follow-up data on violent behavior (ranging from assault to murder) were collected from Royal Canadian Mounted Police files. The reliability and predictive utility of the VRAG have been demonstrated for several other populations, including mentally disordered offenders in Sweden (Gratin et al. 2000), previously incarcerated sex offenders (Hanson and Harris 1998; Rice and Harris 1997), and wife assaulters (Hilton et al. 2001). The VRAG directs evaluators to 12 items that are scored and then assigned weightings by using a simple procedure designed by the instrument's creators. Unlike the items in the HCR-20, items and weightings in the VRAG were empirically derived, based on what the instrument's creators found had worked in their original data sample. The instrument's creators found, for example, that having schizophrenia *decreased* the risk of future violence, so having this diagnosis was weighted so as to lower predicted risk of violence. Available research (e.g., Rice and Harris 1995) suggests accuracy levels for the VRAG that are comparable to those for the HCR-20.

"Psychopathy" appears as an element in both the HCR-20 and the VRAG. It turns out that an evaluee's psychopathy score, as measured by the Hare Psychopathy

Checklist—Revised (PCL-R; Hare 1991) or the Psychopathy Checklist—Screening Version (PCL:SV; Hart et al. 1995), is itself a decent predictor of violent behavior (Grann et: al. 1999), though perhaps not as accurate a predictor as are the HCR-20 and VRAG (e.g., Douglas et al. 1999; Glover et al. 2002; Hilton et al. 2001). To use the PCL-R, the evaluator takes interview information and collateral data (from clinical files, police records, etc.) to assign scores of 0, 1, or 2 to 20 items, so that a total PCL-R score ranges from 0 to 40. The PCL-R items refer to two "factors" that characterize PCL-R–defined psychopathy: 1) callous, unremorseful use of others (as reflected, e.g., in glibness, lying, manipulation of others, lack of remorse, and unwillingness to accept responsibility) and 2) a chronically unstable and antisocial lifestyle (as reflected in, e.g., early behavioral problems, stimulation seeking, impulsiveness, and multiple sexual relationships).

Iterative Classification Tree

The Iterative Classification Tree (ICT) method (Monahan et al. 2000; Steadman et al. 2000) represents another potentially useful way of assessing violence risk. Using a sequence set out by the classification tree, an evaluator asks an initial question about an evaluee. Depending on the answer to the first question, the evaluator asks one of two second questions and continues with this procedure until the evaluee is classified in one of the terminal categories on the ICT's branches. Membership in particular categories allows the assignment of evaluees to subgroups with risks that are lower than, higher than, or not distinguishable from the full group's base rate of violence.

Although the authors claim a high level of accuracy for their risk assessment scheme (AUC=0.80–0.82), their ICT was designed specifically for their test sample, and their statistical analyses do not tell us how well their ICT would perform in another sample (Mossman 2000). As a result, they appropriately caution users that the accuracy of the ICT in "other types of clinical setting (e.g., forensic hospitals) is unknown" (Monahan et al. 2000, p. 318).

Instruments Designed to Predict Sexual Offender Recidivism

The Sex Offender Risk Appraisal Guide (SORAG; Quinsey et al. 1998), Rapid Risk Assessment for Sexual Offense Recidivism (RRASOR; Hanson 1997), and Static-99 (Hanson and Thornton 2000) are three of the currently available actuarial instruments designed to predict recidivism in individuals convicted of sexual offenses. All appear to have modestly-better-than-chance accuracy in predicting who will reoffend over long periods (10 years or more) of community release. The SORAG is very similar to the VRAG, and the latter instrument may indeed be as good as the former at predicting sexual recidivism (Hall and Ebert 2002; Rice and Harris 1997, 2002). The RRASOR and Static-99 direct evaluators to just a few historical items about the offender—in the case of the RRASOR, number of prior sex offenses, age, sex of victim(s), and relationship to victim(s)—and yield scores that are significantly correlated with long-term likelihood of recidivism.

Clinical Judgment or Actuarial Method?

If a psychiatrist has a choice between using clinical judgment or actuarial measures to assess violence risk, which method is better? The best current answer is "We're not sure, but probably the actuarial method." The reason is that, in a broad variety of prediction tasks, actuarial methods consistently yield better predictions than those made by unaided clinicians (Grove and Meehl 1996). For those who are not familiar with studies comparing clinical and actuarial predictions, this finding may come as a surprise. After all, clinical judgments presumably incorporate things such as detailed lessons from experience, human pattern recognition abilities, and subtle nuances that simple formulas leave out: It would seem, therefore, that clinical predictions *must* be more accurate than predictions generated by algorithms or formulas.

The psychological literature strongly suggests that the opposite is true, however. The reason may be that clinicians do not assign proper significance to the kinds of information used in actuarial prediction formulas or that clinicians may just not reliably and consistently weight the information they use. In most cases, making a prediction may be more like figuring out a grocery bill than deciding whether a portrait accurately depicts its subject. It is very difficult to program a computer to identify faces (something people do easily and well), but when it comes to calculating a grocery bill, checking prices and using a simple calculator will be much more accurate than eyeballing a shopping cart and estimating the total cost (Dawes et al. 1989).

Some authors (e.g., Gardner et al. 1996; Harris et al. 2002; Mossman 1994a; Quinsey et al. 1998) have interpreted available research as indicating that actuarial measures are superior to clinical judgments in predicting future violence. On the basis of their own research findings and the general finding that actuarial measures outperform clinical predictions, Quinsey and colleagues (1998) have argued for "the complete replacement of existing practice with actuarial methods" (p. 171).

As Litwack (2001) [Chapter 16 of this collection] has pointed out, however, only a few studies have directly compared clinical and actuarial predictions of violence, and these have not demonstrated the clear superiority of either approach. Thus, although research suggests that actuarial methods are superior to clinical judgments in many prediction tasks, we cannot be sure that this general finding applies to predicting violence. "Assessments of dangerousness are inherently different from many other predictive tasks, in ways that make it very difficult to meaningfully compare clinical and actuarial assessments," argues Litwack. Moreover, "even the best studied and validated actuarial tool for assessing dangerousness, the [VRAG] . . . has not been demonstrated as suitable for practical purposes in many instances, or to be superior to clinical assessments." Given the currently available evidence, concludes Litwack, the call for replacement of clinical assessment by actuarial methods is "premature" [page 281 of this collection]. Litwack believes, however, that available evidence has shown that instruments such as the PCL-R and the HCR-20 "can enhance a variety of dangerousness risk assessments," and he feels that clinicians who perform "risk assessments have a professional responsibility to be aware of the advantages and limitations of using such risk assessment tools" [p. 312].

Even if their predictive superiority is unclear, actuarial methods have other advantages over clinical judgment. When used properly, actuarial methods are impartial, systematic, and thorough. They also have the virtue of "transparency," in that they use fairly objective data and an explicitly prescribed method of combining those data. This makes actuarial methods and their results open to inspection, questioning, and, when necessary, critique. Finally, actuarial methods allow for an approach to judgments about future violence called "structured risk assessment" (Hanson and Thornton 2000) or "structured clinical judgment" (Douglas and Kropp 2002; Kropp et al. 2002). Indeed, the designers of the Static-99 and the HCR-20 believe that actuarial measures should be used only as a first step in evaluating violence risk, "as an aide-mémoire and as a research instrument" (Webster et al. 1997, p. 5). Actuarial scales force the evaluator to proceed from and give appropriate consideration to a set of known factors associated with violence risk. But the evaluator then may (and usually should) consider additional factors specific to an evaluee's situation—for example, dynamic factors not included in the risk assessment, characteristics and availability of known potential victims, the evaluee's known response to treatment, the evaluee's anticipated future situation, and the degree to which the actuarial measure fits the population from which the evaluee is drawn—to make an ultimate judgment about violence risk. Most important, the power of actuarial instruments should not lead evaluators to ignore common sense. Sometimes data that do not appear in an actuarial instrument—for example, a clearly stated intent to kill someone following an acute precipitant—put a person at high, imminent risk to act violently. As Hart (1999) has pointed out, assessors would be negligent if they ignored an individual's prior history of violence or homicidal ideation and threats, variables that have been shown to be linked to violence (Grisso et al. 2000).

THE PRACTICAL USEFULNESS OF PREDICTIONS

The success of actuarial measures such as the HCR-20 and the VRAG in sorting violent from nonviolent individuals clearly indicates that long-term predictions of violence can be accurate. Yet clinicians should not overestimate the usefulness of these instruments. To understand why, consider two more hypothetical psychiatrists, Dr. Jones and Dr. Smith, who have created a hypothetical actuarial measure, the Violence Prediction Scale (VPS), to make decisions concerning their patients' future violence. After thorough testing, Drs. Jones and Smith have learned that the VPS performs as well as or better than other currently available instruments: its ROC curve has an AUC of 0.83. The ROC curve for the VPS passes through the point where the FPR is 0.25 and the TPR is 0.75, and Drs. Jones and Smith decide to use the VPS score corresponding to this cut-off as their decision threshold. They now plan to evaluate inpatients for whom they are responsible. From past experience, they know that one out of four of the inpatients (25%) will engage in a seriously violent act, a base rate of violence that is typical in studies of inpatients (Borum 1996) [Chapter 3 of this collection].

Imagine two situations in which the doctors might put the VPS to use. In the first situation, Dr. Jones must assign 160 new, simultaneously arriving inpatients to treatment units. One hundred of the available hospital beds are in general treatment units, and 60 of the available beds are in special care units. The special care units have been specially designed and staffed, and they reduce patients' violence by 50% compared with what it would otherwise be. If Dr. Jones were to assign patients to the special and general units at random, the rate of violence for the 60 patients in the special care unit would be 1 out of 8 (i.e., half the base rate = 0.125) and 8 patients would become violent. On the general treatment units, 25 of the 100 patients would become violent. Overall, the rate of violence would be 33 out of 160 patients. But by using the VPS, Dr. Jones can divide the patients into two subgroups: a 60-member "predicted violent" group for whom the rate of violence is 0.50 (1 out of 2), and a 100-member "predicted non-violent" group for whom the rate is 0.10 (1 out of 10). If the "predicted violent" patients are placed in special care, their rate of violence is halved from what it would otherwise be, so only 15 of them become violent. On the general units, 10 "predicted nonviolent" patients become violent. The system is imperfect, but by using the VPS, Dr. Jones has reduced the total rate of violence by one-quarter (from 33 to 25 patients out of 160).

Dr. Jones's clinical task—evaluating 160 new arrivals and assigning them to one of two types of treatment units—is not the sort of problem that most clinicians encounter. A more typical problem is the task faced by Dr. Smith. He, too, is responsible for 160 inpatients, but his patients are placed in similar treatment units. (For purposes of this illustration, it does not matter whether the patients are already present in the hospital or arrive individually over a period of time.) Like Dr. Jones, Dr. Smith can use the VPS to sort the patients into a "high risk" group, 50% of whose members will act violently, and a "low risk" group, of whom 10% will be violent. But how might Dr. Smith react to this information? He probably would be more concerned about those patients to whom the VPS assigns a 50% chance of becoming violent. But would he want to do *nothing* about the potential dangerousness of the "low-risk" patients, who have (only) a 10% risk of acting violently? If the violent behavior of one of these "low-risk" patients resulted in a *Tarasoff*-type lawsuit, Dr. Smith probably would not want to tell jurors that having a 1-in-2 chance of serious violence implied a need for special attention, but a 1-in-10 chance was too low to warrant thoughtful efforts to prevent harm to others. Under most circumstances, it would be hard to justify treating patients with a 10% risk of serious violence very differently from those with a 50% risk. For both groups of patients, Dr. Smith—and most real-life psychiatrists—would probably exercise similar precautions when formulating inpatient treatment, making follow-up plans, and completing other treatment arrangements.

CONCLUSION

Two decades ago, G. E. Dix (1983) wrote, "Intuition suggests that psychiatrists' predictive ability is substantially greater when it is called into play concerning the short-term risk posed by persons whose assaultive tendencies are related to symptoms of identifiable serious mental illnesses" (p. 256). Yet research since the mid-1990s has suggested that persons' likelihood of being violent also is a function of several enduring characteristics. Psychiatric impairments affect how well a person can interpret behavior, resolve conflicts, and get along with others (Swanson et al. 1998), which may explain why having a mental illness statistically increases a person's violence risk. Other enduring individual variables that statistically influence the likelihood of violence (e.g., sex, age, level of education, and income level) provide information that helps make reasonable statements about an individual's long-term violence risk. As a result, simple "actuarial" prediction tools that focus on known risk factors can help clinicians identify patients with higher or lower probabilities of becoming violent.

Recent research suggests that actuarial tools may well let clinicians make better predictions than they would by using their unaided clinical judgment. Yet clinicians may often find that predictions made with these tools do not change how they manage patients, because for typical clinical tasks even fairly accurate prediction techniques may not sort patients into subgroups with meaningfully different levels of risk.

The practical value of violence prediction measures may inhere in the help they give psychiatrists in focusing on important aspects of clinical management. Noncompliance with treatment and substance abuse—two items found in the HCR-20—are risk factors for violent behavior following hospital discharge (Steadman et al. 1998; Swartz et al. 1998). By addressing these problems (e.g., by finding ways to improve patients' adherence to community treatment and avoidance of intoxicants), mental health professionals might reduce their patients' risk of acting violently. Of course, improving compliance and preventing substance abuse are good things for patients, whether or not these interventions reduce violence. Perhaps the greatest current value of actuarial prediction instruments rests not in their predictive powers but in their ability to translate what current research tells us about violence risk into knowledge that clinicians can use to make evidence-based decisions about treatment.

KEY POINTS

- Recent publications suggest that short-term and long-term predictions of violence have comparable, better-than-chance levels of accuracy.
- In recent years, researchers have developed "actuarial" instruments for conducting risk assessments.
- These actuarial instruments, which are based on established risk factors for violence, probably lead to assessments that are more accurate than assessments based solely on clinical judgment.
- Using actuarial methods may help psychiatrists improve their assessments of the risk of violence.
- Actuarial instruments also may help clinicians identify factors that can potentially be addressed in treatment and should be considered in any violence risk assessment.

PRACTICE GUIDELINES

1. When making formal assessments of the risk of violence, familiarize yourself with actuarial prediction instruments.
2. When conducting a risk assessment, focus on research-proven factors that influence an individual's risk of violence.
3. Consider using actuarial prediction tools in standard risk assessments when possible, because these tools force you to proceed from and give appropriate consideration to a set of known factors associated with violence risk.
4. Consider additional factors specific to an evaluee's situation—for example, the availability of known potential victims—when making judgments about violence risk.

REFERENCES

Bartels SJ, Drake RE, Wallach, MA, et al: Characteristic hostility in schizophrenic outpatients. Schizophr Bull 17:163–171, 1991

Belfrage H, Fransson G, Strand S: Prediction of violence using the HCR-20: a prospective study in two maximum-security correctional institutions. Journal of Forensic Psychiatry 11:167–175, 2000

Borum R: Improving the clinical practice of violence risk assessment: technology, guidelines, and training. Am Psychol 51:945–956, 1996

Buchanan A, Leese M: Detection of people with dangerous severe personality disorders: a systematic review. Lancet 358:1955–1959, 2001

Dawes RM, Faust D, Meehl PE: Clinical versus actuarial judgment. Science 243:1668–1674, 1989

Dernevik M, Grann M, Johansson S: Violent behaviour in forensic psychiatric patients: risk assessment and different risk-management levels using the HCR-20. Psychology, Crime and Law 8:93–111, 2002

Dix GE: A legal perspective on dangerousness: current status. Psychiatric Annals 13:243–256, 1983

Douglas KS, Kropp PR: A prevention-based paradigm for violence risk assessment: clinical and research applications. Criminal Justice and Behavior 29: 617–658, 2002

Douglas KS, Webster CD: The HCR-20 violence risk assessment scheme: concurrent validity in a sample of incarcerated offenders. Criminal Justice and Behavior 26:3–19, 1999

Douglas KS, Ogloff JRP, Nicholls TL, et al: Assessing risk for violence among psychiatric patients: the HCR-20 risk assessment scheme and the Psychopathy Checklist: Screening Version. J Consult Clin Psychol 67:917–930, 1999

Doyle M, Dolan M, McGovern J: The validity of North American risk assessment tools in predicting inpatient violent behaviour in England. Legal and Criminological Psychology 7:141–154, 2002

Gardner W, Lidz CW, Mulvey EP, et al: Clinical versus actuarial predictions of violence in patients with mental illness. J Consult Clin Psychol 64:602–609, 1996

Glover AJJ, Nicholson DE, Hemmati T, et al: A comparison of predictors of general and violent recidivism among high risk federal offenders. Criminal Justice and Behavior 29:235–249, 2002

Grann M, Langstrom N, Tengström A: Psychopathy (PCL-R) predicts violent recidivism among criminal offenders with personality disorders in Sweden. Law Hum Behav 23(2):205–217, 1999

Grann M, Belfrage H, Tengström A: Actuarial assessment of risk for violence: predictive validity of the VRAG and the historical part of the HCR-20. Criminal Justice and Behavior 27:97–114, 2000

Grisso T, Davis J, Vesselinov R, et al: Violent thoughts and violent behavior following hospitalization for mental disorder. J Consult Clin Psychol 68:388–398, 2000

Grove WM, Meehl PE: Comparative efficiency of informal (subjective, impressionistic) and formal (mechanical, algorithmic) prediction procedures: the clinical-statistical controversy. Psychology, Public Policy, and Law 2:293–323, 1996

Hall HV, Ebert RS: Violence Prediction: Guidelines for the Forensic Practitioner. Springfield, IL, Charles C Thomas, 2002

Hanley JA, McNeil BJ: The meaning and use of the area under a receiver operating characteristic (ROC) curve. Radiology 143:29–36, 1982

Hanson RK: The Development of a Brief Actuarial Risk Scale for Sexual Offender Recidivism (User Report 97–04). Ottawa, Ontario, Department of the Solicitor General of Canada, 1997

Hanson RK, Harris A: Dynamic Predictors of Sexual Recidivism (User Report No 1998–01). Ottawa, Ontario, Solicitor General Canada, 1998

Hanson RK, Thornton D: Improving risk assessments for sex offenders: a comparison of three actuarial scales. Law Hum Behav 24:119–136, 2000

Hare RD: Manual for the Hare Psychopathy Checklist—Revised. Toronto, Ontario, Multi Health Systems, 1991

Harris GT, Rice ME, Cormier CA: Prospective replication of the Violence Risk Appraisal Guide in predicting violent recidivism among forensic patients. Law Hum Behav 26:377–394, 2002

Hart SD: Assessing violence risk: thoughts and second thought (review of *Violent Offenders: Appraising and Managing Risk*). Contemporary Psychology 44:486–488, 1999

Hart SD, Cox DN, Hare RD: The PCL:SV—Psychopathy Checklist: Screening Version. Toronto, Ontario, Multi Health Systems, 1995

Haywood TW, Kravitz HM, Grossman LS, et al: Predicting the "revolving door" phenomenon among patients with schizophrenic, schizoaffective, and affective disorders. Am J Psychiatry 152:856–861, 1995

Heller v Doe, 509 U.S. 312 (1993)

Hilton NZ, Harris GT, Rice ME: Predicting violence by serious wife assaulters. Journal of Interpersonal Violence 16:408–423, 2001

Kropp PR, Hart SD, Lyon DR: Risk assessment of stalkers: some problems and possible solutions. Criminal justice and Behavior 29:590–616, 2002

Litwack TR: Actuarial versus clinical assessments of dangerousness. Psychology, Public Policy, and Law 7:409–443, 2001

Lusted LB: ROC recollected. Med Decis Making 4:131–135, 1984

Monahan J: The Clinical Prediction of Violent Behavior (DHHS Publ No ADM 81–921). Rockville, MD, National Institute of Mental Health, 1981.

Monahan J, Steadman HJ, Appelbaum PS, et al: Developing a clinically useful actuarial tool for assessing violence risk. Br J Psychiatry 176:312–319, 2000

Mossman D: Assessing predictions of violence: being accurate about accuracy. J Consult Clin Psychol 62:783–792, 1994a

Mossman D: Further comments on portraying the accuracy of violence predictions. Law Hum Behav 18:587–593, 1994b

Mossman D: Commentary: Assessing the risk of violence—are "accurate" predictions useful? J Am Acad Psychiatry Law 28:272–281, 2000

Mossman D, Somoza E: ROC curves, test accuracy, and the description of diagnostic tests. J Neuropsychiatry Clin Neurosci 3:330–333, 1991

Quinsey VL, Harris GT, Rice ME, et al: Violent Offenders: Appraising and Managing Risk. Washington, DC, American Psychological Association, 1998

Rice ME, Harris G: Violent recidivism: assessing predictive validity. J Consult Clin Psychol 63:737–748,1995

Rice ME, Harris GT: Cross-validation and extension of the Violence Risk Appraisal Guide for child molesters and rapists. Law Hum Behav 21:231–241, 1997

Rice ME, Harris GT: Men who molest their sexually immature daughters: is a special explanation required? J Abnorm Psychol 111:329–339, 2002

Shah SA: Dangerousness: a paradigm for exploring some issues in law and psychology. Am Psychol 33:224–238, 1978

Somoza E, Mossman D: Introduction to neuropsychiatric decision making: binary diagnostic tests. J Neuropsychiatry Clin Neurosci 2:297–300, 1990

Somoza E, Mossman D: ROC curves and the binormal assumption. J Neuropsychiatry Clin Neurosci 3:436–439, 1991

Steadman HJ, Mulvey EP, Monahan J, et al: Violence by people discharged from acute psychiatric inpatient facilities and by others in the same neighborhoods. Arch Gen Psychiatry 55:393–401, 1998

Steadman HJ, Silver E, Monahan J, et al: A classification tree approach to the development of actuarial violence risk assessment tools. Law Hum Behav 24:83–100, 2000

Swanson JW: Mental disorder, substance abuse, and community violence: an epidemiological approach, in Violence and Mental Disorder: Developments in Risk Assessment. Edited by Monahan J, Steadman HJ. Chicago, IL, University of Chicago Press, 1994, pp 101–136

Swanson JW, Borum R, Swartz MS, et al: Psychotic symptoms and disorders and the risk of violent behavior in the community. Criminal Behaviour and Mental Health 6:317–338, 1996

Swanson JW, Swartz M, Estroff S, et al: Psychiatric impairment, social contact, and violent behavior: evidence from a study of outpatient-committed persons with severe mental disorder. Soc Psychiatry Psychiatr Epidemiol 33 (suppl 1):S86–S94, 1998

Swartz MS, Swanson JW, Hiday VA, et al: Violence and severe mental illness: the effects of substance abuse and nonadherence to medication. Am J Psychiatry 155:226–231, 1998

Swets JA: ROC analysis applied to the evaluation of medical imaging techniques. Invest Radiol 14:109–121, 1979

Tarasoff v Regents of the University of California, 551 P.2d 334 (Calif. 1976)

Tengström A: Long-term predictive validity of historical factors in two risk assessment instruments in a group of violent offenders with schizophrenia. Nord J Psychiatry 55:243–249, 2001

Webster CD, Douglas KS, Eaves E, et al: HCR-20: Assessing Risk for Violence, Version 2. Burnaby, British Columbia, Mental Health, Law and Policy Institute, Simon Fraser University, 1997

SUGGESTED READINGS

Douglas KS, Kropp PR: A prevention-based paradigm for violence risk assessment: clinical and research applications. Criminal Justice and Behavior 29:617–658, 2002

Grove WM, Meehl PE: Comparative efficiency of informal (subjective, impressionistic) and formal (mechanical, algorithmic) prediction procedures: the clinical-statistical controversy. Psychology, Public Policy, and Law 2:293–323, 1996

Litwack TR: Actuarial versus clinical assessments of dangerousness. Psychology, Public Policy, and Law 7:409–443, 2001 [Chapter 16 of this collection]

Quinsey VL, Harris GT, Rice ME, et al: Violent Offenders: Appraising and Managing Risk. Washington, DC, American Psychological Association, 1998

Swanson JW: Mental disorder, substance abuse, and community violence: an epidemiological approach, in Violence and Mental Disorder: Developments in Risk Assessment. Edited by Monahan J, Steadman HJ. Chicago, IL, University of Chicago Press, 1994, pp 101–136

Webster CD, Douglas KS, Eaves E, et al: HCR-20: Assessing Risk for Violence, Version 2. Burnaby, British Columbia, Mental Health, Law and Policy Institute, Simon Fraser University, 1997

Portions of this chapter are adapted from Mossman D: "Assessing Predictions of Violence: Being Accurate About Accuracy." Journal of Consulting and Clinical Psychology *62:783–792, 1994; Mossman D: "Commentary: Assessing the Risk of Violence—Are 'Accurate' Predictions Useful?"* Journal of the American Academy of Psychiatry and the Law *28:272–281, 2000; and Mossman D: "Evaluating Violence Risk 'by the Book': A Review of HCR-20: Assessing Risk for Violence, Version 2 and the Manual for the Sexual Violence Risk-20."* Behavioral Sciences and the Law *18:781–789, 2000.*

6

The Accuracy of Predictions of Violence to Others

CHARLES W. LIDZ, EDWARD P. MULVEY AND WILLIAM GARDNER

ABSTRACT

OBJECTIVE—*To assess the accuracy of clinicians in predicting violence in mental patients. Specifically, to determine if clinicians can predict violence when variation in rates of violence attributable to age, race, and sex is controlled.*

DESIGN—*Two samples of psychiatric patients, matched on age, race, sex, and admission status, were followed up in the community during a 6-month period. One group included individuals assessed by psychiatric emergency department clinicians as likely to be violent to another person during the follow-up period; the other was a comparison group. Patients provided self-reports of violent incidents, and a "collateral," ie, an individual with detailed knowledge of the patient's life, provided this same information. Official records were also reviewed.*

SETTING—*Patients were recruited in the emergency department of a metropolitan psychiatric hospital. Patients and collaterals were interviewed in their homes or in public places in the community.*

PATIENTS OR OTHER PARTICIPANTS—*A consecutive sample of individuals coming into a psychiatric emergency department during daylight and evening shifts was obtained. A*

Reprinted with permission. Journal of the American Medical Association, 269 *(8), 1007–1011. Copyright © 1993, American Medical Association. All rights reserved.*

total of 2452 patients were approached for consent and 1948 consented. A final sample of 357 patients whom clinicians assessed as likely to be violent and their matched comparison patients were included.

MAIN OUTCOME MEASURES—*Patients', collaterals', and official records' reports of incidents in which the patient laid hands on another person or threatened someone with a weapon.*

RESULTS—*Violence during the follow-up period was reported in approximately 45% of the cases: 36% in the comparison group and 53% in the cases predicted to be violent. Overall clinical accuracy was significantly better than chance, but predictions of female patients' violence were not better than chance.*

CONCLUSIONS—*The level of patient violence reported using self-reports and collateral reports was higher than has been obtained using other methods. Clinical judgment adds to predictive accuracy, but overall accuracy was modest and particularly low for female patients.*

Mental patients are feared, in part because they are thought to be violent.[1] Whether these patients are more violent than nonpatients is the subject of considerable research and debate [2,3] but the belief has supported legal practices, such as involuntary civil commitment, and made predicting violence toward others part of a mental health clinician's role.[4-6] Nonetheless, there is little definitive knowledge about how accurately clinicians make predictions of future violence by patients toward others.[7]

What research does exist is discouraging regarding clinicians' present predictive practices. A series of studies done mostly in the 1970s reported that, at best, clinicians are twice as likely to be wrong as right when stating that a mental patient will be violent in the community.[8] Explanations for this low clinical accuracy abound,[7,9,10] but the belief in the low accuracy of these assessments is so widely accepted that no new studies of clinical predictions of patient violence in the community have been reported since 1979.[11] Indeed it has been suggested that simple actuarial schemes for predicting violence might do as well as clinicians in certain situations.[12-14]

These studies raised the issues and framed the debate surrounding the clinical prediction of violence, but they have substantial methodological problems. They have mainly been retrospective analyses that used indirect and potentially inaccurate measures of both clinicians' predictions and patient violence.[15-23] These studies are, therefore, likely to have been biased toward an underestimate of the accuracy of clinical prediction and to have produced misleading estimates of the associations between case characteristics and violence.

In general, the early studies of clinical prediction of community violence did not obtain predictions directly from clinicians but instead inferred them from the disposition of the case. If patients were judged committable as dangerous to others, they were assumed to have been predicted to be violent. Patients who were not committed as dangerous to others were assumed to have been predicted not violent.

Unfortunately, these methods for inferring a clinical prediction may have produced patient samples with considerable heterogeneity regarding the clinicians' actual assessments of their potential violence. Patients are often released despite clinicians' concerns that they may become violent [24] Similarly, clinicians may commit patients as dangerous to others without considering the patient highly likely to commit a violent act, and other patients thought to be likely to commit a violent act might sign themselves in voluntarily.[25,26]

Perhaps a more serious flaw in previous research was that the early studies of clinical accuracy measured violent behavior using police arrests, commitment hearings reports, or clinical records. These sources of information may severely underestimate the rates of community violence committed by patients.[27] Indeed, surveys of mental patients about community violence suggest that the rate of violence is much higher than is evident from official records.[28–30]

The results presented here are the initial findings from a large research project designed to assess clinician accuracy in predicting community violence by mental patients. This study sought to measure both clinical judgment and patient violence more accurately than in previous studies, using interviews with clinicians to measure their predictions and interviews with patients and collaterals, as well as official records, to measure violent incidents.

This article focuses on two issues. First, it assesses the level of predictive accuracy that clinical judgment adds over and above that achievable by consideration of basic actuarial characteristics of the patient. Second, it compares the accuracy of clinical judgment across patient groups segregated according to demographic variables thought to be related to violence.

METHODS

The study was done in a large university-based hospital with responsibility for an urban catchment area. During a 2-year period, research staff approached 2452 psychiatric emergency department patients who were between the ages of 14 and 65 years and lived within the county in which the hospital was located, and 1948 (79%) consented to take part in the study. The research protocol was approved by the appropriate institutional review board, and consent was obtained from patients after the nature of the study had been explained. The consenters were similar to the refusers, although the former were more likely to be African American (39% vs 32%) and young (40% vs 27% less than 27 years old). This may reflect our payment of $40 for three 1-hour interviews, which was presumably more attractive to poorer patients.

Routine procedure in the emergency department was that nurse-clinicians or junior residents saw all patients first and interviewed them in detail. The clinician then presented the case to the attending psychiatrist, who reinterviewed the patient and came to a disposition with the clinician. After a disposition was decided on, our researchers asked both the clinician and attending psychiatrist independently to assess potential patient violence toward others during the next 6 months. The resulting scales from the clinician and attending psychiatrist were summed to generate a score between 0 and 10 that reflected the concerns of the two professionals who handled the case. Clinicians' and attending psychiatrists' ratings correlated ($r=.68$). A total of 148 different clinicians and 67 different attending psychiatrists produced the ratings of the 714 matched cases discussed here.

Patients who received a summed rating of at least 3 were included in the predicted-violent group (n=564). The cut-off of 3 was chosen after extensive pretesting and interviews with clinicians who described the lower ratings as reflecting minor concerns about violence. Each predicted patient was then matched on sex, race, age (within 10 years), and admission status (admitted or not admitted) with a patient that received no concern about violence from either staff member. Patients with summed ratings of 1 or 2 were not followed in either group. The matching procedure meant that differences between the predicted and comparison groups in rates of violence could not result from differences in the sex, race, age, and admission status of predicted and comparison patients. Thus, if higher rates of violence were found in the predicted patients, it must reflect clinicians' detection of information about patients' dangerousness that was independent of these demographic characteristics.

We then attempted to interview each predicted and comparison patient three times during the next 6 months. In addition, we interviewed another person (the collateral) whom the patient identified as knowing the most about what happened to him or her. It was thus possible to have six follow-up interviews (three patient and three collateral) for each case. Each interview gathered information about changes in the patient's life and details of violent incidents that might have occurred during the previous 2 months. In addition, we collected reports of violent incidents from police, commitment, and hospital records.

Only cases with three or more of the six possible interviews (at least one of these being with the patient) and that had been matched were considered here. Of the 564 predicted patients, 131 either dropped out of the study or could not be found before three interviews were completed. Additionally, 76 predicted patients could not be matched (primarily young admitted men) leaving us with an eventual sample of 357 matched pairs. There were slight differences between the final predicted and comparison groups both as to when the last interview was completed (180.5 days after the emergency department visit for the predicted group and 182.2 days for the comparison group) and in the percentage completing all six interviews (predicted, 62%, and comparison, 66%) possibly leading to a small underestimate in the rate of violence in the predicted group as compared with the comparison group.

Of the sample of 357 matched pairs, 48% were African American, 60% were men, and the mean age was 28 years. Of the predicted patients, 529 had been hospitalized previously, 83% had a history of violence recorded in the medical record, 22% were brought in after a violent incident, and 189 had a prior arrest for a violent crime. Of the comparison patients, 48% had been hospitalized previously, 36% had a history of violence recorded in the medical record, only 0.03% were brought in after a violent incident, and 10% had a prior arrest for a violent crime. Patients were not matched by diagnosis. Admission diagnoses for both groups are presented in Table 1.

TABLE 1

Frequency of Diagnostic Groups Among Predicted and Comparison Patients

DIAGNOSIS	PREDICTED GROUP, %	COMPARISON GROUP, %
Schizophrenia	15.0	16.3
Affective disorder	15.9	29.7
Substance abuse	41.0	30.6
Personality disorder	13.9	6.6
Other	14.2	16.6
Total	**100.0**	**100.0**

A patient was judged to have been involved in a violent incident during the follow-up period if an official record, the patient, or the collateral reported that the patient had laid hands on another person with violent intent or threatened someone with a weapon. Verbal threats, incidents in which the patient was the victim of violence or did not engage in a violent act, and parental discipline were excluded. Of those patients for whom such violence was reported, 80% had incidents more serious than a push, shove, or kick, and 24% had incidents involving weapons, rape, attempted homicide, or assaults requiring medical treatment.

RESULTS

Level of Reported Violence

We found a higher level of violence than in previous studies of the accuracy of clinical predictions of dangerousness. Table 2 shows the relationship between predictions of violence and occurrences of violent incidents. Violent incidents were reported in approximately 45% of the cases: 36% of the comparison cases and 53% of the predicted cases. Because of the sampling procedure, these cases overrepresent the patients who are of the age, race, and sex about whom staff are most concerned. Nevertheless, the rate of violence is startling. In order to assess the impact of diagnosis on violence, we looked separately at the relationship in both predicted and comparison groups. Schizophrenic patients were less violent in both groups (predicted, $\chi^2=15.21$; $df=1$; $P<.0001$; and comparison, $\chi^2=8.59$; $df=1$; $P<.004$). Patients with a personality disorder were more violent in the predicted group only ($\chi^2=3.84$; $df=1$; $P<.05$), perhaps because a history of violence is a diagnostic sign for some personality disorders.

TABLE 2

Occurrence of Violent Incidents for Predicted and Comparison Patients: Counts of Matched Pairs

WAS COMPARISON PATIENT VIOLENT?	WAS PREDICTED PATIENT VIOLENT?		TOTAL (%)
	NO	YES	
No	111	117	226 (63.9)†
Yes	56	73	129 (36.1)
Total (%)	**167(46.8)**	**190(53.2)***	**357 (100.0)**

*The positive predictive value of clinical judgments of violence.
†The negative predictive value of clinical judgments that patients will not be violent.

Overall Predictive Accuracy

To assess the accuracy of clinical judgments, we calculated the sensitivity and specificity of the clinicians' predictions (the positive and negative predictive values of clinical predictions are also presented in Table 2, where they are, respectively, the marginal rate of violence among the predicted patients and the marginal rate of nonviolence among the comparison patients). Sensitivity is the number of true positives (Table 2, the 190 predicted patients who were violent) divided by the sum of the true positives and the false negatives (i.e., the 190 + 129 violent patients), which is 60%. Specificity is the number of true negatives (the 228 comparison patients who were not violent) divided by the sum of the true negatives and the false positives (the 228 + 167 nonviolent patients), which is 58%. Because this sample may have a higher prevalence of violent patients than an unselected emergency department population, clinical predictions of unselected emergency department patients may be more specific and less sensitive than these values.

Because our sample contains matched pairs of patients predicted to be violent or nonviolent, random predictions by clinicians would have a sensitivity and specificity of 50%. If clinical predictions are better than chance, however, then the rate of violence among predicted patients will be greater than among the comparison patients, which implies that both sensitivity and specificity will be greater than 50%. McNemar's test was used to determine whether the rate of violence of the predicted patients differed from the rate in the matched comparison patients (or, equivalently, whether clinical judgments were better than chance when race, age, and sex were controlled by matching). The significant result (χ^2=21.51; df=1; P<.001) indicated that clinicians were above chance in their predictions of violence (equivalently, we can reject the null hypothesis that sensitivity and specificity equaled 50%). Although the significant relationship between predictions and incidents indicates that clinicians can predict dangerousness at a better than chance level even when demographic factors are controlled, the relatively low sensitivity and specificity of their predictions shows that there is substantial room for improvement.[31]

Predicted and comparison patients also differed in their rates of violence when their most violent acts were broken down into three levels of seriousness (Table 3; $\chi^2=36.9$; $df=3$; $P<.001$).[32] The violent acts of comparison patients were more likely to be acts less serious than a hit or strike (30% of comparison patients' violent acts vs 12% for predicted patients), whereas the acts of predicted patients were more frequently a hit or strike (61% of predicted patients' violent acts vs 50% for comparison patients) or serious violent acts (27% vs 19% for comparison patients).

TABLE 3
Seriousness of Violent Incidents for Predicted and Comparison Patients: Counts of Matched Pairs

SERIOUSNESS OF COMPARISON PATIENT VIOLENCE	SERIOUSNESS OF PREDICTED PATIENT VIOLENCE				
	NO INCIDENT	MINOR VIOLENCE	HIT/ STRIKE	SERIOUS VIOLENCE	TOTAL (%)
No incident	111	16	70	29	226 (63.7)
Minor violence	19	1	12	7	39 (11.0)
Hit/strike	26	4	23	12	65 (18.3)
Serious violence	11	2	9	3	25 (7.0)
Total (%)	167 (47.0)	23 (6.5)	114 (32.1)	51 (14.4)	355 (100.0)

We also assessed whether clinicians were more accurate in predicting violence among those patients with whom they had great concern about violence. We split the matched pairs on the basis of the summed concern score of the patient predicted to be violent (low-concern pairs included patients judged dangerous with summed scores of less than 6; high-concern pairs included dangerous patients with scores of 6 through 10). Clinical judgments were no more accurate when the level of concern about a patient judged dangerous was high than when it was low. This suggests that whereas the presence or absence of a concern about violence is informative about the likelihood of violence, the level of a clinician's concern does not improve predictive accuracy.

Predictive Accuracy within Subgroups

To assess whether the accuracy of clinical judgments varied depending on the gender, race (whites vs African Americans), or age of the patients, we performed tests within subgroups to determine whether predicted patients were more violent than comparison patients.

The accuracy of clinicians' predictions was little affected by patients' race. The rates of violence were similar for African Americans and whites in both predicted (white, 54%, and African American, 52%) and comparison (white, 34%, and African American, 38%) groups. The sensitivity (white, 61%, and African American, 58%) and specificity (white, 59%, and African American, 56%) of the assessments were also close in both subgroups. Sensitivities and specificities were significantly greater than 50% by McNemar's test for both groups (whites, $\chi^2=14.41$; $df=1$; $P<.0001$; and African Americans, $\chi^2=7.38$; $df=1$; $P<.007$). To determine whether clinicians might have been more accurate in predicting violence among whites, we tested the homogeneity across racial groups of the (McNemar) statistics measuring accuracy within each group,[33] but found no significant difference.

Patients' age also did not affect the accuracy of prediction. We split the sample into young (n=193) and old (n=164) pairs at a cutoff based on the mean across pairs of the mean within-pair age (28 years 4 months). Younger patients were more violent than older patients (57% of young patients vs 30% of old patients). Sensitivities (59% for young and 60% for old) and specificities (62% for young and 54% for old) were significantly greater than chance in each group (for young, $\chi^2=16.32$; $df=1$; $P<.0001$; and for old, $\chi^2=5.71$; $df=1$; $P<.02$). The statistics measuring accuracy within groups did not differ significantly across age group.

The accuracy of clinical judgment may have been affected, however, by patient gender. Surprisingly, the level of violent incidents among women was higher (49%) than among men (42%) (Table 4). Clinicians, however, predicted violence for only 22% of the larger set of women who consented to participate in the study compared with 45% of the men who consented. Clinicians were fairly accurate at picking which men would be violent. The sensitivity of assessments of male patients was 63% and the specificity 60%, values that are significantly greater than 50% ($\chi^2=21.74$; $df=1$; $P<.0001$). Among women, however, sensitivity and specificity were 54% and 53%, respectively, values that do not differ significantly from 50% ($\chi^2=2.52$; $df=1$; $P<.20$). Thus, while the data indicate that clinicians are above chance when predicting violence among male patients, there is no evidence that they can predict female violence successfully. The disparity between the percentage of women predicted to be violent and the percentage with a violent event and the low sensitivity and specificity among women suggests that clinicians were not only substantially underpredicting the levels of female violence but were also using the wrong cues in choosing the cases thought likely to be violent. The data do not, however, clearly support the claim that clinicians can actually predict male violence more accurately than female violence because the test of homogeneity of McNemar statistics was not significant ($\chi^2=3.11$; $df=1$; $P=.08$).

The data indicate that clinical predictions of patient violence are better than chance, at least for male patients. Does clinical judgment, however, offer any advantage over just predicting future violence based on a history of violence? The answer is not clear. The sensitivity of a prediction using history as the predictor seems better (69%), but the specificity (48%) is considerably weaker. The higher sensitivity and lower specificity of predictions from reported histories of violence presumably reflect the higher base rate of violent histories (60%, whereas only 50% of our sample was predicted by clinicians to be violent).

TABLE 4

Occurrence of Violent Incidents for Predicted and Comparison Patients:
Gender Differences

		WAS PREDICTED PATIENT VIOLENT?		
GENDER	WAS COMPARISON PATIENT VIOLENT?	NO	YES	TOTAL (%)
Women	No	39	40	79 (55.2)†
	Yes	27	37	64 (44.8)
	Total (%)	66 (46.2)	77 (53.8)*	143 (100.0)
Men	No	72	77	149 (69.6)†
	Yes	29	36	65 (30.4)
	Total (%)	101 (47.2)	113 (52 .8)*	214 (100.0)

*The positive predictive values of clinical judgments of violence in each gender.
†The negative predictive values of clinical judgments that patients will not be violent.

Do clinicians' judgments predict patients' violence when information about patients' histories is statistically controlled? To check this, we split the pairs into two groups. In one group (n=171 pairs), the predicted patient had a history of reported violence, while the comparison patient had no reported history of violence. In this history-present group, the clinicians' judgments may have resulted from the differences in the patients' histories of violence. The history-absent group (n=186 pairs) included pairs in which neither patient had a history of violence, in which both patients had been violent, or in which the comparison patient had been violent but the predicted patient had not. In the history-absent group, therefore, histories of violence could not have been the basis for the differential prediction. If history were the basis of accurate judgments, one would expect clinicians' judgments to be substantially more accurate among the history-present than history-absent pairs. Among the history present group, sensitivity was 63% and specificity was 59% (values were significantly greater than 50%; $\chi^2=16.67$; $df=1$; $P<.0001$). However, clinician accuracy was also better than chance in the history-absent group (sensitivity, 56%, and specificity, 56%; $\chi^2=5.73$; $df=1$; $P<.02$), and the difference between the within-history-group McNemar tests was nonsignificant. The data indicate, therefore, that accuracy is better than chance even when clinicians are not predicting on the basis of history (or age, race, or sex).

COMMENT

This study provides a more valid assessment of clinical accuracy in predicting violence toward others by mental patients by using direct clinical judgments of potential violence and self-reports and collateral reports of community violence. The findings provide important leads for efforts to improve the prediction of violence.

First, using self-reports and collateral reports suggests that the level of violence among patients may be higher than expected. In prior studies, the rates of violence ranged from 14% to 41% among those predicted to be violent and from 8% to 31% in comparison groups. The studies with the higher rates used samples of forensic patients rather than general populations of psychiatric patients, thus raising the expected base rate of violence in those samples. However, since the samples followed here were selected by generating clinical concern or for having the same demographic characteristics as those individuals, we cannot use these data to assess the true rate of violence among the mentally ill or determine whether mental patients are more violent than non-mentally ill individuals.[34]

What this study does show is that clinical judgment has been undervalued in previous research. Not only did the clinicians pick out a statistically more violent group, but the violence that the predicted group committed was more serious than the acts of the comparison group. Nonetheless, the low sensitivity and specificity of these judgments show that clinicians are relatively inaccurate predictors of violence. Whether the accuracy of clinical judgment is adequate to justify its use in short-term or long-term civil commitment (or even the death penalty, as is done in some jurisdictions) is beyond the scope of this article.

The data also suggest, however, that the accuracy of clinical predictions can be improved. Judgments about male patients have some modest clinical utility, but clinicians had great difficulty predicting violence in women. It appears that clinicians may not only underestimate the prevalence of violence among female patients but also fail to notice cues that could distinguish which women would be violent. This finding substantiates an argument made by Monahan[8] a decade ago that faulty assessments of base rate information may be the origin of many errors in the clinical assessment of dangerousness. The variability in clinical accuracy across a demographic variable in this study suggests that the cues considered by clinicians in predicting violence should be tailored to the types of cases at hand. For example, if reliable cues predicting violence toward others by female patients can be identified, it may be possible to train clinicians to recognize them and thereby improve the accuracy of clinical predictions.

REFERENCES

1. Rosen G. *Madness in Society: Chapters in the Historical Sociology of Mental Illness.* Chicago, Ill: University of Chicago Press; 1968.
2. Krakowski M, Volavka J, Brizer D. Psychopathology and violence: a review of literature. *Compr Psychiatry.* 1986;27:131–148.
3. Morse SJ. A preference for liberty: the case against involuntary civil commitment of the mentally disordered. *Calif Law Rev.* 1982:54, 70, 87–93.
4. Monahan J, Shah S. Dangerousness and commitment of the mentally disordered in the United States. *Schizophr Bull.* 1989;15:541–553.
5. Poythress N. Avoiding negligent release: contemporary clinical and risk management strategies. *Am J Psychiatry.* 1990;147:994–997.
6. Mulvey EP, Lidz CW. Back to basics: a critical analysis of dangerousness research in a new legal environment. *Law Hum Behav.* 1985;9:209–219.
7. Monahan J. Risk assessment among the mentally disordered: generating useful knowledge. *Int J Law Psychiatry.* 1988;11:249–257.

8. Monahan J. *The Clinical Prediction of Violent Behavior.* Washington, DC: US Government Printing Office; 1981.

9. Meehl PE, Rosen A. Antecedent probability and the efficiency of psychometric signs, patterns, or cutting scores. *Psychol Bull.* 1955;52:194–203.

10. Mulvey EP, Lidz CW. Clinical considerations in the prediction of dangerousness in mental patients. *Clin Psychol Rev.* 1984;4:379–401.

11. Monahan J, Steadman HJ. Toward a rejuvenation of risk assessment research. In: Monahan J, Steadman HJ, eds. *Violence and Mental Disorder: Developments in Risk Assessment.* Chicago, Ill: University of Chicago Press. In press.

12. Ewing C. 'Dr Death' and the case for an ethical ban on psychiatric and psychological predictions of dangerousness in capital sentencing proceedings. *Am J Law Med.* 1983;4:407–428.

13. Faust D, Ziskin J. The expert witness in psychology and psychiatry. *Science.* 1988;241:31–35.

14. Grisso T, Appelbaum PS. Is it unethical to offer predictions of future violence? *Law Hum Behav.* 1992;16:621–634.

15. Kozol HL, Boucher RJ, Garofalo RF. The diagnosis and treatment of dangerousness. *Crime Delinq.* 1972;18;371–392.

16. Steadman HJ, Cocozza J. *Careers of the Criminally Insane.* Lexington, Mass: Lexington Books; 1974.

17. Dix GE. Determining the continued dangerousness of psychologically abnormal sex offenders. *J Psychiatry Law.* 1975;3:327–344.

18. Quinsey VL, Warneford A, Preusse M, Link N. Released Oak Ridge patients: a follow-up study of review board discharges. *Br J Criminol.* 1975;15:264–270.

19. Cocozza J, Steadman H. The failure of psychiatric predictions of dangerousness: clear and convincing evidence. *Rutgers Law Rev.* 1976;29:1084–1101.

20. Steadman HJ. A new look at recidivism among Patuxent inmates. *Bull Am Acad Psychiatry Law.* 1977;5:200–209.

21. Thornberry T, Jacoby J. *The Criminally Insane: A Community Follow-up of Mentally Ill Offenders.* Chicago, Ill: University of Chicago Press; 1979.

22. Sapejak D, Maurice R, Webster C, Jensen F. Clinical predictions of dangerousness: two-year follow-up of 408 pre-trial forensic cases. *Bull Am Acad Psychiatry Law.* 1983;11:171–181.

23. Quinsey V, Maguire A. Maximum security psychiatric patients Acruarila and clinical prediction of dangerousness. *J Interpersonal Violence.* 1986;1:143–171.

24. Lidz CW, Mulvey EP. Dangerousness and the decision to release. Read before the XII International Congress of Law and Psychiatry; June 22, 1986; Montreal, Quebec.

25. Segal S, Watson M, Goldfinger S, Averbuck D. Civil commitment in the psychiatric emergency room, II: mental disorder indicators and three dangerousness criteria. *Arch Gen Psychiatry.* 1988;45:753–758.

26. Lidz CW, Mulvey EP, Appelbaum PS, Cleveland S. Commitment: the consistency of clinicians and the use of legal standards. *Am J Psychiatry.* 1989;146:176–181.

27. Mulvey EP, Lidz CW. Measuring patient violence in dangerousness research. *Law Hum Behav.* In press.

28. Bland R, Orn H. Family violence and psychiatric disorder. *Can J Psychiatry.* 1986;9:129–137.

29. Tardiff K, Sweillam A. Assaultive behavior among chronic inpatients. *Am J Psychiatry.* 1982;11:13–49.

30. Klassen D, O'Connor W. Assessing the risk of violence in released mental patients: a cross-validation study. *Psychol Assess J Consult Clin Psychol.* 1990;1:75–81.

31. Weinstein MC, Fineberg HV. *Clinical Decision Analysis.* Philadelphia, Pa: WB Sounders Co; 1980.

32. Bishop YMM, Fienberg SE, Holland PW. *Discrete Multivariate Analysis.* Cambridge, Mass: MIT Press; 1975.

33. Holford TR. The analysis of pair-matched case-control studies. *Biometrics.* 1978;34:665–672.

34. Swanson J, Holzer C, Ganju V, Jono R. Violence and psychiatric disorder in the community: evidence from the Epidemiological Catchment Area Surveys. *Hosp Community Psychiatry.* 1990;41:761–770.

7

Violent Recidivism of Mentally Disordered Offenders: The Development of a Statistical Prediction Instrument

GRANT T. HARRIS, MARNIE E. RICE AND VERNON L. QUINSEY

ABSTRACT: *Multivariate techniques were used to derive and validate an actuarial instrument for the prediction of violent postrelease offenses by mentally disordered offenders. The 618 subjects were a heterogeneous group of men who had been charged with serious offenses. Approximately half had been treated in a maximum security psychiatric institution and the rest had been briefly assessed prior to imprisonment. The actuarial instrument consisted of 12 variables and significantly predicted violent outcome in each of five subgroups. The instrument's practical application and its use in clinical appraisals of dangerousness are discussed.*

The law requires that predictions of dangerousness be made in many circumstances. Courts, parole boards, psychiatric review boards, and individual clinicians are called on to decide, at least partly for the protection of the public, who is to be incarcered or institutionalized and for how long. As is the case in virtually every decision-making situation that has been examined, statistical prediction has been found to be more accurate than expert clinical judgment (Gottfredson, 1987). Over the past several decades, there have been many attempts to derive statistical or actuarial methods to predict the level of risk that offenders present to the community. Most of the instruments have been

Reprinted by permission of Sage Publications. Criminal Justice and Behavior, 20 *(4), 315–335. © 1993 American Association for Correctional Psychology.*

designed to predict criminal recidivism of any kind. It was not until the 1970s and 1980s, however, that statistical prediction instruments were systematically applied in practice and, with the use of these instruments, the predictive accuracy of general criminal recidivism is now routinely in the 60% to 80% range (Andrews, 1989).

Such instruments have been far less successful, however, at predicting violent recidivism (Holland, Holt, Levi, & Beckett, 1983; Nuffield, 1982). There is also general agreement that clinical prediction in this area is extremely poor (Steadman, 1987). At the same time, it is violence that the public and decision makers most want to predict and prevent. Therefore, any progress toward the development of a useful instrument for predicting violent recidivism would be most welcome, and recent reviews (e.g., Monahan & Steadman, in press) have suggested several methodological improvements for future research.

One of the biggest problems in the area of prediction of violence has been the problem of low base rates (Quinsey, 1980; Steadman, 1987). Typically, the likelihood of violent recidivism in a sample of offenders is so low that it is hard to improve on the prediction that no one will commit a violent offense (Steadman, 1983). Thus, for example, in a study of over 1,000 Canadian federal inmates, the predictive abilities of three statistical devices for identifying violent recidivists were so poor that none of the instruments could be recommended (Nuffield, 1982).

In a series of follow-up studies recently completed in Ontario, however, rates of violent recidivism ranging from 16% to 77% have been reported (Harris, Rice, & Cormier, 1991; Quinsey & Maguire, 1986; Rice & Harris, 1992; Rice, Harris, & Cormier, 1992; Rice, Harris, Lang, & Bell, 1990; Rice, Harris, & Quinsey, 1990; Rice, Quinsey, & Harris, 1991; Rice, Quinsey, & Houghton, 1990). In some of these studies (Rice et al., 1992; Rice, Harris, Lang, & Bell, 1990; Rice, Harris, & Quinsey, 1990; Rice et al., 1991), the usefulness of a large number of variables suggested by the literature on the prediction of dangerousness (Monahan, 1981; Quinsey, 1984) has been examined in an attempt to identify which variables, taken separately and in combination with other variables, best predict violent recidivism among mentally disordered offenders and their nonmentally disordered criminal counterparts.

The purpose of the present study was to combine some of these samples and their common variables to obtain a large data set for the construction of a statistical instrument for the prediction of violent criminal recidivism. The value of such an instrument, if sufficiently accurate, would lie in its application to new cases. Individuals receiving low scores on such an instrument would be candidates for relatively short sentences, early release, or less intensive community supervision. On the other hand, offenders with high scores would be candidates for longer sentences, preventive detention, or intensive community supervision.

METHOD

Subjects

The subjects have been described in detail elsewhere (Rice et al., 1992; Rice, Harris, Lang, & Bell, 1990). Briefly, the initial subject pool was comprised of two groups: (a) 371 men (of whom 332 eventually had an opportunity to recidivate; see below) admitted for treatment to a maximum security psychiatric institution in Ontario between 1965 and 1980 and (b) 324 men (of whom 286 had an opportunity to recidivate) who had been admitted only for a brief pretrial psychiatric assessment. Each of the men in the second (assessed) group was matched to a man in the first (treated) group according to the following criteria: (a) each had received the same criminal charge for his index offense, (b) both had the same score (within 20%) on a measure of their frequency and severity of both past violent and nonviolent criminal activity (Akman & Normandeau, 1967), (c) both were the same age (within 1 year), and (d) their index offenses occurred within 12 months of each other. Background and offense data for the subjects are shown in Table 1. These two groups were used in the present study to ensure that the resulting instrument would be applicable not just to forensic psychiatric patients but to serious offenders in general who might be referred to forensic clinicians for appraisals of dangerousness and/or pretrial clinical assessments. Men who had no opportunity to recidivate were dropped from the study, leaving a final sample of 618.

The data presented in Table 1 show that the subjects were a group of serious offenders; all had been charged with a serious criminal offense and 85% had been charged with at least one violent offense (the current offense, a prior offense, or both). Of the remaining 15%, 6% had well-documented acts of interpersonal violence without criminal charges. In addition, 3% had been charged with arson, 2% with robbery, and 3% with weapons offenses (all of which would qualify as violence in some studies). Absent from this sample were offenders whose only crimes involved drug offenses, drunken driving, and property and economic offenses. Table 1 shows that many subjects had failed on prior conditional release or had escaped from custody; many had committed homicide; most had used a weapon in their index (i.e., current) offense; many were assessed as having antisocial, pro-criminal values; most qualified for a psychiatric diagnosis of personality disorder or, less commonly, schizophrenia; and many had a serious alcohol abuse problem. Consequently, any statistical prediction instrument resulting from analysis of this sample cannot be expected to generalize to offenders with less serious criminal histories or, of course, to persons without any criminal conduct. However, because of the ways in which patients were referred to our institution (some for treatment, some for only a brief assessment), we believe that the sample was representative of offenders incarcerated for serious crimes.

TABLE 1

Comparison Between Subjects Who Recidivated Violently
and Those Who Did Not

| VARIABLE | SUBJECTS | | |
	RECIDIVISTS[a] (n = 191)	NONRECIDIVISTS[a] (n = 427)	t OR χ^2
CHILDHOOD HISTORY			
Highest school grade	8.0 (2.5)	9.0 (2.4)	4.67*
Elementary school maladjustment	2.6 (1.2)	1.8 (1.1)	7.88*
Teen alcohol abuse score	1.5 (1.1)	1.2 (.93)	2.55
Socioeconomic status	318(139)	310 (161)	n.s.
Childhood aggression	3.2 (1.9)	2.3 (1.7)	6.06*
Behavior problems	3.5 (2.6)	2.0 (5.3)	3.71*
Suspended or expelled (%)	25	14	11.68*
Arrested under age 16 (%)	42	19	38.21*
Separation from parents under age 16 (%)	55	28	38.17*
Parental crime (%)	13	6	6.82
Parental psychiatric history (%)	16	12	n.s.
Parental alcoholism (%)	51	37	9.29
ADULT ADJUSTMENT			
Longest employment (mo)	30 (83)	66 (127)	3.44*
Admissions to corrections	1.7 (2.2)	.81 (1.8)	5.31*
Psychiatric admissions	1.1 (2.0)	1.3 (2.4)	n.s.
Alcohol abuse score	2.2 (1.6)	1.8 (1.6)	3.16
Impulsivity score	3.1 (1.8)	2.3 (1.7)	4.90*
Property offense history	7.2 (14.9)	2.9 (7.8)	4.62*
Violent offense history	3.3 (7.7)	1.9 (6.4)	2.41
Never married (%)	70	50	20.23*
Previous violent offense (%)	35	23	10.94*
Ever fired (%)	34	34	n.s.
Escaped from an institution (%)	24	11	17.69*
Failure on prior conditional release (%)	43	20	36.69*
Lived alone (%)	46	37	4.10
INDEX OFFENSE			
Age at index offense	23.5 (7.2)	29.7 (11.9)	6.63*
Victim injury	3.6 (2.4)	4.4 (2.2)	4.04*
Seriousness of index offense	19.4 (19.3)	22.1 (20.9)	n.s.
Violent offense (%)	76	85	7.46*
Victim knew offender (%)	28	42	11.11*
Female victim (%)	39	51	7.07*
Weapon used (%)	61	70	4.89
Sexual motive (%)	14	7	8.24
Alcohol involved (%)	51	43	n.s.
ASSESSMENT RESULTS			
IQ	97 (17)	99 (14)	n.s.
Level of Supervision Inventory	19.8 (8.1)	15.5 (8.5)	5.81*
Psychopathy Checklist	21 (8.7)	14 (9.0)	8.47*
Elevation on MMPI Scale 4 (%)	30	22	5.59
DSM-III schizophrenia (%)	12	28	18.68*
DSM-III personality disorder (%)	55	28	41.12*
Procriminal values (%)	50	29	13.61*
Attitude unfavorable to convention (%)	48	29	21.03*

Note: Numbers under *t* or χ^2 are significant ($p < .05$) *t*s, *df* > 100, for continuous variables, or χ^2 (1, *N* > 500) for dichotomous variables for the comparison between entries in the first two columns. Asterisks indicate significant differences after a Bonferroni correction.

a. Numbers under these columns are means (accompanied by *SD*s) for continuous variables and percentages for dichotomous variables (indicated by %).

Finally, it is important to note that the study variables (excluding recidivism) reflected only data available at the time the subject was referred to our institution. Some subjects remained for several years afterward to participate in treatment, whereas virtually all of the others were imprisoned for several years. The mean length of time between index offense and the point at which subjects first had an opportunity to recidivate was 5.31 years (*SD* = 4.32). The clinical and administrative characteristics of the study institution have been described elsewhere (Quinsey, 1981; Rice & Harris, 1993). Published data have indicated that treatment in the institution was at best weakly related to recidivism (Rice et al., 1992; Rice, Quinsey, & Houghton, 1990).

Study Variables

All study variables (including the revised Psychopathy Checklist and *DSM-III* diagnosis), except those pertaining to recidivism, were coded retrospectively and exclusively from descriptive material contained in institutional files by a team of three research assistants who had extensive experience and training (mean greater than 3 years) as data coders for similar research projects. The clinical files have formed the basis for several other studies (e.g., Quinsey & Maguire, 1986; Rice & Harris, 1991). The institutional files included information from a variety of sources (e.g., psychosocial histories, information from other institutions, police reports, psychological test reports, questionnaires from patients' families). Most of the variables used in this study (shown in Table 1) are self-explanatory. However, a few require some additional explanation.

Elementary school maladjustment was rated on a 4-point scale from *none* (0) to *serious discipline and/or attendance problems* (3). Socioeconomic status was the highest rank order of either parent's occupation while the subject lived at home, according to the Blishen Scale (Blishen & McRoberts, 1976). Childhood behavior problems was the sum of items endorsed for the 12 problem behaviors noted before age 15 for a *DSM-III* diagnosis of antisocial personality disorder. Teen alcohol abuse was rated on a 4-point scale from *never drank* (0) to *serious drinking problem* (3). Separation from parents was scored as present if it occurred due to divorce, abandonment, or institutionalization before the subject turned 16. Adult aggression was rated on a 7-point scale from *no aggression* (1) to *occasional or frequent extreme aggression* (7). Level of Supervision Inventory was a modification of Andrews's (1982) 55-item scale (approximately 20% of the items were altered slightly). Property and violent offense history were summaries of criminal charges history using a modification (available from the authors) of Akman and Normandeau's (1967) seriousness scale. Victim injury was rated on a 7-point scale from *no injury* (1) to *death with mutilation* (7), following Quinsey and Chaplin (1982).

The revised 20-item version of the Psychopathy Checklist (PCL-R; Hare, 1991) was used to measure psychopathy. When individual items could not be coded (< 5%), scores were prorated. Although the PCL-R is often completed with an interview, scores in this study were based entirely on file information. Elsewhere, we have presented data showing that this method yields acceptable predictive validity (Harris et al., 1991) and the same psychometric properties (Harris, Rice, & Quinsey, in press) as the conventional method. The coding of diagnosis, including personality disorder, employed *DSM-III* criteria applied to file data available at the time of admission; it was not based on the diagnosis made by hospital physicians. Attitude supportive of crime was measured using an item from the Level of Supervision Inventory indicating procriminal, antisocial values (Andrews, 1982).

A separate team of three research assistants gathered all the outcome information and sent it for coding to the first team. Outcome data were obtained from the files of the coroner's office, the Lieutenant Governor's Board of Review (which maintains information about every insanity acquittee in Ontario), the Royal Canadian Mounted Police (a national database of criminal arrests and convictions including INTERPOL reports), the National Parole Service of Canada, and provincial correctional and parole systems. Childhood history, adult adjustment, offense variables, and assessment variables were coded by the first team before recidivism data were obtained and coded to prevent inadvertent contamination of the historical variables by raters' knowledge of recidivism.

In coding recidivism, subjects were classified as violent failures if they incurred any new charge for a criminal offense against persons or were returned to a maximum security institution for violent behavior against persons that, in the judgment of the first team of raters, would otherwise have resulted in a criminal charge for an offense against persons. Violent offenses included all assaults and sexual assaults, armed robbery, forcible confinement, threatening, and pointing a firearm, but did not include possession of a weapon, robbery, or arson. We employed a dichotomous outcome variable (violent recidivism or not) because simple dichotomies of outcome have been found to perform as well as more sophisticated methods among correctional populations (Wormith & Goldstone, 1984). A subject was deemed to have an opportunity to recidivate when he was released to the street or was placed in a halfway house or an open psychiatric ward.

Interrater Reliability

Twenty subjects were randomly chosen for an interrater reliability check. One rater (the one who coded the largest number of subjects) rated all 20 of the subjects selected for the reliability check, and each of the other two raters rated 10. Mean Pearson correlation coefficients were computed for continuous variables, and kappa (a statistic not subject to bias due to low base rates) for categorical variables (including recidivism). For all variables, the reliability criterion was set at .70, and variables not reaching this criterion were dropped from the study. For all variables retained, the mean correlation coefficient was .90 and the mean kappa statistic was .83.

Actuarial Prediction

We sought to derive a prediction instrument that would work well for serious offenders in general and that used a variety of predictors applicable to a variety of offenders. Approximately one third of the present subjects were men who had been acquitted on a criminal offense because of insanity. The data were subjected to preliminary analyses to determine whether the relationships between study variables and violent recidivism were different for the insanity acquittees and the other men, and they were not. Thus, in the remainder of the present report, data from the insanity acquittees were combined with those of the other subjects to derive a statistical prediction instrument. A multi-variate approach was employed to select variables for inclusion in the prediction instrument. To select a reduced set of variables to be used in the final analysis, a separate stepwise discriminant analysis[1] (α to enter and remove = .25) using each of the four sets of variables shown in Table 1 (childhood history, adult adjustment, index offense, and assessment results) was conducted for each of five groups of subjects who had an opportunity to recidivate. The five groups were: (a) the entire sample ($N = 618$), (b) the treated subjects ($n = 332$), (c) the assessed subjects ($n = 286$), (d) a randomly selected half of the entire sample, and (e) the remaining half of the entire sample. Based on order of entry in stepwise analyses, up to four variables were selected from each variable set for each group. Because stepwise multivariate results are often unstable, only those variables (of the 19 candidate variables) that were selected by at least three of the five analyses of the different subject groups were allowed to enter into the final stepwise multiple discriminant analysis.

RESULTS

At the last follow-up, in April 1988, the average time at risk was 81.5 months ($SD = 60.6$). A total of 191 (31%) of the at-risk subjects were violent failures. Table 2 shows the univariate comparisons between those subjects who exhibited violent recidivism and those who did not. Because of the number of comparisons, the Bonferroni correction procedure was applied ($\alpha = .001$).

The final discriminant analysis using the entire sample identified 12 variables for inclusion in the final statistical prediction instrument. These variables and their relationship with violent recidivism for the entire sample are indicated in Table 2. The multiple correlations for a final discriminant function using the 12 variables selected in the analysis using the entire sample but applied to each of the subsamples are shown in Table 3.

Although the multiple discriminant approach as used above is sound, multivariate functions generally perform much less well on cross-validation (i.e., when used on a new sample from the same population). Part of the reason for this has to do with the fact that when there are many potential variables considered for inclusion, some that enter into the final equation happen by chance to be important for the particular sample selected, but would not turn out to be important in a new sample. We partially accounted for this possibility by eliminating from consideration those variables that added to the multiple R for two or fewer of the subsamples considered in this study. However, another reason that multiple discriminant solutions tend to shrink on cross-validation has to do with the weighting of the variables. In the final discriminant function, the weights of each of the selected variables is maximized so as to provide the best possible fit for the particular sample used. Just as in the selection of variables, there is a certain amount of capitalization on chance in the selection of the best weights. Therefore, to reduce the amount of shrinkage that would be expected on cross-validation due to the calculation of weights, we used two different approaches.

TABLE 2

Univariate Correlations Between Each Final Predictor Variable and Violent Recidivism Plus Multiple Correlations Achieved with the Addition of Each

VARIABLE	r^a	R^b
Psychopathy Checklist	.34	—
Separation from parents under age 16	.25	.406
Victim injury in index offense	−.16	.429
DSM-III schizophrenia	−.17	.439
Never married	.18	.446
Elementary school maladjustment	.31	.450
Female victim-index offense	−.11	.454
Failure on prior conditional release	.24	.456
Property offense history	.20	.457
Age at index offense	−.26	.458
Alcohol abuse history	.13	.459
DSM-III personality disorder	.26	.459

a. For all rs, $p < .05$.
b. For all Rs, $p < .0001$.

In the first procedure, we assigned unitary weights to each of the selected variables. That is, we constructed an equation that forced each predictor to participate equally. This approach yields a liberal estimate of the effects of predictive shrinkage that would occur on cross-validation (Tatsuoka, 1988). We did this by first standardizing each variable (i.e., converting each to a z score with a mean of 0 and a standard deviation of 1). Then, for each subject, a score was obtained by summing his standard scores for each variable. The sum of these variables was significantly correlated, $r(618) = .44$, with violent recidivism. The performance of this unitary weight equation (in terms of the correlation between total score and violent recidivism) with each of the construction samples is shown in Table 3. The entire range of scores on the unitary weight equation was divided into nine steps or "bins" of equal size; the rate of violent recidivism for subjects at each step is shown in the top panel of Figure 1. Also shown are the number of subjects assigned to each of the nine steps. It may be seen that the equation performed well, in that it assigned subjects to all levels of risk and that the probability of violent recidivism increased steadily from near 0 to 100% as scores on the prediction equation increased.

TABLE 3

Correlations Between the Final 12 Predictor Variables and Violent Recidivism for Multiple Discriminant Function (Weighted) and the Final Statistical Instrument Using Unitary Weights (Unweighted)

SAMPLE	WEIGHTED		UNWEIGHTED
	n	R^a	r^a
All subjects	618	.459	.424
Treated subjects	332	.527	.462
Subjects assessed only	286	.454	.370
1st random subjects	307	.522	.477
2nd random subjects	311	.432	.370

a. For all correlations, $p < .001$.

The other method of using the 12 variables to construct a prediction equation was described by Nuffield (1982). According to this method, predictor variables are selected based on univariate correlations with violent recidivism and then are weighted in proportion to their abilities to discriminate recidivists from nonrecidivists. Although the 12 variables we used were selected by a multivariate rather than univariate procedure, all were significant at least at the .05 level before a Bonferroni correction was applied. The value of using the variables selected by the multivariate procedure was that it reduced the number of variables for inclusion in the prediction in a way that eliminated redundant variables. Then, following Nuffield (1982), the recidivism rates for each value (or range of values) of each of the 12 predictor variables were determined. For every difference (plus or minus) of more than 5% from the mean overall violent recidivism rate (31%), a weighting of one was added. Thus, for example, for the variable "never married," subjects who had married had a violent recidivism rate of 21% (two full increments of 5% below the mean), and those who had not married had a recidivism rate of 38% (one full increment of 5% above the mean). Thus, for that variable, a subject who had married would obtain a score of –2, whereas a subject who had never married would obtain a score of +1. The variable with the highest possible range of scores using this method was the Psychopathy Checklist (because it had the highest correlation with violent recidivism), and possible scores on this variable ranged from –5 to +12. Using this method with each of the 12 final variables resulted in a risk score that ranged between –27 and +35. (A copy of the final scoring key can be obtained from the authors.) The correlation between scores on this prediction equation and violent recidivism was .44, identical to the correlation obtained using the unitary weight method described above. The violent recidivism rates for nine equal-size bins, each encompassing a range of 8 points, are illustrated in the middle panel of Figure 1. Again, it may be seen that the Nuffield equation performed well in terms of assigning subjects to risk levels, and that actual violent recidivism increased steadily with predicted risk level. Indeed, because the performance of this equation was at least as good as the unitary weight version, and because this method is easier to apply to new samples, we decided to adopt this equation based on the Nuffield method as our prediction instrument.

Because the set of 12 predictor variables contains information that is often unavailable without a detailed history and specialized diagnostic procedures, it is of interest to know how well violent recidivism could have been predicted from routinely available information. When the PCL-R, *DSM-III* diagnosis, and childhood variables (all of which require detailed psychosocial histories) were dropped, the Nuffield procedure applied to the remaining seven variables yielded a score that had a correlation of $r(618) = .36$ with violent recidivism. The performance of this more limited equation is summarized in the bottom of Figure 1. It can be seen that, although still adequate, there was no subgroup in which all members reoffended violently.

Psychometric Properties

The mean score on the final actuarial instrument was .91 ($SD = 12.9$). If a prediction instrument is to be used in making decisions about individual cases, issues of measurement error should be addressed. The first such issue pertains to the standard error of measurement (SEM; i.e., the relationship between a subject's hypothetical "true" score and his actual obtained score). The SEM is a function of both the standard deviation and the reliability of a measure. The reliability of the final prediction instrument using the Nuffield method was evaluated by comparing final scores based on the two independent coders described above. The resulting interrater reliability was a Pearson correlation coefficient of .90. Thus the SEM for the instrument was equal to $SD\sqrt{1-r} = 4.1$. This SEM is small enough to ensure that an individual subject's true score lay close to his obtained score.

The second issue pertains to the confidence one may place in the obtained violent failure rates for the samples of subjects in each bin shown in the middle panel of Figure 1. The magnitudes of such confidence intervals depend on the degree of confidence desired, the variability of violent recidivism, and the number of subjects in the bin. The 95% confidence intervals for each bin are shown in the figure. Most noteworthy is the fact that most adjacent confidence intervals do not show great overlap. Thus the data presented here suggest that the final prediction instrument possesses acceptable psychometric properties. That is, the levels of relative risk identified by the instrument are discriminably different from each other. Also, the standard error of measurement possessed by the instrument suggests that individual subjects can be assigned reliably to levels of risk.

Of course, a crucial psychometric issue is predictive validity. Table 4 presents the accuracy with which violent recidivism was predicted (using the final instrument) in the entire sample for each of several cutoff scores. The results illustrate the usual trade-off between sensitivity (i.e., the proportion of violent recidivists identified) and specificity (i.e., the proportion of nonrecidivists correctly identified) obtained with any test. They

FIGURE 1

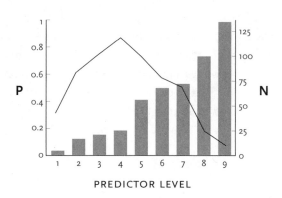

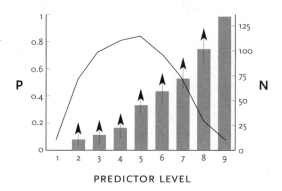

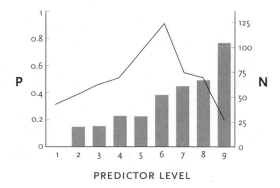

The performance of the unitary weight statistical prediction equation using z scores (top panel), the final statistical instrument using the Nuffield method to weight variables (middle panel), and the final instrument using a reduced set of seven variables (bottom panel).

Note: Bars indicate the probability of violent recidivism *(P)* for subjects at each of nine equal size steps. The solid line indicates the number of subjects *(N)* in each step or bin. Arrows in the middle panel indicate the 95% confidence intervals for the violent recidivism rates for subjects in each bin.

indicate that, assuming approximately an equivalent cost of misses (i.e., false negatives) and false alarms (i.e., false positives), good performance was obtained when the cutoff score was set so that the selection rate was equal to the base rate of violent recidivism. This cutoff corresponded to the boundary between the fifth and sixth bins in the middle panel of Figure 1. At that cutoff score, total accuracy was almost maximized whereas both a low false positive rate and reasonable sensitivity were maintained. Examination of the binomial effect size (the likelihood of violence both above and below the cutoff; Rosenthal, 1990) for cutoff scores around the base rate reveals that subjects above the cutoff exhibited more than twice the rate of violent recidivism (69%) than subjects below the cutoff (31%).

TABLE 4

Predictive Accuracy of the Final Instrument at Varying Criteria for a Prediction of Violent Recidivism

CUTOFF SCORE	PERCENTAGE CORRECT	FALSE POSITIVES	SENSITIVITY	SPECIFICITY	ϕ^a
20th percentile	47	.64	.95	.25	.24
40th percentile	61	.57	.87	.49	.34
60th percentile	70	.49	.72	.69	.38
Base rate	73	.45	.60	.78	.37
80th percentile	74	.39	.41	.88	.33

a. For all phi coefficients, $p < .001$.

DISCUSSION

The multiple discriminant analyses using 12 predictor variables yielded a multiple R of .459 in the whole sample and multiple Rs ranging from .432 to .527 in the various subsamples. When each variable was allowed to participate equally in the prediction (done by transforming scores on all variables to z scores), the correlations with violent recidivism ranged from .370 to .477. The application of the Nuffield (1982) method (which is much easier to use with new samples) resulted in an equation with perform-ance identical to that obtained using the z-score method. These values translate into a classification accuracy of about 75%. These modest decrements in performance obtained using the z-score or Nuffield methods rather than using the weightings obtained from the multivariate analyses are very close to what might be expected if full cross-validations using the multivariate equation were conducted with independent but similar samples of offenders (Kerlinger & Pedhazur, 1973). A reduced equation using only seven easily obtained variables showed some decrement in performance but still exhibited some ability to discriminate between subjects who recidivated and those who did not.

It should be noted that recidivism could be evaluated only for those offenders who had been released. Preliminary comparisons between the 618 subjects and 67 other men who qualified as subjects but were never released revealed a few significant differences. The largest difference between the released and retained groups was in the seriousness of the index offense. Although this variable was negatively related to recidivism, the retained group had higher seriousness of index offense scores. Similarly, degree of victim injury and having a female victim were negatively related to violent recidivism, but retained offenders were more likely to have caused serious injury and to have had a female victim than released subjects. The only significant difference between released and retained subjects that, according to our prediction instrument, indicated that the retained subjects would have had higher rates of violent recidivism was that fewer of the retained subjects had been married. Because there were so few unreleased subjects, we believe that the prediction instrument would have performed equally well if all 685 potential subjects had had an opportunity to reoffend.

The issue of generalization to other populations warrants further comment. At first glance it might seem that, because all had been psychiatric patients, some were psychotic, and some were found insane, the present subjects were very different from criminal offenders in general. Without doubt, the present subjects comprised only dangerous offenders, each of whom had already committed at least one serious offense. It is not at all clear, however, that the present subjects differed materially from serious offenders found in prison. There are several bases for this statement: First, the majority (55%) of the present sample (all of the assessed and many of the treated subjects) were not insane but had been convicted. Second, most (58%) of the insanity acquittees were not psychotic but had been found insane based on psychiatric testimony that they had severe antisocial personality disorders. Third, although a significant minority (about 30%) of the present subjects did qualify for a *DSM-III* diagnosis of psychosis, recent studies (Hodgins, 1990) indicate that a surprisingly large proportion (as high as 25%) of prison inmates also qualify for *DSM-III* psychotic diagnoses. That proportion might be even higher among serious offenders. Fourth, questions about the comparability of serious offenders among prison inmates and forensic psychiatric patients are very difficult to evaluate because very few investigators have published data on the demographic, social, criminal, or psychiatric histories of serious offenders from either population. We have reported elsewhere (Harris, Rice, Quinsey, Chaplin, & Earls, 1992) that sex offenders in our population and sex offenders in a Canadian prison were indistinguishable on variables reflecting criminal, demographic, and social history. Fifth, most of the present findings pertaining to individual predictor variables (age, marital status, psychopathy, criminal history, failure on prior conditional release, alcohol use, antisocial conduct in childhood) and recidivism have been reported by other investigators studying offender populations exclusively in prisons. In summary, we believe there are good grounds to anticipate that the present results will generalize both to mentally disordered offenders from other jurisdictions *and* to serious offenders in prison populations. Of course, further research is required to test our expectation.

The prediction equation used only static linear predictive relationships and did not include interactions. Results from our earlier work (Harris et al., 1991), for example, suggested that age and psychopathy interacted in their effects on violent recidivism such that, among nonpsychopaths (i.e., those scoring less than 25 on the PCL-R), rates of violent recidivism declined with age whereas among psychopaths, there was no such decline. Further research is required to incorporate such interactive variables into the statistical prediction of violent recidivism.

Another task of future research is to establish prediction equations for more homogeneous subgroups of offenders that have high enough base rates of violent offending to permit a meaningful increase in predictive accuracy. For example, several investigators have reported that child molesters with male victims are at greater risk to recidivate than those with only female victims (Furby, Weinrott, & Blackshaw, 1989; Quinsey, 1986; Rice, Quinsey, & Harris, 1991) and that sex offenders with more deviant sexual preferences are more likely to fail (Rice, Harris, & Quinsey, 1990; Rice et al., 1991). Thus a prediction equation for sex offenders might profitably employ additional aspects of offense history and phallometric data as predictors. Similarly, different variables may be necessary to accurately predict violent recidivism among arsonists compared to violent robbers compared to spouse murderers.

The level of accuracy attained by the actuarial model raises the issue of its practical applications, of which there are several. Actuarial models can be used in such policy decisions as the determination of the level of perimeter security required to safely contain offenders within an institution. With respect to treatment, actuarial predictors of risk can be used to identify groups of offenders for whom specialized treatment or supervision are required. For example, it has been suggested that treatments designed to alter risk of recidivism are more effective when directed toward higher- rather than lower-risk offenders (Andrews, 1989).

How might statistical predictions be used in making release and disposition decisions about individual offenders? Because the actuarial instrument developed in the present study was not perfectly accurate, and recognizing that each individual is unique, one might be tempted to ignore statistical predictions and base decisions solely on clinical judgment and intuition. However, such a strategy would inevitably result in more errors (greater risk to the public, more unnecessary incarceration, or both) than would the use of an actuarial instrument. That is, the data on the prediction of violence indicate that clinicians are insensitive to variations in the base rate of violent offending, show poor agreement among themselves, make the same judgments as laypersons, and are less accurate than actuarial models (Faust & Ziskin, 1988; Quinsey & Ambtman, 1979; Quinsey & Maguire, 1986), a series of findings that is consistent with a much larger literature on human judgment in probabilistic situations.

Clinical judgment can be improved, however, through the use of actuarial information; this has been referred to as "structuring discretion" (Gottfredson, Wilkins, & Hoffman, 1978). In this approach to decision making about an individual, an actuarial estimate of risk is used to anchor clinical judgment. More specifically, clinicians can use dynamic (changeable) information such as progress in treatment, change in procriminal attitudes, and the amount and quality of supervision in the postrelease environment to adjust the risk level computed by the actuarial prediction instrument. If adjustments are made conservatively and *only* when a clinician believes, on good evidence, that a factor is related to the likelihood of violent recidivism in an individual case, predictive accuracy may be improved.

What about offenders who are classified as high risk but who would not in fact recidivate upon release (i.e., the false positives)? Because being a high risk does not mean that a person will necessarily commit a new violent offense, decisions should be made that protect the public while reducing the human cost of false positives (Quinsey & Walker, 1992). We believe that there are a few offenders whose offenses are so serious and their actuarial risk scores so high that they are proper candidates for incapacitation (through indefinite incarceration). Of course, it is not for researchers or clinicians, but rather for the courts and other judicial bodies, to decide how serious the history and how high the risk must be before incapacitation is imposed. Otherwise, actuarial measures of risk are best suited for ensuring that more intensive treatments and more rigorous supervisory methods are employed with the offenders who need them the most, those of high risk.

NOTE

1. It might be argued that logistic regression would have been the more appropriate multivariate technique. We performed all of the analyses with logistic regression, and the variables selected and their order were always identical to the results from the multiple discriminant analyses. We preferred multiple discriminant analyses because they readily yield Rs and permit evaluation of the proportions of shared variance and because we did not intend to use the beta weights from either analysis.

REFERENCES

Akman, D. D., & Normandeau, A. (1967). The measurement of crime and delinquency in Canada: A replication study. *British Journal of Criminology, 7,* 129–149.

Andrews, D. A. (1982). *The Level of Supervision Inventory.* Toronto: Ministry of Correctional Services (Ontario).

Andrews, D. A. (1989). Recidivism is predictable and can be influenced: Using risk assessments to reduce recidivism. *Forum on Corrections Research, 1,* 11–18.

Blishen, B. R., & McRoberts, H. A. (1976). A revised socioeconomic index for occupations in Canada. *Canadian Review of Sociology and Anthropology, 13,* 71–79.

Faust, D., & Ziskin, J. (1988). The expert witness in psychology and psychiatry. *Science, 241,* 501–511.

Furby, L., Weinrott, M. R., & Blackshaw, L. (1989). Sex offender recidivism: A review. *Psychological Bulletin, 105,* 3–30.

Gottfredson, S. D. (1987). Statistical and actuarial considerations. In F. Dutile & C. Foust (Eds.), *The prediction of violence* (pp. 71–81). Springfield, IL: Charles C Thomas.

Gottfredson, D. M., Wilkins, L. T., & Hoffman, P. B. (1978). *Guidelines for parole and sentencing: A policy control method.* Toronto: Lexington Books.

Hare, R. D. (1991). *The Revised Psychopathy Checklist.* Toronto: Multi-Health Systems.

Harris, G. T., Rice, M. E., & Cormier, C. (1991). Psychopathy and violent recidivism. *Law and Human Behavior, 15,* 625–637.

Harris, G. T., Rice, M. E., & Quinsey, V. L. (in press). Psychopathy as a taxon: Evidence that psychopaths are a discrete class. *Journal of Consulting and Clinical Psychology.*

Harris, G. T., Rice, M. E., Quinsey, V. L., Chaplin, T. C., & Earls, C. (1992). Maximizing the discriminant validity of phallometric assessment. *Psychological Assessment, 4,* 502–511.

Hodgins, S. (1990). Prevalence of mental disorders among penitentiary inmates in Quebec. *Canada's Mental Health, 38,* 1–4.

Holland, T. R., Holt, N., Levi, M., & Beckett, G. E. (1983). Comparison and combination of clinical and statistical predictions of recidivism among adult offenders. *Journal of Applied Psychology, 68,* 203–211.

Kerlinger, F. N., & Pedhazur, E. J. (1973). *Multiple regression in behavioral research.* New York: Holt, Rinehart & Winston.

Monahan, J. (1981). *Predicting violent behavior: An assessment of clinical techniques.* Beverly Hills, CA: Sage.

Monahan, J., & Steadman, H. (Eds.). (in press). *Violence and mental disorder: Developments in risk assessment.* Chicago: University of Chicago Press.

Nuffield, J. (1982). *Parole decision-making in Canada: Research towards decision guidelines.* Ottawa: Ministry of Supply and Services Canada.

Quinsey, V. L. (1980). The baserate problem and the prediction of dangerousness: A reappraisal. *Journal of Psychiatry and Law, 8,* 329–340.

Quinsey, V. L. (1981). The long term management of the mentally disordered offender. In S. J. Hucker, C. D. Webster, & M. Ben-Aron (Eds.), *Mental disorder and criminal responsibility* (pp. 137–155). Toronto: Butterworths.

Quinsey, V. L. (1984). Politique institutionelle de liberation: Identification des individus dangereux: une revue de la literature (Institutional release policy and the identification of dangerous men: A review of the literature). *Criminologie, 17,* 53–78.

Quinsey, V. L. (1986). Men who have sex with children. In D. Weisstub (Ed.), *Law and mental health: International perspectives* (pp. 140–172). New York: Pergamon.

Quinsey, V. L., & Ambtman, R. (1979). Variables affecting psychiatrists' and teachers' assessments of the dangerousness of mentally ill offenders. *Journal of Consulting and Clinical Psychology, 47,* 353–362.

Quinsey, V. L., & Chaplin, T. C. (1982). Penile responses to nonsexual violence among rapists. *Criminal Justice and Behavior, 9,* 312–324.

Quinsey, V. L., & Maguire, A. (1986). Maximum security psychiatric patients: Actuarial and clinical prediction of dangerousness. *Journal of Interpersonal Violence, 1,* 143–171.

Quinsey, V. L., & Walker, W. D. (1992). Dealing with dangerousness: Community risk management strategies with violent offenders. In R. DeV. Peters, R. J. McMahon, & V. L. Quinsey (Eds.), *Aggression and violence throughout the life span* (pp. 244–262). Newbury Park, CA: Sage.

Rice, M. E., & Harris, G. T. (1991). Firesetters admitted to a maximum security psychiatric institution: Characteristics of offenders and offenses. *Journal of Interpersonal Violence, 6,* 461–475.

Rice, M. E., & Harris, G. T. (1992). A comparison of criminal recidivism among schizophrenic and nonschizophrenic offenders. *International Journal of Law and Psychiatry, 15,* 397–408.

Rice, M. E., & Harris, G. T. (1993). Ontario's maximum security hospital at Penetanguishene: Past, present and future. *International Journal of Law and Psychiatry, 16,* 195–215.

Rice, M. E., Harris, G. T., & Cormier, C. (1992). Evaluation of a maximum security therapeutic community for psychopaths and other mentally disordered offenders. *Law and Human Behavior, 16,* 399–412.

Rice, M. E., Harris, G. T., Lang, C., & Bell, V. (1990). Recidivism among male insanity acquittees. *Journal of Psychiatry and Law,* pp. 379–403.

Rice, M. E., Harris, G. T., & Quinsey, V. L. (1990). A followup of rapists assessed in a maximum security psychiatric facility. *Journal of Interpersonal Violence, 5,* 435–448.

Rice, M. E., Quinsey, V. L., & Harris, G. T. (1991). Sexual recidivism among child molesters released from a maximum security institution. *Journal of Consulting and Clinical Psychology, 59,* 381–386.

Rice, M. E., Quinsey, V. L., & Houghton, R. (1990). Predicting treatment outcome and recidivism among patients in a maximum security token economy. *Behavioral Sciences and the Law, 8,* 313–326.

Rosenthal, R. (1990). How are we doing in soft psychology? *American Psychologist, 45,* 775–777.

Steadman, H. J. (1983). Predicting dangerousness among the mentally ill: Art, magic and science. *International Journal of Law and Psychiatry, 6,* 381–390.

Steadman, H. J. (1987). How well can we predict violence for adults? A review of the literature and some commentary. In F. Dutile & C. Foust (Eds.), *The prediction of criminal violence* (pp. 5–19). Springfield, IL: Charles C Thomas.

Tatsuoka, M. M. (1988). *Multivariate analysis.* New York: Macmillan.

Wormith, J. S., & Goldstone, C. S. (1984). The clinical and statistical prediction of recidivism. *Criminal Justice and Behavior, 11,* 3–34.

8

Forecasting Recidivism in Mentally Ill Offenders Released from Prison[1]

GREGG J. GAGLIARDI, DAVID LOVELL, PAUL D. PETERSON,
AND RON JEMELKA

ABSTRACT: *Little research has focused on assessing the risk of mentally ill offenders (MIOs) released from state prisons. Here we report findings for 333 mentally ill offenders released from Washington State prisons. Logistic regression identified sets of variables that forecasted felony and violent reconviction as accurately as state-of-the-art risk assessment instruments. Sums of simple recoded versions of these variables predicted reoffense as well as complex logistic regression equations. Five of these 9 variables were found to be relative protective factors. Findings are discussed in terms of the value of stock correctional variables in forecasting risk, the need to base actuarial risk assessments on local data, the importance of protective factors in assessing MIO risk, and the need for dynamic, situational, and clinical variables that can further sharpen predictive accuracy of emergent risk in the community.*

KEYWORDS: *mentally ill offenders; recidivism; prediction.*

The last two decades have witnessed a surge of interest in whether mentally ill persons pose an increased risk of dangerousness, and how to best assess and manage that risk. Although there has been a spate of research on the dangerousness of the mentally ill (Hodgins, 1993; Link & Stueve, 1994; Martel, Rosner, & Harmon, 1995; Otto, 1992,

Reprinted with kind permission of Springer Science and Business Media. Law and Human Behavior, 28 *(2), 133–155.* © 2004 *American Psychology-Law Society/Division 41 of the American Psychology Association.*

1994, 2000; Swanson, Holzer, Ganja, & Jono, 1990), on factors associated with risk in mixed populations of mentally disordered and nondisordered offenders (Quinsey, Harris, Rice, & Cormier, 1998; see Harris, 2000 for review), in populations of civilly committed persons (Monahan et al., 2001), in inmates released from maximum security hospitals (Quinsey et al., 1998; Villaneueve & Quinsey, 1995), or in undifferentiated populations of mentally ill offenders (MIOs; Bonta, Law, & Hanson, 1998), there has been comparatively little work on the risk of MIOs released from prisons. We have found only a handful of such studies.

There are good reasons for believing that mentally ill prisoners represent a different population than conditionally released insanity acquitees, involuntarily committed psychiatric patients, or offenders released from maximum security hospitals. Unlike most civilly committed patients, inmates have usually been imprisoned following conviction for a serious felony offense. Also, mentally ill prisoners usually have substantial criminal histories and are more likely than other inmates to have been incarcerated for a violent offense (Ditton, 1999). Furthermore, unlike MIOs in maximum-security hospitals, mental health treatment may not be readily available to MIOs in general prisons, and when provided it may be nominal or limited to managing acute psychiatric emergencies. Unlike treatment in state or private psychiatric hospitals, mental health treatment in prison is customarily not accredited by powerful regulatory bodies such as the Joint Commission on the Accreditation of Healthcare Organizations (JCAHO) or Centers for Medicaid and Medicare Services (CMS; formerly the Health Care Financing Administration, HCFA). Moreover, unlike civilly committed persons, mentally ill prisoners are usually released without conditions such as improved mental functioning, decreased dangerousness, or the availability of a suitable less-restrictive placement. They are generally released under the authority of administrative boards or panels according to the legal conditions of their sentence, not on the basis of clinical judgment. Finally, and most important, civilly committed persons, insanity acquitees, and patients released from maximum security hospitals are usually released with a mental health aftercare plan involving substantial treatment in the community, whereas mentally ill prisoners may be released with little or no mental health aftercare planning or actual receipt of social services in the community (Lamb, Weinberger, & Gross, 1999).

Looking at published studies of the recidivism of mentally ill prisoners, Silver, Cohen, and Spodak (1989) reported a 5-year arrest recidivism rate of 73.3% for 135 MIOs released from Maryland state prisons compared to rates of 65.4 and 54.3% for nonmentally disordered prisoners ($n = 127$) and persons acquitted by reason of insanity ($n = 127$), respectively. Factors associated with recidivism were not reported. In a second study of mentally ill prisoners, Feder (1991a, 1991b) followed 147 MIOs released from New York state prisons into the community. She found that at 18 months postrelease 64% of the MIOs were rearrested and 48% were rehospitalized, compared with rates of rearrest and hospitalization of 60 and 1%, respectively for 400 non-MIOs. Status as an MIO was not associated with arrest recidivism; age at release and prior adult incarceration were the only variables significantly associated with new arrests for either group.

Although Jacoby and Kozie-Peak (1997) reported recidivism outcomes for MIOs released from prisons, their sample size was only 27 and their community follow-up interval was short, only 18 months. Nevertheless, they reported that 63% of the MIOs were rearrested and 33% rehospitalized during follow-up. In another small-N study, Wilson, Tien, and Eaves (1995) reported that of 59 MIOs released from prison, those 26 who received postrelease treatment services logged an average of 80 days in jail during follow-up, whereas 33 who did not accumulated an average of 213 days in jail during follow-up. Most recently, Hartwell (2003) has reported early outcomes for 226 mentally ill inmates released from Massachusetts correctional facilities assigned to the Forensic Transitions Team program, an MIO community transitions program that is operated by the Massachusetts Department of Mental Health. At the time of her report, these MIOs had been followed for only 3 months in the community. The early outcome picture showed that those serving sentences for index misdemeanors were more likely than felons to be reincarcerated, and those serving sentences for index felonies were more likely to be hospitalized over the first 3 months of follow-up in the community. Contrary to expectation, mental health symptoms and service needs were not related to short-term post release outcomes, although having a history of mental health services prior to the index incarceration was associated with reincarceration, and female MIOs had a disproportionate rate of incarceration (36%) compared to their percentage in the sample (22%).

The need for better understanding of MIOs is underscored by high prevalence rates of serious mental disorders in U.S. prisons. Available point prevalence estimates suggest that 6–16% of U.S. prisoners are mentally ill (Ditton, 1999; Monahan & Steadman, 1983; Steadman, 1982). U.S. Department of Justice reports that at yearend 2001 there were an estimated 1,406,031 inmates in state and federal prisons (Harrison & Beck, 2002), which yields an estimated 84,000 to 225,000 mentally ill prisoners. In 2000, there were an estimated 571,000 state prison inmates released to the community (Beck, Karberg, & Harrison, 2002, Table 8, p. 7). An estimated 91,000 (16%) of them released that year—a small city—were MIOs.

There can be little doubt that State agencies, communities, law enforcement agencies, community correction agencies, community mental health agencies, and practitioners are very concerned about safe management of MIOs released from prison to the community. Indeed, prejudices that hinder community treatment of the mentally ill (Wolff, Pathere, Craig, & Leff, 1996a, 1996b, 1996c), may be even more severe for MIOs released from prison because these MIOs may be perceived as greater risks to public safety (Lamb et al., 1998, 1999). Community agencies and providers may be understandably reluctant to provide outpatient mental health treatment for MIOs released from prison. For example, in the State of Washington one insurance carrier has refused to provide liability coverage for providers (and another raised rates for community agencies) who would treat MIOs released from prison under that state's Dangerous Mentally Ill Offender law (SSB 5011; Phipps & Gagliardi, 2002, p. 17). Community perceptions of increased liability are likely to continue to promote risk avoidance as a preferred risk management strategy. To the extent that identification and efficacious treatment of MIOs might actually reduce recidivism, risk avoidance ironically increases the likelihood of the feared outcomes that motivated that strategy in the first place. If we wish to encourage better treatment of the mentally ill released from prison, we need to better assess the risk they pose.

In this report we describe recidivism risk findings from Washington State's Community Transitions Study (CTS; Lovell, Gagliardi, & Peterson, 2002). The original purpose of the CTS was to track a variety of community outcomes for 333 MIOs released from Washington prisons; it was not originally designed as a recidivism risk study. Consequently, the only variables available for risk analysis were variables of the type routinely found in most correctional records systems. Although this limitation prohibited study of some important clinical variables and their potential unique association with recidivism, it also permitted a real world inquiry into the usefulness of stock correctional records in forecasting MIO recidivism.

METHOD

Study Sample

Human subjects review boards at the University of Washington (UW), The Department of Corrections (DOC), and the Department of Social and Health Services (DSHS) separately examined and approved our study. Subjects comprised all identifiable MIOs released from Washington prisons in 1996 and 1997. Although DOC had set up screening and treatment programs for mentally ill prisoners, prisoner mental health status was not established as part of its classification system until 1997. We therefore had to devise ways of identifying potential subjects and checking their mental health status with evidence available through DOC's Offender-Based Tracking System (OBTS) and archived medical records.

For purposes of our study, mental illness was defined as a major thought or mood disorder that substantially impairs daily functioning and requires continuing treatment. From lists provided by DOC's Office of Planning and Research, we used sets of OBTS indicators—mental health bed residency, use of psychotropic medications, and intake screening flags—to identify 590 candidate MIOs released in 1996 and 1997. Archived medical charts were then reviewed for more specific evidence of mental illness, operationally defined as meeting two of three criteria below:
1. More than 30 days in a prison residential mental health treatment program;
2. Prescription of qualifying dosages of listed psychotropic medications,[2] and
3. A recorded diagnosis of schizophrenia, other psychotic disorder, bipolar disorder, major depression, dementia, or borderline personality disorder.

There were 259 subjects certified as mentally ill via chart review; an additional 78 whose charts were unavailable for review were certified on the basis of electronic records including progress notes. Four (4) subjects were dropped from the study because they were civilly committed immediately upon release or very shortly thereafter. A total of 333 inmates were included in the study.

Thirty percent (30%) of the sample of released inmates was female, a percentage three times higher than the percentage of women released from Washington prisons in 1996–97. Seventy-two percent (72%) of our MIOs (vs. 67% of general population inmates released in 1996–97) were Caucasian. MIO index crimes were the same as general population offenders, with the exception of slightly more sex offenses (14% vs. 10%) and somewhat fewer drug offenses (29% vs. 39%). On average they had served slightly more time in prison at the time of release (28 vs. 23 months). MIOs were similar to general population offenders released during 1996–97 in terms of age (33 years old) and prior convictions ($M = 4.4$ and 4.2, respectively).

Thirty-one percent (31%) of our MIOs carried a diagnosis of schizophrenia or another psychotic disorder, 21% had a diagnosis of depression, 17% had a diagnosis of bipolar disorder, and 8% had another qualifying diagnosis. In 23% of the cases, a formal *DSM* diagnosis could not be found. About 70% of our subjects had received some residential mental health treatment in prison, usually ranging from 6 months to 1 year, although women MIOs spent considerably less of their time in a prison residential mental health treatment program than did men (20% vs. 41%, p < .001). Of those MIOs whose medical charts were examined (176 men and 83 women), a substance abuse problem was noted in 75% of the cases. At the time of release, 38% of our sample was prescribed antipsychotic medications, 26% mood stabilizers, and 40% antidepressants. For 26% of the men and 36% of the women, there either were no discharge medications or the discharge medication was not recorded.

Data Collection and Statistical Analyses[3]

For correctional and demographic data, we relied primarily on DOC records; Washington State criminal history records were provided by the Washington State Institute for Public Policy (WSIPP). Postrelease criminal event data were gathered over a postrelease tracking period of 27–55 months ($M = 39$ months) using WSIPP databases for Washington records and National Crime Information Center (NCIC) databases for out-of-state offenses. Only those events that resulted in a conviction were counted as instances of recidivism. We counted one event, the most serious one, per offense date. Recidivism was classified as follows:

Felony recidivism: Conviction of any felony crime
Violent recidivism: Conviction of a violent felony crime or violent misdemeanor crime

For initial recidivism analyses, we selected several dozen prerelease variables that had a previously reported or a plausible hypothesized association with recidivism.

In preparation for the logistic regression analyses reported below, we examined the frequency distributions of the continuously distributed independent variables and the relationship of these variables to the dependent variable to assure a meaningful linear relationship. This is important because when a continuous independent variable is entered into a logistic regression, interpretation of the estimated coefficient depends on the unit of the independent variable and its scale in the dependent variable (Hosmer & Lemeshow, 1989, pp. 57, 88–91).[4]

Several of our continuous independent variables were recoded to simplify and clarify the interpretation of their coefficients in the logistic regression: age at first offense (recoded into three dichotomous variables), age at release (recoded into three dichotomous variables), prison infraction rate (recoded into three dichotomous variables), and prison mental health bed residence (recoded into a single dichotomous variable). A list of prediction variables and their precise definitions following recoding is provided in the data dictionary in Appendix A.

Pearson product moment correlations between the selected variables and recidivism were calculated. Those variables that correlated with felony or violent recidivism ($p < .05$) were retained for logistic regression analyses, which were conducted using SAS© version 8.2 PROC LOGISTIC. For those variables retained for subsequent analyses, there was a complete set of data for each subject. Consequently, there is no missing data in the analyses reported below.

As a safeguard to the logistic regressions reported below, several diagnostic indices were calculated for the set of independent variables using the collinearity diagnostics option in SPSS© 11.0. The highest condition index was 13.5, substantially below the cutoff of 30 recommended by Tabachnick and Fidell (1996, pp. 86–87); no root number had any more than one variance proportion greater than .50; the lowest tolerance statistic was .536, substantially above the value of .40 recommended by Allison (1999, p. 50). Consequently, the interrelationships among the independent variables were not of the type or severity to jeopardize analysis with logistic regression.

Logistic regression model development proceeded in two stages. First, variables with significant univariate correlations with the target dependent variable were entered into the equation simultaneously. Next, those variables whose coefficients were at least marginally significant ($p < .10$ based on the Wald chi-square) were retained and entered into a forward logistic regression analysis with the variable entry criterion set at .10. The forward logistic regression analysis was motivated by (1) a desire to find the smallest number of independent variables necessary to fit logistic regression models to the data, (2) our interest in the priority or importance of the retained variables in forecasting recidivism, and (3) our interest in calculating predictive accuracy statistics at each stage of variable entry into the model.

In addition to conducting logistic regressions, we conducted ROC analyses (Receiver Operating Characteristic; for an accessible introduction to ROC analysis see Swets, Dawes, & Monahan, 2000), using logistic regression scores, and scales derived from simple sums of recoded versions of the variables that survived the logistic regressions, to predict recidivism. Briefly, as it relates to this study, the ROC is an x–y plot of the true positive rate (i.e., sensitivity) against the false positive rate (i.e., 1-specificity) for each numerical value of the predictor measure. Thus, the ROC portrays the predictive accuracy of a measure across its entire range rather than limiting the accuracy assessment to a classification decision rule based on a chosen cut score. The Area Under the ROC (known as the AUC), is independent of both the base rate of the criterion or dependent variable (in this case, recidivism) and the selection ratio (i.e., any chosen cut score). The AUC is particularly useful as a standard of comparison for determining the relative accuracy of different methods or measures of prediction, especially across situations where base rates or selection ratios differ.

RESULTS AND DISCUSSION

MIO Recidivism

Over the 27–55 month follow-up period, renewed involvement with the criminal justice system was the norm for our MIOs: there were 258 MIOs (77%) who were arrested or charged with a new crime. Excluding charges that were dismissed or not pursued, or for which no disposition was known, there were 231 (69%) found guilty of a supervision violation or new crime. There were 135 (41%) convicted of a new felony offense, but, only 76 (23%) committed a violent reoffense (misdemeanor or felony) against persons. Of the 76 violent recidivists, 32 (10%) committed a violent felony, whereas the remaining 44 (13%) committed violent misdemeanors. The most serious kinds of violent recidivism were one MIO convicted of murder, two convicted of first-degree rape, two convicted of first-degree robbery, and one convicted of first-degree assault. The remaining 26 violent felony recidivists were convicted of lesser assaults, second-degree robbery, weapons charges, or harassment.

It is of interest to compare the reconviction rates of the MIOs with the remaining general population (GP) offenders ($N = 10,809$) released from Washington prisons in 1996 and 1997, followed to the same date postrelease. Data on out-of-state convictions, which comprised 2% of the MIO's felony recidivism, were not available for the GP offenders, which reduced their estimated recidivism rates. Thirty-eight percent of the GP offenders were convicted of a new felony (vs. 41% of the MIOs; $Z = 1.11, p > .10$) and 10% of the GP offenders (vs. 10% of the MIO) were convicted of a new violent felony. Thus, contrary to widespread community belief about the dangerousness of the mentally ill, our mentally ill inmates were neither more likely nor more serious recidivists than general population inmates.

Correlates of Felony and Violent Recidivism

Fourteen variables were significantly correlated ($p < .05$) with felony or violent recidivism. Table 1 presents the recidivism rates associated with the dichotomous variables, whereas Table 2 presents the means and standard deviations of continuously distributed variables for felony and violent recidivists versus nonrecidivists. Pearson correlations with felony and violent recidivism are presented for each variable. Although we tested a number of clinical variables (e.g., diagnoses of thought disorder, mood disorder, or personality disorder) at the first stage of data analysis described earlier, none reached statistical significance. In passing, however, we note that because clinical variables were not reliably recorded in DOC records this resulted in large amounts of missing data, which reduced the power of statistical tests of their association with recidivism. Thus, for all practical purposes there was no real opportunity to study clinical correlates of recidivism in this sample.

TABLE 1
Recidivism Rates among Subjects According to Categorical Prediction Variables ($N = 333$)

CHARACTERISTIC	FELONY RECIDIVISM RATES			VIOLENT RECIDIVISM RATES		
	YES	(NO)	r	YES	(NO)	r
Female	.45	(.39)	ns	.13	(.27)	−.16
Age 1st offense ≤25	.49	(.28)	.21	.30	(.12)	.20
Age 1st offense ≥36	.06	(.44)	−.23	.06	(.25)	−.13
First-time sex offender	.05	(.45)	−.26	.08	(.25)	−.13
Low infraction rate	.29	(.48)	−.20	.13	(.29)	−.19
Mental health unit residence	.34	(.55)	−.20	.25	(.18)	ns
Age at prison release ≤25	.50	(.38)	ns	.47	(.17)	.29

Note: For categorical variables, the values represent the rate of recidivism among subjects with the characteristic, and in parentheses, the rate of recidivism among subjects with the complementary characteristic; for example, for female gender, the rate in parentheses is the rate of recidivism among males. The r is a Pearson product moment correlation between the variable and the recidivism outcome. Correlation coefficients larger than .1070, .1410, and .1795 are significant at $p < .05$, $p < .01$, and $p < .001$, respectively.

TABLE 2
Scores of Recidivist and Nonrecidivist Subjects on Continuous Prediction Variables ($N = 333$)

	FELONY RECIDIVISM: $M(SD)$			VIOLENT RECIDIVISM: $M(SD)$		
	YES	NO	r	YES	NO	r
Past misdemeanors	3.89 (4.04)	.94 (3.94)	.23	4.03 (5.09)	2.35 (3.67)	.17
Past felonies	4.98 (2.5)	2.84 (2.31)	.40	4.80 (2.86)	3.4 (2.44)	.23
Prior violent felonies	0.79 (1.23)	0.59 (0.82)	ns	1.21 (1.5)	0.51 (0.76)	.29
Past drug felonies	1.50 (1.52)	0.56 (1.03)	.35	0.76 (1.20)	0.99 (1.4)	ns
Past sex felonies	0.096 (0.38)	0.29 (0.52)	−.20	025 (0.59)	0.20 (0.44)	ns
Felony versatility score	1.85 (0.67)	1.44 (0.62)	.31	1.89 (0.72)	1.52 (0.64)	.23
Index Time served (days)	671.4 (614.9)	948.4 (1092.6)	−.15	691.8 (657.5)	878.1 (1003.0)	ns

Note: Past felonies, past drug felonies, and past sex felonies include the index offense. Prior violent felonies are all felony offenses against persons (violent or sex felonies) *preceding* the index offense. The r is a Pearson product moment correlation between the variable and the recidivism outcome. Correlation coefficients larger than .1075, .1410, and .1795 are significant at $p > .05$, $p < .01$, and $p < .001$, respectively.

Correlations with recidivism ranged from −.26 to .40. For the most part, the magnitude and sign of those variables' association with risk is similar to that previously reported over many years of recidivism research (Gendreau, Little, & Goggin, 1996; also, see Bonta et al., 1998). Criminal history variables tended to have the strongest associations with recidivism, a finding also consistent with much past literature.

Curiously, status as a first-time sex offender was negatively associated with both felony (−.26) and violent (−.13) recidivism; number of past sex offenses was negatively correlated with felony recidivism (−.20), and not significantly correlated with violent recidivism. A history of any (a day or more) mental health unit residence in prison (dichotomously coded) was significantly negatively correlated with felony recidivism (−.20), but not significantly correlated with violent recidivism. The amount of time served on the index sentence (in days) was significantly negatively correlated with felony recidivism (−.15), but not correlated with violent recidivism.

Logistic Regression

Felony Model

Two logistic regression models were developed; one for felony recidivism and another for violent recidivism. Table 3 presents a summary of the findings for the forward felony logistic regression model. Changes in the percentage of variance explained (ΔR^2), normally reported at each step of a forward ordinary least squares regression, cannot be meaningfully interpreted in logistic regression because the dichotomous nature of the dependent variable imposes a ceiling on the maximum obtainable R^2. As an alternative to this truncated R^2, Allison (1999, p. 56) recommends calculating the generalized R^2, also known as the Coefficient of Determination (Cox & Snell, 1989), as an omnibus index of predictive power.

TABLE 3

Final Model: Stepwise Logistic Regression Results for Felony Recidivism

STEP	VARIABLE	B	WALD	p	ODDS RATIO	CD	ROC AREA
0	Intercept	−0.4799	1.42	.2342			
1	Past felonies	0.2392	17.60	<.0001	1.27	.159	.770
2	Past drug felonies	0.4183	14.90	<.0001	1.52	.221	.797
3	Low infraction rate	−0.9588	9.38	.0022	0.383	.242	.807
4	Prison mental health unit	−0.9730	9.48	.0021	0.378	.263	.817
5	Old age at 1st offense	−2.267	6.18	.0129	0.104	.283	.824
6	First-time sex offender	−1.698	4.91	.0267	0.183	.299	.828
Goodness of fit criterion	df	χ^2	p				
Hosmer–Lemeshow	8	13.66	.0911				

Note: Variables are listed in order of the forward regression steps at which they appeared. The logistic regression coefficients (B), Wald, p, and odds ratios describe the variable in the final model (Step #6); the CD and Area under the ROC curve (AUC) describe the strength of the model at the indicated step, when the variable was added. See the coding table for precise definitions of the variables. The odds ratio is adjusted for other variables in the model. CD is the coefficient of determination (Cox & Snell, 1989).

At the conclusion of the forward logistic regression, the felony model contained six variables, presented in order of forward selection: (1) number of previous felonies, (2) number of previous drug felonies, (3) low infraction rate, (4) residence in a prison mental health unit, (5) older age at first offense, and (6) status as a first-time sex offender. The Hosmer–Lemeshow goodness of fit statistic (Hosmer & Lemeshow, 1989, pp. 140–145) showed that the model adequately fit the data, $\chi^2(8) = 13.66, p > .0911$.

Several features of Table 3 are worth highlighting. First, four of the independent variables had negative coefficients, suggesting that they were relative protective factors:[5]

(1) low infraction rate, (2) prison mental health bed residence, (3) old age at first offense, and (4) status as a first-time sex offender. Second, number of previous felonies by itself resulted in impressive prediction of felony recidivism. The ROC area under the curve (AUC) measure of .770 at this step was substantially greater than chance (.5, $p < .000$). This is not surprising given that the univariate correlation of this variable with felony recidivism was .40. Third, at a descriptive level, the size of the AUC tended to grow slowly after number of previous felonies (AUC = .770) and number of previous drug felonies (AUC = .797) were added to the model. When the largest six-variable model was reached, a final AUC of .828 was obtained.[6] The Coefficient of Determination for the final model was .299, which adjusted for attenuation using Nagelkerke's correction based on the maximum possible R^2 (SAS Institute, 1999, p. 1948), would amount to an R^2 of .403.

Violence Model

Table 4 presents a summary of findings for the violence logistic regression model. Table 4 is identical in structure to Table 3. At the conclusion of this logistic regression, five variables were included in the model, presented in order of forward selection: (1) young age at release, (2) felony versatility score, (3) female gender, (4) low infraction rate, and (5) status as a first time sex-offender. Three of the five independent variables were relative protective factors: (1) female gender, (2) low infraction rate, and (3) status as a first-time sex offender. The final five-variable model fit the data well, as shown by the Hosmer–Lemeshow goodness of fit test, $\chi^2(8) = 5.06, p > .7513$. Predictive accuracy as gauged by the Coefficient of Determination (.170), the Nagelkerke adjusted R^2 (.259) and the AUC (.779) was good. The first variable selected by the forward selection procedure, young age at release, resulted in a proportionately larger AUC (.640, $p < .000$) but the addition of other variables resulted in comparatively larger incremental contributions to predictive accuracy than was the case for the felony model.

Relative Protective Factors

Rogers (2000) has cogently argued that a selective focus on risk factors, to the exclusion of protective factors, biases risk assessment in the direction of overpredicting dangerousness. Such overprediction not only decreases forecasting accuracy but it potentially leads to unfair handling by the criminal justice system (Silver & Miller, 2002).

Of the nine variables applied in the logistic regressions, four that have often been

TABLE 4

Final Model: Stepwise Logistic Regression Results for Violent Recidivism

STEP	VARIABLE	B	WALD	p	ODDS RATIO	CD	ROC AREA
0	Intercept	−2.123	25.80	<.0001			
1	Young age at release	1.396	19.03	<.0001	4.04	.074	.640
2	Felony versatility	0.6982	11.05	<.0009	2.01	.109	.706
3	Female	−1.111	9.37	.0022	.329	.133	.743
4	Low infraction rate	−0.8091	6.01	.0142	.445	.152	.759
5	First-time sex offender	−1.512	5.29	.0214	.220	.170	.779
Goodness of fit criterion	df	χ^2	p				
Hosmer–Lemeshow	8	5.06	.7513				

Note: Variables are listed in order of the forward regression steps at which they appeared. The logistic regression coefficients (B), Wald, p, and odds ratios describe the variable in the final model (Step #5); the CD and Area under the ROC curve (AUC) describe the strength of the model at the indicated step, when the variable was added. See the coding table for precise definitions of the variables. The odds ratio is adjusted for other variables in the model. CD is the coefficient of determination (Cox & Snell, 1989)

reported as risk factors were again found to be risk factors, but the remaining five were found to be relative protective factors. Although these protective factors generally entered the logistic regression at later steps than risk factors, many of them were associated with substantially lowered risk for reoffense.[7] For example, only 13% of the female MIOs were reconvicted of a violent offense (vs. 27% of the males; unadjusted odds ratio of 2.52; 95% CI = 1.31–4.85); only 5% of first-time sex offenders were reconvicted of a felony offense (vs. 45% of the non-first-time sex offenders; unadjusted odds ratio of 15.28; 95% CI = 3.62–64.59); and only 8% were reconvicted of a violent reoffense (vs. 25% of the others; unadjusted odds ratio of 3.96; CI = 1.19–13.26); only 6% of those who committed their first offense at age 36 or older were reconvicted of a felony offense (vs. 44% of the others; unadjusted odds ratio of 12.34; 95% CI = 2.90–52.52); only 29% of MIOs with one or fewer prison infractions per year were convicted of a new felony offense (vs. 48% of the others; unadjusted odds ratio of 2.35; 95% CI = 1.47–3.75); and only 11% were convicted of a new violent offense (vs. 31% of the others; unadjusted odds ratio of 2.72; 95% CI = 1.51–4.93); only 34% of MIOs with any time at all time in a prison mental health unit were convicted of a new felony offense (vs. 55% of MIOs who spent no time in a prison mental health unit; unadjusted odds ratio of 2.35; 95% CI = 1.46–3.77).

Although our data do not permit us to test causal hypotheses about relative protective factors, these findings leave little room for doubt about the importance of identifying and assessing actuarial factors that are related to lower risk. Whether these same variables would function as relative protective factors for other populations of MIOs, or in other settings, or jurisdictions outside of Washington State is unknown. It is possible that some of them (e.g., status as a first-time sex offender, and history of residential mental health treatment in prison) are related to the auspices under which mental health services are provided to mentally ill prisoners in Washington State (see

Morrissey, Swanson, Goldstrom, Rudolph, & Manderscheid, 1993) or to the manner in which Washington State has chosen to identify, treat and manage its MIOs, particularly MIO sex offenders.

Are Complex Logistic Regression Equations Really Necessary to Forecast Risk?

As is widely known, the magnitude of regression coefficients can shrink substantially on cross-validation. Dawes and Corrigan (1974) were among the first to argue that for many applied prediction problems a preoccupation with regression weights is misplaced, because unit weights or even random weights often yield acceptable prediction. They argued that what is most crucial is (1) whether an independent variable is truly associated with the criterion variable and (2) the direction (positive or negative) of the association. To calculate simple risk scores that don't rely on logistic regression coefficient weights, we recoded variables in our logistic regression equations using a method similar to those employed by Burgess (1928) and Nuffield (1982).[8]

Appendix B shows how we recoded the original logistic regression variables into new ones based on the relationship between the original variable and observed recidivism. In most cases, it was possible to recode the new variable +1, −1 or 0, depending on its relationship to recidivism relative to the 99% CI around the recidivism baseline. However, for one of the continuous variables (number of previous felonies) recoding the variable in this manner would have discarded important covariation related to recidivism. Hence for this variable it was necessary to follow a slightly different method as described further in Appendix B.

To compare the predictive accuracy of simple risk scores with the corresponding risk scores based on the logistic regression equations, we plotted comparative ROCs for the two methods for felony recidivism (Fig. 1) and violent recidivism (Fig. 2).[9] All of the AUCs were large and highly significant ($p < .000$, all tests), and pairs of AUCs for the same prediction task were very comparable in magnitude. This is not surprising given the high correlations between the simple risk scores and equation-based scores; $r = .923$ and $.915$, for the pairs of felony and violence scores, respectively.

To provide statistical tests of the predictive accuracy of the simple risk scores versus the equation-based risk scores, we conducted two new logistic regressions in which we entered both types of risk score as variables into logistic regression to predict felony and violent recidivism. We also tested the difference in the size of the AUCs for the two types of risk score for felony and violent recidivism using a statistical for test correlated ROCs recommended by Hanley and McNeil (1983).

The logistic regressions used a backwards elimination procedure in which step one contained the simple risk score and the equation-based risk score and step two removed the equation-based risk score leaving only the simplified risk score in the logistic regression equation. In both cases, removal of the equation-based risk score failed to make a difference, with a nonsignificant change in −2 Log likelihood following removal of the equation-based score in each case (change in $\chi^2(1) = -.432$, $p < .511$; change in $\chi^2(1) = -.050$, $p < .823$; felony and violent reoffense analyses, respectively). There were

FIG. 1
Felony ROC Curves

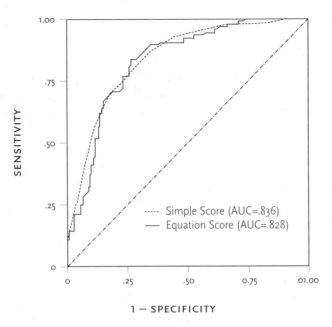

ROC curves for the felony logistic regression equation score versus the simple felony risk scale score.

FIG. 2
Violence ROC Curves

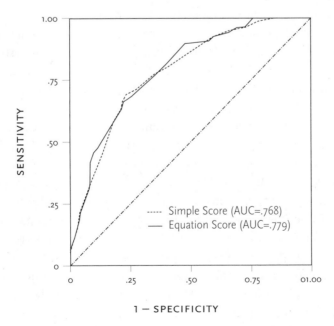

ROC curves for the violence logistic regression equation score versus the simple violence risk scale score.

no statistically significant differences in pairs of AUCs for felony or violent reoffense ($Z = .664$, p = .507 [two-tailed]; $Z = .489$, $p = .625$ [two-tailed]; felony and violent reoffense ROC AUCs respectively). Thus, the simple risk scores forecasted felony and violent recidivism as well as the more complex scores derived from the logistic regression equations.

The relationship between the simple felony risk score and felony recidivism is depicted in Fig. 3 in the form of two overlapping frequency distributions of risk scores for recidivists and nonrecidivists, and the probability of recidivism as a function of risk score is plotted on the secondary y-axis. Fig. 4 shows these frequency distributions and probability of violent recidivism for the simplified violence risk scores. This method of presenting the data shows both the mix of recidivists to nonrecidivists at each score level and the numerical consequences of using any score for classification or decision-making purposes, as well as depicts the relationship between the score and recidivism.

As can be seen in Figs. 3 and 4, the higher the score the greater the percentage of recidivists. Of those scoring at the top two highest scores (10 and 11) on the felony graph and those scoring at the top score (6) on the violence graph, all or nearly all were reconvicted. Of those with extremely low scores (0 and 1 on the violence graph; 0 and 1 on the felony graph) none were reconvicted. Intermediate probabilities of reconviction, including some fairly high rates and low rates, are also seen for the next highest and lowest scores, and rates near baseline recidivism (baserate = 41% for felony reconviction; 23% for reconviction of a violent offense) are seen for the middle-most scores. Although highly accurate prediction was possible for a small percentage of individuals with very high or low scores, the majority of MIOs received risk scores at the middle levels of the scales where discrimination between recidivists and non-recidivists is less accurate.

[Although creating a new risk tool was not one of the goals of this study, there is some practical value in considering how well our simple risk scores perform relative to published risk assessment tools. It will be recalled that our AUC for forecasting violence using the simple scores was .77 (see Fig. 2); for forecasting new felonies it was .84 (see Fig. 3). These AUC statistics are quite comparable to those reported for state-of-the art risk assessment instruments.[10] For example, on the basis of a compilation of 26 Violence Risk Appraisal Guide (VRAG) replication studies, Harris, Rice, and Cormier (2002, http://www.mhcp-research.com/forcon2.pps) reports ROC AUCs that average about .75 to .79; the ROC AUC for the HCR-20 reported by Douglas, Ogloff, and Nichols (1999) ranges from .76 to .80; Hanson and Thornton (2000) report that the AUCs for three of the most common actuarial tools used with sex offenders range from .65 to .74; the AUC for the Spousal Assault Risk Appraisal (SARA; Kropp & Hart, 2000) is .70. The AUC for violence of .80 in the VRAG replication study (Harris et al., 2002), and the AUC of .82 reported for the MacArthur Iterative Classification Tree (ICT; Steadman et al., 2000) are slightly higher than our AUC of .77. The multiple ICT model method (AUC = .88; Monahan et al., 2001, p. 123) provides the only clear example of substantially better violence prediction.

FIG. 3
Felony Risk Score

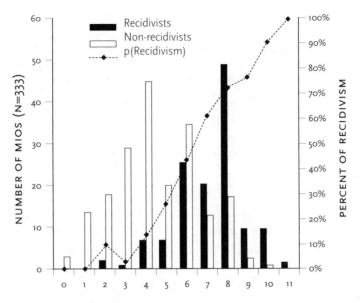

Felony risk scale score by number of MIOs with the score for felony recidivists and nonrecidivists. Secondary Y-axis plots probability of felony recidivism as a function of the felony risk scale score.

FIG. 4
Violence Risk Score

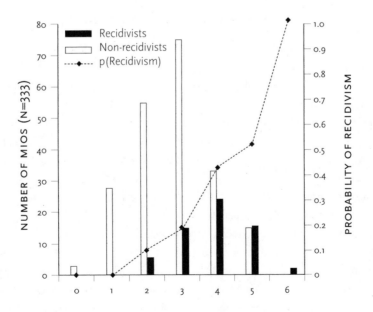

Violence risk scale score by number of MIOs with the score for violent and nonviolent recidivists. Secondary Y-axis plots probability of violent recidivism as a function of the violence risk scale score.

CONCLUSIONS

Study Limitations

Before proceeding we identify two important limitations of our study. First, our identification of MIOs was based upon a review of existing DOC records, not on individual clinical assessments. Ideally, one would conduct structured clinical interviews of a large random sample of inmates and prospectively follow them into the community. Among other things, this would have made possible a better study of diagnostic and other clinical variables as potential risk factors or protective factors. However, assuming a point prevalence rate of 10% serious mental illness in prison inmates, this would have required performing clinical assessments of about 3300 inmates to include 333 MIOs in the sample.

Second, we have not cross-validated our findings on a new sample of MIOs. Although bootstrapping methods can be used to generate estimates of central tendency and confidence intervals, we chose not to use bootstrapping. Unlike the national multisite study of Steadman et al. (2000), that reported bootstrapped confidence intervals for various Iterative Classification Tree (ICT) risk categories, our sample of 1996–97 release cohorts was drawn from a single agency, Washington State Department of Corrections. Consequently, any peculiarities or biases in our sample would only have been recursively resampled in the bootstrapping procedure. In our view, the only sensible cross-validation strategy is to draw new samples of MIOs from other states or study additional cohorts of Washington MIOs, research of ours that is currently in progress.

Major Findings and Their Implications

It is clear that Washington's mentally ill inmates are at no greater risk of recidivism than ordinary inmates. Given this finding, societal concerns that mentally ill inmates represent a particularly dangerous group of offenders are, at the least, questionable. Indeed, including history or diagnosis of mental illness as a per se risk factor for estimating future violence in correctional populations, as is done in the case of the Level of Supervision Inventory—Revised (LSI-R, items 48, 49, 50), the HCR-20 (item H6), and SVR-20 (item 4), may not only unfairly prejudice mentally ill offenders but it may even degrade predictive accuracy.

Our findings also show that a handful of ordinary correctional records can be as accurate as more complex risk tools in forecasting recidivism. This has important implications for correctional settings where large numbers of inmates must be assessed under tight budgetary constraints. If predicting likelihood of reoffense is the main goal or *only* goal of using a risk instrument, tools based on data routinely available in institutional databases have a decided advantage over tools that must be individually administered by a professional.[11] Unless one risk tool is markedly superior to others in a given setting, the choice of tool would seem obvious: use the least costly one.

Silver and Chow-Martin (2002) have recently shown that multiple ICT models formed from 10 ordinary correctional variables achieved high levels of accuracy for predicting rearrest and reimprisonment for 1,170 New Jersey Department of Corrections inmates. Indeed, one multiple ICT model achieved an AUC of .90 in predicting 1-year prison returns. Whether any of their ICT models would work equally well outside of New Jersey is, of course, unknown. As Silver and Chow-Martin point out, differences in offender demographics, and differences in social and economic conditions could affect which variables and models work best for different states. Our findings, therefore, along with those of Silver and Chow-Martin, not only emphasize the practicality of risk forecasting using ordinary correctional data but also stress the importance of developing actuarial models based on *local* data.

We are confident that most large institutions possess sufficient information in their electronic databases to construct their own actuarial risk equations or risk scores tailored to fit their population, setting and community release environment. What remains for these institutions to complete this task is the motivation to collect recidivism data to develop and test risk models. The economic, social, and legal advantages of using locally developed actuarial models over published, but locally untested, tools for risk decision-making are compelling.

Where Do We Go from Here?

In a highly influential paper, Monahan and Steadman (1996) analogized the task of violence risk assessment to weather prediction. We suggest, however, a distinction between broad enduring meteorological patterns or trends—what we commonly call climate—and acute or emergent fluctuations and changes: that is, weather. Keeping this distinction in mind, the reliance of current risk tools on static factors means that what current risk tools forecast is not the "weather" at all, but "climate." We should, not be disappointed therefore, to find that tools developed to predict climate don't predict the weather very well. Taking gender as an example, we should no more expect male gender to predict a violent act than expect geography to predict a tornado. Certainly, no competent meteorologist would base an actual tornado or hurricane forecast on geography, even though tornadoes are more frequent in Oklahoma or Kansas and hurricanes on the Gulf coast.

It is widely known that the prediction of destructive weather events requires timely, local meteorological data; not just knowledge of climate, season, or national weather patterns. As Monahan (2002) has pointed out, weather forecasting is one profession where over-rides based on "clinical review and revision" can sometimes improve predictive accuracy. Indeed, knowledge of local conditions and patterns may be what allows experienced meteorologists to revise and improve upon the accuracy of temperature and precipitation forecasts generated by the National Weather Service (Carter & Polger, 1986, cited in Monahan, 2002; for analyses that decompose human forecasting skill into constituent parts see: Heideman, Stewart, Moninger, & Reagan-Cirincione, 1993; Stewart & Lusk, 1994).

In recent years, a burgeoning literature on dynamic risk factors has emerged (e.g., see Andrews & Bonta, 1994; Bonta et al., 1998; Gendreau et al., 1996; Hanson & Harris, 1998, 2000; Quinsey et al., 1998, chaps. 10 &11; Zamble & Quinsey, 1997). Unhappily, when clinical or dynamic factors have been compared with static factors in risk fore-casting studies they have generally been assessed only once, which necessarily forces them to function like static variables in prediction equations. Considering the long forecast intervals of most risk studies, it is not surprising that statically measured clinical or dynamic variables would perform relatively poorly. Indeed, expecting a statically measured clinical variable (e.g., score on a mood state scale) to forecast a temporally remote event is a bit like expecting one's body temperature on January 1st to predict influenza next winter, notwithstanding the fact that an elevated body temperature is a highly reliable *proximal* sign that one is coming down with an infectious disease.

A remaining task for clinical evaluators is a how to integrate dynamic factors with static factors. Although dynamic risk factors may be included along with static factors on some risk scales or, alternatively, clinical findings taken into consideration as supple-mentary data to an actuarial risk assessment based on static factors, it is unclear how or even whether to combine the data from these two sources. Should one simply add up all of the factors regardless of source? Should some factors be given more weight than others based upon empirical relationships or using clinical judgment? Or, should clinical adjustment to an actuarial tool be discouraged until such adjustment is shown to enhance predictive validity? There are no simple answers to these questions.

To our knowledge no tool has yet been developed that truly satisfies the needs of clinical providers charged with treating MIOs in the community; namely, the need to assess risk on a continuing basis over months or even years. We believe that it may be possible to construct a practical risk assessment tool that combines static and dynamic factors, one that might permit something akin to a synoptic weather forecast. To do so will not only require identifying dynamic variables that forecast offending, but it will require taking frequent local "readings" of these dynamic variables, and, finally, it will require a rational, quantitative basis for integrating the static and dynamic risk factors. Proportional hazards regression, a powerful model developed by Cox (1972), is particularly well suited to accomplish this task. Not only does the concept of hazard comport well with how most people intuitively understand the vicissitudes of risk (see Allison, 1997, pp. 17–19), but the proportional hazards model can accommodate static and time-dependent (changing dynamic) covariates in the *same* model to yield a single estimate of risk at a given point in time. Brown (2002) has recently demon-strated the usefulness of proportional hazards regression in studying a combination of static and time-dependant (dynamic) covariates in Canadian male offenders. In her study of time to failure in released general population offenders, static variables yielded an AUC of .79, but the addition of several time-dependant covariates increased the AUC to .90. However, the dynamic risk factors were assessed at only three points in time: pre-release, 1-month and 3-months post release. It is possible that more frequent assessment of dynamic risk factors in the community (e.g., monthly or weekly)—as would be the case for diligent clinical supervision—would lead to even more accurate forecasts of hazard to offend and better timed opportunities for intervention.

Data Dictionary

CATEGORICAL VARIABLES

Age 1st offense ≤25	Age at first recorded conviction for a criminal offense ≤25 (Y/N)
Age 1st offense ≥36	Age at first recorded conviction for a criminal offense ≥36 (Y/N)
Age at prison release ≤25	Age at release from index conviction ≤25 (Y/N)
First-time sex offender	First recorded sex offense conviction (Y/N)
Female	DOC records report inmate is female (Y/N)
Low infraction rate	Rate of DOC institutional infractions ≤1 per year (Y/N)
Mental health unit residence	Time spent in a DOC mental health unit on index conviction ≥1 day (Y/N)

CONTINUOUS VARIABLES

Felony versatility score	Number of felony categories (1–4) in which the offender has a past[12] felony conviction (drug, property, violent nonsex, sex)
Index time served	Number of days of sentence served on index crime before release
Past drug felonies	Number of past felony convictions for drug offenses
Past felonies	Number of past felony convictions regardless of category
Past misdemeanors	Number of past misdemeanor convictions regardless of category
Past sex felonies	Number of past convictions for felony sex offenses
Prior violent felonies	Number of convictions for violent felonies (regardless of type) before index conviction

APPENDIX B
Recoding Original Variable Values Into Simple Risk Scores

VARIABLE	VALUE	RECODED SCORE	RECIDIVISM
Felony prediction (baserate)			**41%**
Past felonies	1–2	−1	13%
	3–4	1	57%
	5+	2	71%
Past drug felonies	0	−1	28%
	1	0	39%
	2+	1	70%
Prison mental health unit	N	1	55%
	Y	−1	34%
Low infraction rate	N	1	48%
	Y	−1	29%
First-time sex offender	N	0	45%
	Y	−1	5%
Old age at 1st offense	N	0	44%
	Y	−1	6%
Violence prediction (baserate)			**23%**
Young age at release	N	0	17%
	Y	1	47%
Felony versatility	1	−1	13%
	2	0	29%
	3–4	1	44%
Female	N	0	27%
	Y	−1	13%
Low infraction rate	N	0	29%
	Y	−1	13%
First-time sex offender	N	0	25%
	Y	−1	8%

Note: The 99% CI for baseline felony recidivism is 34–48%. The 99% CI for baseline violent recidivism is 17–29%. For levels of the dichotomous variables, a −1, 0 or +1 was assigned depending on whether the recidivism associated with that level of the variable was above the CI (+1), below the CI (−1), or within the CI (0). For one of the continuous variables (prior felonies), an additional level (+2) was assigned for those with five or more felonies based on the high associated rate of recidivism (71%) and the difference (14%) between that rate and the next lowest level (57%). Total scores for the recoded felony prediction score ranged from −6 to +5 with (M = −0.39, SD = 2.38); total scores for the recoded violence prediction score ranged from −3 to +3 (M = −0.003, SD = 1.20). To eliminate negative scores, a constant (6.0 or 3.0; felony and violence scores, respectively) was added to each score, yielding a felony risk scale that ranges from 0 to 11 (M = 5.6, SD = 2.38) and a violence risk scale that ranges from 0 to 6 (M = 3.0, SD = 1.20).

NOTES

1. An earlier partial analysis of the recidivism data was included in a more general report on the Community Transitions Study in *Psychiatric Services*, 53 (10), 1290–1296. Some of these findings were also presented at the National Association of State Mental Health Program Directors Forensic Division Conference, September 24, 2002, Seattle, Washington and at The American Psychology Law Society Biennial Conference, March 9, 2002, Austin, Texas.
2. A complete list of these medications and qualifying dosage regimens is available by request from the authors.
3. Data collection was a complex, time-consuming process that is more fully described in a monograph length presentation of the findings that is available by request from the authors.

4. An example involving the relationship of age at first offense and recidivism helps make this clear. In the present data set, age at first offense was negatively correlated with both felony recidivism (−.28) and violent recidivism (−.28). However, careful examination of segments of the scale of this variable showed that age ≤25 was positively correlated with felony and violent recidivism (.21 and .20 respectively), age ≥36 was negatively correlated with felony (−.23) and violent (−.14) recidivism, and age 26–35 was uncorrelated with recidivism. This is not an unusual finding, having been previously reported by Beck and Shipley (1997) in their large study of recidivism in 16,000 state and federal prisoners.

5. Whether a variable ought to be categorized a protective factor versus a risk factor ultimately depends not on how it is coded but on its causal relationship with the dependent variable. For example, female gender (here coded 1 = female vs. 0 = male) could just as easily have been coded as male gender (1 = male vs. 0 = female). The second way of coding would, however, have missed the fact that being female is associated with a level of violence risk that is significantly below the general baseline risk for violence in our MIOs and our intuition that there is something about being female that reduces violence risk. In epidemiological research there are usually persuasive biological grounds for a trait being categorized a risk factor or protective factor. Thus, elevated cholesterol increases coronary artery disease via the promotion of plaque formation in coronary arteries and regular aerobic exercise decreases coronary artery disease by changing the ratio of high-density lipoproteins to low-density lipoproteins, which tends to reduce plaque formation, etc. In recidivism and violence risk research, persuasive causal explanations of the relationships between the independent and dependent variable are lacking, nor are there any well-formed, falsifiable theories of criminality or violence that generate truly causal hypotheses (for an informative struggle to test two well known "theories" of criminality see Krauss, Sales, Becker, & Figueredo, 2000). In the absence of good theory, we resort to coding risk and protective factors on the basis of whether the trait, albeit intuitively coded, is significantly above or below the baseline. Future research that tests causal hypotheses generated by well-formed theories of recidivism or violence will ultimately reject or support our intuitive coding of variables as risk factors versus protective factors. We use the adjective "relative" in "relative protective factors" to denote the fact that we have coded these factors relative to the baseline for the event of interest.

6. Each AUC was significantly greater than chance (p < .000 all comparisons). We do not report tests of the significance of differences between AUCs (Hanley & McNeil, 1983) here because this type of nonparametric test is not the statistical test of choice for variables in a logistic regression analysis. Here we present AUCs mainly for descriptive purposes because AUC has become somewhat of a standard gauge in risk prediction studies (e.g., see Mossman's meta-analysis [Mossman, 1994], which uses the AUC as a standard for comparing studies and variable domains).

7. The reader may wonder why the large differences in recidivism proportions reported for these variables didn't result in larger odds ratios in the logistic regression tables. Here it is important to remember that the odds ratios in logistic regression are tested against the size of their standard error, and importantly they are also adjusted for the other variables in the equation.

8. We don't pretend to have eliminated the need for cross-validation of our findings because the association and direction of association of a variable with the criterion may not replicate in a new sample. Here, our intent is merely to reduce reliance on logistic regression coefficients, which can't help but overfit the data, and to explore the utility of a simpler method for calculating risk scores that is easier for evaluators and decision makers to understand. A cross validation study is underway.

9. Plotting of the pairs of ROCs, and calculation of their AUCs, was completed in SPSS© 11.0. The AUC values for the ROCs based on the logistic regression scores differ slightly from those calculated by SAS©PROC LOGISTIC and reported for the last step of the logistic regression in Tables 3 and 4.

10. In fairness to published risk assessment tools, it is possible that had they been used with our sample they may have outperformed our equations or simple risk scores. For studies that compare some well-known risk tools in the same sample see Kroner and Mills (2001) and Glover, Nicholsen, Hemmati, Brenfeld, and Quinsey (2002).

11. As an illustration, assume that 10% of U.S. prisoners are mentally ill. On the basis of DOJ estimates that there were 1,406,031 inmates in state and local prisons in 2001, mass testing of all of the MIOs would require about 140,000 risk assessments. Although work estimates are not available for most risk tools, the Department of Research at the Penetanguishene Mental Health Centre has estimated that to complete a VRAG, "it requires, on average, approximately 2.5 person days to

complete a suitable psychosocial history" (http://www.mhcp-research.com/vragsum.htm). On the basis of these estimates, VRAG assessment of 140,000 MIOs would require 350,000 person days, or about 960 person years of work. Indeed, the Hare Psychopathy Checklist–Revised (PCL-R) alone (VRAG item 12; HCR-20 item H7) would, according to Multi Health Systems, require 150 to 180 min. per administration (http://www.mhs.com/), or about 14,500–17,500 person days (39–48 person years) of work. These estimates do not include the time necessary to train professionals or supervise paraprofessionals in the administration of these instruments, nor do they include the cost of some instruments themselves (e.g., PCL-R).

12. All variable names with the modifier "past" include the index conviction.

REFERENCES

Allison, P. D. (1997). *Survival analysis using the SAS System: A practical guide.* Cary, NC: SAS Institute.

Allison, P. D. (1999). *Logistic regression using the SAS System: Theory and applications.* Cary, NC: SAS Institute.

Andrews, D. A., & Bonta, J. L. (1994). *The psychology of criminal conduct.* Cincinnati, OH: Anderson.

Beck, A. J., Karberg, J. C., & Harrison, P. M. (2002). *Prison and jail inmates at midyear 2001* (NCJ No. 191702).Washington, DC: U.S. Department of Justice, Bureau of Justice Statistics Bulletin.

Beck, A. J., & Shipley, B.E. (1997). *Recidivism of prisoners released in 1983* (NCJ No. 116261). Washington, DC: U.S. Department of Justice, Bureau of Justice Statistics Special Report.

Bonta, J., Law, M.,& Hanson, K. (1998). The prediction of criminal and violent recidivism among mentally disordered offenders. *Psychological Bulletin, 123,* 123–142.

Brown, S. L. (2002). The dynamic prediction of criminal recidivism: A three-wave prospective study. Unpublished doctoral dissertation, Queen's University, Kingston, Ontario.

Burgess, E. M. (1928). Factors determining success or failure on parole. In A. A. Bruce, E. W. Burgess, & A. J. Arn (Eds.), *The working of the intermediate sentence law and the parole system in Illinois* (pp. 205–249). Springfield, IL: State Board Parole.

Cox, D. R. (1972). Regression models and life tables (with discussion). *Journal of the Royal Statistical Society, B34,* 187–220.

Cox,D. R., & Snell, E. J. (1989). *Analysis of binary data* (2nd ed., pp. 208–209). London: Chapman & Hall.

Dawes,R. M., & Corrigan,B. (1974). Linear models in decision making. *Psychological Bulletin, 81,* 95–106.

Ditton, P. M. (1999). *Mental health and treatment of inmates and probationers* (NCJ Publication No. 174463).Washington, DC: U.S. Department of Justice, Bureau of Justice Statistics Special Report.

Douglas, K., Ogloff, J., & Nichols, T. (1999). Assessing risk for violence among psychiatric patients: The HCR-20 Violence Risk Assessment Scheme and the Psychopathy Checklist: Screening version. *Journal of Consulting and Clinical Psychology, 67,* 917–930.

Feder, L. A. (1991a). A comparison of the community adjustment of mentally ill offenders with those from the general population: An 18-month follow-up. *Law and Human Behavior, 15*(5), 477–493.

Feder, L. A. (1991b). A profile of mentally ill offenders and their adjustment to the community. *Journal of Psychiatry and the Law, 19,* 79–98.

Gendreau, P., Little, T., and Goggin, C. (1996). A meta-analysis of the predictors of adult offender recidivism: What works! *Criminology, 34,* 575–607.

Glover, A. J. J., Nicholson, D. E., Hemmati, T., Bernfeld, G. A., & Quinsey, V. L. (2002). A comparison of predictors of general and violent recidivism among high-risk federal offenders. *Criminal Justice and Behavior, 29*(3), 235–249.

Hanley, J. A., & McNeil, B. J. (1983). A method of comparing the areas under receiver operating characteristic curves derived from the same cases. *Radiology, 148,* 839–843.

Hanson, R. K., & Harris, A. J. R. (1998). *Dynamic predictors of sexual recidivism* (User Report 1998–01). Ottawa: Department of the Solicitor General of Canada.

Hanson, R. K., & Harris, A. J. R. (2000). *The Sex Offender Need Assessment Rating (SONAR): A method for measuring change in risk levels.* Ottawa: Department of the Solicitor General of Canada.

Hanson, R. K., & Thornton, D. (2000). Improving risk assessments for sex offenders: A comparison of three actuarial scales. *Law and Human Behavior, 24*(1), 199–236.

Harris, G. T., Rice, M. E., & Cormier, C. A. (2002). Prospective replication of the VRAG and clinical judgment in the prediction of violent recidivism among forensic patients. *Law and Human Behavior, 26,* 377–394.

Harris, V. (2000). Insanity acquitees and rearrest: The past 24 years. *Journal of the American Academy of Psychiatry and the Law, 28*(2), 225–231.

Harrison, P. M., & Beck, A. J. (2002). *Prisoners in 2001* (NCJ Publication No. 195189). Washington, DC: U.S. Department of Justice, Bureau of Justice Statistics Special Report.

Hartwell, S. (2003). Short-term outcomes for offenders with mental illness released from incarceration. *International Journal of Offender Therapy and Comparative Criminology, 47*(2), 145–158.

Heideman, K. F., Stewart, T. R., Moninger, W. R., & Reagan-Cirincione, P. (1993). The Weather Information and Skill Experiment (WISE): The effect of varying levels of information on forecast skill. *Weather and Forecasting, 8,* 25–36.

Hodgins, S. (Ed). (1993). *Mental disorder and crime.* London, UK: Sage.

Hosmer, D. W., & Lemeshow, S. (1989). *Applied logistic regression.* New York: Wiley.

Jacoby, J. E., & Kozie-Peak, B. (1997). The benefits of social support for mentally ill offenders: Prison-to community transitions. *Behavioral Science and the Law, 15,* 483–501.

Krauss, D. A., Sales, B. D., Becker, J. V., and Figueredo, A. J. (2000). Beyond prediction to explanation in risk assessment research: A comparison of two explanatory theories of criminality and recidivism. *International Journal of Law and Psychiatry, 23*(2), 91–112.

Kroner, D.G., & Mills, J. F. (2001).The accuracy of five risk appraisal instruments in predicting institutional misconduct and new convictions. *Criminal Justice and Behavior, 28*(4), 471–489.

Kropp, P. R., & Hart, S. D. (2000). The Spousal Assault Risk Assessment (SARA) Guide: Reliability and validity in adult male offenders. *Law and Human Behavior, 24*(1), 101–118.

Lamb, R. H., Weinberger, L. E., & Gross, B. H. (1998). Persons with severe mental illness in jails and prisons: A review. *Psychiatric Services, 49*(4), 483–492.

Lamb, R. H., Weinberger, L. E., & Gross, B. H. (1999). Community treatment of severely mentally ill offenders under the jurisdiction of the criminal justice system: A review. *Psychiatric Services, 50*(7), 907–913.

Link, B. G., & Stueve, A. (1994). Psychotic symptoms and the violent/illegal behavior of mental patients compared to community controls. In J. Monahan & H. J. Steadman (Eds.), *Violence and mental disorder: Developments in risk assessment,* (pp. 137–160) Chicago, Ill.: University of Chicago Press.

Lovell, D., Gagliardi, G. J., & Peterson, P. D. (2002). Recidivism and use of services among persons with mental illness after release from prison. *Psychiatric Services, 53*(1), 1290–1296.

Martell, D. A., Rosner, R.,& Harmon, R. B. (1995). Base-rate estimates of criminal behavior by homeless mentally ill persons. *Psychiatric Services, 46*(6), 596–601.

Monahan, J. (1981). *Predicting violent behavior: An assessment of clinical techniques.* Beverly Hills, CA: Sage.

Monahan, J. (2002) Violence risk assessment. In Goldstein, A. (Ed.), *Handbook of psychology: Vol. 11. Forensic psychology (chap. 24)* (pp. 527–540). New York: Wiley.

Monahan, J., & Steadman, H. J. (1983). *Mentally disordered offenders.* New York: Plenum.

Monahan, J., & Steadman, H. J. (1996). Violent storms and violent people: How meteorology can inform risk communication in mental health law. *American Psychologist, 51,* 931–938.

Monahan, J., Steadman, H. J., Silver, E., Appelbaum, P. S., Clark Robbins, P., Mulvey, E. P., et al. (2001). *Rethinking risk assessment: The MacArthur study of mental disorder and violence.* New York: Oxford.

Morrisey, J. P., Swanson, J.W., Goldstrom, I., Rudolph, L., & Manderscheid, R.W. (1993). *Mental Health, Statistical note No. 207. Overview of mental health services provided by state adult correctional facilities: United States, 1998.* Rockville, MD: Center for Mental Health Services

Mossman, D. (1994). Assessing prediction of violence: Being accurate about accuracy. *Journal of Consulting and Clinical Psychology, 62,* 783–792.

Nuffield, J. (1982). *Parole decision-making in Canada: Research towards decision guidelines* (Cat. No. JS-22-65/1982E). Ottawa: Communications Branch, Minister of Supply and Services Canada.

Otto, R. K. (1992). Prediction of dangerous behavior: A review and analysis of "second generation" research. *Forensic Reports, 5,* 103–133.

Otto, R. K. (1994). On the ability of mental health professionals to "predict dangerousness": Commentary on interpretations of the "dangerousness" literature. *Law and Psychology Review, 18*, 43–68.

Otto, R. K. (2000). Assessing and managing violence risk in outpatient settings. *Journal of Clinical Psychology, 56*(10), 1239–1262.

Phipps, P., & Gagliardi, G. J. (2002). *Implementation of Washington's dangerous mentally ill offender law: Preliminary findings* (Document No. 02-03-1901). Olympia, WA: Washington State Institute for Public Policy.

Quinsey, V. L., Harris, G. T., Rice, M. E., & Cormier, C. A. (1998). *Violent Offenders: Appraising and managing risk.* Washington, DC: American Psychological Association.

Rogers, R. (2000). The uncritical acceptance of risk assessment in forensic practice. *Law and Human Behavior, 24*(5), 595–605.

SAS Institute. (1999). SAS/STAT® *User's guide, version 8* (p. 1948). Cary, NC: SAS Institute.

Silver, E., & Chow-Martin, L. (2002). A multiple models approach to assessing recidivism risk: Implications for judicial decision making. *Criminal Justice and Behavior, 29*(5), 538–568.

Silver, E., Mulvey, E.P., & Swanson, J. (2002). Neighborhood structural characteristics and mental disorder: Faris and Dunham revisited. *Social Science and Medicine, 55*(8), 1457–1470.

Silver, S. B., Cohen, M. I., & Spodak, M. K. (1989). Follow-up after release of insanity acquittees, mentally disordered offenders, and convicted felons. *Bulletin of the American Academy of Psychiatry and the Law 17*(4), 387–400.

Steadman, H. J. (1982). Mentally disordered offenders: A national survey of patients and facilities. *Law and Human Behavior, 6*, 31–38.

Steadman, H. J., Silver, E., Monahan, J., Appelbaum, P. S., Robbins, P. C., Mulvey, E. P., et al. (2000). A classification tree approach to the development of actuarial violence risk assessment tools. *Law and Human Behavior, 24*(1), 83–100.

Stewart, T. R., & Lusk, C. M. (1994). Seven components of judgmental forecasting skill: Implications for research and the improvement of forecasts. *Journal of Forecasting, 13*, 579–599.

Swanson, J., Holzer, C., Ganja, V., & Jono, R. (1990). Violence and psychiatric disorder in the community: Evidence from the Epidemiologic Catchment Area Surveys. *Hospital and Community Psychiatry, 41*, 761–770.

Swets, J. A., Dawes, R., & Monahan, J. (2000). Psychological science can improve diagnostic decisions. *Psychological Science in the Public Interest, 1*, 1–26.

Tabachnick, B. G., & Fidell, L. S. (1996). *Using multivariate statistics* (3rd ed.). New York: HarperCollins.

Villaneueve, D., & Quinsey, V. L. (1995). Predictors of general and violent recidivism among mentally disordered prison inmates. *Criminal Justice and Behavior, 22*, 397–410.

Wilson, D., Tien, G., & Eaves, D. (1995). Increasing community tenure of mentally ill offenders: An assertive case management program. *International Journal of Law and Psychiatry, 18*(1), 61–69.

Wolff, G., Pathare, S., Craig, T., & Leff, J. (1996a). Community attitudes to mental illness. *British Journal of Psychiatry, 168*, 183–190.

Wolff, G., Pathare, S., Craig, T., & Leff, J. (1996b). Community knowledge of mental illness and reaction to mentally ill people. *British Journal of Psychiatry, 168*, 191–198.

Wolff, G., Pathare, S., Craig, T., & Leff, J. (1996c). Public education for community care: A new approach. *British Journal of Psychiatry, 168*, 441–468.

Zamble, E., & Quinsey, V. L. (1997). *The criminal recidivism process.* Cambridge, UK: Cambridge University Press.

III

Clinical Prediction and Assessment

Section III

Introduction

In this section's first chapter, **William H. Reid** (Chapter 9) echoes Shah's earlier idea that there is much that clinicians and decision makers can do to improve the integrity of their violence risk assessments. However, he emphasizes that this does not necessarily imply that prediction accuracy will rise. He believes that risk assessment can be approached logically and that it is therefore a task that can be accomplished within reasonable limits. He lists concretely what can be done (e.g., carefully using diagnostic classifications, evaluating patients' post-discharge living conditions, assessing their responsiveness to treatment). In his view, the aim in making accurate prediction assessments is to match the patient with a group of people who pose similar levels of risk so that management and security decisions are as fair and accurate as possible. By closely monitoring and appropriately treating patients, the clinician or administrator will have the best possible chance of averting serious incidents or tragedies.[1]

Reid offers a "rant" against relying on "checklists" of risk factors as the "sole basis for [making] important decisions about safety and therapeutics" (page 188)[2] He emphasizes the importance of good clinical thinking, careful review of records, interaction with colleagues, detailed observations and corroboration of findings. His reminder that " [r]isk assessment is not a 3-minute exercise" (page 189) is aptly put.

The manner in which countertransference can infiltrate a therapeutic environment and result in counter-therapeutic and sometimes even punitive treatment is a subject dealt with in two classic psychoanalytically oriented papers (see Main, 1957 and Adler, 1972). How clinicians sometimes view their patients in a negative or pejorative light is not a subject that has received extensive research (though see Pfäfflin, 1979; Pfohl, 1978; Menzies, 1989). **Glyn Lewis** and **Louis Appleby** (Chapter 10) use a vignette study to examine the extent to which people with personality disorders may be disadvantaged. They invited a group of psychiatrists to rate a single written case vignette. The vignette was modified slightly (e.g., the key case included a diagnosis of personality disorder; in another instance the diagnosis was depression; in another, no diagnosis was offered). When the participants completed a rating scale designed to elicit assessment and management opinions, the data clearly showed that the psychiatrists were the most negative when the vignette included the term "personality disorder."

Lewis and Appleby conclude that "personality disorder" is not a scientifically established category and that affixing such a label to patients diminishes their chance of receiving help and support. Despite advances in diagnostic precision around personality disorders (e.g., American Psychiatric Association, 2000), clinicians' assessments can still be influenced by their countertransference. A clinician's countertransference— particularly when assessing people with personality disorders—can result in the patient being unfairly treated and/or unnecessarily detained.

Lewis and Appleby's piece is included in this collection to remind us that it is not always possible, or even wise under some circumstances, to detach ourselves from personal feelings about particular patients. Just as certain crimes tend to elicit abhorrence in even seasoned clinicians, so too do the attitudes and behaviours of particular patients. Not all clinicians, perhaps especially those in the forensic and correctional fields, are ideally suited to offer informed, disinterested opinion on people's potential violence and related risks. In fairness, some cases should be referred to colleagues, and certainly a second opinion should be solicited in cases where there is even a hint of possible bias.

Dale E. McNiel, **Amanda L. Gregory**, **Judy N. Lam**, **Renée L. Binder** and **Glenn R. Sullivan** (Chapter 11) contest the impression, left by the chapters in Section II, that clinicians really are capable of predicting violence. Like the chapter that follows, the McNiel et al. piece focuses on *short-term* prediction in "real world" clinical circumstances. The design of their study is sufficiently straightforward that it could be implemented in most practical clinical circumstances. Obviously, to do a prospective study there must be some defined predictor variables and some defined outcome variables. In this case, the authors chose to use the HCR-20, the 12-item Screening Version of the Hare PCL-R (Hart et al., 1995) and a five-item device called the Violence Screening Checklist (McNiel et al., 1988). Nurses completed the outcome measure using a device called the Overt Aggression Scale (Yudofsky et al., 1986). Participants consisted of 100 patients admitted to a locked, short-term, psychiatric unit for behavioural emergencies. The authors found that each of the three scales was associated with the likelihood of violence. The current clinical factors of the five-item (clinical) scale of the HCR-20 had appreciable predictive power, more so than the historical, "static" factor scale. (This scale is based on "static" factors that cannot possibly change because of events and conditions that occurred in the past.) The authors conclude that there is a role for developing decision support tools (page 219) in short-term assessments for violence.

These tools are particularly critical in cases where there has been acute exacerbation of a mental disorder, such as those studied in this project, rather than in situations where there is chronic risk.

The study by **David Watts**, **Morven Leese**, **Stuart Thomas**, **Zerrin Atakan** and **Til Wykes** (Chapter 12) has similarities to the research by McNiel and his group. The research by Watts and colleagues was also conducted in the "real world" setting of an acute psychiatric unit. While most practising clinicians will likely not share the authors' appetite for statistical "model building," studies in which clinicians work in close collaboration with researchers greatly improve our understanding of violence risk assessment and management. The authors themselves point to this state of affairs when they say "one problem bedeviling risk prediction studies is that they take place in the real world, in clinical settings, and cannot be of purely experimental design" (page 224). The practical problem is that once violence potential has been identified, clinicians and officials in the legal system have to work to prevent its occurrence. Intervening usually averts actual violence, so what might have been a true positive then becomes a false positive.

Watts and his colleagues used nurses as raters, since they are often the ones who do violence risk assessments on emergency psychiatric units. A hundred patients consecutively admitted to two locked units served as the study sample. An interesting feature of this project was the use of two definitions of violence—actual assault versus aggressive behaviour. Using various predictive and outcome measures, the researchers found that roughly one-third acted violently, one-third acted aggressively and one-third were completely non-violent.

The results from this admittedly small, as-yet unreplicated, study suggest that the factors predictive of violence of one type or the other and non-violence "do not fit neatly on a continuum" (page 231). The implications of this are profound. The findings suggest that when considering candidate factors in violence risk assessments, outcome measures should be carefully defined in advance. The arguably amorphous (and outdated) notion of "dangerousness" will not suffice. Given the heterogeneity of problematic and aggressive conduct and the spectrum of severity for each behaviour, it seems logical that different risk factors might be predictive of different behaviours, although some overlap between categories can be expected. Following Hart et al. (2003), clinicians need to specify who might be violent, in what way, under what conditions, against whom and over what period of time, when making forecasts during violence assessments.

Watts et al., like McNiel et al., found that the historical variable of pre-admission violence, though associated significantly with subsequent violence on the units, was not the most powerful variable in predicting future violence. Rather, a measure of hostile-suspiciousness predicted actual assaults; a measure of withdrawal-retardation was the best predictor of aggressive behaviour; and a measure of anxiety-depression was the factor most strongly associated with non-violence (see Table 3, page 228). This kind of research is important because it suggests that not all stipulated risk factors will act in the same way given different measures of outcome.

Richard Rogers (Chapter 13) recommends cautious diligence in approaching the task of violence risk assessment, and reminds his readers that there can be big gaps between ideal and actual practices. As well, he calls for a more discerning attitude toward the many violence risk evaluation devices now available (e.g., see Bloom et al., Section I). Rogers notes that most of these devices place too much weight on static factors and that other more dynamically oriented schemes may rest too heavily on the "assumption of additivity" (page 234) (i.e., the more factors operating, the higher the risk).[3] A major feature of his argument is that too much emphasis is placed on risk factors at the expense of protective factors (e.g., social relations, self-esteem, religious beliefs and the extent to which the patient is accepted by his or her parents). He calls for "balanced" evaluations that account for both of these types of factors. Rogers also points out that protective and risk factors may depend on the age of the patient, and may vary according to the patient's gender and the choice of outcome criteria. In his view, it is also important not to over-rely on total scores from measures such as the Hare PCL-R and the HCR-20. Assessors need to consider how scores from individual items are interrelated, as this may have more predictive power than the total score.

Certainly Rogers argues that over-emphasizing static risk factors "may produce lopsided assessments and resource allocations" (page 237). Courts and clinicians can become preoccupied with static factors, such that certain patients who pose minimal violence risks are assessed more conservatively and are thus unduly restricted (both within the institution and in the community) and/or precluded from community placement. These forensic patients can consume considerable mental health resources, despite often posing less risk of violence than their civil counterparts. With many contemporary risk assessment schemes, it is impossible to avoid assigning high risk scores without fully considering protective factors: this results in overdetection and over-supervision. Rogers offers some helpful "questions to consider" when conducting violence risk assessments (see Table 1, page 242).

The chapter by **Tonia L. Nicholls**, **Johann Brink**, **Sarah I. Desmarais**, **Christopher D. Webster** and **Mary-Lou Martin** (Chapter 14) addresses some of the challenges and possibilities raised by the authors of the five preceding chapters in this section. It is based on a relatively new structured professional judgment (SPJ) device called the Short-Term Assessment of Risk and Treatability (START; Webster et al., 2004). Without ignoring historical, static factors, START offers a set of 20 dynamic variables. These are conceptualized in six main areas: health concerns, mental/emotional state, substance use, vocational/leisure skills, community living skills/activities of daily living and reintegration risks. Each of the 20 factors is scored separately for strengths and vulnerabilities (on 0, 1 or 2 scales).[4] This scheme also allows assessors to record "signature risk signs";[5] it invites evaluators to consider a range of risk besides violence against others, and focuses on treatment planning.

Although the START scheme has not acquired substantial scientific and professional support, it represents an up-to-date attempt to deal with some of the important issues raised by William Reid, Glyn Lewis, Dale McNiel, David Watts, Richard Rogers and their respective colleagues. The START scheme offers a vision of what interdisciplinary SPJ devices might look like in the future.

NOTES

1. It is remarkable how closely patients can be followed. Recently, Schubert et al. (2006) demonstrated that it is possible to have sustained *weekly* contact with patients in the community.
2. Robert Hare once published his regret at having deemed the PCL-R to be a "checklist" (1998, pages 112–113). The authors of the HCR-20 resist the device being cast in these terms, and they deplore it being used by those who lack training, experience and the willingness to make constant reference to the manual. Yet even they refer to the HCR-20 as a "checklist" (page 10).
3. The HCR-20 does in fact offer specific advice on this front. Its authors point out that, while generally the more factors operating the greater the risk (i.e., the additivity principle), there will be many exceptions to this rule (i.e., cases where individual item scores are low but overall risk estimation is appropriately considered high; see Webster et al., 1997).
4. In fact, the chapter on START included here uses an earlier scoring system in which the same zero served both scales (i.e., a continuous five-point scale). This means that each item had to be scored either for strengths or for vulnerabilities. When the scales are separated (i.e., two three-point scales), it is possible to score for both strengths and vulnerabilities on a particular item.
5. Many people signal, wittingly or unwittingly, when they are about to become angry, have relapses in psychiatric symptoms, harm themselves, take drugs and so on. Often these signals are unique to that individual. Such signs are very important clinically and, once noted to be reliable, should be conveyed to people who could be affected (e.g., members of staff, family members, employers).

REFERENCES

Adler, G. (1972). Helplessness in the helpers. *British Journal of Medical Psychology, 45,* 315–326.

American Psychiatric Association. (2000). *Diagnostic and Statistical Manual of Mental Disorders* (4th ed., text rev.). Washington, DC: Author.

American Psychological Association (APA) Presidential Task Force on Evidence-Based Practice. (2006). Evidence-based practice in psychology. *American Psychologist, 61,* 271–285.

Hare, R.D. (1998). The Hare PCL-R: Some issues concerning its use and misuse. *Legal and Criminological Psychology, 3,* 99–119.

Hart, S.D., Cox, D. & Hare, R.D. (1995). *The Hare Psychopathy Checklist: Screening Version* (PCL:SV). Toronto: Multi-Health Systems.

Hart, S.D., Kropp, P.R. & Laws, D. (2003). *The Risk for Sexual Violence Protocol.* Burnaby, B.C.: Mental Health Law and Policy Institute, Simon Fraser University.

Main, T.F. (1957). The ailment. *British Journal of Medical Psychology, 30,* 129–145.

McNiel, D.E., Binder, R.L. & Greenfield, T.K. (1988). Predictors of violence in civilly committed acute psychiatric patients. *American Journal of Psychiatry, 145,* 965–970.

Menzies, R.J. (1989). *Survival of the Sanest: Order and Disorder in a Pretrial Psychiatric Clinic.* Toronto: University of Toronto Press.

Pfäfflin, F. (1979). The contempt of psychiatric experts for sexual convicts: Evaluation of 963 files from sexual offence cases in the state of Hamburg, Germany. *International Journal of Law and Psychiatry, 2,* 485–497.

Pfohl, S.J. (1978). *Predicting Dangerousness: The Social Construction of Psychiatric Reality.* Lexington, MA: Lexington Books.

Schubert, C.A., Mulvey, E.P., Lidz, C.W., Gardner, W.P. & Skeem, J.L. (2006). Weekly community interviews with high-risk participants. *Journal of Interpersonal Violence, 20,* 632–646.

Webster, C.D., Douglas, K.S., Eaves, D. and Hart, S.D. (1997). *HCR-20: Assessing Risk for Violence, Version 2.* Burnaby, B.C.: Mental Health, Law, and Policy Institute, Simon Fraser University.

Webster, C.D., Martin, M-L., Brink, J., Nicholls, T.L. & Middleton, C. (2004). *Short-Term Assessment of Risk and Treatability (START): An Evaluation and Planning Guide.* Port Coquitlam, BC: Forensic Psychiatric Services Commission.

Yudofsky, S.C., Silvers, J.M., Jackson, W., Endicott, J. & Williams, D. (1986). The Overt Aggression Scale for the objective rating of verbal and physical aggression. *American Journal of Psychiatry, 143,* 45–49.

9

Risk Assessment, Prediction, and Foreseeability

WILLIAM H. REID

Risk assessment is a hot topic in both clinical and forensic psychiatry. It is usually framed in terms of prediction (e.g., predicting suicide, predicting dangerousness, predicting relapse). This month, in spite of nearly axiomatic views that psychiatrists and other clinicians can't predict dangerousness or suicide, I'll briefly discuss some ways in which we can assess risk and some common misunderstandings about our "predictions."

No, I'm not going to say we know which patients will meet (or cause) tragedy and when they'll do it. The subtle wording shift in the preceding paragraph—from "predict" to "assess risk"—is the key. Clinician-readers know that we assess risk in many different situations, from admission evaluations to commitment opinions to decisions about patient passes and discharge.

Sometimes, of course, risk assessment is very hard. It is unreasonable to expect a clinician or clinical team to come up with the right answer every time. Sometimes there is no right answer at all. We'll focus on the idea that risk assessment is logical and can often be done well.

EXPERIENCED CLINICIANS ARE FAIRLY GOOD ASSESSORS

One commonly hears or reads, sometimes from reputable sources, that psychiatrists and

Reprinted with permission. Journal of Psychiatric Practice, 9 *(1), 82–86. © 2003 Lippincott Williams & Wilkins.*

psychologists are poor predictors of risk, and that "studies show" they predict no more accurately than some laypersons. Such statements are at best incomplete and often either misconstrue the concept of risk assessment or are simply not true, depending on the situation and parameters described. The clinical and statistical literature strongly suggests that experienced clinicians are fairly good at assessing risk of suicide and violence.[1, 2]

GROUPS AT RISK VS. PREDICTING INDIVIDUAL BEHAVIOR

Clinical risk assessment does not imply predicting specific acts or outcomes—that's a different, much harder, task—but rather it involves trying to place the patient with an appropriate group that has greater or lesser *total* risk. The risk group may be broad (such as people with major depressive disorder) or narrow (such as people at imminent risk of suicide). Risk assessment (as contrasted with prediction) is not as good as having a crystal ball for individual patient behavior, but it is very useful.

> A man with severe delusional disorder had been hospitalized against his will for several years, based on two episodes of assault before admission, severe delusions of persecution, mood instability and irritability, and repeated written threats to kill a number of people. Although he had not committed a violent act in the hospital for many months, his psychiatric symptoms had not changed significantly during his stay. He refused treatment, but was not sufficiently ill to have his refusal overridden by an order to force medications (which might not have been effective in any event).
>
> At his commitment hearing, held before a jury, his attorney asked the forensic experts testifying for the State whether or not they could really "predict" that he would harm others as a result of his mental disorder, much less do so at some particular time in the near future. They answered that they had not attempted to predict any particular act of violence, but rather had come to the opinion that he was part of a group of patients who, as a group, could be expected to be associated with far more violence than the general population, and substantially more than most other patients.
>
> The question before the doctors—and the jury—was not whether or not the patient was clearly and convincingly* going to commit some specific harm as a result of his illness, but whether or not he was accurately viewed as part of *a group of people whose members were at markedly increased risk for such behavior.* In his case, factors such as his past behavior and threats, their seriousness, his diagnosis, his refusal of treatment, the absence of symptom change, the high probability that his disorder and symptoms would not change within the foreseeable future, and the likelihood that he would not participate in outpatient

treatment or monitoring all mitigated toward considering him sufficiently dangerous to remain in the hospital. The jury voted to continue his commitment.

Doctors place people in risk groups all the time, and we do a pretty good job so long as we choose the breadth of the risk category wisely. Internists do it based on things like cholesterol and blood pressure and routinely use those assessments to recommend or provide care and treatment. Some risks suggest simple, general action (e.g., notifying the patient of abnormal lipid levels and making recommendations). Others, such as acute chest pain with certain ECG changes, mandate rapid, often intrusive intervention. One doesn't expect a physician to predict a specific stroke or myocardial infarction, but a doctor who offers nothing to a patient with obvious risk is likely to be practicing outside the standard of care.

The parallels with psychiatric and psychological practice are obvious. If a prematurely-discharged suicidal patient kills himself on the way home from the hospital, the words "we can't predict suicide" ring hollow.

THE "NO-BETTER-THAN-A-COIN-TOSS" FALLACY

A number of older papers and reports assert that psychiatrists and psychologists are no better than laypeople, or even the toss of a coin, at predicting suicide or other violence.[3] The reports often say something like "Only 48% of the people predicted to be violent actually assaulted anyone in the year following discharge." Of course, such a finding does not really imply that the doctors did not do better than chance, but it makes a good "sound bite." Many people, including a few clinicians, take it to mean that we might as well flip coins as we deal with danger or suicide and patients.

Here's the fallacy: Let's say one assesses 1,000 random patients for discharge. Most, by far, will not be significantly violent during a given period (say, 1 year). If each is viewed separately, it is indeed futile to try to "predict dangerousness" for every person in the group. *But narrowing the field would be very useful.*

Among other things, we can:
- fairly reliably classify patients by general diagnosis and severity of illness (e.g., presence of psychosis, delusions of persecution, severe depression, or unstable mood)
- associate some of those disorders with traits of concern, such as instability, treatment refractoriness, unpredictability, or particular behaviors
- search their past histories for evidence of significant treatment or violence
- consider our—and/or the treatment team's—personal experience with each patient
- assess patients' responsiveness to treatment
- assess psychological factors that are sometimes associated with self-harm, aggression, impulsiveness, assaultiveness, and the like
- evaluate patients' post-discharge living conditions and circumstances, including presence and availability of family or other caregivers

- estimate many patients' responses to, or behaviors in, important post-discharge situations (such as intoxication or marital disputes)
- estimate whether or not patients are likely to participate in follow-up care, and whether or not intensive monitoring or care (such as by an ACT team) is available
- consider (but not overuse) factors such as age and gender.

When experienced clinicians carry out these assessments and considerations, with adequate information, it becomes fairly straightforward to match the patient with an appropriate risk group. The narrower the group, the more useful it is for making decisions about individual patients.

Note that we have not predicted suicide or violence, but we have done something almost as useful: *We have highlighted a group that deserves important attention.* When clinicians can do that, but neglect to do so without good reason, they are likely to be practicing outside the standard of care.

But what about that pesky "coin toss"? Only half the patients named actually went on to commit mayhem or suicide.

Look at it this way: It is good practice indeed when one can move at-risk patients from a large, heterogenous group (for which the chance of mayhem or suicide is, say, 5%, and where the risks are obscured by the "noise" of extraneous information and larger numbers) to a much smaller but more worrisome group in which the chance of such problems is, say, 48%. Once that is done, treatment and protective options become much clearer than before.

There is one more statistical point related to the fallacy. As Norko and Baranoski pointed out in a recent paper,[4] *once someone has been placed in a high-risk group, his or her risk usually decreases.* Suicide and other tragedies are often prevented by the closer monitoring, more intensive treatment, and greater attention such patients and groups receive. Many patients who *appear* to have been "false positives" would have experienced bad outcomes had they not been recognized.

"RISK FACTOR" CHECKLISTS AND ACTUARIAL INSTRUMENTS

I am concerned about the overuse, and sometimes inappropriate use, of checklists and actuarial instruments to try to predict occurrences like suicide, violence, or criminal recidivism. One should avoid relying completely on them and understand their shortcomings.

Checklists concern me because their positive attributes (such as making sure that staff think about risk and certain items correlated with it) sometimes fail to overcome their negative ones. To the extent that they are used as reminders or memory joggers for experienced evaluators, they're fine. It may also be good for less experienced screeners to keep checklists handy for reporting information to their supervisors.† It is usually foolish, however, to make a simple checklist one's sole basis for important decisions about safety and therapeutics. Using such checklists as a hospital's or clinic's primary means of documenting suicide or other risk assessment may soothe some hospital attorneys, but these lists are not sufficient in and of themselves.

Why the rant about checklists? Isn't it true that they are designed to be part of a balanced system of care and protection?

Sure, just as it's true that Cap'n Crunch cereal can be part of a balanced breakfast. But if that's all we feed the kids (and it's tempting for busy moms), we're asking for trouble.

Here are several potential shortcomings.

- *Accepting a false sense of security.* Too many care staff and treatment teams (and a few psychiatrists) believe a low checklist score means they don't have to worry. The checklist is not a substitute for clinical thought, review, interaction, and corroboration.
- *Using undertrained monitoring staff.* Facilities and treatment teams may assume that the checklist can be administered by relatively unsophisticated employees, and that the written items decrease or eliminate the need for assessments by more senior staff (a poor way to cut staffing budgets).
- *Confusing clarity with validity.* Checklists usually have well-defined parameters that appear to lead to unambivalent results, often in just a few typed lines on a page. Real symptoms, signs, feelings, and impulses aren't so easy to understand.
- *Relying on other people's work* instead of following up with one's own. Busy doctors and other decision-making clinicians sometimes rely solely on what they hear in treatment team meetings or read on brief checklists. Such communications are an important part of overall care and extend the doctor's eyes and ears, but we must be careful about the validity and completeness of the information we use to make important decisions.
- *Relying on patients' statements.* This is a big one. I am continually amazed at the number of staff and clinicians whose safety decisions rely heavily on patients' own statements that they're not suicidal (or homicidal). Suicidal patients do not always tell nurses or clinicians the truth about their future plans. There are usually many other sources of information available for clinical decision making; use them.
- *Asking the patient a few short questions* rather than communicating and corroborating with other history and observations. Risk assessment is not a 3-minute exercise.
- *Using the list once a day and assuming that's enough.* I recently reviewed a case in which a suicidality checklist was completed early each morning. The patient said he was not planning to kill himself, although the chart indicated that his mood and impulsivity fluctuated substantially from day to day, and sometimes from hour to hour. A few hours later, group leaders documented signs of suicide risk. Nevertheless, the early-morning checklist result was used more than 12 hours later as the basis for allowing him to work unaccompanied in a kitchen, where he drank a large quality of cleaning solution and almost died.

"Actuarial" instruments use historical data alone to place patients or inmates into groups of greater, or lesser, concern. They don't require a patient interview and usually depend largely on "static" characteristics (see below) of the person being assessed. Many have been validated on large groups; others have not. It is important to know whether or not a particular one (e.g., the VRAG, Static-99 or RRASOR) has been adequately validated on patients or inmates similar to the person being evaluated. Although such assessments are popular because of their simplicity, low cost, and concrete results, overreliance on them is common and recent studies have questioned their accuracy, particularly in correctional settings.[5]

Actuarial instruments convey a superficial impression of science and objectivity which is welcome as we wrestle with clinical nuance and emotion (and particularly as clinicians and the institutions in which they work strive to reduce their liability). Factor weighting and formulas make the results seem legitimate when they may or may not be. Brevity and simplicity make some instruments so cheap and easy to use that they are routinely included in evaluations whether or not their results are valid. Once such a result becomes part of a patient's or inmate's official record, it is likely to influence future evaluators for a long time.

Static and Dynamic Factors. Actuarial instruments, and some checklists, rely heavily on assumptions about certain items in the patient's history that do not change (i.e., are "static"), that those items are relevant to the behavior being predicted or risk being assessed, and that current or future factors (such as treatment or supervision) will not affect risk. One's gender and prior job history, for example, are immutable. Other items that are fairly indelible, yet have great effect on the results of many actuarial assessments, include such things as history of past violence or arrests and socioeconomic status. Although these are often statistically associated with accurate group predictions of assault or recidivism, static factors alone (as expressed in the instruments now available) should not be one's primary basis for individual prediction.

> A 35-year-old man had a history of sudden angry outbursts which had led to several serious assaults, arrests, and involuntary hospitalizations. Diagnosed with schizophrenia and schizoaffective disorder at various times over the years, he was noted to have a normal gross neurological exam and electroencephalogram (EEG).
>
> He was eventually evaluated by a behavioral neurologist who performed a more specific kind of electroencephalography, found a subtle focal abnormality, and diagnosed an ictal instability which was successfully treated with a new medication. His EEG reverted to normal and he was discharged. He has had no more violent episodes during several years of follow-up.

Had the patient in the above vignette been assessed using solely static information, he would have found it very difficult to secure discharge. His violent history, repeated episodes, and the unpredictability of his episodes, coupled with his past diagnosis and gender, placed him in a very high violence risk category on any of a number of actuarial instruments, when in fact his risk was markedly decreased by dynamic factors such as a fresh clinical assessment, new findings, and a more appropriate treatment.

FORESEEABILITY AND PREDICTABILITY

Negligence lawsuits, such as those alleging malpractice, often hinge on whether or not some damage (such as a suicide) was foreseeable. Colleagues often ask how anyone could be expected to predict a specific event as complicated as suicide, especially when it occurs days or weeks after the clinician saw the patient.

That's not how the law defines "foreseeable" in most malpractice contexts. It doesn't refer to predicting a specific act at a specific time, but rather to whether or not the doctor reasonably recognized, and adequately dealt with, a particular level of danger.

Moreover, we must deal with patients' unpredictability. Unpredictability can be very dangerous. Only a fool would leave a small child alone with dangerous things, even if the chance of serious injury or death were relatively small. When seriously ill patients are unpredictable, clinicians and hospitals should be very cautious. When the environment into which they are placed is dangerous or unpredictable as well, that caution should increase.

THE LAST WORD

Psychiatrists and other clinicians perform risk assessments in many clinical settings. The point is to use the right terms and goals (e.g., risk assessment rather than specific prediction) and to do it well.

NOTES

* "Clear and convincing" evidence is the burden of proof required of the State in almost all civil commitment proceedings.

† Note the important difference between first-line screeners, who take information and have a threshold for reporting it to others, and triage clinicians, who make rapid decisions about condition and referral for emergency care (and thus should be among the most experienced clinicians available).

REFERENCES

1. Haim R, Rabinowitz J, Lereya J, et al. Predictions made by psychiatrists and psychiatric nurses of violence by patients. *Psychiatr Serv* 2002;53:622–4.
2. Hoptman MJ, Yates KF, Patalinjug MB, et al. Clinical prediction of assaultive behavior among male psychiatric patients at a maximum-security forensic facility. *Psychiatr Serv* 1999;50:1461–6.
3. Faust D, Ziskin J. The expert witness in psychology and psychiatry. *Science* 1988;241:31–5.
4. Norko M, Baranoski M. Understanding risk assessment. Course, Annual Meeting of the American Academy of Psychiatry and the Law, Newport Beach, CA, October, 2002.
5. Barbaree HE, Seto MC, Langton CM, et al. Evaluating the predictive accuracy of six risk assessment instruments for adult sex offenders. *Crim Justice Behav* 2001;28:490–521

10

Personality Disorder: The Patients Psychiatrists Dislike

GLYN LEWIS AND LOUIS APPLEBY

ABSTRACT: *A sample of psychiatrists was asked to read a case vignette and indicate likely management and attitudes to the patient on a number of semantic-differential scales. Patients given a previous diagnosis of personality disorder (PD) were seen as more difficult and less deserving of care compared with control subjects who were not. The PD cases were regarded as manipulative, attention-seeking, annoying, and in control of their suicidal urges and debts. PD therefore appears to be an enduring pejorative judgement rather than a clinical diagnosis. It is proposed that the concept be abandoned.*

Personality disorder is an established clinical diagnosis, surviving in both ICD-9 (World Health Organization, 1978) and DSM-III (American Psychiatric Association, 1980). In 1974, Shepherd & Sartorius concluded: "Despite diagnostic imprecision and terminological confusion it is indisputable that some working concept of psychopathic personality is essential for the practice of clinical psychiatry."

A number of criticisms have been made of the concept of personality disorder (PD). Firstly, it is an unreliable diagnosis, in part due to rather vague definitions (e.g. Kreitman *et al*, 1961; Walton & Presly, 1973; Lewis, 1974), and remains so, despite attempts at greater precision, for instance in DSM-III (American Psychiatric Association, 1980; Mellsop *et al*, 1982). Secondly, the concept of personality that underlies this clinical

Reprinted with permission. British Journal of Psychiatry, 153, 44–49. © 1988 Royal College of Psychiatrists.

term has been increasingly abandoned by most social psychologists (e.g. Mischel, 1968), who cite evidence showing that people do not behave similarly in different situations.

But there is a more serious criticism in the literature, that personality disorder is a derogatory label that may result in therapeutic neglect (Gunn & Robertson, 1976). Kendell (1975*a*), in his influential monograph on diagnosis, says "it is true that several of our diagnostic terms, like hysteric and psychopath, have acquired pejorative connotations even among psychiatrists." Although this argument is usually applied to antisocial PD, it is relevant to many of the other categories. For instance, Parry (1978) writes of alcoholics with personality disorder "they are of course, totally unreliable and their protestations are rapidly shown to be shallow insincerities." Hysterical PD in some accounts is a parody of supposed feminine characteristics (Chodoff & Lyons, 1958). Inadequate personality disorder, the term itself a critical judgement, has been described as an "addiction to help," and further that "young inadequate women may become prolific producers of children with whom they seek unsuccessfully the kind of intimacy they cannot achieve elsewhere" (Howard, 1985). Although ICD-9 (World Health Organization, 1978) has changed the name to asthenic, the concept of inadequate PD remains unchanged: "a weak inadequate response to the demands of daily life" (World Health Organization, 1978).

Among all this controversy, there is, surprisingly, one area of relative agreement; that personality disorder is not a mental illness (Lewis, 1974). Although Henderson (1939) and Cleckley (1976) regard PD as an illness, there has recently been an increasing consensus distinguishing PD from illness. Even Walton (1978), who has criticised PD, wrote "The Personality Disorders . . . take the form of recurrent disturbance in relationships with other people and is not a form of illness."

Many authorities have found mental illness difficult to define (Lewis, 1953; Wootton, 1959; Kendell, 1975*b*; Farrell, 1979). However, one aspect of the concept is that the mentally ill are seen as less responsible and less in control of their actions. Weiner (1980) has argued that the inference that someone is in "control" is an important determinant in whether that person is given help. His subjects were more likely to help, and were more sympathetic to, someone who appeared ill (uncontrollable) than someone who appeared drunk (controllable). Thus, distinguishing PD patients from those with mental illness could lead to lack of sympathy and blame because of judgements that their actions are under control.

This study was both an empirical test of whether PD is a pejorative term, and an examination of the hypothesis that patients labelled as PD are thought to be more in control of their actions. A sample of psychiatrists was given different short case vignettes and then asked to complete a questionnaire assessing their attitudes towards the case. Using vignettes in this way allowed us to control for possible confounding variables, and forced the psychiatrists to use their stereotypes of PD to complete the questionnaire.

METHOD

Sample

Psychiatrists (240), who lived in England, Wales, or Scotland, were randomly selected from the membership list of the Royal College of Psychiatrists (approximately 12% of total; Department of Health and Social Security, 1987). Those who were described as registrars, who were retired, or were listed as being child psychiatrists, were excluded from the sample (but several child psychiatrists were included in the sample because they were not listed as such). Subjects were randomly allocated one of the six brief case histories, which they were asked to read before completing and returning an accompanying questionnaire. They were told that we were interested in how experience influenced the practice of psychiatrists, and were asked to provide details about previous qualifications and experience in psychiatry and in other specialties. The real purpose of the study was explained only to those receiving case 4 (see below).

Case Histories

The six case histories differed from each other in only one or two particulars. Each history contained the information which a general practitioner's (GP's) letter might provide about a depressed patient. The amount of information was deliberately restricted, to encourage subjects to draw inferences based on pre-existing attitudes.

The first case history was as follows:

> A 34-year-old man is seen in out-patients. He complains of feeling depressed, and says he has been crying on his own at home. He is worried about whether he is having a nervous breakdown, and is requesting admission. He has thought of killing himself by taking an overdose of some tablets he has at home. He has taken one previous overdose, 2 years ago, and at that time he saw a psychiatrist who gave him a diagnosis of personality disorder. He has recently gone into debt and is concerned about how he will repay the money. He is finding it difficult to sleep and his GP has given him some nitrazepam. He thinks these have helped a little and is reluctant to give them up.

The other cases were modified from the first as follows:

Case 2
No previous diagnosis was mentioned.

Case 3
Previous diagnosis was given as depression.

Case 4

Information as for case 1 was given, but the subjects were told that we were interested in the labelling effect of certain psychiatric diagnoses and were asked not to let themselves be influenced by previous labels.

Case 5

Information as for case 2 was given, except that the patient was female.

Case 6

Information as for case 2 was given, except that the word "man" in the opening sentence was changed to "solicitor."

Questionnaire

The questionnaire consisted of 22 semantic differentials, with a 6-point scale, designed to elicit one aspect of the assessment or management of the case. Some of the items placed more emphasis on practical management issues (e.g. antidepressant prescription, psychotherapy referral), but most asked directly about attitudes to the patient (e.g. likely to annoy, attention-seeking, etc.). A full list is given in Table 1. The semantic differentials were scored so that a higher score represented responses that were more rejecting or that indicated lack of active treatment. For instance, a response at the end of the scale "overdose would be an attention-seeking act" scored 6 and a response at the end "overdose would be a genuine suicidal act" was scored 1. Each subject was asked to complete the questionnaire and then choose a diagnosis from a list of depression, anxiety, adjustment reaction, drug dependence, personality disorder, and neurasthenia.

RESULTS

Characteristics of the Sample

Of the sample, 72% (173 of 240) returned completed questionnaires and a further 9% (22) refused to participate, usually complaining that there was insufficient clinical information on which to base judgements. Overall it was a very experienced sample, with a mean of 16.5 years psychiatric practice.

Previous diagnosis of personality disorder

The principal experimental concern was to see whether the previous diagnosis of personality disorder affected the psychiatrists' attitudes. Preliminary analysis illustrated that all statistically significant differences between the cases depended on the presence or absence of the PD diagnosis, so cases 1 and 4 were combined as group PD ($n = 58$) and the remainder, receiving cases 2, 3, 5, and 6 were combined as group NoPD ($n = 115$).

The means of group PD were higher (i.e. more critical) than those of NoPD on all but 1 of the 22 items as shown in the first two columns of Table 1. Individual one-way analyses of variance showed a significant difference between groups PD and NoPD on 16 of the 22 semantic differentials. The *F* ratios of these one-way analyses are in column 3 of Table 1.

These results confirm the hypothesis: when psychiatrists were given a previous diagnosis of personality disorder, their attitudes to the patient were less favourable. This occurred irrespective of whether they were informed of our interest in unfavourable attitudes towards PD (case 4). Furthermore, PD had a much more powerful effect on these attitudes than did sex and class.

TABLE 1

Means and Results of Analysis of Variance

STATEMENT ABOUT PATIENT	GROUP/MEANS		ONE-WAY ANOVA (F RATIOS)	TWO-WAY ANOVA
	PD	NoPD	GROUP	DIAGNOSIS
Manipulating admission	3.41	2.75	14.2***	4.6***
Unlikely to arouse sympathy	3.50	2.61	15.0***	2.8*
Taking an overdose would be attention-seeking	3.67	3.18	7.1**	6.4***
Should be discharged from out-patient follow-up	2.05	1.65	7.0**	1.5
Would not like to have in one's clinic	2.96	2.45	7.2**	2.0
Poses difficult management problem	3.89	2.95	19.2***	2.0
Likely to annoy	3.14	2.59	7.0**	2.9*
Unlikely to improve	2.54	2.00	13.7***	3.6**
Cause of debts under patient's control	4.36	4.04	3.9*	1.4
Not mentally ill	3.67	2.96	9.8**	9.4***
Case does not merit NHS time	3.00	2.67	5.3*	2.7*
Unlikely to complete treatment	3.76	2.61	42.9***	3.8**
Unlikely to comply with advice/treatment	3.45	2.69	21.6***	3.8**
Suicidal urges under patient's control	3.48	3.18	2.7	3.1*
Likely to become dependent on one	4.09	3.94	0.2	1.0
Condition not severe	3.60	3.12	10.3**	4.5***
Admission not indicated	4.03	3.41	3.6	2.2
Not a suicide risk	3.44	3.07	4.3*	4.1**
Does not require sickness certificate	3.00	2.44	3.8	3.6**
Dependent on benzodiazepines	3.26	3.14	0.9	1.9
Psychotherapy referral not indicated	3.54	3.55	0.0	1.5
Antidepressants not indicated	3.77	3.12	6.6*	5.8***

*P<0.05; **P<0.01; ***P<0.001.

ANOVA = analysis of variance; PD = personality disorder; NoPD = no personality disorder.

Higher values indicate greater agreement with Statement; there was a 6-point scale between the two statements of the semantic differential.

Diagnosis Made by Respondents: Its Relationship to Attitudes

At the end of the semantic differential, the psychiatrists were asked to make a provisional diagnosis. Sixty-three per cent made a diagnosis of depression. The respondents in Group PD were more likely than those in Group NoPD to make the diagnosis of adjustment reaction ($\chi^2 = 14.4$; d.f. = 3; $P < 0.001$; Table 2). Because of this relationcship, two-way analyses of variance were performed, entering the group effect first. This allowed us to examine the effects of diagnosis independent of the group effect. The results are shown in the fourth column of Table 1.

TABLE 2

The Relationship Between the Diagnosis Made by the Psychiatrists and Their Attitudes to the Case

	GROUP PD		GROUP NoPD	
	NUMBER OF CASES	MEAN OF VARIABLES (S.E.M.)	NUMBER OF CASES	MEAN OF VARIABLES (S.E.M.)
Depression	25	3.03 (0.11)	64	2.59 (0.07)
Personality disorder	7	3.48 (0.18)	4	3.30 (0.37)
Anxiety state	3	3.88 (0.30)	8	3.27 (0.09)
Adjustment reaction	16	3.76 (0.36)	9	3.09 (0.18)
Neurasthenia	2	3.07 (0.36)	2	3.61 (0.97)
Drug dependence	0	—	1	3.0

The significant semantic differential items have been summed for each subject and the means for each diagnostic group are given here. Higher values indicate more critical attitudes (see Table 1).

The mean values (Table 2) show that the diagnosis of depression was associated with the least-critical attitudes. Personality disorder, adjustment reaction, and anxiety had higher scores than depression, but the small sample size makes it impossible to say whether there were any real differences between these diagnoses. Table 2 gives an overall picture of the results, obtained by calculating the means of the sum of the significant variables in each diagnostic category.

Although the diagnosis of depression was associated with more favourable attitudes overall, a previous diagnosis of PD (Group PD) still resulted in more critical attitudes, even when the psychiatrists' own diagnosis was depression (Table 2). This result was confirmed by the analysis of variance, for there was only one semantic differential that showed a significant group by diagnosis interaction, the item "manipulating admission" ($F = 2.89$; $P < 0.05$) and even here, the mean of subjects who diagnosed depression in group PD (mean = 3.00) was still higher than those in group NoPD (mean = 2.55; $t = 2.74$; $P < 0.01$). The vast majority of the attitudes showed no such interaction and it is clear that the group effect of previous diagnosis was independent of the effect of the "current" diagnosis made by the psychiatrists. It indicates that PD still had an effect on attitudes even though it was not the psychiatrists' own diagnosis.

The diagnosis of adjustment reaction was commoner in the group that had been given a previous diagnosis of PD, and adjustment reaction was associated with more critical attitudes. This suggests that adjustment reaction could be a diagnosis applied to depressive symptoms in those whose fundamental disturbance is seen as of the personality rather than due to illness.

The more-experienced psychiatrists had less-critical attitudes on a number of items, e.g. "annoying," "not mentally ill," "condition not severe." Such cross-sectional data though, could reflect changes in medical education rather than experience.

Perception of Control and Personality Disorder

The correlations between individual items provide some confirmation of the suggested link between mental illness and control (Table 3). "Not mentally ill" was correlated with items implying the patient had control over his or her behaviour (items 2–5 in Table 3). Weiner's (1980) model also predicts that perceived control should be associated with lack of sympathy (items 8 and 9) and so make it less likely that the psychiatrist would consider helping (items 6 and 7). Of the correlation coefficients in Table 3, 31 of 36 are significant at the 5% level.

TABLE 3
Correlations Between Selected Items

ITEM	CORRELATION (r) [1]							
	2	3	4	5	6	7	8	9
1. Not mentally ill	0.40	0.35	0.19	0.40	0.23	0.27	0.25	0.28
2. Taking an overdose would be attention seeking		0.51	0.28	0.39	0.31	0.31	0.41	0.30
3. Manipulating admission			0.27	0.37	0.36	0.36	0.23	0.10
4. Cause of debts under patient's control				0.31	0.04	0.14	0.23	0.21
5. Suicidal urges under patient's control					0.12	0.29	0.17	0.19
6. Should be discharged from out-patient follow up						0.29	0.25	0.06
7. Case does not merit NHS time							0.25	0.24
8. Unlikely to arouse sympathy								0.37

DISCUSSION

This study supports the view that psychiatrists form pejorative, judgemental, and rejecting attitudes towards those who have been given a diagnosis of personality disorder. Patients previously labelled as personality disordered were seen as manipulative, difficult to manage, unlikely to arouse sympathy, annoying, and not deserving NHS resources. Psychiatrists viewed them as uncompliant, not accepting advice, and having a poor prognosis. They were more likely to be discharged from follow-up examination, and suicide attempts were seen as attention-seeking rather than "genuine." Requests for admission were thought to be manipulative, and the patients were judged less mentally ill, and their problems less severe.

At the end of the questionnaire, the subjects were asked to make their own diagnosis; analysis of the results indicated that these attitudes to PD were apparent regardless of the psychiatrists' own diagnosis. One cannot argue therefore, that the features shown above are the real features of personality disorder.

The results show that the past diagnosis of PD was more important in determining these attitudes than sex, class, and giving a previous diagnosis of depression. Informing the respondents of our main experimental concerns did not affect attitudes.

Methodological Issues

Case vignettes have been used in previous studies of decision-making by psychiatrists (Mayou, 1977) and physicians (O'Toole et al, 1983). This method allows a fully controlled experimental study, and usually produces results consistent with behavioural observations (e.g. Weiner, 1980). Although a case vignette does not provide as much information as a clinical interview, it cannot create attitudes that do not already exist.

Unambiguous semantic differentials are an accepted method of measuring attitudes. The validity of the scales is supported by the results, for instance, that psychotherapists were more likely to refer for psychotherapy, and biological psychiatrists were more likely to prescribe antidepressants. Attitudes are an important determinant of behaviour (e.g. Nisbett & Ross, 1980) and an important area of study in their own right, particularly in psychiatry, where rejecting and pejorative attitudes would be noted by patients because of non-verbal cues, although the psychiatrists' overt behaviour might be unchanged.

Categories of Personality

The case vignette used here did not specify a category of PD nor provide any information that might support any particular PD diagnosis. This is consistent with the practice of many psychiatrists, who use the term without subdividing PD into categories.

The present study therefore extends Gunn & Robertson's (1976) assertion on the label "psychopath" to the overall term of personality disorder that "what is conveyed . . . is that the patient is difficult and probably unpleasant"; although it does not exclude the possibility that some types of personality disorder are less damning than others.

Personality Disorder and Mental Illness

How has a term, which appears at first sight to bring together a group of deviant types of behaviour, come to be a derogatory label? We argue here, with supportive evidence from the study, that the answer lies in the assumption that PD is not a mental illness, and the consequent attributions of control.

The PD patients were judged less mentally ill, and were seen as being in control of their debts and suicidal urges. They were thought to be manipulating and attention-seeking, both expressions implying control of behaviour. Perceived control and absence of "illness" were also significantly correlated with lack of help-giving and sympathy, consistent with Weiner's (1980) model.

Sociologists (e.g. Scheff, 1963) usually think of mental illness as a stigmatising label, but for the psychiatrists in this study it was associated with favourable attitudes. This does not imply that there is no stigma to mental illness; rather that "abnormal" behaviour may be relatively excused if attributed to mental illness. For a psychiatrist, someone who is mentally ill requires professional help, including the sympathy and acceptance that doctors are expected to provide.

Although mental illness is a concept without rigid boundaries (Farrell, 1979), doctors appear to distinguish between those that are ill and those that are not. Furthermore, the unreliability of the PD diagnosis suggests that the rules employed are arbitrary. This view would be ethically acceptable, although scientifically dubious, if its only consequence were a caring, sympathetic attitude to those whose behaviour fell within the illness boundary. However, this study demonstrates that patients receiving a non-illness, PD diagnosis may be rejected and viewed with therapeutic pessimism even when they have psychiatric symptoms. Those labelled as personality disordered appear to be denied the benefits of being regarded as ill, but also denied the privilege of being regarded as "normal."

In clinical practice, judgements are frequently made on whether a patient is in control of his or her actions, and so responsible for them. For example, if a patient considered ill breaks a window, his action may automatically be attributed to his illness; he is therefore not responsible and is not blamed. For the patient thought to have a PD, there may be an equivalent automatic assumption: he is responsible and deserves blame for his actions.

Each case vignette described the same symptoms and so the effect of the PD label on attitudes was seen to override the patient's complaints. It has been suggested that those diagnosed as personality disordered are less likely to receive treatment for depression despite having depressive symptoms (Slavney & McHugh, 1974; Thompson & Goldberg, 1987). Here, prescription of antidepressants and outpatient follow-up examination was less likely in group PD. The PD label appears to reduce the importance attributed to symptoms, perhaps by providing alternative explanations: for instance, that the patient is attention-seeking or manipulative, that their symptoms are less genuine.

CONCLUSION

This study adds to the criticism of the personality-disorder diagnosis. We have suggested that because it is seen as distinct from mental illness, it implies control and responsibility, and encourages rejection. Most seriously, it leads to pejorative attitudes.

We suggest that the clinical diagnosis of personality disorder has no justification and should be abandoned. No physicist would claim that an electron was any more worthwhile than a positron, but psychiatrists appear to prefer one diagnosis to another. A scientific classification loses credibility if it contains value judgements or moral statements. A classification based on symptoms should be more reliable, and encourage a sympathetic approach to treatment.

REFERENCES

American Psychiatric Association (1980) *Diagnostic and Statistical Manual of Mental Disorders* (3rd edn) (DSM-III). Washington DC: APA.

Chodoff, P. & Lyons, H. (1958) Hysteria, the hysterical personality and hysterical conversion. *American Journal of Psychiatry,* 114, 734–740.

Cleckley, H. (1976) *The Mask of Sanity* (5th edn). St Louis: C. V. Mosby.

Department of Health and Social Security (1987) Medical and dental staffing prospects in the NHS in England and Wales in 1986. *Health Trends,* 19, 1–7.

Farrell, B. A. (1979) Mental illness: a conceptual analysis. *Psychological Medicine,* 9, 21–35.

Gunn, J. & Robertson, G. (1976) Psychopathic personality: a conceptual problem. *Psychological Medicine,* 6, 631–634.

Henderson, D. K. (1939) *Psychopathic States.* New York: W. W. Norton.

Howard, C. (1985) The "inadequate personality." In *Handbook of Psychiatry, vol. 4. The Neuroses and Personality Disorders* (eds G. F. M. Russell & L. A. Hersov). Cambridge: Cambridge University Press.

Kendell, R. E. (1975a) *The Role of Diagnosis in Psychiatry.* Oxford: Blackwell Scientific Publications.

—— (1975b) The concept of disease and its implications for psychiatry. *British Journal of Psychiatry,* 127, 305–315.

Kreitman, N., Sainsbury, P., Morrissey, J., Towers, J. & Scrivener, J. (1961) The reliability of psychiatric diagnosis. *Journal of Mental Science,* 107, 887–908.

Lewis, A. (1953) Health as a social concept. *British Journal of Sociology,* 4, 109–124.

—— (1974) Psychopathic personality: a most elusive category. *Psychological Medicine,* 4, 133–140.

Mayou, R. (1977) Psychiatric decision making. *British Journal of Psychiatry,* 130, 374–376.

Mellsop, G., Varghese, F., Joshua, S. & Hicks, A. (1982) The reliability of axis II of DSM-III. *American Journal of Psychiatry,* 139, 1360–1361.

Mischel, W. (1968) *Personality and Assessment.* New York: Wiley.

Nisbett, R. & Ross, L. (1980) *Human Inference: Strategies and Shortcomings of Social Judgement.* Englewood Cliffs, NJ: Prentice Hall.

O'Toole, R., Turbett, P. & Nalepka, C. (1983) Theories, professional knowledge and diagnosis of child abuse. In *The Dark Side of Families: Current Family Violence Research.* (eds D. Finkelhor, R. J. Gellis, G. T. Hottaling & M. A. Straus). Beverly Hills: Sage.

Parry, R. A. (1978) Alcoholism. In *Companion to Psychiatric Studies* (2nd edn) (eds A. Forrest, J. Afleck & A. Zealley). Edinburgh: Churchill Livingstone.

Scheff, T. J. (1963) The role of the mentally ill and the dynamics of mental disorder. *Sociometry,* 26, 436–453.

Shepherd, M. & Sartorius, N. (1974) Personality disorder and the "International Classification of Diseases." *Psychological Medicine,* 4, 141–146.

Slavney, P. R. & McHugh, P. R. (1974) The hysterical personality: a controlled study. *Archives of General Psychiatry,* 30, 325–329.

Thompson, D. J. & Goldberg, D. (1987) Hysterical personality disorder: the process of diagnosis in clinical and experimental settings. *British Journal of Psychiatry*, 150, 241–245.

Walton, H. J. (1978) The psychoneuroses. In *Companion to Psychiatric Studies* (2nd edn) (eds A. Forrest, J. Affleck & A. Zealley). Edinburgh: Churchill Livingstone.

——& Presly, A. S. (1973) Use of a category system in the diagnosis of abnormal personality. *British Journal of Psychiatry*, 122, 259–268.

Weiner, B. (1980) A cognitive (attribution)–emotion–action model of motivated behaviour: an analysis of judgements of help giving. *Journal of Personality and Social Psychology*, 39, 186–200.

Wootton, B. (1959) *Social Science and Social Pathology*. London: George Allen.

World Health Organization (1978) *Mental Disorders: Glossary & Guide to their Classification in Accordance with the Ninth Revision of the International Classification of Diseases* (ICD-9). Geneva: World Health Organization.

11

Utility of Decision Support Tools for Assessing Acute Risk of Violence

DALE E. McNIEL, AMANDA L. GREGORY, JUDY N. LAM,
RENÉE L. BINDER AND GLENN R. SULLIVAN

ABSTRACT: *The authors evaluated the utility of 3 decision support tools for assessing acute risk of violence in patients undergoing behavioral emergencies that warranted hospitalization. Information available at the time of admission to a short-term psychiatric unit was coded from the medical charts of 100 patients using the Historical, Clinical, Risk Management–20 (HCR-20), the Hare Psychopathy Checklist–Screening Version (PCL-SV), and the McNiel–Binder Violence Screening Checklist (VSC). Nurses rated violence that later occurred during hospitalization with the Overt Aggression Scale. Scores on all 3 instruments were associated with the likelihood of violence. The strongest predictive relationships were obtained for indices of clinical risk factors rather than historical risk factors. The results suggest that decision support tools, particularly those that emphasize clinical risk factors, have the potential to improve decision making about violence risk in the context of behavioral emergencies.*

Clinicians frequently are required to make decisions about their patients' risk of violence, especially when presented with behavioral emergencies that may require psychiatric hospitalization. In view of the well-known limitations of unaided clinical

Reprinted with permission. The official citation that should be used in referencing this material is McNiel, D.E., Gregory, A.L., Lam, J.N. Binder, R.L. & Sullivan, G.R. (2003). Utility of decision support tools for assessing acute risk of violence. Journal of Consulting and Clinical Psychology, 71 (5), 945–953. © 2003 by the American Psychological Association Inc.

judgment in assessing violence risk (cf. McNiel, Lam, & Binder, 2000), considerable research attention has been focused recently on development of tools to improve decision making about patients' potential for violence (McNiel et al., 2002; Swets, Dawes, & Monahan, 2000). Despite significant advances in this area, obstacles remain in translating research on violence risk assessment into improvements in clinical practice. For example, research has supported several instruments as adding useful information to the risk assessment process, but they have been validated against the occurrence of violence that occurs over the long term, from several months to multiple years after the assessment. Examples include the MacArthur Iterative Classification Tree approach (Monahan et al., 2001; Steadman et al., 2000), the Historical, Clinical, Risk Management–20 (HCR-20; Webster, Douglas, Eaves, & Hart, 1997), the Violence Risk Appraisal Guide (Harris, Rice, & Quinsey, 1993; Quinsey, Harris, Rice, & Cormier, 1998), the Spousal Assault Risk Assessment Guide (Kropp, Hart, Webster, & Eaves, 1999), and the Hare Psychopathy Checklist—Screening Version (PCL-SV; Hart, Cox, & Hare, 1995). The utility of such instruments for evaluation of patients' short-term, acute risk of violence, an important aspect of clinical practice in emergency and inpatient psychiatric settings, is unknown. This study evaluates the usefulness of three structured risk assessment tools for measuring acute risk of violence, that is, within the next few days to weeks after the evaluation.

Clinicians who provide service to acutely mentally ill patients are frequently required to manage violent behavior. For example, Lehmann, McCormick, and Kizer (1999) surveyed 166 Veterans Health Administration facilities and found that of 32,771 incidents involving battery or physical assaults, 43% occurred in psychiatric units and 13% in admission or triage areas. In a survey of the directors of 20 psychiatric emergency rooms from across the United States, Binder and McNiel (1999) found that all of the directors indicated that managing violence was a routine component of their work. Moreover, violence represents a common cause of injury to staff in emergency and inpatient settings (Erdos & Hughes, 2001; Lam, McNiel, & Binder, 2000). At the time of hospital admission, staff must make rapid assessments of patients' potential for violence to make important decisions concerning issues such as whether to initiate civil commitment, what level of security is needed during hospitalization, and whether to act on a duty to protect third parties from any threatened violent behavior. Trends in utilization review and restrictions in third-party payment for hospitalization have resulted in reductions in lengths of psychiatric inpatient stay to an average of approximately 8 days in the United States (HCIA, 1999). Consequently, to be useful in this context, risk assessment tools must yield information about short-term potential for violence.

To address the limitations of unaided clinical judgment, researchers have developed a number of instruments to improve decision-making about violence risk or studied them for their usefulness for this purpose, with civil (as opposed to criminal) patients. McNiel and Binder (1994a) used an *actuarial* approach, in which items on the assessment instrument are weighted according to a fixed and explicit algorithm (cf. Grove & Meehl, 1996), in developing a five-item Violence Screening Checklist (VSC) based on a previous study of statistical prediction of violence among civilly committed patients (McNiel,

Binder, & Greenfield, 1988). The VSC received support as an indicator of violence risk in a new sample of hospitalized patients (McNiel & Binder, 1994a). Another approach is *structured professional judgment*, in which the instrument is intended to guide a clinician's inquiry to include a preestablished list of risk factors selected from the existing research and professional literature. Webster et al. (1997) developed the HCR-20, which consists of 20 historical, clinical, and risk management variables. Douglas, Ogloff, Nicholls, and Grant (1999) found that scores on the HCR-20 predicted violence within 2 years after discharge from civil psychiatric hospitals. Similarly, the PCL-SV, which consists of 12 items measuring antisocial behaviors and traits comprising the construct of psychopathy (Hart et al., 1995), has been found to predict violence during the first year after discharge from civil psychiatric hospitals and had the strongest bivariate association with postdischarge community violence of a multitude of potentially relevant risk factors studied in the MacArthur Violence Risk Assessment Study (Monahan et al., 2001). Despite their promise for assessment of more chronic risk of violence, whether these newer measures represent valid indicators of acute risk of violence (e.g., during brief psychiatric hospitalization) is unknown.

This study used a retrospective design to evaluate the validity of the HCR-20 and PCL-SV as indicators of patients' risk for violence during short-term psychiatric hospitalization and to compare them with an actuarial tool developed for application in this setting, the VSC.

METHOD

Participants and Procedure

The setting was a locked, university-based, short-term psychiatric inpatient unit. The study involved retrospectively summarizing information that is routinely collected in the course of providing clinical care to patients. The study protocol was approved by the Committee on Human Research of the University of California, San Francisco.

The occurrence of various aggressive behaviors is recorded by nursing staff at the end of each 8-hr shift on a widely used measure of inpatient aggression with documented reliability and validity, the Overt Aggression Scale (Silver & Yudofsky, 1991; Yudofsky, Silver, Jackson, Endicott, & Williams, 1986). For this study, the definition of *violence* was operationalized as physical attacks on persons (i.e., a score of ≥ 1 on the Physical Aggression Against Other People subscale of the Overt Aggression Scale).

We used a retrospective case-control method of sampling. We selected all unduplicated cases who had been physically assaultive during 1998. This represented 50 cases, 10% of the 523 unduplicated patients admitted during 1998. Then, using a table of random numbers, we randomly selected a comparison group of 50 nonviolent patients from the remaining 473 patients admitted during 1998.

Review of the medical charts of the 100 patients in the study group showed the following characteristics. Fifty-three percent were women and 47% were men. Twenty-two percent were married or cohabiting and 78% were single, divorced, or widowed. Fifty-four percent were Caucasian, 19% Asian, 18% African American, and 9% of other ethnic backgrounds. The mean age was 45.7 years (SD = 17.2 years), with a range of 19 to 89 years. Clinical diagnoses, based on the *Diagnostic and Statistical Manual of Mental Disorders* (4th ed.; *DSM–IV*; American Psychiatric Association, 1994), included schizo-phrenic disorders (n = 26); bipolar disorder, manic episode (n = 15); other mood disorders (n = 29); substance-related disorders (n = 27); psychotic disorder not otherwise specified (n = 20); adjustment disorders (n = 7); anxiety disorders (n = 8); dementia or delirium (n = 8); and other disorders (n = 6). (The total number of diagnoses exceeds the number of participants in the study group because of comorbidity.) Twenty-three percent of the study group were involuntarily civilly committed on grounds that included dangerousness to others, 66% were civilly committed on the basis of dangerousness to self and/or grave disability, and 11% were hospitalized voluntarily. The median length of hospitalization was 9.5 days.

Measures

HCR-20 (Version 2)

The HCR-20 represents a strategy for coding 20 variables that the authors determined had support in the research literature as indicators of violence risk. The scale includes 10 Historical items (previous violence, young age at first violent incident, relationship instability, employment problems, substance use problems, major mental illness, psycho-pathy, early maladjustment, personality disorder, and prior supervision failure), five Clinical items (lack of insight, negative attitudes, active symptoms of major mental illness, impulsivity, and unresponsive to treatment), and five Risk Management items (plans lack feasibility, exposure to destabilizers, lack of personal support, noncompliance with remediation attempts, and stress). Each item is coded on a 3-point scale, with a range of 0 (*available information contraindicates the presence of the item*), 1 (*available information suggests the possible presence of the item*), and 2 (*available information indicates the presence of the item*). Douglas et al. (1999) rated the HCR-20 on the basis of the files of 193 patients who had been civilly committed for a mean of 273 days and followed them in the community for a mean of 626 days. Receiver operating characteristic (ROC) analyses showed the HCR-20 to be strongly associated with violence, with areas under the curve (AUCs) ranging from .76 to .80.

PCL-SV

The PCL-SV has demonstrated reliability and validity as a measure of psychopathy (Hart et al., 1995). The instrument consists of 12 items, scored on a similar 0–2 scale as the HCR-20. Items on Part 1 concern emotional and interpersonal traits (superficial, grandiose, deceitful, lacks remorse, lacks empathy, and does not accept responsibility). Part 2 concerns behavioral traits (impulsive, poor behavioral controls, lacks goals, irresponsible, adolescent antisocial behavior, and adult antisocial behavior). Although a semistructured interview may be used to elicit information, file data including collateral information are considered essential for the ratings.

The predecessors of the PCL-SV were the Psychopathy Checklist (Hare, 1980) and the Psychopathy Checklist—Revised (PCL-R; Hare, 1991), which have received extensive support as indicators of community violence and general recidivism in male criminal offenders (Hemphill, Templeman, Wong, & Hare, 1998; Salekin, Rogers, & Sewell, 1996). Hart et al. (1995) developed the PCL-SV to assess for psychopathy in noncriminal contexts and to screen for psychopathy in offender populations. Hart et al. (1995) reported that the PCL-SV is highly correlated with the PCL-R total score (weighted mean r of .80), has a similar factor structure, and has a similar pattern of correlations with external criteria such as crime and violence. Although the base rate of a diagnosis of psychopathy in civil psychiatric settings tends to be low (less than 10% of patients in the normative studies reported in the PCL-SV manual met a threshold of ≥ 18), PCL-SV scores have been found to measure subthreshold psychopathic traits that correlate with violence. We are aware of publications based on two research projects that have examined the relationship of PCL-SV scores and violence in general civil psychiatric settings. In the above-mentioned follow-up study of hospitalized patients by Douglas et al. (1999), PCL-SV scores predicted community violence during a follow-up period of an average of 626 days, with AUCs ranging from .73 to .79. In the other major project, the MacArthur Risk Assessment Study (Skeem & Mulvey, 2001), 1,136 patients were followed up for the first year after discharge from short-term civil psychiatric hospitalization. They found an AUC of .73 for the PCL-SV total score. In addition, they found that scores on Part 2 (termed Antisocial Behavior) of the PCL-SV predicted violence more strongly than Part 1 (termed Emotional Detachment).

VSC

The VSC consists of five items that had been identified in a previous study of statistical prediction of violence among 238 civilly committed psychiatric inpatients (McNiel et al., 1988) and were validated with a new sample of 338 patients (McNiel & Binder, 1994a). The items include the following: (a) history of physical attacks and/or fear-inducing behavior during the 2 weeks before hospital admission, (b) absence of recent suicidal behavior (this item is checked if the patient has *not* shown recent suicidal behavior), (c) schizophrenic or manic diagnosis, (d) male gender, and (e) currently married or cohabiting. The items are worded so that a positive answer to each question increases the likelihood of violence (scored as a 1) and a negative answer is scored as a 0. When evaluated against the criterion of physical attacks in a general inpatient population in which 24% of the patients physically attacked people, scores on the tool had a sensitivity of .55, specificity of .64, false-positive rate of .68, false-negative rate of .18, positive predictive value of .41, negative predictive value of .82, total predictive value of .61, and relative improvement over chance of .25 (McNiel & Binder, 1994a).

Preliminary analyses of the VSC in the present study suggested the desirability of elimination of the item concerning marital status from the measure because of the absence of a significant bivariate correlation between marital status and violence in this sample. However, to permit comparisons with previous research, we initially report the analyses with the original five-item version. Under the final heading of the Results section, we also report analyses with the revised version, the Violence Screening Checklist—Revised (VSC-R), which consists of the first four items described in the previous paragraph.

Several previous researchers have rated the HCR-20 (Douglas et al., 1999), the PCL-SV, the family of PCL scales (Douglas et al., 1999; Grann, Langstrom, Tengstrom, & Stalenheim, 1998; Gretton, McBride, Hare, O'Shaughnessy, & Kumka, 2001), and the VSC (McNiel & Binder, 1994a) on the basis of file data including collateral information, although interviews may also be used to supplement the file data. This study involved rating the scales on the basis of notes and forms filled out by clinicians at the time patients were admitted to the hospital. The ratings were completed by two doctoral students in clinical psychology, who had been trained in the use of the measures. At the time of the ratings, the raters were blind with regard to whether the patients later became violent. Before beginning collection of data for the study, their ratings of four practice charts showed an interrater agreement, measured by the intraclass correlation coefficient (ICC_1; Bartko & Carpenter, 1976), of .96 on the HCR-20 and .84 on the PCL-SV. Similarly, examination of their interrater agreement on five charts that were part of the study group showed ICCs of .78 on the HCR-20, .77 on the PCL-SV, and 1.0 on the VSC. As only one rating was used for each patient, ICC_1 is the actual reliability of the ratings. For descriptive purposes, it is worth noting that estimates of the reliability of averaged ratings (ICC_2) were .98 for the HCR-20 and .91 for the PCL-SV practice charts and .88 on the HCR-20, .87 on the PCL-SV, and 1.0 on the VSC for the charts that were part of the study.

Overview of Data Analysis

We used several methods of data analysis. To describe the bivariate associations between the scores on the risk assessment tools and whether the patients became violent, we developed a correlation matrix using Kendall's tau correlations. Then, we conducted multivariate logistic regression analyses incorporating all three of the tools to determine their independent contributions to assessing violence risk when considered concurrently. To further illustrate the relationship between the risk assessment tools and violence, we also undertook ROC analysis, which describes predictive accuracy in a way that is less dependent on the base rate of violence in the sample than correlational approaches (Hanley & McNeil, 1982; Rice & Harris, 1995). We characterized the ROC analysis using the AUC, which is the probability that a randomly selected violent patient will have been evaluated by the risk-assessment tool as at higher risk than a randomly selected nonviolent patient (Swets, 1986). Using the AccuROC program (Vida, 1997), we computed separate AUCs for each risk assessment tool, then compared whether they differed using the chi-square statistic. Finally, we computed traditional accuracy statistics (Baldessarini, Finkelstein, & Arana, 1983), including sensitivity, specificity, positive predictive value, negative predictive value, false positive rate, and total predictive value to illustrate the correspondence between violence and scores on the risk assessment tools at different cutoffs.

RESULTS

Descriptive Statistics

For the study group as a whole, the mean scores (with standard deviations in parentheses) on the HCR-20 were 18.0 (6.6) for the total score, 7.1 (3.5) for the Historical items, 6.1 (2.3) for the Clinical items, and 4.8 (2.3) for the Risk Management items. The mean score on the VSC was 2.1 (1.3). Mean scores on the PCL-SV were 9.1 (5.1) for the total score, 4.7 (3.0) for Part 1, and 4.5 (2.8) for Part 2. Five percent ($n = 5$) of the patients exceeded the cutoff score of ≥ 18 recommended by Hart et al. (1995) for a strong indication of psychopathy on the PCL-SV. This is similar to the base rate of psychopathy found in other civil psychiatric samples (Hart et al., 1995).

Correlation Analysis

As shown in Table 1, the VSC showed a significant and moderate to large (Cohen, 1992) association with the likelihood of later violence. The HCR-20 total score was significantly correlated with likelihood of violence, but this was due primarily to the Clinical items of the scale, which had a higher correlation with violence than did the total score. Neither the Historical items nor the Risk Management items of the HCR-20 were significantly correlated with violence. The PCL-SV total score was not significantly correlated with violence. However, analysis of the PCL-SV subscales shows that although Part 2 was not associated with violence, Part 1 did show a significant correlation of small to medium magnitude (Cohen, 1992). Consistent with expectations based on the internal consistency that the authors of the scales have reported, Table 1 shows that HCR-20 subscales tended to correlate more with each other than with the other scales, as did the PCL-SV subscales. (Note that in correlations shown in Table 1 between the PCL-SV scales and the HCR-20 total score and HCR-20 Historical items, the Psychopathy item was removed from the HCR-20 scores to avoid redundancy, as one of the 10 Historical items is Psychopathy.)

Kendall's tau correlations between the items on the VSC and violence were as follows: history of physical attacks and/or fear-inducing behavior within the 2 weeks before hospital admission ($\tau = .26$, $p = .000$), absence of recent suicidal behavior ($\tau = .40$, $p = .000$), schizophrenic or manic diagnosis ($\tau = .39$, $p = .000$), male gender ($\tau = .18$, $p = .067$), and currently married or cohabiting ($\tau = -.15$, $p = .143$).

TABLE 1

Intercorrelations Among Risk Assessment Tools and the Occurrence of Violence

VARIABLE	1	2	3	4	5	6	7	8	9
1. Violence	—	.22*	.09	.41**	.13	.16	.23**	.07	.38**
2. HCR-20 total score		—	.68**	.59**	.66**	.61**	.51**	.59**	.26**
3. HCR-20 H Scale			—	.27**	.39**	.56**	.39**	.62**	.17**
4. HCR-20 C Scale				—	.43**	.40**	.44**	.28**	.34**
5. HCR-20 R Scale					—	.47**	.39**	.47**	.15*
6. PCL-SV total score						—	.76**	.73**	.23**
7. PCL-SV Part 1							—	.43**	.27**
8. PCL-SV Part 2								—	.16*
9. VSC									—

Note: Kendall's tau correlations. To avoid redundancy, the Psychopathy item was removed from the HCR-20 Total Score and HCR-20 H Scale in correlations with the PCL-SV total score, PCL-SV Part 1 score, and the PCL-SV Part 2 score. HCR-20 = Historical, Clinical, Risk Management–20; HCR-20 H Scale = HCR-20, Historical Items Scale; HCR-20 C Scale = HCR-20, Clinical Items Scale; HCR-20 R Scale = HCR-20, Risk Management Items Scale; PCL-SV total score = Hare Psychopathy Checklist—Screening Version Total Score; PCL-SV Part 1 = Hare Psychopathy Checklist—Screening Version, Part 1 Score; PCL-SV Part 2 = Hare Psychopathy Checklist—Screening Version, Part 2 Score; VSC = McNiel–Binder Violence Screening Checklist.

$* p < .05.$ $** p < .01.$

Logistic Regression Analysis

Table 2 shows the results of a multivariate logistic regression analysis in which violence was predicted based on the total scores on the PCL-SV, the HCR-20, and the VSC.[1] In this model, the VSC had a substantial relationship with violence, but the PCL-SV and the HCR-20 did not make independent contributions to violence prediction.

TABLE 2

Summary of Logistic Regression Analysis Predicting Violent Behavior of 100 Patients Based on Three Decision Support Tools

VARIABLE	B	SE	WALD STATISTIC	p
HCR-20	0.096	0.060	2.532	.112
PCL-SV	−0.063	0.078	0.653	.419
VSC	0.660	0.191	11.884	.001
Constant	−2.516	0.751	11.226	.001

Note: HCR-20 = Historical, Clinical, Risk Management-20; PCL-SV = Hare Psychopathy Checklist—Screening Version; VSC = McNiel–Binder Violence Screening Checklist.

Although the manual for the PCL-SV (Hart et al., 1995) and previous work using the HCR-20 (Douglas et al., 1999) with civil psychiatric patients have focused primarily on total scores of these measures in investigating their validity, our correlation analyses suggested the potential value of examining the subscales of these tools. Because certain subscales had stronger bivariate correlations with violence than the total scores on the HCR-20 and PCL-SV, we conducted additional multivariate logistic regression analyses using the subscale scores. Table 3 shows the results of a multivariate logistic regression analysis in which violence was predicted on the basis of subscales of the HCR-20, subscales of the PCL-SV, and the VSC. In this model, only the Clinical items of the HCR-20 and the VSC made independent contributions to violence prediction.

TABLE 3

Summary of Logistic Regression Analysis
Predicting Violent Behavior of 100 Patients
Based on the VSC and Subscales of the HCR-20 and PCL-SV

VARIABLE	B	SE	WALD STATISTIC	p
HCR-20				
H Scale	0.006	0.118	0.002	.962
C Scale	0.509	0.161	10.045	.002
R Scale	−0.125	0.145	0.743	.389
PCL-SV				
Part 1	0.022	0.113	0.036	.849
Part 2	−0.088	0.160	0.300	.584
VSC	0.497	0.204	5.932	.015
Constant	−3.272	0.884	13.701	.000

Note: VSC = McNiel–Binder Violence Screening Checklist; HCR-20 = Historical, Clinical, Risk Management–20; HCR-20 H Scale = HCR-20, Historical Items Scale; HCR-20 C Scale = HCR-20, Clinical Items Scale; HCR-20 R Scale = HCR-20, Risk Management Items Scale; PCL-SV Part 1 = Hare Psychopathy Checklist—Screening Version, Part 1 Score; PCL-SV Part 2 = Hare Psychopathy Checklist—Screening Version, Part 2 Score.

ROC Analysis

As noted above, the AUC refers to the probability that a randomly selected violent patient will have scored higher on the risk-assessment tool than a randomly selected non-violent patient. The AUC can range from .0 (*perfect negative prediction*) to .5 (*accuracy not improved over chance*) to 1.0 (*perfect positive correlation*). Table 4 shows that total scores on the HCR-20 and the VSC had AUCs that differed significantly from the line of no information, and there was a trend that did not reach traditional significance levels for the total score on the PCL-SV to enhance predictive accuracy. The VSC had a predictive relationship with violence that was significantly stronger than the PCL-SV total score.

TABLE 4
Areas Under the Curve (AUCs)
of Receiver Operating Characteristic Analyses
for the HCR-20, PCL-SV, and VSC
as Predictors of Short-Term Violence Risk

MEASURE	AUC	SE	95% CI	p
HCR	.65	.06	.54–.76	.005
PCL-SV$_a$	.61	.06	.50–.72	.061
VSC$_a$	.74	.05	.68–.86	.000

Note: Measures that share a subscript *a* differ from each other significantly (*p* < .05). HCR-20 = Historical, Clinical, Risk Management–20; HCR = HCR-20 (except in the analysis contrasting the HCR with the PCL-SV, in which the psychopathy item was removed from the HCR); PCL-SV = Hare Psychopathy Checklist—Screening Version; VSC = McNiel–Binder Violence Screening Checklist; CI = confidence interval.

Subsidiary ROC analyses of the HCR-20 subscales showed AUCs of .56 for the Historical items, .77 for the Clinical items, and .58 for the Risk Management items. On the PCL-SV, the AUC of Part 1 was .66 and of Part 2 was .55. Of these subscales, only the HCR-20 Clinical items and Part 1 of the PCL-SV differed significantly ($p < .01$) from the line of no information.

Traditional Accuracy Statistics

Table 5 shows the classification accuracy of total scores on the HCR-20, the PCL-SV, and the VSC at different cutoffs. All three measures demonstrate the expected tradeoff between sensitivity and specificity as different cutoffs are used. (These values are presented for illustrative purposes, as our study design set the rate of violence at 50%. In clinical settings with lower base rates of violence, the positive predictive power of the tools would be expected to be lower; Baldessarini et al., 1983). Consistent with previous research (McNiel & Binder, 1994a), comparison of the sensitivity and specificity of the VSC at different cutoffs showed that the effectiveness of the tool for identifying which patients would and would not become violent was best if a score of 2 or less was considered low risk and of 3 or more was considered high risk. Although less clear-cut, a cutoff of 8 or more on the PCL-SV for predicting violence appeared to achieve the optimal balance between sensitivity and specificity in this sample. This threshold for predicting violence with the PCL-SV is similar to that obtained in other research with civil psychiatric patients predicting postrelease violence in community settings (Douglas et al., 1999; Skeem & Mulvey, 2001), although the specificity of the PCL-SV at this threshold was stronger in those previous studies. Compared with research using the HCR-20 with long-term community follow-up (Douglas et al., 1999), the HCR-20 had generally lower levels of sensitivity and specificity in this sample.

TABLE 5

Traditional Indices of Predictive Accuracy for Violence at Different Cutoffs of the HCR-20, PCL-SV, and VSC

MEASURE AND CUTOFF	SENSITIVITY	SPECIFICITY	POSITIVE PREDICTIVE VALUE	NEGATIVE PREDICTIVE VALUE	FALSE-POSITIVE RATE	TOTAL PREDICTIVE VALUE
HCR-20						
10	1.00	.18	.55	1.00	.82	.59
15	.76	.48	.59	.67	.52	.62
20	.48	.68	.60	.57	.32	.58
25	.24	.82	.57	.52	.18	.53
PCL-SV						
4	.96	.26	.56	.87	.74	.61
8	.64	.50	.56	.58	.50	.57
12	.36	.70	- .55	.52	.30	.53
16	.16	.90	.62	.52	.10	.53
VSC						
1	.94	.16	.47	.73	.84	.55
2	.78	.58	.65	.73	.42	.68
3	.64	.80	.76	.69	.20	.72
4	.24	.92	.75	.55	.08	.58

Note: Scores ≥ cutoff are classified as high risk. Sensitivity = probability that the test will give a positive result when the patient later does become violent. Specificity = probability that the test will give a negative result when the patient later does not become violent. Positive predictive value = probability of becoming violent when the test is positive. Negative predictive value = probability of not becoming violent when the test is negative. False positive rate = probability that a person with a positive test result will not become violent. Total predictive value = likelihood any test result will be correct. HCR-20 = Historical, Clinical, Risk Management–20; PCL-SV = Hare Psychopathy Checklist—Screening Version; VSC = McNiel–Binder Violence Screening Checklist.

VSC-R

A four-item revised version of the VSC, which omits the marital status item, was somewhat more closely related to violence than the original five-item version of the VSC. The VSC-R and VSC, respectively, had Kendall's tau correlations with whether patients became violent of .44 and .38 and AUCs of .77 and .74. Although replication is needed, these results suggest that the four-item VSC-R captures the information relevant to violence risk as well as the original version, and it has the benefit of greater brevity.

In a multivariate logistic regression analysis in which violence was predicted on the basis of total scores on the VSC-R, PCL-SV, and HCR-20, the VSC-R had a substantial relationship with violence ($B = 0.856$, $SE = 0.217$, Wald statistic = 15.557, $p = .000$), but the PCL-SV and HCR-20 did not make independent contributions to violence prediction. Similarly, in a multivariate logistic regression analysis predicting violence on the basis of two subscales of the PCL-SV, the three subscales of the HCR-20, and the total score on the VSC-R, the only variables with a significant relationship with violence were the VSC-R ($B = 0.689$, $SE = 0.222$, Wald statistic = 9.645, $p = .002$) and the Clinical items of the HCR-20 ($B = 0.496$, $SE = 0.166$, Wald statistic = 8.893, $p = .003$).

Table 6 shows traditional accuracy statistics for the VSC-R, as well as the Clinical items of the HCR-20. On the VSC-R, the optimal tradeoff between sensitivity and specificity appeared to be if a score of 2 or more was considered high risk and a score of less than 2 was considered low risk. Setting a threshold of 7 or greater on the Clinical items of the HCR-20 as high risk and less than 7 as low risk appeared to achieve a balance of sensitivity and specificity in this study group.

TABLE 6

Traditional Indices of Predictive Accuracy for Violence at Different Cutoffs of the Clinical Subscale of the HCR-20 and the VSC-R

MEASURE AND CUTOFF	SENSITIVITY	SPECIFICITY	POSITIVE PREDICTIVE VALUE	NEGATIVE PREDICTIVE VALUE	FALSE-POSITIVE RATE	TOTAL PREDICTIVE VALUE
HCR-20 C Scale						
3	.98	.12	.53	.86	.88	.55
5	.86	.44	.61	.76	.56	.71
7	.62	.80	.76	.68	.20	.71
9	.28	.92	.78	.56	.08	.60
VSC–R						
1	.94	.22	.55	.79	.78	.58
2	.74	.70	.71	.73	.30	.72
3	.62	.84	.79	.69	.16	.73
4	.18	.98	.90	.54	.02	.58

Note: Scores ≥ cutoff are classified as high risk. HCR-20 C Scale = Historical, Clinical, Risk Management–20 Clinical Items Scale; VSC-R = McNiel–Binder Violence Screening Checklist—Revised.

DISCUSSION

The promise of psychological science for improving human judgments through development of decision support tools is being increasingly recognized, particularly in the area of violence-risk assessment (Swets et al., 2000). The results of this study suggest that this potential may be realized in the area of short-term risk assessment, in that the risk assessment tools showed a reliable association with the likelihood of violence during brief hospitalization. However, our findings suggest that tools that are optimal for assessment of acute violence risk in persons suffering exacerbations of major mental illness may not be the same as for assessing more chronic risk. The results suggest that decision support tools that incorporate clinical variables are of relatively greater utility in the setting of short-term risk assessment for violence by people with active major mental illness. In our study, the Clinical items of the HCR-20 were predictive of violence, whereas other research applying the HCR-20 to assessment of long-term risk has found the Historical items to be more predictive (Douglas et al., 1999). Similarly, the

PCL-SV, which has been shown to be a robust indicator of violence during the first year following discharge from civil hospitals (Skeem & Mulvey, 2001), had a modest predictive association with violence in this sample, which did not add incremental validity when considered concomitantly with a tool weighted more toward clinical dimensions, the VSC-R (or the VSC). It is possible that in a person experiencing active phases of decompensation, the clinical features such as acute schizophrenic or manic symptoms or recent behavioral dyscontrol overshadow background traits as indicators of violence potential (McNiel & Binder, 1994b). In any event, although other research has suggested that decision support tools emphasizing historical and trait factors may be quite useful in evaluating the risk of violence over the next several months to years of people who have been treated and deemed ready for discharge, our findings suggest that other considerations come to bear with actively mentally ill people who are being considered for hospital admission. Among such individuals, evidence-based decision support tools will prompt the clinician to attend to aspects of mental disorder and recent behavior that are associated with short-term violence risk.

The VSC was developed and validated in the short-term inpatient setting. Hence, the meaning of the scores on this tool are likely affected by the setting and base rates of different clinical phenomena in this setting. Items such as a recent history of violence may indicate an increase in acute risk for reasons such as that a patient who manifests behavioral dyscontrol as a component of an episode of decompensation is at risk of further dyscontrol until the episode is brought into remission. Similarly, absence of recent suicidal behavior may increase the risk of acute risk of violence during short-term hospitalization because patients who exhibit suicidal behavior show more internalizing problems in the short term, leaving the remainder of the patients with an overrepresentation of those whose episode of illness is marked by externalizing behavior.

The meaning of an item such as schizophrenic or manic diagnosis, in application of the VSC in the present context, generally connotes that the individual is in an acute exacerbation of the disorder. The significance of such a diagnosis for violence risk may be different if the disorder is in remission and the individual is no longer experiencing active symptoms. The phasic nature of major mental disorders such as these may account for some of the discrepancies that have been reported in the literature about the relationship between diagnosis and violence. A meta-analysis of 116 studies by Douglas and Hart (1996) found that, on average, psychosis was reliably associated with a two- to threefold increase in the risk of violence. However, findings about the association of major mental disorders such as schizophrenia and bipolar disorder vary across individual studies. For example, some have found a diagnosis of schizophrenia to be associated with higher rates of violence (Arseneault, Moffitt, Taylor, & Silva, 2000; Eronen, Hakola, & Tiihonen, 1996; Swanson, 1994) and others have found the opposite association (Lidz, Mulvey, & Gardner, 1993; Monahan et al., 2001; Quinsey et al., 1998). Multiple methodological and sampling issues likely affect these disparate findings. It may be that active symptomatology associated with episodes of exacerbation of schizophrenic or manic disorders is more relevant to acute violence risk than whether the person carries the diagnosis (Link, Monahan, Steuve, & Cullen, 1999; McNiel &

Binder, 1994b; Swanson et al., 1997). This conclusion is further supported by the finding in this study that the Clinical items of the HCR-20 (which include information regarding active symptoms of mental illness) also predicted acute risk of violence.

The sensitivity of our study for identifying historical and trait indicators of violence potential may have been restricted by limitations in the extent of information that was available to the clinicians. As a practical matter, clinicians must often make decisions in the setting of behavioral emergencies on the basis of limited information. At the time of hospital admission, only limited information may be available about historical variables such as whether the patient engaged in adolescent antisocial behavior or engaged in a first violent incident at a young age. Nevertheless, as our study relied on the information that was available to the clinicians and recorded in the patients' charts, the findings are likely to be generalizable to the types of decisions that clinicians are expected to make in this context. It is of some interest to note that the VSC and the VSC-R, which are briefer and rely on information readily available to clinicians evaluating patients who are undergoing emergencies, had as strong or stronger predictive relationships with violence as the other tools, which call for more detailed background information. However, the predictive value of the Clinical items from the HCR-20 and the VSC appear complementary, given that each of these measures made independent contributions to prediction of violence in the multivariate logistic regression analyses.

Considered in light of past research, the present findings provide support for the HCR-20 approach to violence-risk assessment, particularly analysis of subscale patterns. That is, the Historical items and Risk Management items but not the Clinical items previously have been found to predict chronic risk of violence after civilly committed patients have been discharged to the community (Douglas et al., 1999). As stabilization of clinical symptoms is typically a factor in decisions about release, the reduced level of symptoms present at the time of hospital discharge may provide little useful information about an individual's chronic risk; at that point in patients' course of illness, their Historical risk factors appear to be of greater relevance. On the other hand, we found the Clinical items to be strong predictors of acute risk of violence in a study group that manifested sufficient decompensation to warrant hospitalization on a locked inpatient unit, generally on the basis of emergency civil commitment. Taken together, these findings suggest that the HCR-20 has flexibility that is desirable for its application in different settings and that the significance of elevations of its subscales for violence risk assessment in mentally disordered individuals varies as a function of phase of illness and clinical context.

In our study group, the component of the PCL-SV that had a modest relationship with violence was Part 1, which corresponds to emotional and interpersonal traits such as grandiosity and lacking empathy. Part 2, which corresponds to behavioral traits such as a history of adolescent and adult antisocial behavior and irresponsibility, did not predict violence. This finding is in contrast to other research with less acute patients, which has found Part 2 to be a stronger predictor of violence during the first year after discharge from civil hospitals (Skeem & Mulvey, 2001). Plausible hypotheses that could explain this discrepancy include (a) state variables (i.e., the acute symptoms that characterize an episode of decompensation) may overshadow trait variables in determining patients' short term risk for violence; (b) in the course of evaluating an individual in the context of a behavioral emergency, detailed background information about the patient's long-standing personality traits may not be available, attenuating the sensitivity of efforts to assess for the remote behavioral history relevant to assessing Part 2, the psychopathic behavioral traits; and (c) given that clinicians evaluating patients for hospitalization may have limited information about their baseline functioning, clinicians may have difficulty determining the extent to which a psychopathic emotional feature such as grandiosity represents a longstanding trait or an acute symptom. Apparently in recognition of some of these issues, the researchers in the MacArthur Violence Risk Assessment Study, who followed up patients to assess their rates of community violence during the first year after hospital discharge, did not attempt to rate the PCL-SV until 2½ to 4 months after the patients had been released from the hospital (Skeem & Mulvey, 2001, p. 361).

Although this study evaluated the predictive validity of three decision support tools considered in isolation, additional research would be helpful to determine whether use of such tools leads to clinicians making better decisions about the assessment and management of violence risk. These tools are intended to be used as decision aids and can be conceptualized as having the potential to add useful information to the comprehensive assessments of violence risk that are expected of clinicians, which need to consider an array of dispositional, personal history, clinical, and contextual issues (McNiel, 1998; Monahan et al., 2001; Tardiff, 1996).

Limitations of this study include its reliance on record review as a data source. It is possible that the tools might not perform in the same fashion if patients were rated and then followed prospectively. On the other hand, the method used in this study avoids the complication that if a clinician using such tools were to determine that a patient was at high risk, the clinician would have an obligation to attempt to prevent the expected violence, thereby attenuating the measured predictive validity of the tool. Another limitation of this study is that the generalizability of the findings to other settings besides acute hospital wards is unknown. For example, other research suggests that in community settings where patients have access to drugs and alcohol, substance abuse is an especially important indicator of chronic risk of violence (Monahan et al., 2001). However, the short-term inpatient setting is important in its own right, given the potential for injury, deprivation of liberty, and cost of care associated with violence risk assessment in this context.

NOTE

1. As one of the HCR-20 items is Psychopathy, we recomputed all of the regression analyses after excluding the Psychopathy item from the HCR-20 to avoid redundancy with the PCL-SV. This did not alter the pattern of the results from that shown in Tables 2 and 3; the same variables independently predicted violence whether or not the Psychopathy item was removed from the HCR-20.

REFERENCES

American Psychiatric Association. (1994). *Diagnostic and statistical manual of mental disorders* (4th ed.). Washington, DC: Author.

Arseneault, L., Moffitt, T. E., Taylor, P. J., & Silva, P. A. (2000). Mental disorders and violence in a total birth cohort: Results from the Dunedin study. *Archives of General Psychiatry, 57,* 979–986.

Baldessarini, R., Finkelstein, S., & Arana, G. (1983). The predictive value of diagnostic tests and the effect of prevalence of illness. *Archives of General Psychiatry, 40,* 569–573.

Bartko, J. J., & Carpenter, W. T. (1976). On the methods and theory of reliability. *Journal of Nervous and Mental Disease, 163,* 307–317.

Binder, R. L., & McNiel, D. E. (1999). Contemporary practices in managing acutely violent patients in 20 psychiatric emergency rooms. *Psychiatric Services, 50,* 1553–1554.

Cohen, J. (1992). A power primer. *Psychological Bulletin, 112,* 155–159.

Douglas, K. S., & Hart, S. D. (1996, March). *Major mental disorder and violent behaviour: A meta-analysis of study characteristics and substantive factors influencing effect size.* Poster presented at the biennial meeting of the American Psychology-Law Society, Division 41, American Psychological Association, Hilton Head, SC.

Douglas, K. S., Ogloff, J. P., Nicholls, T. L., & Grant, I. (1999). Assessing risk for violence among psychiatric patients: The HCR-20 violence risk assessment scheme and the Psychopathy Checklist: Screening Version. *Journal of Consulting and Clinical Psychology, 67,* 917–930.

Erdos, B. Z., & Hughes, D. H. (2001). Emergency psychiatry: A review of assaults by patients against staff at psychiatric emergency centers. *Psychiatric Services, 52,* 1175–1177.

Eronen, M., Hakola, P., & Tiihonen, J. (1996). Mental disorders and homicidal behavior in Finland. *Archives of General Psychiatry, 53,* 497–501.

Grann, M., Langstrom, N., Tengstrom, A., & Stalenheim, E. G. (1998). Reliability of file-based retrospective ratings of psychopathy with the PCL-R. *Journal of Personality Assessment, 70,* 416–426.

Gretton, H. M., McBride, M., Hare, R. D., O'Shaughnessy, R., & Kumka, G. (2001). Psychopathy and recidivism in adolescent sex offenders. *Criminal Justice and Behavior, 28,* 427–449.

Grove, W., & Meehl, P. E. (1996). Comparative efficacy of informal (subjective, impressionistic) and formal (mechanical, algorithmic) prediction procedures: The clinical-statistical controversy. *Psychology, Public Policy, and Law, 2,* 293–323.

Hanley, J. A., & McNiel, B. J. (1982). The meaning and use of the area under a receiver operating characteristic (ROC) curve. *Radiology, 143,* 29–36.

Hare, R. (1980). A research scale for the assessment of psychopathy in criminal populations. *Personality and Individual Differences, 1,* 111–119.

Hare, R. (1991). *The Hare Psychopathy Checklist—Revised.* Toronto, Ontario, Canada: Multi-Health Systems.

Harris, G. T., Rice, M. E., & Quinsey, V. L. (1993). Violent recidivism of mentally disordered offenders: The development of a statistical prediction instrument. *Criminal Justice and Behavior, 20,* 315–335.

Hart, S. D., Cox, D., & Hare, R. D. (1995). *Manual for the Screening Version of the Hare Psychopathy Checklist—Revised* (PCL-SV). Toronto, Ontario, Canada: Multi-Health Systems.

HCIA. (1999). *Psychiatric length of stay by diagnosis, United States, 1999.* Baltimore: Author.

Hemphill, J., Templeman, R., Wong, S., & Hare, R. (1998). Psychopathy and crime: Recidivism and criminal careers. In D. Cooke, A. Forth, & R. Hare (Eds.), *Psychopathy: Theory, research, and implications for society* (pp. 374–399). Dordrecht, the Netherlands: Kluwer Academic.

Kropp, P. R., Hart, S. D., Webster, C. W., & Eaves, D. (1999). *Spousal Assault Risk Assessment: User's guide* (3rd ed.). Toronto, Ontario, Canada: Multi-Health Systems.

Lam, J. N., McNiel, D. E., & Binder, R. L. (2000). The relationship between patients' gender and violence leading to staff injuries. *Psychiatric Services, 51,* 1167–1170.

Lehmann, L. S., McCormick, R. A., & Kizer, K. W. (1999). A survey of assaultive behavior in Veterans Health Administration facilities. *Psychiatric Services, 50,* 384–389.

Lidz, C. W., Mulvey, E. P., & Gardner, W. (1993). The accuracy of predictions of violence to others. *Journal of the American Medical Association, 269,* 1007–1011.

Link, B. G., Monahan, J., Steuve, A., & Cullen, F. T. (1999). Real in their consequences: A sociological approach to understanding the association between psychotic symptoms and violence. *American Sociological Review, 64,* 316–332.

McNiel, D. E. (1998). Empirically based clinical evaluation and management of the potentially violent patient. In P. K. Kleespies (Ed.), *Emergencies in mental health practice: Evaluation and management* (pp. 95–116). New York: Guilford Press.

McNiel, D. E., & Binder, R. L. (1994a). Screening for risk of inpatient violence: Validation of an actuarial tool. *Law and Human Behavior, 18,* 579–586.

McNiel, D. E., & Binder, R. L. (1994b). The relationship between acute psychiatric symptoms, diagnosis, and short-term risk of violence. *Hospital and Community Psychiatry, 45,* 133–137.

McNiel, D. E., Binder, R. L., & Greenfield, T. K. (1988). Predictors of violence in civilly committed acute psychiatric patients. *American Journal of Psychiatry, 145,* 965–970.

McNiel, D. E., Borum, R., Douglas, K. S., Hart, S. D., Lyon, D., Sullivan, L. E., & Hemphill, J. F. (2002). Risk assessment. In J. P. Ogloff (Ed.), *Taking psychology and law into the 21st century: Reviewing the discipline— A bridge to the future* (pp. 147–170). New York: Plenum.

McNiel, D. E., Lam, J. N., & Binder, R. L. (2000). Relevance of interrater agreement to violence risk assessment. *Journal of Consulting and Clinical Psychology, 68,* 1111–1115.

Monahan, J., Steadman, H. J., Silver, E., Appelbaum, P. S., Robbins, P. C., Mulvey, E. P., et al. (2001). *Rethinking risk assessment: The MacArthur study of mental disorder and violence.* New York: Oxford.

Quinsey, V., Harris, G., Rice, M., & Cormier, C. (1998). *Violent offenders: Appraising and managing risk.* Washington, DC: American Psychological Association.

Rice, M. E., & Harris, G. T. (1995). Violent recidivism: Assessing predictive validity. *Journal of Consulting and Clinical Psychology, 63,* 737–748.

Salekin, R., Rogers, R., & Sewell, K. (1996). A review and meta-analysis of the Psychopathy Checklist and Psychopathy Checklist—Revised: Predictive validity of dangerousness. *Clinical Psychology: Science and Practice, 2,* 203–215.

Silver, J. M., & Yudofsky, S. C. (1991). The Overt Aggression Scale: Overview and guiding principles. *Journal of Neuropsychiatry and Clinical Neuroscience, 3* (Suppl. 1), 22–29.

Skeem, J. L., & Mulvey, E. P. (2001). Psychopathy and community violence among civil psychiatric patients: Results from the MacArthur Violence Risk Assessment Study. *Journal of Consulting and Clinical Psychology, 69,* 358–374.

Steadman, H. J., Silver, E., Monahan, J., Appelbaum, P. S., Robbins, P., Mulvey, E. P., et al. (2000). A classification tree approach to the development of actuarial violence risk assessment tools. *Law and Human Behavior, 24,* 83–100.

Swanson, J. W. (1994). Mental disorder, substance abuse, and community violence: An epidemiological approach. In J. Monahan & H. J. Steadman (Eds.), *Violence and mental disorder: Develop-ments in risk assessment* (pp. 101–136). Chicago: University of Chicago Press.

Swanson, J., Estroff, S., Swartz, M., Borum, R., Lachiocotte, W., Zimmer, D., & Wagner, R. (1997). Violence and severe mental disorder in clinical and community populations: The effects of psychotic symptoms, comorbidity, and lack of treatment. *Psychiatry, 60,* 1–22.

Swets, J. A. (1986). Form of empirical ROCs in discrimination and diagnostic tasks: Implications for theory and measurement of performance. *Psychological Bulletin, 99,* 181–188.

Swets, J. A., Dawes, R. M., & Monahan, J. (2000). Psychological science can improve diagnostic decisions. *Psychological Science in the Public Interest, 1,* 1–26.

Tardiff, K. (1996). *Concise guide to assessment and management of violent patients* (2nd ed.). Washington, DC: American Psychiatric Press.

Vida, S. (1997). AccuROC nonparametric receiver operating characteristic analysis (Version 3.1) [Computer software]. Montreal, Quebec, Canada: Accumetric.

Webster, C. D., Douglas, K. S., Eaves, D., & Hart, S. D. (1997). *HCR-20: Assessing risk for violence* (Version 2). Burnaby, British Columbia, Canada: Simon Fraser University, Mental Health, Law, and Policy Institute.

Yudofsky, S. C., Silver, J. M., Jackson, W., Endicott, J., & Williams, D. (1986). The Overt Aggression Scale for the objective rating of verbal and physical aggression. *American Journal of Psychiatry, 143,* 35–39.

12

The Prediction of Violence
in Acute Psychiatric Units

DAVID WATTS, MORVEN LEESE, STUART THOMAS,
ZERRIN ATAKAN AND TIL WYKES

ABSTRACT: *This is a prospective longitudinal study addressing the issue of predicting violence within two weeks of admission to two psychiatric units. Predictors of violence in 100 consecutive admissions were collected at baseline and tested on an outcome of violence. Risk factors were analyzed using logistic regression models and cross-validated using jack-knifing techniques. Two separate definitions of violence were used, actual assault on another person and aggressive behavior including attempted assault, violence to property and specific threats. Thirty-two patients actually assaulted, 41 behaved aggressively and 27 were completely non-violent. Two models were developed to predict membership according to these definitions. A single model based on a three-category outcome compared unfavorably with the two-model approach. Although the presence of recent pre-admission violence had some predictive value for both models, clinical variables were most predictive. "Non-violence" and "violence" appeared to be two separate states, and did not fit neatly on to a continuum. The two models were statistically robust, but should be tested prospectively on larger samples.*

Issues of replicability and generalizability remain significant stumbling blocks for implementing violence risk assessments in routine clinical practice, with cross validation

Reprinted with permission. International Journal of Forensic Mental Health, 2 (2), 173–180. © 2003 International Association of Forensic Mental Health Services.

proving problematic even with similar populations (Monahan, 1997). These issues may account for the numerous variables put forward as predictive in violence risk prediction studies. According to Menzies and Webster (1995) virtually every variable looked at has, in one study or another, shown a degree of relation to future violence. Epidemiological studies of violence have generally demonstrated that the risk factors for violence within a mentally ill population (age, sex, employment status, criminal history) are the same as for the whole population, and are therefore of little practical benefit for a clinician making an individual clinical judgment.

What remains apparent from the literature is the need to take the base rates (prevalence) of violence in the population into consideration when interpreting the predictive accuracy of a risk assessment. One relatively established method for approaching these difficulties is to use Receiver Operating Characteristic (ROC) Curves (Mossman, 1994; Rice & Harris, 1995). Alternatively, an index of effectiveness (Hasselblad & Hedges, 1995) can similarly be calculated using measures of sensitivity and specificity and interpreted in the same manner as effect sizes (Cohen, 1992).

In a rapidly expanding evidence base on violence risk assessment (e.g. Monahan et al., 2002), the field of acute inpatient violence remains relatively rarely studied. There have been a number of surveys of inpatient violence (e.g. Owen et al., 1998) and several studies addressing the accuracy of clinician's assessment of violence potential. Of particular importance are the studies of McNiel and Binder (1994, 1995, 1998) in which they identified those characteristics that clinicians feel are pertinent to the prediction of violence and evaluated their accuracy.

One problem bedeviling risk prediction studies is that they take place in the real world, in clinical settings, and cannot be of purely experimental design. That is, when a clinician makes an assessment that an individual is highly likely to commit a violent act of some sort, they are bound to "act on that assessment, thus altering the outcome" (Davison, 1997, p. 202). In any setting, a range of interventions is likely to follow to prevent the predicted outcome from occurring, potentially increasing false positive rates. To attempt to alleviate this methodological problem, in this study we did not dichotomize the sample into two groups, the violent and non-violent, but into three: those that actually assaulted another person, those that behaved aggressively and those that were completely non-aggressive. The overall aim of this study was to identify (a) patients likely to be completely non-aggressive and (b) patients likely to actually assault, despite targeted clinical interventions, during the first two weeks of admission to two locked psychiatric units.

METHOD

Sample

The sample comprised 100 consecutive direct admissions from the community to two locked psychiatric units. The two units were very similar in terms of size, degree of physical security, access criteria, and operating policies, and covered neighboring catchment areas of similar social deprivation and ethnic mix. Patients readmitted during the study period and patients transferred to the units from other inpatient services were excluded from the study.

Eighty-four percent of the 100 participants were male. Forty-six were aged between 18 and 30, the other 54 being 31 years or older ($M = 30$, range 18–63). According to ICD-10 category diagnoses the majority, 68%, had a diagnosis of schizophrenia, with an additional 23% being classified as having affective disorder. A total of 48% were Black Caribbean, 18% White, and 18% Black African; 78% were single. They were representative of people admitted to the units within the respective catchment areas with high levels of social deprivation and psychiatric morbidity. However, there was an over-representation of people from ethnic minorities and they tended to be slightly younger than people in touch with the services as a whole (Wykes et al., 2000).

Measures and Procedure

At admission, a nurse rated their likelihood of being violent in the first two weeks of admission using a 10-point scale. Ratings between 0 (no risk) and 10 (maximum risk) were possible. Nursing staff were selected as raters because they are most frequently responsible for completing violence risk assessments in the UK (Watts et al., 2003), particularly in emergency mental health settings.

Risk factors of interest were selected on the basis of clinical significance and of a review of the literature, with particular emphasis on previous studies of in-patient violence (McNiel & Binder, 1995). Ratings of psychopathology and observed behavior problems were assessed with the Expanded Brief Psychiatric Rating Scale (BPRSE; Ventura et al., 1997) and Social Behaviour Schedule (SBS; Wykes & Sturt, 1986). Training was provided to raters for the BPRSE and interrater reliability was tested prior to data collection. The Nurses' Observation Scale for Inpatient Evaluation (NOSIE-30; Honigfeld et al., 1966) was completed 72 hours after admission as a rating of observed behavior problems. Violent and aggressive behavior was recorded using the Overt Aggression Scale (OAS; Yudofsky et al., 1986). This was adapted to be completed once every twenty-four hours, recording the total number of violent incidents, the most severe incident, clinical interventions and whether any of the incidents had the potential to escalate in severity. Sociodemographic and clinical history information was informed by previous studies. Pre-admission violence was recorded using the Modified Overt Aggression Scale (MOAS; Ratey & Gutheil, 1995), scored like the OAS but with weightings added to violent incidents of greater severity in the 24 hours prior to admission. BPRSE scores were high ($M = 56.97$, $SD = 12.31$) reflecting the acute nature of the population admitted to these units. SBS scores were also higher than expected for inpatient populations ($M = 26.32$, $SD = 6.85$). High NOSIE scores ($M = 97.98$, $SD = 28.84$) were mostly explained by high positive symptom scores, again reflecting the highly symptomatic nature of the sample. The distribution of the MOAS scores indicated that violence reported prior to admission was distributed across a range of scores rather than bimodally ($M = 10.74$, $SD = 7.19$). This makes it a useful variable in the modeling analyses and an improvement on previous measures based on three categories (no violence, aggressive behaviour and actual violence).

The two operational definitions of violence used in this study were derived from the OAS (Yudofsky et al., 1986). "Actual assault" was fulfilled if the violence met the criteria for OAS categories 4(ii) (actual assault without injury), 4(iii) (actual assault causing mild to moderate injury) and 4(iv) (actual assault causing severe injury). "Aggressive behavior" was fulfilled if the violence met the criteria for categories 1(iv) (clear threats of violence), 2(iv) (sets fires, throws objects dangerously) and all categories of physical violence.

Strategy for Model Development

Two logistic regression models were developed in parallel. A third outcome in which violence was divided into three categories (actual assault, aggressive behavior falling short of actual assault and no violence) was also considered. The logistic regression models were developed using STATA, version 6 (Stata Corp, 1999). The first model sought to identify those with a propensity to actually assault, the second those who were unlikely to behave aggressively. The parameters of the models were presented in two ways, first using the default probability of 0.5, then using probability cut-offs focusing on sensitivity to identify the two groups defined above.

Univariate analyses were performed with potential predictor variables, chosen *a priori* on clinical grounds. Variables included were age; BPRSE total score and symptom cluster scores (agitation-excitement, withdrawal-retardation, anxious-depression, hostile-suspiciousness and thinking disturbance); ICD-10 diagnosis; ethnicity; level of family support; gender; lifetime history MOAS score; marital status; total MOAS score; NOSIE total, positive factor, and negative factor scores; SBS total score and social mixing score; and severity of drug and alcohol use. Individual variables found to be significantly univariately correlated with either of the two dependent variables were included in two logistic regression models using backward stepwise methods. Sensitivity/ specificity plots, Receiver Operator Characteristic (ROC) curves, and test properties were calculated, for two choices of cut-off probability. The test properties were jackknifed by successively leaving out each case from the analysis, re-estimating parameters and averaging results (Lachenbruch & Michie, 1986). An overall index of effectiveness (Hasselblad & Hedges, 1995) and AUC of the ROC curve were also computed (Rice & Harris, 1995).

Ideally, a single model would predict the definitely violent and the definitely non-violent groups. Therefore, while it had been envisaged a priori that two models would be necessary, multiple and ordered logistic regression (Agresti, 1996) were also performed to check if a single model could replace the two separate models. In these supplementary models, the membership of three groups (no violence, aggressive behavior falling short of actual assault, and actual assault) was treated as a single three-category outcome and the six variables used in either Model 1 or Model 2 were entered as potential predictors.

RESULTS

Model 1: Actual Assault

When using a definition of actual assault only, 32 of the 100 patients were classified as being violent. When the definition was broadened to include aggressive behavior, the number classified as violent increased to 73.

This model was aimed at identifying those with a risk of actual assault. The variables univariately significantly associated with the dependent variable of actual assault were total MOAS score; age; ethnicity; hostile-suspiciousness; withdrawal-retardation; total BPRS score; SBS social mixing score; total NOSIE negative factors score; and severity of drug use. The resulting model is shown in Table 1. The area under the ROC curve was 0.84. Test properties, both raw and jack-knifed are shown in Table 2 for the predictions from this model both using the default probability cut-off and a cut-off with 75% sensitivity. Adjusted indices of effectiveness were 1.29 and 0.86 for cut-offs of $p = 0.5$ and $p = 0.4$, respectively, corresponding to a large, albeit less robust, effect size (Hasselblad & Hedges, 1995).

A linear prediction equation was developed for the model using the coefficients of each of the variables in the model to obtain an index score. The linear predictor (IV) for Model 1 was: $0.113 \times$ total MOAS score $- 1.21$ (if age > 30) $- 0.67$ (if Black Caribbean ethnicity) $- 3.0$ (if Black African ethnicity) $- 2.2$ (if other ethnicity) $+ (0.59 \times$ hostile-suspiciousness BPRS score) $- 2.735$ (constant). If IV $> - 0.41$, then the patient would be predicted to be violent (with sensitivity 75%). The linear predictor can be used to obtain a rule corresponding to any other and solving the equation $\log[(p/(1-p)] = $ IN to determine the cutoff (Altman, 1999). For $p = 0.5$ the cut-off is zero.

TABLE 1

Model 1: Actual Assault

	ADJUSTED ODDS RATIO[1]	95% C.I	p
Total MOAS score	1.120	1.031 – 1.218	0.008
Older Age (>31yrs)	0.300	0.104 – 0.857	0.025
Black Caribbean ethnicity[2]	0.511	0.133 – 1.968	0.329
Black African ethnicity[2]	0.052	0.007 – 0.410	0.005
Other ethnicity[2]	0.108	0.013 – 0.879	0.037
Hostile-Suspiciousness BPRSE symptom cluster score	1.800	1.151 – 2.813	0.010

[1] Adjusted for all other risk factors in Model

[2] Compared to White ethnicity

TABLE 2

Test Properties of Model 1

| | DEFAULT CUT-OFF $p = 0.5$ | | CUT-OFF $p = 0.4^2$ (FOR SENSITIVITY C. 75%) | |
	RAW	JACK-KNIFED	RAW	JACK-KNIFED
Sensitivity	50%	44%	75%	56%
Specificity	93%	93%	82%	79%
Positive Predictive Value	76%	78%	67%	56%
Negative Predictive Value	80%	74%	88%	79%
Misclassification Rate	21%	23%	20%	28%
Index of Effectiveness[1]	1.42	1.29	1.43	0.86

[1] See Hassleblad and Hedges (1995).

[2] Chosen on the basis of sensitivity-specificity plot (available from authors).

Model 2: Aggressive Behavior

The variables found to have univariate associations with aggressive behavior were total MOAS score, age, anxious-depression, withdrawal-retardation, total NOSIE positive symptoms score, and SBS social mixing total score. The resulting model is shown in Table 3. The area under the ROC curve was 0.77. Test properties, both raw and jack-knifed are shown in Table 4 for the predictions from this model using both the default probability cut-off (0.5) and a cut-off with 75% specificity. The index of effectiveness of Model 2 was not adversely affected when the data were jack-knifed, thereby suggesting that the moderate effect size was robust.

As before, a linear predictive equation for use as a predictive assessment was developed, using the coefficients from the logistic model. The linear predictor (IN) for Model 2 was: $(0.078 \times \text{total MOAS score}) - 1.09$ (if age > 30) $- (0.67 \times \text{anxious-depression score}) + (0.69 \times \text{withdrawal-retardation score}) + 1.03$ (constant). If IN ≤ 1.10, then the patient would be predicted to be non-violent (with sensitivity 75%). As before, the linear predictor can be used to obtain a rule corresponding to any other probability, with cut-off zero for $p = 0.5$.

TABLE 3

Model 2: Aggressive Behavior

	ADJUSTED ODDS RATIO[1]	95% C.I	p
Total MOAS score	1.08	1.01 − 1.16	0.035
Older Age (>31yrs)	0.34	0.12 − 0.99	0.048
Anxiety-Depression BPRSE symptom cluster score	0.60	0.28 − 0.91	0.024
Withdrawal-Retardation BPRSE symptom cluster score	1.99	0.87 − 4.54	0.104

[1] Adjusted for all other risk factors in the model.

TABLE 4

Test Properties of Model 2

| | DEFAULT CUT-OFF $p = 0.5$ | | CUT-OFF $p = 0.75$[2] (FOR SPECIFICITY C. 75%) | |
	RAW	JACK-KNIFED	RAW	JACK-KNIFED
Sensitivity	92%	92%	66%	62%
Specificity	30%	22%	74%	67%
Positive Predictive Value	78%	76%	87%	83%
Negative Predictive Value	57%	46%	44%	39%
Misclassification Rate	25%	28%	32%	37%
Index of Effectiveness[1]	0.88	0.65	0.94	0.66

[1] See Hassleblad and Hedges (1995).

[2] Chosen on the basis of sensitivity-specificity plot (available from authors); specificity for aggressive behaviour = sensitivity for *non*-aggressive behaviour.

Performance of Models

The AUC of the ROC curves for the two models were consistent with previous studies of violence risk assessment tools (e.g., Dolan & Doyle, 2000, Monahan et al., 2001), and the indices of effectiveness similar to the findings of Buchanan and Leese (1999). The misclassification rates of both models increased after jack-knifing, as would be expected. For Model 2, with a preferred cut-off aimed at giving high (75%) specificity, the mis-classification rate increased modestly from 32% to 37%, with the specificity dropping 7% to 67%. By contrast the misclassification of Model 1 increased from 20% to 28%, with sensitivity dropping 19% to 56%. Thus although Model 1 was superior to Model 2 in terms of overall success rate (and overall effectiveness: 0.86 compared to 0.66), the sensitivity was more drastically affected during the jack-knifing. This may be due to the larger number of parameters estimated in the model.

The predictions made by the two models were compared against the three groups (actual assault, aggressive behavior, and no violence). There was generally high consistency between the results of the two predictions, although 6 of the 100 cases were predicted inconsistently (predicted high risk of actual violence but also predicted high on non-violence). Given that there is a degree of overlap, albeit small, between the two predictors, other types of models aimed at predicting all three categories were investigated.

A Three-Category Model

The outcome variable was split into three categories: 32 who actually assaulted, 41 who behaved aggressively but did not actually assault, and 27 who displayed no violence. Multiple logistic regression comparing the two extreme groups to the middle group was also performed. Ordered logistic regression, in which the three groups were entered in the form of an ordered categorical variable, was also fitted using the same six predictors. The likelihood ratio test comparing the ordered and multiple models was not significant, $\chi^2 = 12.14$, $p = 0.145$, thereby suggesting that the ordered model would be acceptable. However, the success rate was only 20% for aggressive behavior and 76% for actual assault. Variables that were significant in the ordered model were MOAS total, age, ethnic group and hostile suspiciousness. Anxiety-depression and withdrawal-retardation were not significant, possibly explaining the poor success rate in predicting the aggressive behavior group.

DISCUSSION

Clinical interventions routinely used in these services and specific training the staff receive in anticipating and managing violence, are designed to decrease the probability of violence occurring. This study investigated the predictive value of a number of different variables that have an effect *over and above* the reductions produced by such clinical interventions. For this reason two different definitions of violence were included because it was unclear if the restricted definition was missing high probability incidents—that is, potential true positives—through the successful use of preventative measures.

Interpretation of Models

Although in both models, recent pre-admission violence is a significant predictor, it is neither the sole nor the most powerful one. In Model 1 recent pre-admission violence is highlighted as a risk factor, although again not the sole or most significant one. A clinical measure of hostile/suspiciousness was the most powerful predictor of an outcome of actual assault. Of particular interest was the finding that non-white ethnicity was associated with a reduced likelihood of actual assault in the short-term. This finding could be due to a number of reasons, not least of which is Type I error arising from the small sample and over-representation of non-white people (N = 82 in this study) admitted to these services. Indeed when considering ethnicity as a binary variable (white or other), non-white ethnicity only showed weak associations with an actual assault outcome ($p = 0.08$), suggesting that this finding should be treated with caution. In Model 2, a clinical measure of withdrawal-retardation from the BPRSE was the best predictor and high scorers were nearly twice as likely as low scorers to show aggressive behavior. Model 2 also highlights protective factors against any aggressive behavior as older age (>30 years) and higher anxiety/depression scores.

The idea of a continuum of violence from low to medium to high risk was not borne out by this study, as the ordered logistic regression was not as successful as the two separate models. In particular, it failed to pick up anxiety-depression as a factor associated with the absence of violence. This suggests that attempting to predict membership of the two opposite groups (actually violent and the nonviolent, in contrast to the intermediate group) is unlikely to be successful on the basis of a single index. Ordered logistic regression might have been expected to perform well. This was not the case and this seemed to confirm the *a priori* concept that there are two dimensions to the different levels of violence, with anxiety-depression being particularly associated with the "no violence" group.

There are several limitations that should be considered when interpreting these results. First, the overall sample size was relatively small so generalizability to the population from which it was drawn may be limited. Furthermore, an independent test sample was not available to test the robustness of the models developed with respect to other psychiatric units in the same area or other geographical areas. This would have been ideal. However, the jack-knifing procedure provides a more realistic indication of predictive error than using the same data for estimation and testing. This technique demonstrated that the predictive accuracy for both models was quite low. Although Model 1 correctly predicted roughly three-quarters of those who actually assaulted (or not), the low sensitivity and PPV highlight the false positive rate. Model 2 presented similar problems in that it misclassified over a third of the sample as being aggressive or not. The sensitivity and specificity of these models, while not high, was in line with other studies (Buchanan & Leese, 2001).

This study suggests that "non-violence" and "violence" are two separate states that do not fit neatly on a continuum. What this study demonstrated, with a reasonable degree of confidence, is a method of developing scientific support to clinical risk assessment within the population under scrutiny. The two models were relatively robust, as evident from the AUC of the ROC curves and the jack-knifed Indices of Effectiveness, and provided comparable results to other violence risk studies. We envisage that these models could be applied with two alternative objectives in mind. The first, which can be characterized as restrictive, is to minimize the number of false negatives; and the second, which can be characterized as permissive, is to minimize the number of false positives. These models should now be applied at the point of admission and tested against short-term outcomes using a much larger data set.

REFERENCES

Agresti, A. (1996). *An introduction to categorical data analysis.* New York: Wiley.

Altman, D. G. (1999). *Practical statistics for medical research.* London: Chapman and Hall/CRC.

Buchanan, A., & Leese, M. (2001). Detention of people with severe personality disorders: a systematic review. *Lancet, 358,* 1955–1959.

Cohen, J. (1992). A power primer. *Psychological Bulletin, 112,* 155–159.

Davison, S. (1997). Risk assessment and management—a busy practitioner's perspective. *International Review of Psychiatry, 9,* 201–206.

Dolan, M., & Doyle, M. (2000). Violence risk prediction: Clinical and actuarial measures and the role of the Psychopathy Checklist. *British Journal of Psychiatry, 177,* 303–311.

Hasselblad, V., & Hedges, L.V. (1995). Meta-analysis of screening and diagnostic tests. *Psychological Bulletin, 17,* 167–178.

Honigfield, G., Gillis, R., & Klett, C. (1966). NOSIE 30: A treatment sensitive ward behavior scale. *Psychological Reports, 19,* 180–182.

Lachenbruch, P., & Michie, R. M. (1986). Estimation of error rates in discriminant analysis. *Technometrics, 10,* 1–11.

Mc.Niel, D., & Binder R. (1994). The relationship between acute psychotic symptoms, diagnosis and short-term risk of violence. *Hospital and Community Psychiatry, 45,* 133–137.

McNiel, D., & Binder R. (1995). Correlates of accuracy in the assessment of psychiatric inpatients risk of violence. *American Journal of Psychiatry, 152,* 901–906.

McNiel, D., & Binder R. (1998). The relationship between confidence and accuracy in clinical assessment of psychiatric patients' potential for violence. *Law and Human Behavior, 22,* 655–667.

Menzies, R., & Webster C. D. (1995). Construction and validation of risk assessments in a 6 year follow-up of forensic patients. *Journal of Consulting and Clinical Psychology, 63,* 766–778.

Monahan, J. (1997). Actuarial support for the clinical assessment of violence risk. *International Review of Psychiatry, 9,* 167–169.

Monahan, J., Steadman, H. J., Silver, E., Appelbaum, P., Robbins, P., Mulvey, E., Roth, L., Grisso, T., & Banks, S. (2001). *Rethinking risk assessment: The MacArthur study of mental disorder and violence.* New York: Oxford University Press.

Mossman, D. (1994). Assessing predictions of violence: Being accurate about accuracy. *Journal of Consulting and Clinical Psychology, 62,* 783–792.

Owen, C., Tarantello, C., Jones, M., Tennant, C. (1998). Repetitively violent patients in psychiatric units. *Psychiatric Services, 49,* 1458–1461.

Ratey, J. J., & Gutheil, C.M. (1991). The measurement of aggressive behavior: Reflections on the use of the Overt Aggression Scale and the Modified Overt Aggression Scale. *Journal of Neuro-psychiatry & Clinical Neurosciences, 3,* S57–S60.

Rice, M. E., & Harris, G. T. (1995). Violent recidivism: Assessing predictive validity. *Journal of Consulting & Clinical Psychology, 63,* 737–748.

Statacorp. (1999). *Stata statistical software version 6.* College Station, TX: Stata Corporation.

Ventura, J., Lukoff, D., Neuchterlein, K. (1997). Manual for Expanded Brief Psychiatric Rating Scale. *Schizophrenia Bulletin, 7,* 594–602.

Watts D., Bindman J., Slade M., Thornicroft, G. (2003). Clinical Assessment of Risk Decision Support (CARDS): The feasibility of routine risk of violence assessment. Paper under review.

Wykes, T., Leese, M., Taylor, R., & Phelan, M. (2000). Effects of community services on disability and symptoms: The PRiSM psychosis study (4). *British Journal of Psychiatry, 173,* 385–390.

Wykes, T., & Sturt, E. (1986). The measurement of social behaviour in psychiatric patients: an assessment of the reliability and validity of the SBS. *British Journal of Psychiatry, 148,* 1–11.

Yudofsky, S., Silver, J., Jackson, W., Endicott, J., & Williams, P. (1986). The Overt Aggression Scale for the objective rating of verbal and physical aggression. *American Journal of Psychiatry, 186,* 35–39.

13

The Uncritical Acceptance of Risk Assessment in Forensic Practice

RICHARD ROGERS

ABSTRACT: *Forensic psychologists are frequently asked to conduct evaluations of risk assessment. While risk assessment has considerable merit, recent applications to forensic psychology raise concerns about whether these evaluations are thorough and balanced. Forensic adult risk-assessment models stress risk factors, and deemphasize or disregard entirely the other side of the equation: protective factors. Mediating and moderating effects must also be considered. Moreover, base-rate estimates may produce erroneous results if applied imprudently to forensic samples without regard to their unstable prevalence rates or the far-reaching effects of settings, referral questions, and evaluation procedures. Psychologists are offered a preliminary list of relevant issues for evaluating the merits of risk assessment in their forensic practices.*

Freudenburg (1988) in a seminal *Science* article chastised social scientists for not taking into account risk probabilities and risk consequences in their determinations. Psychologists, and especially forensic psychologists, have taken this criticism to heart. In the last decade, several hundred articles have detailed and frequently extolled the virtues and values of risk assessment. Risk assessment is not a unitary construct. Hanson (1998) provided three plausible approaches to risk assessment: (a) a guided

Reprinted with kind permission of Springer Science and Business Media. Law and Human Behavior, 24 (5), 595–605. © 2000 *American Psychology-Law Society/Division 41 of the American Psychology Association.*

clinical approach (expert judgment based on validated risk factors), (b) a pure actuarial approach (predetermined numerical weighting of predictors), and (c) an adjusted actuarial approach (an actuarial prediction that can be modified to take into account potentially important factors). According to Borum (1999), risk assessment refers to probabilistic estimates of a continuous variable (e.g., violence) based on both person-based and situational variables.

This commentary on risk assessment is not intended as a wholesale indictment. Rather, its purpose is to temper the unbridled enthusiasm by articulating the perils and pitfalls regarding any uncritical acceptance of risk assessment. As a concrete example of such unbridled enthusiasm, a 1996 issue of *American Psychologist* devoted most of its pages to the positive aspects of risk assessment. Despite papers by leading forensic experts (e.g., Borum, 1996; Monahan & Steadman, 1996; Schopp, 1996), these otherwise thoughtful papers substantially overlooked any critical analysis of the risks common to risk assessment. This enthusiasm continues unabated. A special issue of *Behavioral Sciences and the Law* (Ewing, 1999) strongly emphasizes the positive aspects of risk assessment.

Much less is known about what occurs with risk assessment in forensic practice. Heilbrun, Philipson, Berman, and Warren (1999) examined how mental health professionals communicated risk assessment to others. Their sample was highly selected, composed of doctoral-level professionals who had completed the Basic Forensic Training Program through the Institute of Law, Psychiatry, and Public Policy at the University of Virginia. Two salient findings emerged: (a) clinicians were markedly divergent in how they utilized and communicated risk assessment, and (b) specific risk factors were addressed by only a minority of respondents. In a factorial design with 222 psychologists, Strohman, O'Neill, and Heilbrun (1999) found that psychologists consider both static (i.e., unmodifiable) and dynamic (i.e., modifiable) risk factors in communicating risk assessments. Interpretations of the results are limited by sample characteristics (35.4% forensic; 84.9% Psy.D.) and the narrow focus of the design (e.g., case vignettes predominated by static and fluid factors).

Our understanding of forensic practice can also be augmented by reviewing the forensic instruments currently available for risk assessment. In this regard, two recent reviews (Borum, 1999; Rosenfeld, 1999) have addressed the primary risk assessment measures: the HCR-20 (Webster, Douglas, Eaves, & Hart, 1997), Rapid Risk Assessment for Sex Offender Recidivism (RRASOR; Hanson, 1997), Sex Offender Risk Assessment Guide (Quinsey, Harris, Rice, & Cormier, 1998), Sexual Violence Risk-20 (SVR-20; Boer, Hart, Kropp, & Webster, 1997), the Spousal Assault Risk Assessment Guide (SARA; Kropp, Hart, Webster, & Eaves, 1999), and Violence Risk Assessment Guide (VRAG; Harris, Rice, & Quinsey, 1993). In general, use of these measures indicates a heavy emphasis on static risk factors (e.g., background characteristics and offense history). With several measures (e.g., SORAG and VRAG), the combination of risk factors is empirically tested, although important issues of generalizability remain.[1] With others (e.g., HCR-20 and SARA), the assumption of additivity (i.e., more indicators equal more risks) is simply postulated, despite extensive problems with multicollinearity.

In the following sections, I examine the important constraints on risk assessment as it is currently conceptualized in forensic practice. With most adult samples, the forensic literature appears content simply to enumerate risk factors with little attention to other critical dimensions of their predictions. Any comprehensive examination of risk factors must also consider protective factors as well as moderator and mediator effects.

PRIZING RISK FACTORS AND NEGLECTING PROTECTIVE FACTORS

Most adult-based studies are unabashedly one-sided; they emphasize risk factors to the partial or total exclusion of protective factors (Sheldrick, 1999). In contrast to risk factors, protective factors reduce the likelihood of a maladaptive outcome. This reduction is achieved by either reducing the effect of risk factors (e.g., Clayton, Leukefeld, Donohew, Bardo, & Harrington, 1995) or by exerting an independent influence on the maladaptive outcome (e.g., Hoge, Andrews, & Leschied, 1996). In both mental health and legal contexts, a balanced evaluation of risk assessment must take into account both risk and protective factors (Laub & Lauritsen, 1994).

Are protective factors merely the absence of risk factors? For example, an Axis II diagnosis is conceptualized as a risk factor in predicting violence on the HCR-20 (Webster et al., 1997). Would the absence of an Axis II disorder be viewed as a protective factor? The answer is partly dependent on the structure and validation of the risk assessment measure. If data are available on how the absence of this specific variable (e.g., absence of Axis II disorders) reduces the risk, then this variable can be construed as a protective factor. More often, however, risk factors are amalgamated into a composite score. Under these circumstances, we cannot test whether absence of a specific risk factor is actually a protective factor. With continuous variables (e.g., age of first arrest), we cannot assume that the variable has equal predictive value as both a risk and protective factor. While studies of psychopathy (Hemphill, Templeman, Wong, & Hare, 1998; Salekin, Rogers, & Sewell, 1996) indicate that high scores are risk factors of violent crimes, it does not necessarily hold that all other scores serve as protective factors. On this point, Hemphill et al. (1998) found that only low, but not average, scores served as protective factors.

Adolescent forensic research underscores the importance of balanced evaluations. Hoge et al. (1996) studied risk and protective factors in a sample of 338 serious juvenile offenders. At follow-up (an interval of 12–18 months), they established several important findings. First, useful protective factors (e.g., positive peer relations) did not overlap with the absence of risk factors (e.g., family conflict). Second, protective factors appeared to be age-specific. Positive response to authority is predictive for youth in their midteens (ages 15–17 years), but not in their early teens (ages 12–14 years; estimated logistic regression coefficients of –0.39 and 0.01, respectively). The first finding addresses the earlier discussion regarding the potential bipolarity of protective-risk factors. The second finding emphasizes the importance of testing protective factors under specific parameters (see subsequent discussion of moderator effects).

Other child and adolescent studies have general implications for risk assessment. For example, Grossman et al. (1992) found that protective factors appear to be context-specific with different protective factors being operative depending on gender and outcome criteria. Protective variables are highly diverse. They may be composed of multiple variables (Felix-Ortiz & Newcomb, 1992) and may include biological, psychological, and social variables (Clayton et al., 1995; Grizenko & Pawliuk, 1994; Werner, 1995).

Despite fewer studies, clinical research with adults has highlighted the importance of protective factors. For example, Plutchik (1995) compiled 10 protective factors that reduce the likelihood of aggressive and suicidal behavior. In noting that many patients with the highest risk factors manifest no evidence of aggression, he concluded, "for most patients the protective factors greatly exceed the risk factors, thus accounting for the relatively low incidence of suicide and violence in our society" (Plutchik, 1995, p. 53). What protective factors might psychologists consider? Dynamic protective factors included social relations, self-esteem, religious beliefs, and parents' acceptance of the patient (Plutchik, 1995).

Even established areas of risk assessment deserve a critical reevaluation. For example, a global measure of psychopathy (i.e., the total score on the Psychopathy Checklist) is established firmly as a risk factor for violence (Hart & Hare, 1996), although its effect sizes range widely by setting (Cohen's d from .42 to 1.92, $M = .79$; Salekin et al., 1996). However, the disaggregation of psychopathy into specific characteristics suggests that simply using global scores may obscure risk assessment. At least with female offenders, individual psychopathic characteristics potentially may contribute to both risk and protective factors (Rogers et al., in press). More specifically, Rogers et al. found one criterion and two subcriteria of psychopathy that are *negatively* associated with physical aggression: (a) sees self as victim of the system (–.70), (b) lacks empathy (–.78), and (c) has little emotion in regard to actions (–.60). While requiring cross-validation, these results indicate the need for forensic psychologists to exercise caution when applying any global criterion as a risk factor.

Risk-only evaluations are inherently inaccurate. As a simple analogy, would most forensic psychologists give credence to a financial planner who dwelled only on their fiscal liabilities to the exclusion of their monetary assets? Predictions based on only one side of the ledger, be it financial or mental health, are markedly constrained in their usefulness. As a concrete example, attempts to rely only on personality characteristics, largely indicative of maladjustment, in the prediction of alcohol abuse have produced meager results (Rogers & Kelly, 1997).

Risk-only risk assessments represent implicitly biased evaluations with grave, often negative consequences to forensic populations. For instance, unwarranted classifications of forensic patients as aggressive are likely to result in marked abridgement of personal freedom. Beyond the direct effects on clients, however, the emphasis on risk factors to the virtual exclusion of protective factors may indirectly exert a widespread and corrosive effect on professionals' perceptions of their clientele. The continued focus on dangerousness hardly engenders a positive view of forensic populations. For example, to search only for risk factors creates unwarranted perceptions of violence and may evoke detrimental countertransference (Madden, Lion, & Penna, 1977). Moreover, many studies have restricted their scope to static risk predictors (e.g., gender, race, and criminal background), thus promoting an image of chronic and irreversible risks (Sullivan, Wells, Morgenstern, & Leake, 1995). Overfocus on risk factors is likely to contribute to professional negativism and result in client stigmatization.

The emphasis on static risk factors also has important implications for assigning risk and evaluating treatment outcome. In an elegant study, Silver, Mulvey, and Monahan (1999) examined risk factors for violence among 293 discharged patients. Their study exemplifies the dangers of relying solely on static risk factors: ethnicity alone resulted in dramatic differences (22.4% for African American versus 9.7% for Anglo American) in risks of violence. However, differences in a dynamic risk factor appears to play an important role in determining risk. When concentrated poverty is considered, the difference in odds ratios between African American and Anglo American is no longer significant. Static factors also limit considerations of treatability. As observed by Becker and Murphy (1998), positive therapeutic change cannot be demonstrated in light of the current focus on static risk factors. However, therapeutic changes may have counterintuitive effects, at least with psychopathic sex offenders (Barbaree, 1999).

Risk-only assessments in risk-averse mental health systems may produce lopsided assessments and resource allocations. Linhorst and Dirks-Linhorst (1997) provided a stark example of how forensic patients found not guilty by reason of insanity (NGRI) now occupy 50% of Missouri's inpatient beds; the competition for inpatient resources results in nonforensic patients being placed on waiting lists. In addition, the forensic patients are higher functioning than nonforensic patients. Indeed, approximately one fourth (26.1%) have mild to no symptoms. Moreover, these patients are less assaultive than their nonforensic counterparts. One critical issue appears to be a preoccupation with risk factors by courts and clinicians to the point that better-functioning NGRI patients are largely precluded from community placement because of their much earlier criminal histories. Extrapolating from the current influx of NGRI patients, all inpatient beds in Missouri will be dedicated to these better-functioning NGRI patients during the next decade. As a parallel, allocation of resources based on risk assessment has led Mississippi to limit inpatient services to only civilly committed patients (Sullivan et al., 1995).

TERRA INCOGNITA: MODERATOR AND MEDIATING EFFECTS

Moderator and mediating effects remain a largely unexplored territory with respect to risk assessment. In their classic paper, Baron and Kenny (1986) carefully differentiated between moderator and mediating effects. As they noted (p. 1174), moderator effects refer to those variables that affect the strength and direction of the relationship between the predictor and the criterion variables. Moderator variables can be either categorical (e.g., race and gender), or continuous (e.g., number of treatment sessions). In the previously cited Silver et al. (1999) study of discharged patients, ethnicity is an important moderator variable.

Mediating effects are intervening variables between independent and dependent variables that influence risk assessment. As observed by Shadish and Sweeney (1991), mediators can result from either the intervention or research processes. In forensic cases, inpatient risk assessments of dangerousness are likely to be influenced by mediating effects (e.g., clinical interventions, such as medication or isolation) that independently affect the aprioristic predictions. In forensic assessments, many sex offenders are likely to experience reactivity to intrusive measures, especially penile plethysmography, that independently may affect their results (Sewell & Salekin, 1997).

Shadish and Sweeney (1991) performed a major meta-analysis of psychotherapy effectiveness and demonstrated the importance of both moderator and mediating variables in predicting effect sizes. They found that the type of measurement appeared to play a significant role; greater effect sizes were reported with (a) more reactivity to the measure, (b) more vulnerability of the measure to manipulation (e.g., clients' self-reports and therapist's ratings), and (c) more targeted treatment goals. In risk assessment, the Shadish and Sweeney results raise alarming possibilities regarding the reactivity and manipulability of the measures. Extrapolating from this research, forensic psychologists would be prudent to consider (a) how clients will react to specific measures and (b) the transparency of specific measures.

Salekin et al. (1996) in a meta-analysis of psychopathy and violent behavior concluded that moderator variables, such as ethnicity and gender, must be taken into account in risk assessments. Despite expressed optimism regarding the use of the Psychopathy Checklist-Revised (PCL-R; Hare, 1991) with African American populations, practitioners cannot assume that similar PCL scores across ethnic identities represent corresponding risk estimates. In an adolescent offender sample, Hicks, Rogers, and Cashel (in press) examined PCL-SV scores for a juvenile maximum security facility. They found that ethnicity was a critical moderator variable; elevated PCL-SV scores were associated with violence in African Americans ($r = 0.57$), but not in European Americans ($r = -0.06$). Gender poses similar problems. Unlike male participants, Salekin, Rogers, and Sewell (1997) found very modest increases in risk estimates for females with high PCL-R scores; these differences remained in a 12-month follow-up (Salekin & Rogers, 1998). What are the practical implications of these studies for forensic psychologists? As noted by Rogers (1995), psychologists are on the safest ground if they limit their risk predictions on the PCL-R to White males with criminal histories.

Several studies have examined directly the role of mediating factors in the assessment of violence. For example, Choice, Lamke, and Pittman (1995) in a national study of 1,836 men found that simple reliance on childhood witnessing of interparental violence to explain subsequent wife battering was relatively unsuccessful ($R^2 = .002$). However, such early experiences contributed to ineffective conflict resolution which resulted in marital distress. Both ineffective conflict resolution and marital distress contributed significantly to the explanation of spousal violence (combined $R^2 = .20$). The implication of this study to forensic practice is readily apparent: parental violence by itself is not likely to be a risk factor for spousal abuse.

Gidycz, Hanson, and Layman (1995) explored possible mediating effects for female survivors of sexual assault. For instance, childhood victimization predicted adolescent victimization, which subsequently prognosticated adult victimization. Most disturbingly, recent adult victimization was a strong predictor (zero-order $r = .59$) of further victimization. Interestingly, childhood victimization without adolescent revictimization was *not* correlated with adult victimization. In this study, any facile assumption of intergenerational violence as a risk factor is likely to result in erroneous conclusions if the mediating effects are not addressed.

PROBLEMS IN APPLYING BASE RATES

Psychologists are frequently counseled to take into account base rates in conducting their risk assessments (Melton, Petrila, Poythress, & Slobogin, 1997). This advice assumes that it is a simple matter to determine which base rates ought to be applied. Hiday (1990) conducted an insightful review of violent behavior among civilly committed inpatients. Even within this circumscribed clinical population, the base rates varied dramatically from 7.5% to 66.7%. Any averaging method is likely to obscure key moderator variables.

Borum's (1999) definition of risk assessment as referring to probabilistic estimates of a continuous variable further complicates the establishment and application of base rates. Ideally, base rates should be established within specific clinical and forensic settings for different levels of violence. This point must be underscored. The definition of violent behavior ranges markedly from belligerent statements to physical assaults (Hiday, 1990; Mulvey & Lidz, 1993). Collapsing verbal threats with physical assaults into a single "violent" category would confound base rates and violate the basic assumptions of risk assessment.

The issue of base rates is also a significant problem in applying clinical research to risk assessment. Rosenfeld (1999) noted that a common solution to relatively low base rates is addressed by artificially increasing the base rates. Increases can be achieved by employing extremely long follow-up periods or decreasing the stringency of the outcome criteria. With the first alternative, use of these base rates from a 5-year follow-up would be inapplicable to risk assessment for civil commitment (i.e., imminently dangerous). As an example of the second, violence might be broadened to include any sexual offense (e.g., pornography and voyeurism).

Forensic psychologists are cautioned that base rates may not be applicable, even if they were known. In forensic settings, a selective process is typically implemented to decide which forensic patients are subjected to a formal risk assessment. Determinants of this selection process are generally nonstandardized, but may include (a) clinically relevant behaviors (e.g., a recent incident of aggression), (b) requests from an external source (e.g., a referral question), (c) subjective impressions (e.g., a staff person feels "scared"), and (d) resource allocation (e.g., an informal triaging of caseload demands and other risk assessment cases). The base rate within the population of mentally disordered offenders or even the specific forensic setting is likely inapplicable to selected risk assessments. This is not a trivial point; the institutional base rate could easily be a small fraction of the base rate for risk assessment cases.

RISKY CONSEQUENCES OF RISK ASSESSMENT

Risk assessment carries two additional risks for forensic psychologists. First, risk probabilities are often misunderstood. Second, some risk measures have a floor effect, assigning low to moderate risk to all mentally disordered persons. The implications of these additional risks for forensic practice are briefly reviewed.

A potentially contentious issue is whether forensic psychologists bear any ethical responsibility for the misuse or misinterpretation by courts and legal professionals. One view is that psychologists "take reasonable steps to prevent others from misusing information these techniques provide" (Ethical Standard 2.02, subsection b; American Psychological Association, 1992). From this perspective, psychologists might well be constrained in offering even well-established probability estimates. Research on prospective jurors (e.g., Faigman & Baglioni, 1988; Smith, Penrod, Otto, & Park, 1996) has demonstrated convincingly that triers of fact do not accurately utilize probabilistic estimates, even when these estimates are explained clearly. An alternative perspective was cogently expressed by an anonymous reviewer, "Psychologists can't prevent the rest of the world from being venal or stupid. If jurors or judges misuse accurately-stated probabilistic information, that's not the psychologist's fault." Clearly, the ethical implications of risk assessment remain unsettled. While ultimately addressed via experimental research and scholarly debate, individual psychologists must decide for themselves the relevance of Ethical Standard 2.02 to forensic conclusions on risk assessment.

Psychologists must wrestle with the misuse of probability estimates even when these estimates are relatively high. Melton et al. (1997, p. 15) illustrate this point with hypothetical data on child sexual abuse profile: depending on the base rates, even a measure with 90% accuracy may result in 68% false-positives. Moreover, this conservative 68% misclassification does not take into account protective factors, moderator effects, or mediating effects.

Clinical and forensic measures often have a floor effect, assigning low to moderate risks to all patient groups. For example, the lowest category of psychopathy may still signal a substantial risk of recidivism. Hart, Kropp, and Hare (1988) examined categories of psychopathy (low, medium, and high) for inmates released on parole or mandatory supervision. The floor effect (.20) was substantial in predicting the likelihood of reincarceration during the first 12 months of release. If an expert opinion took into account these base rates, the lowest possible probability estimate would be 20%. While it is possible that 20% is accurate on an aggregate level, can we justify assigning this floor-effect probability to the most exemplary inmate in whom we have every confidence will not recidivate? As an extreme example, would an inmate with compromised physical functioning (e.g., quadeplegia [*sic*]) warrant this risk estimate? A systematic consideration of protective factors (e.g., treatment gains or physical incapacitation) would likely inform the floor-effect base rates.

Risk assessment in forensic practice is most often construed in terms of the *selection* of individuals composing a particular category. Risk assessment can also be conceptualized as *deselection* (Nietzel & Dillehay, 1986) or exclusion of persons based on defined characteristics. For instance, many half-way houses commonly exclude any patient with a documented risk for violence. Even forensic patients with low risks may be deemed unacceptable. As a further example, Rice and Harris (1997) demonstrated the risk of sexual misconduct among child molesters treated in a maximum security hospital was relatively low during the first 2 years ($\leq .20$), but nearly doubled during the next 7 years. Because many communities are intolerant of even small risks, low probabilities may have far-ranging effects on the release of forensic patients.

FINAL CONSIDERATIONS

Risk assessments are not inherently inaccurate. However, two broad questions appear fundamental when contemplating the use of risk assessment in forensic psychology. First, is the risk assessment fair and balanced? Among many other issues, psychologists may wish to consider the role of protective factors, mediating effects, and moderating effects. Second, is the risk assessment based on relevant and well-established base rates? Base-rate information is likely to be helpful when it takes into account referral questions, setting, and clinical characteristics.

Table 1 summarizes a preliminary list of issues raised by risk assessments. For forensic practice, psychologists will likely select which issues are most salient to their risk assessments. For research, Table 1 provides an initial template of potential issues that deserve painstaking investigations. Despite important advances during the last two decades, systematic research is urgently needed on risk assessment to explore the complex relationships between risk and protective factors and the influences of mediating and moderating effects.

TABLE 1

Risk Assessment for Forensic Purposes: Questions to Consider

1. *Comprehensiveness*: Do predictions
    a. Use both static and dynamic risk factors?
    b. Take into account protective factors?
    c. Assess the effects of intervention?
    d. Specify the conditions under which they are valid?

2. *Measurement*: Do estimates of the index behavior
    a. Use a consensual definition?
    b. Address the imprecision as documented by SEm?
    c. Examine the distribution of scores and express this variability as a range of percentages?
    d. Apply to a particular setting/referral question?
    e. Apply to an evaluatee's gender, ethnicity, and psychiatric background?

3. *Base-rate estimates*: Are such estimates
    a. Aligned with a well-defined referral question?
    b. Established for a specific forensic setting?
    c. Demonstrably stable for that forensic setting?
    d. Specific to sociodemographic and other background variables?

NOTES

1. For example, the VRAG was developed on data from an atypical forensic hospital; its past practices included such nonstandardized treatments as psychedelic drugs and nude marathons.

REFERENCES

American Psychological Association (1992). Ethical principles of psychologists and code of conduct. *American Psychologist, 47,* 1597–1611.

Barbaree, H. E. (1999). Effect of treatment on risk for recidivism in sex offenders. In American Psychological Association (Ed.), *Psychological expertise and criminal justice* (pp. 217–220). Washington, DC: American Psychological Association.

Baron, R. M., & Kenny, D. A. (1986). The moderator–mediator variable distinction in social psychological research: Conceptual, strategic, and statistical considerations. *Journal of Personality and Social Psychology, 51,* 1173–1182.

Becker, J. V., & Murphy, W. D. (1998). What we know and do not know about assessing and treating sex offenders. *Psychology, Public Policy, and Law, 4,* 116–137.

Boer, D. P., Hart, S. D., Kropp, P. R., & Webster, C. D. (1997). *Manual for the Sexual Violence Risk— 20: Professional guidelines for assessing risk of sexual violence.* Burnaby, BC, Canada: Mental Health, Law, and Policy Institute.

Borum, R. (1996). Improving the clinical practice of violence risk assessment. *American Psychologist, 51,* 945–956.

Borum, R. (1999). Advances in the assessment of dangerousness and risk. In American Psychological Association (Ed.), *Psychological expertise and criminal justice* (pp. 465–484). Washington, DC: American Psychological Association.

Choice, P., Lamke, L. K., & Pittman, J. F. (1995). Conflicting resolution strategies and marital distress as mediating factors in the link between witnessing interparental violence and wife battering. *Violence and Victims, 10,* 107–119.

Clayton, R. R., Leukefeld, C. G., Donohew, L., Bardo, M., & Harrington, N. G. (1995). Risk and protective factors: A brief review. *Drugs and Society, 8*, 7–14.

Ewing, C. P. (Ed.) (1999). Threat assessment [Special issue]. *Behavioral Sciences and the Law, 17*(3).

Faigman, D. L., & Baglioni, A. J. (1988). Bayes' theorem in the trial process: Instructing jurors on the value of statistical evidence. *Law and Human Behavior, 12*, 1–17.

Faust, D. (1989). Data integration in legal evaluations: Can clinicians deliver on their premises? *Behavioral Sciences and the Law, 7*, 469–483.

Felix-Ortiz, M., & Newcomb, M. D. (1992). Risk and protective factors for drug use among Latino and White adolescents. *Hispanic Journal of Behavioral Sciences, 14*, 291–303.

Freudenburg, W. R. (1988). Perceived risk, real risk: Social science and the art of probabilistic risk assessment. *Science, 241*, 44–49.

Gidycz, C. A., Hanson, K., & Layman, M. J. (1995). A prospective analysis of relationships among sexual assault experiences: An extension of previous findings. *Psychology of Women Quarterly, 19*, 5–29.

Grizenko, N., & Pawliuk, N. (1994). Risk and protective factors for disruptive behavior disorders in children. *American Journal of Orthopsychiatry, 64*, 534–544.

Grossman, F. K., Beinashowitz, J., Anderson, L., Sakurai, M., Finnin, L., & Flaherty, M. (1992). Risk and resilience in young adolescents. *Journal of Youth and Adolescence, 21*, 529–550.

Hanson, R. K. (1997). *The development of a brief actuarial risk scale for sexual offender recidivism*. Ottawa, ON, Canada: Department of the Solicitor General of Canada.

Hanson, R. K. (1998). What do we know about sex offender risk assessment? *Psychology, Public Policy, and Law, 4*, 50–72.

Hare, R. D. (1991). *Manual for the Hare Psychopathy Checklist-Revised*. Toronto: Multi-Health Systems.

Harris, G. T., Rice, M. E., & Quinsey, V. L. (1993) Violent recidivism of mental disordered offenders: The development of a statistical prediction instrument. *Criminal Justice and Behavior, 20*, 315–335.

Hart, S. D., & Hare, R. D. (1996). Psychopathy and risk assessment. *Current Opinion in Psychiatry, 9*, 380–383.

Hart, S. D., Kropp, P. R., & Hare, R. D. (1988). Performance of male psychopaths following conditional release from prison. *Journal of Consulting and Clinical Psychology, 56*, 227–232.

Heilbrun, K., Philipson, J., Berman, L., & Warren, J. (1999). Risk communication: Clinicians' reported approaches and perceived values. *Journal of the American Academy of Psychiatry and the Law, 27*, 397–406.

Hemphill, J. F., Templeman, R., Wong, S., & Hare, R. D. (1998). Psychopathy and crime: Recidivism and criminal careers. In D. Cooke, A. Forth, & R. Hare (Eds.), *Psychopathy: Theory, research, and implications for society* (pp. 375–398). Dordrecht, Netherlands: Kluwer Academic.

Hicks, M. M., Rogers, R., & Cashel, M. L. (In press). Predictions of violent and total infractions among institutionalized male juvenile offenders. *Journal of the American Academy of Psychiatry and Law.* Hiday, V. A. (1990). Dangerousness of civil commitment candidates: A six-month follow-up. *Law and Human Behavior, 14*, 551–567.

Hoge, R. D., Andrews, D. A., & Leschied, A. W. (1996). An investigation of risk and protective factors in a sample of youthful offenders. *Journal of Child Psychology and Psychiatry, 37*, 419–424.

Koehler, J. J., & Macchi, L. (1997, August). *Improving jurors' comprehension of statistical DNA evidence by inducing an outside perspective.* Paper presented at the American Psychological Association Convention, Chicago.

Kropp, P. R., Hart, S. D., Webster, C. D., & Eaves, D. (1999). *Manual for the Spousal Assault Risk Assessment Guide.* Toronto: Multi-Health Systems.

Laub, J. H., & Lauritsen, J. L. (1994). The precursors of criminal offending across the life course. *Federal Probation, 58*, 51–57.

Linhorst, D. M., & Dirks-Linhorst, P. A. (1997). The impact of insanity acquittees on Missouri's public mental health system. *Law and Human Behavior, 21*, 327–338.

Madden, D. J., Lion, J. R., & Penna, M. W. (1977). Assaults on psychiatrists by patients. *American Journal of Psychiatry, 133*, 422–429.

Melton, G. B., Petrila, J., Poythress, N. G., & Slobogin, C. (1997). *Psychological evaluations for the courts: A handbook for mental health professionals and lawyers (2nd ed.).* New York: Guilford Press.

Monahan, J., & Steadman, H. J. (1996). Violent storms and violent people: How meteorology can inform risk communication in mental health law. *American Psychologist, 51*, 931–938.

Mulvey, E. P., & Lidz, C. W. (1993). Measuring patient violence in dangerousness research. *Law and Human Behavior, 17,* 277–288.

Nietzel, M. T., & Dillehay, R. C. (1986). *Psychological consultation in the courtroom.* New York: Pergamon Press.

Plutchik, R. (1995). Outward and inward directed aggressiveness: The interaction between violence and suicidality. *Pharmacopsychiatry, 28* (Supplement), 47–57.

Quinsey, V. L., Harris, G. T., Rice, M. E., & Cormier, C. A. (1998). *Violent offenders: Appraising and managing risk.* Washington, DC: American Psychological Association.

Rice, M. S., & Harris, G. T. (1997). Cross-validation and extension of the Violence Risk Appraisal Guide for child molesters and rapists. *Law and Human Behavior, 21,* 231–241.

Rogers, R. (1995). *Diagnostic and structured interviewing: A handbook for psychologists.* Odessa, FL: Psychological Assessment Resources.

Rogers, R., & Kelly, K. S. (1997). Denial and misreporting of substance abuse. In R. Rogers (Ed.), *Clinical assessment of malingering and deception* (2nd ed., pp. 108–129). New York: Guilford Press.

Rogers, R., Salekin, R. T., Hill, C., Murdock, M., Sewell, K. W., & Neumann, C. S. (In press). The Psychopathy Checklist—Screening Version: An examination of criteria and subcriteria in three forensic samples. *Criminal Justice and Behavior.*

Rosenfeld, B. (1999). Risk assessment in the wake of *Hendricks.* In American Psychological Association (Ed.), *Psychological expertise and criminal justice* (pp. 451–464). Washington, DC: American Psychological Association.

Salekin, R. T., & Rogers, R. (1998). Psychopathy and recidivism among female inmates. *Law and Human Behavior, 22,* 109–128.

Salekin, R. T., Rogers, R., & Sewell, K. W. (1996). A review and meta-analysis of the Psychopathy Checklist and the Psychopathy Checklist—Revised: Predictive validity of dangerousness. *Clinical Psychology: Science and Practice, 3,* 203–215.

Salekin, R. T., Rogers, R., & Sewell, K. W. (1997). Construct validity of psychopathy in a female offender sample: Multitrait-multimethod evaluation. *Journal of Abnormal Psychology, 106,* 576–585.

Schopp, R. F. (1996). Communicating risk assessments: Accuracy, efficacy, and responsibility. *American Psychologist, 51,* 939–944.

Sewell, K. W., & Salekin, R. T. (1997). Understanding and detecting dissimulation in sex offenders. In R. Rogers (Ed.), *Clinical assessment of malingering and deception* (2nd ed., pp. 328–350). New York: Guilford Press.

Shadish, W. R., Jr., & Sweeney, R. B. (1991). Mediators and moderators in meta-analysis: There's a reason we don't let dodo birds tell us which psychotherapies should have prizes. *Journal of Consulting and Clinical Psychology, 59,* 883–893.

Sheldrick, C. (1999). Practitioner review: The assessment and management of risk in adolescents. *Journal of Child Psychology and Psychiatry, 40,* 507–518.

Silver, E., Mulvey, E. P., & Monahan, J. (1999). Assessing violence risk among discharged psychiatric patients: Toward an ecological approach. *Law and Human Behavior, 23,* 237–255.

Smith, B. C., Penrod, S. D., Otto, A. L., & Park, R. C. (1996). Jurors' use of probabilistic evidence. *Law and Human Behavior, 20,* 49–82.

Strohman, L., O'Neill, M., & Heilbrun, K. (1999, August). *Violence risk communication: A review of the literature.* Paper presented at the Annual Convention of the American Psychological Association, Boston.

Sullivan, G., Wells, K. B., Morgenstern, H., & Leake, B. (1995). Identifying modifiable risk factors for rehospitalization: A case–control study of seriously mentally ill persons in Mississippi. *American Journal of Psychiatry, 152,* 1749–1759.

Webster, C. D., Douglas, K., Eaves, D., & Hart, S. D. (1997). *HCR-20: Assessing risk for violence, version 2.* Burnaby, BC, Canada: Simon Fraser University and Forensic Psychiatric Services Commission of British Columbia.

Werner, E. E. (1995). Resilience in development. *Current Directions in Psychological Science, 4,* 81–85.

14

The Short-Term Assessment of Risk and Treatability (START): A Prospective Validation Study in a Forensic Psychiatric Sample

TONIA L. NICHOLLS, JOHANN BRINK, SARAH L. DESMARAIS,
CHRISTOPHER D. WEBSTER AND MARY-LOU MARTIN

ABSTRACT: *A new assessment scheme—the Short-Term Assessment of Risk and Treatability (START)—presents a workable method for assessing risks to self and others encountered in mentally and personality disordered clients. This study aimed to demonstrate (a) prevalence and severity of risk behaviors measured by the START, (b) psychometric properties of START, (c) similarities and differences in START scores across different mental health professionals, and (d) concurrent validity of START with diverse negative outcomes. Treatment team members completed the 20-item, dynamically focused START for 137 forensic psychiatric inpatients. Prevalence and severity of START risk domains were measured for 51 patients detained in the hospital for 1 year. Results revealed high rates of generally low-level adverse events. With some exceptions, START scores were meaningfully associated with outcomes measured by a modified Overt Aggression Scale.*

KEYWORDS: *forensic assessment; forensic psychiatric patients; structured professional judgment; violence; suicide; self-harm; risk to self and others*

In the past several decades, considerable scholarly attention has been focused on the risks that persons with mental disorders pose to others (e.g., Monahan et al., 2001). Several statistical, mechanical, or actuarial (i.e., using empirically derived variables,

Reprinted by permission of Sage Publications. Assessment, 13 (3), 313–327. © 2006 Sage Publications.

e.g., MacArthur Iterative Classification Tree, Monahan et al., 2001; Violence Risk Appraisal Guide [VRAG], Quinsey, Harris, Rice, & Cormier, 1998) and clinical, professional guidelines have been developed for use in the assessment of risk for general, sexual, and domestic violence with adults (e.g., Forensic Inpatient Observation Scale [FIOS], Timmerman, Vastenburgh, & Emmelkamp, 2001; Historical Clinical Risk—20 [HCR-20], Webster, Douglas, Eaves, & Hart, 1997; Spousal Assault Risk Assessment Guide [SARA], Kropp, Hart, Webster, & Eaves, 1999; Risk of Sexual Violence Protocol [RSVP], Hart, Kropp, & Laws, 2003). In addition, guides also now exist for evaluating the risk to others posed by male and female children and adolescents (e.g., Early Assessment Risk List for Boys [EARL-20B], Augimeri, Koegl, Webster, & Levene, 2001; Early Assessment Risk List for Girls [EARL-21G], Levene et al., 2001; Structured Assessment of Violence Risk in Youth [SAVRY], Borum, Bartel, & Forth, 2003).

Many of these tools are likely best described as Structured Professional Judgment (SPJ) schemes, meaning that they use actuarial scores and structured assessment approaches to inform, not replace, clinical decision making (see Hart, 1998; Douglas, Ogloff, & Hart, 2003). With few exceptions, these instruments, often fashioned after the Psychopathy Checklist—Revised (PCL-R; Hare, 1991, 2003) and HCR-20 (Webster et al., 1997),[1] guide the assessor in considering variables relevant to the risk of violence to others posed by clients but provide few, if any, recommendations for assessing and managing other, common, and often comorbid management concerns (for an exception, see Jail Screening Assessment Tool [JSAT], Nicholls, Roesch, Olley, Ogloff, & Hemphill, 2005). Furthermore, they typically do not give any consideration to clients' strengths (for an exception, see SAVRY, Borum et al., 2003). The Short-Term Assessment of Risk and Treatability (START; Webster, Martin, Brink, Nicholls, & Middleton, 2004) is a structured clinical scheme to organize assessments, guide clinical interventions, and index possible improvement due to therapeutic interventions and other events, as well as map any evidence of mental and behavioral deterioration, across seven often-overlapping risk domains: risk to others, self-harm, suicide, self-neglect, substance abuse, unauthorized leave, and victimization by others. Although the START scheme stresses that it is essential to consider historical factors, the scale itself is composed entirely of dynamic variables scored for strengths and risks simultaneously. In the present article, we provide a review of the rationale for the development of START and describe the results of the first validation study to examine its potential clinical utility with forensic psychiatric patients.

A limitation of available tools intended to inform violence risk assessment and risk management is the restricted attention devoted to dynamic and clinical risk factors. As already noted, historical (e.g., prior aggression) and static (i.e., unchanging, e.g., gender, history of child abuse) predictors of risk provide a vital foundation for any risk evaluation. Yet the value of many such variables is considerably underplayed due to the fact that they offer little guidance for treatment. Recent research also suggests that dynamic, clinical variables contribute appreciably to assessments of acute and short-term violence risk (Gray, Snowden, & MacCulloch, 2004; Grevatt, Thomas-Peter, & Hughes, 2004; McNiel, Gregory, & Lam, 2003; Skeem & Mulvey, 2001) and that stable or static risk predictors such as psychopathy (Douglas, Guy, & Weir, 2005; Edens, Poythress, & Lilienfeld, 1999; Nicholls, Ogloff, & Douglas, 2004), substance abuse, and medication compliance might have less relevance in the inpatient setting than has been found in community follow-up studies (Serper et al., 2005). There is also the point that clients in forensic and correctional institutions have similar psychosocial backgrounds, rife with substance abuse, unstable upbringings, prior aggression to others, and maladaptive social support systems. This can mean that the items included in the many now-available schemes may have a relatively limited ability to distinguish among clients (Ferguson et al., 2005).

In most jurisdictions, mental health professionals have to comment on the need for treatment, potential dangerousness to self and others, and grave inability to care for self (Melton, Petrila, Poythress, & Slobogin, 1997). In comparison to the substantial advances made in assessing (and to a lesser extent managing) risk for violence to others, far fewer efforts have focused on minimizing the likelihood of other negative events, which often are prevalent in the lives of mentally ill individuals. To demonstrate, Brekke, Prindle, Bae, and Long (2001) found that persons who had mental illnesses were 14 times more likely to be the victims of violent crime than they were to be arrested for one. Similarly, the rate of suicide within psychiatric populations rises dramatically when compared to the risk in the general population (Brown, Beck, Steer, & Grisham, 2000).

Largely because of time constraints, the use of structured assessment guides in daily practice is conspicuously rare in the assessment and management of clinical evaluations of many diverse forms of risk to which mental health professionals must attend (e.g., suicide, self-harm, self-neglect; Gunstone, 2003). It is for these reasons that the potential use of a brief guide to assist in these important tasks warrants exploration. In a user satisfaction study described briefly in the START manual (Webster et al., 2004), we found diverse mental health professionals (psychiatrists, nurses, social workers) endorsed the user friendliness of START. The majority of staff (88%) indicated that they had sufficient time to code the form; 82% reported the items were easily applied to the individual patients and completion of START required 8 min on average.

Forensic and civil psychiatric patients, particularly those who are hospitalized, often are severely disabled and present with multiple risks and management challenges, which confront front-line staff and mental health professionals daily. Studies reveal high rates of violence, self-harm, and homelessness among persons with mental disorders (Ash, Galletly, Haynes, & Braben, 2003). Self-harm and suicide attempts (Hill, Rogers, & Bickford, 1996; Vaughan, Pullen, & Kelly, 2000) as well as threats and assaults on staff and copatients (Davies, 2001; Flannery, Hanson, & Penk, 1994) are relatively common occurrences in psychiatric institutions and are known to result in increased sick days, administrative costs, staff turnover, as well as substantial emotional and physical trauma to patients and staff (Hunter & Carmel, 1992; Rice, 1997; Rice & Harris, 1997). These negative events disrupt the clinical milieu, reduce staff morale, and present serious management challenges (Daffern & Howells, 2002). It is noteworthy that research suggests that male and female (Nicholls et al., 2004; Skeem et al., 2005) forensic and civil psychiatric patients (Seto, Harris, & Rice, 2004) present similar challenges for professionals.

Theoretical and empirical evidence shows that inwardly directed aggression (e.g., suicide, self-harm) and outwardly directed aggression (e.g., violence to others) reflect substantial overlap in their precipitating events (e.g., threat, insult) and in the predisposing profile (e.g., mental illness, personality disorder, coping style, impulsivity) of patients prone to exhibit these behaviors (Korn, Botsis, & Kotler, 1992; Links, Gould, & Ratnayake, 2003). Multiple theoretical frameworks have been advanced to explain the co-occurrence of violence against self and violence against others (for a review, see Hillbrand, 2001; also see Korn et al., 1992; Nikolova, Carignan, Moscovitz, & Demers, 2004).

Several studies confirm that clinical characteristics of violence and self-harm/suicide often overlap. Depression is common among people who are suicidal (Hillbrand, Foster, & Hirt, 1988) and also is a risk factor for violence (e.g., child abuse, see Ferguson et al., 2005; homicide-suicide, Hillbrand, 2001; Marzuk, Tardiff, & Hirsch, 1992). Anger is characteristic of people who are violent (Novaco & Renwick, 1998) but is also sometimes evident in individuals who are depressed (Fava, 1990) or suicidal (Goldsmith, Fyer, & Frances, 1990; Tardiff & Sweillam, 1980). Other risk factors such as panic disorders (Korn, Putchik, & Van Praag, 1997), impulsivity (Polvi, 1997; Stälenheim, 2001), substance abuse, child abuse (e.g., Warm, Murray, & Fox, 2003), and personality disorders (Links et al., 2003) are common among individuals who commit self-harm/suicide and among individuals who engage in aggression against others.

Extrapolating from the Epidemiological Catchment Area (ECA) survey (Swanson, Holzer, Ganju, & Jono, 1990) and a meta-analysis performed by Harris and Barraclough (1997), Hillbrand (2001) concluded that in all diagnostic categories, the odds of violence against self and against others are dramatically higher in psychiatric patients than in the general population. He reported that schizophrenia increases the odds of suicide by eight and the risk of violence to others by seven. These findings call into question the appropriateness of focusing our research and intervention efforts on violence risk to others to the relative neglect of other important risk considerations.

In one of the few studies to examine the predictive accuracy of existing structured professional judgment schemes for assessing diverse challenging behaviors in persons with mental disorder, Gray and colleagues (2003) administered some of the most well-established measures available, namely, the PCL-R (Hare, 1991), the H and C scales of the HCR-20 (i.e., HC-15, Webster et al., 1997), the Brief Psychiatric Rating Scale (BPRS, Overall & Gorham, 1962), and the 20-item Beck Hopelessness Scale (BHS, Beck, Weissman, Lester, & Trexler, 1974), to a small sample of mentally disordered offenders ($N = 34$) in the United Kingdom. One of the objectives of their study was to distinguish the relationship between the measures and different forms of violence (violence to others, property damage, verbal aggression, and violence to self). Aggression and self-harm were measured throughout a period of 3 months.

Of importance, Gray et al. (2003) noted that the BHS was significantly correlated with both the HCR-20 and the PCL-R. The BPRS yielded a substantial association with aggression against others ($r = .61$, AUC = .84). This was followed by the HC-15 at $r = .53$ (AUC = .81) and the PCL-R at .35 (AUC = .70). In all three cases, the correlations were statistically significant. The BHS scores did not yield a significant effect when physical aggression served as the outcome measure ($r = .18$, AUC $= .53$). It was, though, the only measure predictive of self-harm ($r = .67$, AUC $= .86$, $p < .001$, for both). The BPRS was found to be a good predictor of verbal aggression ($r = .58$, AUCs $= .81$) and physical violence ($r = .61$, AUCs $= .84$) but was a poor predictor of self-harm. In sum, schemes devised largely to predict violence against others performed as expected; the one scale included to measure self-injury did not have predictive power with respect to forecasting other-directed violence but was observed to have a substantial relationship with self-harm. Although it should be noted that this study was limited by its small sample size and a lack of clarity with regard to what was categorized as physical aggression, the results suggest that mental health professionals can enhance their ability to assess and manage the multiple risks presented by many clients so long as they are able and willing to use several separate measures, a proposal unlikely to be met with much enthusiasm among clinicians.

It was a consideration of all these issues that prompted the recent development of the START (Webster et al., 2004; for an overview of START's development, see Webster, Nicholls, Martin, Desmarais, & Brink, in press). The current study was designed as a first step in exploring the concurrent validity of the START in regard to inpatient risks to self and others among forensic psychiatric patients. Specific objectives were to (a) provide the first descriptive data available on the START, (b) report the prevalence and severity of the START risk domains in a sample of forensic psychiatric patients, (c) study the validity and reliability of START to determine if it has predictive accuracy according to dependent variables measured using a modified version of the Overt Aggression Scale (OAS; Yudofsky, Silver, Jackson, Endicott, & Williams, 1986), and (d) examine the extent to which externalizing and internalizing risks overlap.

METHOD

Participants

START Assessments

The sample of 137 patients ($n = 122$ men, 15 women) for which data are reported here was collected at the Forensic Psychiatric Hospital in British Columbia, Canada. All patients were under the authority of the British Columbia (BC) Review Board as a result of having been deemed Not Criminally Responsible on Account of Mental Disorder (i.e., Canada's insanity defence) or Unfit to Stand Trial by the courts. All such patients appear before the Review Board at least annually, with some having their progress and legal status reviewed more than once per year.[2]

We asked the treatment team members (i.e., psychiatrist, social worker, and senior nurse) of every patient who appeared before the Review Board throughout a 6-month period to complete the START just prior to the hearing date. The decision to use the Review Board hearing as the point of assessment for this study was a choice of convenience and ecological validity; it coincided with the time when the team conducted their formal risk assessment in preparation for the report to the Board and were most familiar with the patient's mental status and degree of progress. A total of 221 Review Board hearings were held at the forensic hospital between January and June 2003. To avoid double-counting adverse events during the follow-up period, we included nonduplicated patients only.[3] With three people on each team, we could, therefore, have as few as zero START forms or as many as three forms returned for a single patient.

A total of 331 START forms were completed by nine psychiatrists, eight senior nurses, and six social workers[4] for the 137 (122 men, 15 women) patients who appeared before 157 Review Boards. These were typically men (89%) with schizophrenia (83%) who often had comorbid substance-use disorder(s) (45%; see Table 1). On average, the men were 38.31 ($SD = 11.25$) years old and the women were 39.61 ($SD = 11.44$) years old. The mean length of stay in the hospital prior the Review Board hearings was 1,096.18 days ($SD = 1,834.41$, range = 21-14,502). Index offences were primarily for crimes against persons: 40% assault, 20% criminal harassment, 15% murder, and 10% mischief.[5] The Review Board hearing outcomes for male patients were as follows: custody = 85 (69.7%), conditional discharge = 31 (25.4%), absolute discharge = 3 (2.5%), reserved = 2 (1.6%), and fit to stand trial = 1 (.8%). Six women (40.0%) were given custody dispositions, eight women (53.3%) received conditional discharges, and one woman (6.7%) received an absolute discharge.

Validation Sample

Of the 137 patients in the initial START assessment sample, 51 patients who remained in-hospital throughout the duration of the follow-up period were included in the validation sample. As with the initial START assessment sample, these were typically men (90%) with schizophrenia (85%), more than half of whom had comorbid substance-use disorder(s) (55%; see Table 1). On average, patients in the validation sample were 40.11 years of age ($SD = 11.57$) and their mean length of stay in the hospital prior the Review Board hearings was 1,610.43 days ($SD = 1,732.90$, range = 36-8,297). Index offences were primarily for violent offences: 40% assault, 20% criminal harassment, 14% murder, and 10% mischief.

TABLE 1

Primary and Secondary Diagnoses of Forensic Psychiatric Inpatients by Attending Physicians at the Time of Discharge or Most Recent Review Board Hearing

	ALL PATIENTS		VALIDATION SAMPLE	
	n	%	*n*	%
PRIMARY DIAGNOSIS				
Schizophrenia	75	54.7	29	56.9
Schizophrenia spectrum	30	21.9	14	27.5
Other psychotic disorders	8	5.8	1	2.0
Due to medical condition	2	1.5	0	0.0
Depressive disorders	4	2.9	0	0.0
Bipolar disorders	8	5.8	1	2.0
Substance abuse disorders	3	2.2	1	2.0
Disorders diagnosed in childhood	3	2.2	3	5.9
Delirium/dementia	1	0.7	1	2.0
Personality disorder mixed	1	0.7	0	0.0
Sexual disorders	2	1.5	1	2.0
SECONDARY DIAGNOSIS				
Schizophrenia spectrum	1	1.0	0	0.0
Other psychotic disorders	3	2.9	0	0.0
Due to medical condition	3	2.9	2	3.9
Depressive disorders	4	3.8	2	3.9
Bipolar disorders	2	1.9	1	2.0
Substance abuse disorders	68	64.8	21	55.3
Disorders diagnosed in childhood	5	4.8	3	5.9
Delirium/dementia	2	1.9	0	0.0
Personality disorder/traits	13	12.4	8	21.1
Sexual disorders	2	1.9	1	2.0
Anxiety disorders	2	1.9	0	0.0

Note: All patients: primary diagnoses *N* = 137 (122 men, 15 women), secondary diagnoses *N* = 105 (93 men, 12 women). Validation sample: primary diagnoses *N* = 51 (48 men, 3 women), secondary diagnoses *N* = 38 (35 men, 3 women).

Measures

START

The START (Webster et al., 2004) scheme is designed to structure regular clinical assessments (i.e., treatment planning, progress evaluations, and assessments of risk to self and others). Evaluators consider the patient's strengths and risks on each of the 20 dynamic items to assess and manage risk to others, self-harm, suicide, unauthorized leave, self-neglect, substance abuse, and victimization by others. At the time this study was initiated, the START used a continuous 6-point scale (i.e., +++ at one pole indicating a considerable strength and − − − at the other pole indicating a substantial risk). Total scores reflect the sum of the individual 20 START items and range from 0 to 120.[6] For patients for whom multiple STARTs were completed, scores reflect an average of the raters' assessments.

Overt Aggression Scale—Revised

The Overt Aggression Scale (OAS) was designed to assess observable aggressive or violent behavior rather than tendencies. It consists of four categories: (a) verbal aggression, (b) physical aggression against objects, (c) physical aggression against self, and (d) physical aggression against other people. Each category of aggressive behavior is rated according to its severity on a 4-point scale from *least severe* (1) to *most severe* (4). We operationalized the dependent variables using a rating scale that the researchers developed by modifying Yudofsky et al.'s (1986) OAS to capture the START risk domains. The modified OAS is intended as an outcome measure for use in clinical practice and validation research with the START; it is available for use in the START workbook (see Appendix C, Webster, et al., in press). To circumvent the challenge of capturing low base rate behaviors and the erroneous false positives that occur in inpatient settings, we expanded our outcome measures to include suicide attempts and attempted unauthorized leave.

When coded from files, the interrater reliability of the OAS has been reported to be high (Intraclass Correlation Coefficient [ICC] = .82; Serper et al., 2005). A graduate-level research assistant with a master's degree in psychology who was trained to complete the modified OAS and blind to the START and modified OAS scores coded a subset of 10 files. In this study, the ICC for the two independent ratings of the OAS was acceptable at .70.

PROCEDURE

Approval for the study was obtained from the University of British Columbia Behavioural Research Ethics Board and the Forensic Psychiatric Services Commission of British Columbia Research Committee.

START Assessments

Following training workshops by one of the START authors, treatment team members were asked to complete the START on all of their patients scheduled to appear before the Review Board between January and June 2003. A research assistant sent START forms and reminders to the team members as scheduled hearings approached. The START ratings were completed independently by individual treatment team members. Ratings reflected treatment team meeting discussions with the patients and a review of file information as part of their routine diagnostic and risk evaluations in preparation for the Review Board hearings. Each member of the team was asked to complete the START ratings independently prior to the date of each patient's hearing and submit it to the research assistant through the hospital mail. In this way, we hoped to obtain three independent STARTs for each patient.

Follow-Up Data Collection

From the date of the Review Board hearing, outcome data on the revised OAS were collected for approximately 1 year ($M = 45.5$ weeks, $SD = 14.7$, $Mdn = 52$ weeks, range $= 1–52$ weeks) on all patients available for follow-up ($N = 129$).[7] Due to the broad range of follow-up length and the fact that we had few patients available for analyses of community adjustment, we conducted our validation analyses on the subsample of patients who received a custodial disposition and remained in the hospital throughout the duration of the 1-year period ($n = 51$).

Follow-up data were collected from clinical-legal files at the hospital and from all community forensic clinics in the BC lower mainland. A bachelor's level psychology research assistant with several years of forensic research experience was trained to review the files and complete the revised OAS by one of the authors. The research assistant, who was blind to the START evaluations, reviewed social, psychiatric, psychological, and legal reports; existing criminal records; and nursing notes to code the revised OAS. It was unnecessary to obtain updated, formal criminal records separately because all of these patients were under the care of the Forensic Psychiatric Services Commission, and this being so, any new charges or convictions were reported to their treatment teams and recorded on file.

ANALYSES

All analyses were conducted using SPSS 13.0 for Windows. Psychometric properties (e.g., distribution and reliability) of the START represent an important aspect of the project given that this is the first study examining this instrument. The facets of reliability examined included internal consistency, item homogeneity, and interrater reliability. Internal consistency was tested using Cronbach's alpha; we report mean interitem correlations as a measure of item homogeneity and intraclass correlation coefficients as a measure of interrater reliability. Using the subsample of patients detained in the hospital on custodial dispositions, we conducted validation analyses to examine the relationship between START total scores and individual risk estimates and the risk behaviors measured on revised OAS and with which the instrument is hypothesized to be associated (e.g., violence, self-harm, unauthorized leave, etc.). The principle means of analyzing predictive validity of the START was Receiver Operating Characteristic (ROC) analyses, the preferred method of evaluating the accuracy of assessment instruments (Hart, 1998; Mossman, 1994). The Area Under the Curve (AUC) reflects the probability that a randomly selected, truly violent patient will have been determined to be higher risk than a randomly selected, truly nonviolent patient (Swets, 1986). We also present point biserial correlations between the continuous predictor (START total score) and the dichotomous outcomes (presence or absence of challenging behaviors on the OAS).

RESULTS

Descriptive Information

Prevalence and Severity of Negative Outcomes

Nearly two thirds of the 51 inpatients engaged in some challenging behavior ($n = 33$, 64.7%) during the 1-year follow-up period. Not surprisingly, verbal aggression ($n = 31$, 60.8%) was the most common, followed by physical aggression against others ($n = 20$, 39.2%) and property damage ($n = 19$, 37.3%). Many patients also engaged in other behaviors that put their own safety and treatment progress at risk. None of the patients sampled attempted or completed suicide, although approximately 1 in 10 patients were identified by staff as requiring exceptional supervision for suicide/self-harm risk ($n = 6$, 11.8%). Six patients attempted ($n = 1$, 2.0%) or successfully took unauthorized leave ($n = 5$, 9.8%). Results of the revised OAS also indicated that several clients were using substances ($n = 18$, 35.3%) and/or neglecting their self-care ($n = 18$, 35.3%). It is noteworthy that the forensic psychiatric inpatients in this study were just as likely to be victimized by others ($n = 25$, 49.0%) or to engage in self-neglect ($n = 18$, 35.3%) as they were to commit physical aggression against others ($n = 20$, 39.2%).

Despite relatively high base rates in several of the START risk categories, results of the revised OAS indicated that the bulk of patients' aggression against self and others, as well as the other negative outcomes evidenced during follow-up, were of mild to moderate severity (see Table 2). To demonstrate, just 5.9% of the patients committed aggression against objects that was categorized in the two highest severity bins of the OAS (levels 3 and 4), and only 3.9% of the patients committed physical aggression against others that was categorized in level 4 (i.e., resulting in serious injury). None of the patients were classified in level 4 for physical aggression against self, self-neglect, physical aggression against others, or inappropriate sexual behavior.

START Scores in Forensic Psychiatric Inpatients

We present scores for the entire sample of patients for whom we had START assessments available ($N = 137$) and for the subsample of patients available for inpatient follow-up validation analyses ($n = 51$). Of the 137 patients sampled, 23 (16.8%) were rated high risk to others, 1 (.01%) patient was assessed as high risk for self-harm, none of the patients were rated high risk for suicide, and 15 (10.9%) were determined to be high risk to take unauthorized leave. The means and standard deviations of the item and total scores on the START are presented in Table 3. There was considerable dispersion in the scores, even in this sample of inpatient forensic psychiatric patients in which one might expect to see scores clumping at the extreme and providing little discriminating information.

TABLE 2

Nature and Severity of Aggression and Challenging Behaviors in a Forensic Psychiatric Inpatient Sample: Measured with the Modified Overt Aggression Scale

REVISED OAS CATEGORY & SEVERITY	FREQUENCY ($N = 51$)	
	n	%
Any challenging behavior	33	64.7
Verbal aggression[a]	31	60.8
Level 1	16	31.4
Level 2	18	35.3
Level 3	24	47.1
Level 4	14	27.5
Physical aggression—objects	19	37.3
Level 1	14	27.5
Level 2	14	27.5
Level 3	3	5.9
Level 4	2	3.9
Physical aggression—self	9	17.6
Level 1	3	5.9
Level 2	7	13.7
Level 3	1	2.0
Level 4	0	0.0
Physical aggression—others	20	39.2
Level 1	16	31.4
Level 2	17	33.3
Level 3	9	17.6
Level 4	0	0.0
Self-neglect	18	35.3
Level 1	12	23.5
Level 2	5	9.8
Level 3	5	9.8
Level 4	0	0.0
Substance use	18	35.3
Level 1	17	33.3
Level 2	6	11.8
Level 3	1	2.0
Level 4	1	2.0
Victimized by others	25	49.0
Level 1	7	13.7
Level 2	15	29.4
Level 3	11	21.6
Level 4	2	3.9
Sexual aggression	2	3.9
Level 1	1	2.0
Level 2	1	2.0
Level 3	0	0.0
Level 4	0	0.0

Note: OAS = Overt Aggression Scale.

a. Although the OAS includes verbal aggression to self in Level 4 of verbal aggression, verbal aggression in this table refers only to aggression to others.

TABLE 3

START Scores in a Sample of Forensic Psychiatric Inpatients

START ITEM	ALL PATIENTS (N = 137)				VALIDATION SAMPLE (N = 51)		
	M	(SD)	M	(SD)	RANGE	ICC	CITC
Insight	3.97	(1.26)	4.60	(1.19)	2–6	.65	.52
Attitudes	3.53	(1.10)	3.95	(1.20)	1–6	.73	.48
Mental state	3.49	(1.28)	4.17	(1.37)	0–6	.73	.50
Emotional state	3.33	(1.01)	3.82	(1.04)	1–6	.71	.54
Substance use	3.32	(1.44)	3.28	(1.85)	0–6	.89	.11
Impulse control	3.70	(1.06)	4.03	(1.23)	0–6	.56	.59
Treatability	3.37	(1.14)	3.98	(1.24)	0–6	.54	.66
Plans	3.61	(1.09)	4.32	(1.15)	0–6	.70	.58
External triggers	3.92	(0.79)	3.89	(1.24)	0–6	.27	.39
Social support	3.32	(1.07)	3.68	(1.32)	0–6	.58	.31
Material resources	3.33	(0.96)	3.56	(1.37)	0–6	.66	.60
Relationships	3.66	(0.91)	3.92	(1.12)	0–6	.46	.51
Social skills	3.46	(1.02)	3.89	(1.15)	1–6	.55	.41
Occupational	3.61	(1.04)	3.77	(1.52)	0–6	.42	.44
Recreational	3.46	(0.83)	3.60	(1.29)	0–6	.04	.43
Med. Adherence	3.33	(1.09)	3.68	(1.19)	1–6	.43	.27
Rule adherence	3.46	(1.02)	3.76	(1.22)	0–6	.69	.68
Coping	3.70	(0.92)	4.06	(1.07)	0–6	.79	.75
Self–care	2.90	(1.11)	3.23	(1.14)	0–6	.69	.36
Conduct	3.30	(1.04)	3.50	(1.39)	0–6	.59	.48
Total START	69.83	(14.62)	78.66	(13.18)	48–110	.87	—

Note: START = Short-Term Assessment of Risk and Treatability; ICC = intraclass correlation coefficient; CITC = corrected item-total correlation.

START Risk Estimates across Diverse Professional Groups

We had 23 mental health professionals who returned a total of 111 START forms reflecting their assessments of the patients detained in custody by the review boards ($n = 51$). Table 4 presents the frequency and proportion of patients rated low, moderate, or high on each of the four risk domains (risk to others, risk of self-harm, risk of suicide, and risk to take unauthorized leave) by professional group (all raters, psychiatry, nursing, and social work). As can be seen, the number of risk estimates available for analyses varied by profession. For instance, we received a total of 103 STARTs that included an evaluation of risk of harm to others: 40 from psychiatrists, 36 from nurses, and 27 from social workers. According to the ratings averaged across the professional groups, most assessments indicated little risk of self-harm ($n = 84$, 80%), suicide ($n = 89$, 85%), or unauthorized leave ($n = 66$, 64%); however, 50% ($n = 51$) of the assessments noted moderate risk to others and nearly one in every five reflected a concern that the patient presented a substantial risk to others (17%, $n = 17$).

A review of the data presented in Table 4 demonstrates considerable concordance between evaluations of forensic psychiatric inpatients' risk for harm to others, self-harm,

TABLE 4

A Comparison of START Risk Estimates in a Sample of Forensic Psychiatric Inpatients across Professional Groups

STRUCTURED PROFESSIONAL JUDGMENT OF RISK BY PROFESSION

START RISK DOMAIN	n	ALL RATERS (N = 23)		
		LOW n (%)	MOD. n (%)	HIGH n (%)
Risk to others	103	35 (34)	51 (50)	17 (17)
Self-harm	105	84 (80)	21 (20)	0 (0)
Suicide	105	89 (85)	16 (15)	0 (0)
Unauthorized leave	104	66 (64)	29 (28)	9 (9)

START RISK DOMAIN	n	PSYCHIATRISTS (n = 9)		
		LOW n (%)	MOD. n (%)	HIGH n (%)
Risk to others	40	6 (15)	26 (65)	8 (20)
Self-harm	40	32 (80)	8 (20)	0 (0)
Suicide	40	32 (80)	8 (20)	0 (0)
Unauthorized leave	40	23 (58)	15 (38)	2 (5)

START RISK DOMAIN	n	NURSES (n = 8)		
		LOW n (%)	MOD. n (%)	HIGH n (%)
Risk to others	36	18 (50)	12 (33)	6 (17)
Self-harm	37	30 (81)	7 (19)	0 (0)
Suicide	37	33 (89)	4 (11)	0 (0)
Unauthorized leave	37	24 (65)	7 (19)	6 (16)

START RISK DOMAIN	n	SOCIAL WORKERS (n = 6)		
		LOW n (%)	MOD. n (%)	HIGH n (%)
Risk to others	27	11 (41)	13 (41)	3 (11)
Self-harm	28	22 (79)	6 (21)	0 (0)
Suicide	28	24 (86)	4 (14)	0 (0)
Unauthorized leave	27	19 (70)	7 (26)	1 (4)

Note: N = 51 inpatients. Mod = Moderate. The number of Short-Term Assessments of Risk and Treatability (STARTs) completed varied by profession: all raters combined n = 111, psychiatrists n = 42, case managers n = 37, social workers n = 32.

suicide, and violence across the three professional groups, with the one exception being psychiatrists ratings of patients' risk of violence to others. Although not presented in Table 4, we found that the mean START total scores for psychiatrists' assessments ($M = 82.17$, $SD = 11.92$) were higher than for those completed by nurses ($M = 76.94$, $SD = 12.23$) and social workers ($M = 76.03$, $SD = 15.08$); however, pairwise comparisons indicated that START total scores did not vary significantly across professional groups.

TABLE 5

Psychometric Characteristics of the Short-Term Assessment of Risk and Treatability (START) in a Sample of Forensic Psychiatric Inpatients by Profession of Rater

PROFESSION	N	M	SD	RANGE	MIC	M CITC	ALPHA
All assessors	111	76.71	13.70	48–110	.27	.48	.87
Psychiatrists	42	79.29	13.07	55–108	.18	.38	.80
Nurses	37	75.92	13.60	57–110	.30	.52	.88
Social workers	32	74.25	15.03	48–105	.40	.61	.92

Table header spanning: PSYCHOMETRIC CHARACTERISTICS OF START

Note: $N = 51$ inpatients. MIC = mean interitem correlation, CITC = corrected item-total correlation. Ns reported refer to the number of assessments.

Structural Reliability

Table 5 presents the psychometric properties of the START, including descriptive and structural reliability characteristics. An interrater reliability check was conducted on all assessors ($n = 111$ START forms) who completed STARTs for the patients available for inpatient follow-up ($n = 51$) and individually for each of the professional groups (START forms: psychiatrists $n = 42$, case managers $n = 37$, social workers $n = 32$). The interrater reliability between the three assessor professions using the intraclass correlation coefficient was $ICC_2 = .87$, $p < .001$. Table 5 also presents the internal consistency (Cronbach's alpha) of the total START scores for all raters ($\alpha = .87$) and for psychiatrists ($\alpha = .80$), case managers ($\alpha = .88$), and social workers ($\alpha = .92$). Item homogeneity was measured using the mean interitem correlation. With the exception of psychiatrists (MIC = .18), the MIC exceeded .20, generally recognized to reflect a unidimensional scale, and the findings are well within the range of MIC reported in the PCL:SV manual (Hart, Cox, & Hare, 1995, p. 38) and in research with the HCR-20 (see Douglas et al., 2005). These findings are generally consistent with similar measures also intended to structure clinical decision making, such as the HCR-20 Violence Risk Assessment Scheme (Webster et al., 1997; see Douglas et al., 2005).

Relationship Between START and Aggression Against Others, Aggression Against Self, and Other Challenging Behaviors in an Inpatient Forensic Psychiatric Sample

The mean START scores of patients who aggressed against others were significantly higher than for those patients who remained incident free during the follow-up period. The findings held true across multiple types and severities of challenging behaviors: any aggression to others ($M = 65.86$ vs. 75.66, $p = .001$), verbal aggression ($M = 66.82$ vs. 75.86, $p = .001$), aggression against objects ($M = 68.00$ vs. 77.90, $p = .001$), physical aggression against others ($M = 68.25$ vs. 76.32, $p = .001$), violence against others

TABLE 6

The Relationship Between the Short-Term Assessment of Risk and Treatability (START) and Challenging and Aggressive Behaviors in Forensic Psychiatric Patients

MODIFIED OAS	ALL PATIENTS BEFORE REVIEW BOARD (n = 129)				INPATIENT VALIDATION SUBSAMPLE (n = 51)			
	r_{pb}	AUC	95% CI	SE_{AUC}	r_{pb}	AUC	95% CI	SE_{AUC}
Verbal aggression—others	.27***	.67	.61–.73***	.033	.27	.72	.58–.86***	.072
Physical aggression—objects	.27***	.69	.62–.76*	.037	.14	.67	.52–.83*	.077
Physical aggression—others	.23***	.65	.57–.72***	.037	.21	.70	.55–.85**	.076
Sexually inappropriate[a]	.12*	.65	.43–.86	.108	.30*	.92	.79–1.05*	.066
Self-harm	.16**	.66	.54–.77**	.059	.22	.67	.50–.84	.088
Attempt unauthorized leave[a]	.18**	.77	.62–.93**	.080	.18	.92	.85–1.00	.038
Take unauthorized leave	.03	.52	.43–.62	.049	−.13	.31	.13–.50	.095

NOTE: OAS = Overt Aggression Scale; r_{pb} = point biserial correlation coefficient; AUC = area under the receiver operating curve; CI = confidence interval; SE = standard error.

a. Note that in the inpatient sample, only two patients were sexually inappropriate and just one patient attempted unauthorized leave, indicating that the results are likely biased and extremely unstable.

*p < .05. **p < .02. ***p < .001.

($M = 69.12$ vs. 81.82, $p = .001$), and sexual aggression ($M = 70.24$ vs. 80.63, $p = .05$). Mean START scores also differed significantly between patients who aggressed against themselves and those who did not, $t (n = 51) = 2.61$, $p = .01$. It is noteworthy that we found a significant difference between the total START scores of patients who attempted to take unauthorized leave (86.89) and those who did not (70.07; $p < .001$).

Results of the univariate analyses (correlations and ROC) of concurrent validity of the START in relation to the modified OAS can be found in Table 6. Tests of the association between START and the OAS for all 129 patients for whom we had combined information about inpatient and community outcome revealed promising results. With the exception of unauthorized leave, the START total scores were found to have moderate and generally statistically significant relationships with the risk behaviors measured with the OAS.

When we examined the inpatient behavior of the sub-sample of 51 patients who received custody dispositions and who were detained in the hospital for the entire 1-year follow-up period, we found further evidence of the strength and direction of the relationship between the START and challenging inpatient behaviors we hypothesized. Results in Table 6 show moderate-sized point biserial correlation coefficients that generally did not reach significance. The ROC analyses, perhaps less affected by base rates, also were moderate to moderate/large but generally were statistically significant.

Overlapping Risks

One of the primary rationales for the START and the aims of this study is to better understand the extent to which challenging behaviors in psychiatric populations overlap with one another and can inform risk assessment and risk management efforts. To clarify, we hypothesized that many forensic psychiatric patients would present with multiple management concerns. For instance, patients who engaged in aggression against others were predicted also to be likely to commit self-harm or suicide as well as engaging in other behaviors likely to present management concerns (e.g., unauthorized leave) and/or interfere with their treatment and recovery (e.g., substance use). As expected, there was a great deal of correspondence between the various negative outcomes throughout the 1-year follow-up period. A considerable proportion of the patients who physically aggressed against others also were using substances (35.0%), neglecting their self-care (45.0%), and/or were victimized by others (70.0%). Similarly, the majority of patients who took unauthorized leaves also were found to be using substances (80.0%) and to have physically aggressed against others (80.0%). Of interest, patients who engaged in self-harm or who were identified by staff as being at risk for suicide/self-harm also were likely to express externalized aggression (84.6%). Of the nine patients (17.6%) who committed acts of self-harm, seven (77.8%) also were found to have been physically aggressive to others. Six patients were identified as being at risk for suicide/self-harm, and of these, five (83.3%) engaged in some form of aggression at least once during the approximately 1-year study period.

Using the phi coefficient, the correlation matrix in Table 7 demonstrates the inter-relationships between aggression against self and aggression against others in the subsample of forensic psychiatric inpatients (n =51). As expected, we found evidence of substantial associations between internalized and externalized aggression. Patients who were physically aggressive to others also were likely to have committed self-harm (φ = .37, p = .008). We found that self-harm was associated with multiple forms of aggression against others, although the relationships did not all reach significance (verbal φ = .27, p = .059; property φ = .60, p < .001; sexual φ = .17, p = .23). Similarly, patients who were physically aggressive to others were also at greater risk to be victimized themselves (φ = .34, p = .016).[8]

DISCUSSION

In an era of financial restraint, deinstitutionalization, and subsequent decreased access to inpatient health-care, administrators and practitioners are keen to identify procedures that promote evidence-based practice and comprehensive care. As such, strategies that effectively assist in the management of multiple challenging behaviors known to reduce treatment effectiveness and prevent release, or conversely, increase patients' strengths, are promising developments and worthwhile endeavors. The assessment and management of violence among mentally and personality disordered

TABLE 7

Phi Correlation Coefficients Between the START Risk Behaviors: Relationship Between Aggression to Others, Self-Harm, and Other Risk Behaviors in a Sample of Forensic Psychiatric Inpatients ($n = 51$)

START RISK ESTIMATE

OAS ITEM/DEPENDENT VARIABLE	VERBAL	OBJECTS	PHYSICAL	SEXUAL	SELF-HARM	UL	SA	NEGLECT	VICTIM
Risk to others									
Verbal aggression		.45***	.65***	.16	.27	.27	.01	.01	.37**
Aggression against objects			.54***	.26	.60***	.02	−.06	.11	.30*
Physical aggression to others				.25	.37**	.28*	−.01	.16	.34**
Sexually inappropriate behavior					.17	−.07	−.15	.06	.00
Self-harm						.02	−.13	.09	.27
Unauthorized Leave (UL)							.31*	.03	.20
Substance Abuse (SA)								−.03	.26
Self-Neglect (Neglect)									.10
Victimized by Others (Victim)									

Note: OAS = Overt Aggression Scale. Suicide is a Short-Term Assessment of Risk and Treatability (START) risk estimate but was not included in the analyses because there was no evidence any of the patients attempted or completed suicide during the follow-up period. Note that not all of these variables are included in analyses of concurrent validity owing to the fact that they were not included on the version of START used at the time this study was conducted.

$*p \leq .05$. $**p \leq .02$. $***p \leq .001$.

clients has consumed the literature in recent years. In contrast, efforts to implement tools into daily practice that assist clinicians to identify and manage other relevant mental health risks have lagged behind advances in violence risk assessment research and practice. A better understanding of the multiple challenges confronting a client and the treatment team is likely to improve violence risk assessment accuracy, risk management, the therapeutic alliance, as well as guiding treatment and treatment evaluation, all of which increase the likelihood of improved mental health status, community release, and cost-effectiveness.

Professionals in community clinics and inpatient forensic psychiatric settings are mandated to provide care that encompasses much more than dangerous, aggressive, and violent behavior. In line with our review in the introduction to this article, scholars (Apter et al., 1991; Hillbrand, 1992, 1995, 2001; Links et al., 2003; Plutchik, 1995) have asserted for more than a decade that there is a need for further investigation into the relationship between violence directed outwardly and self-destructive forms of violence and the development and testing of appropriate assessment and management tools. Hillbrand (2001) recommends that assessments of risk for violence to self and others ought to go hand-in-hand.

This study investigated the psychometric properties of a new instrument intended to guide assessment and management of diverse populations of mentally and personality disordered persons and intended to act as a clinical indicator of treatment progress. Our primary interest was to examine the utility of using START to identify patients who are at risk for diverse challenging behaviors, including aggression and violence, self-harm, suicide, and unauthorized absences. Our results provide preliminary evidence for the validity and practicality of considering these issues simultaneously with an instrument such as the START.

The fact that the scores of the patients detained in custody were generally higher than that of the entire sample of patients appearing before the review board in a 6-month period offers preliminary evidence of the concurrent validity of the START (i.e., presumably, higher risk patients would be more likely to be detained). Furthermore, there was considerable dispersion in the START scores, suggesting that the measure is potentially useful for distinguishing between patients, even in an inpatient population with a lengthy history of mental health problems and contact with the criminal justice system (see Hart et al., 1995, p. 41). This is an important finding, suggesting that the START is a useful method of identifying patients with greatest need and a useful means of allocating scarce resources. Furthermore, the descriptive statistics for the items demonstrate that there is not an extreme endorsement frequency for any items, at least not so extreme as to affect the measure's validity or reliability. Despite the fact that staff did not have access to the complete START manual (Webster et al., 2004), which had not been published at the time the study was conducted, raters were able to achieve acceptable levels of interrater reliability and the instrument appears to have structural reliability rivaling established instruments that use a similar approach and are intended to identify personality disorders (e.g., PCL:SV, Hart et al., 1995) and violence risk (HCR-20, Webster et al., 1997; see Douglas et al., 2005). Furthermore, our concurrent validity results suggest that START might be a valid means of assessing and monitoring forensic psychiatric patients. Our current research efforts are focused on examining the START's dynamic items as a useful means of monitoring patient progress and planning for effective interventions as well as comparing and contrasting the importance of considering patients' strengths in combination with their risks.

Thinking of aggression against others, aggression against self, and other risk behaviors (e.g., substance abuse, self-neglect, unauthorized leave) together has important implications for assessment, management, and prevention strategies. Current practices tend to emphasize the differences in the presentation and needs of patients who commit violence and those who demonstrate self-destructive behaviors, to the neglect of similarities. Hillbrand's (2001) comprehensive review of homicide-suicide and other co-occurring forms of aggression against self and aggression against others coupled with our findings, and that of previous studies (e.g., Lewinsohn, Rohde, & Seeley, 1994), including longitudinal research (Mann, Waternaux, Haas, & Malone, 1999), demonstrates that externalized and internalized aggression are not completely distinct and knowledge of one might inform assessments of the other. The START provides a multidimensional approach to assessing, managing, and treating risk-related behavior and improving the prognosis of psychiatric patients, potentially, across seven risk domains.

Planning for effective treatment with clients who present with multiple challenging behaviors is difficult. Forensic psychiatric services are intended to do more than simply manage the risk patients pose to the public—they should work to restore and maintain the mental health and well-being of patients. The Gray et al. (2003) study confirmed that efforts to make use of available tools to evaluate co-occurring risk among mentally and personality disordered patients would be a time-consuming exercise requiring the use of multiple tools for each risk category. In light of the co-occurring risky behaviors common to civil and forensic psychiatric patients (Seto et al., 2004) and the need for a suitable tool for informing short-term assessment and treatment of complex and inter-mingled risks (Gray et al., 2003; Hillbrand, 2001), the authors developed the START as a structured professional judgment guide to extend the use of evidence-based decision support tools to inform therapeutic assessments and risk reduction efforts (Webster et al., 2004). A review of the extant literature on the theoretical and empirical etiologies and comorbidity of multidimensional risks among patients with mental and personality disorders suggests that such an approach might have wide application with civil, forensic, and correctional clients. The present study provides preliminary evidence that START risk categories are not uncommon in a forensic inpatient setting and often co-occur in individual patients, presenting exceptional management and treatment challenges that require holistic approaches to care.

This study had the advantage of being prospective, and although we were studying low base rate behaviors, we amassed information on multiple outcome measures relevant to a single risk category to capture variables that are otherwise difficult to assess in relatively small sample sizes (e.g., attempting to take unauthorized leave as well as successful unauthorized leaves, being placed on self-harm/suicide watch in addition to self-harming behaviors). We also had the advantage of in vivo (i.e., interview + file review) START assessments completed by the treatment teams as part of their routine diagnostic evaluations in preparation for the review board hearings. Although this reflects strong ecological validity, the study nonetheless suffered other limitations.

Our results should be considered with several caveats in mind. First, these findings doubtless reflect an underestimation of the prevalence of inpatient aggression because we did not complete patient and/or collateral interviews (Monahan et al., 2001). Investigators have cautioned that hospital charts and incident reports reflect underreporting of inpatient aggression (Ehmann et al., 2001). Second, generalizability is limited to inpatient forensic psychiatric populations of primarily male schizophrenic patients.

Having been conducted in a Canadian forensic psychiatric inpatient setting, the study will need to be replicated in other settings (e.g., civil psychiatric hospitals) as well as testing the utility in other cultures and legal jurisdictions. Finally, although having the START completed by practicing attending mental health professionals following team meetings reflects the manner in which START is intended to be used, our design might very well have inflated interrater agreement and/or our results might underestimate interdisciplinary professional differences.

NOTES

1. Although it should be noted that the Psychopathy Checklist—Revised (PCL-R) is not a risk assessment instrument, it would be difficult to deny that the Psychopathy Checklist (PCL) family of instruments (PCL, PCL-R, PCL:Screening Version [PCL:SV]) and other early instruments such as the HCR-20 have had a dramatic influence on the development of many of the risk assessment manuals that have been produced in recent years (e.g., the 0, 1, 2 coding; use of ~20 items with brief coding descriptions).

2. In Canada, there are three potential dispositions resulting from a Review Board hearing. Custody dispositions require that the individual resides at a psychiatric hospital under the care of a treatment team. A Conditional Discharge indicates that the patient will reside in the community while remaining under the care and supervision of a treatment team and reporting regularly to a forensic psychiatric clinic. An Absolute Discharge indicates that the patient is no longer compelled to be under the care of a treatment team and has no further duty to report to the court or the Review Board.

3. If a patient had more than one hearing during the study period, we used the hearing for which the most team members had completed the Short-Term Assessment of Risk and Treatability (START), and if those were equal, we used their latest hearing. Excluding duplicated patients reduced the sample to 157 patients with at least one appearance before the tribunal; however, no forms were submitted on behalf of 19 patients and 1 patient was excluded due to too few START items completed, leaving a sample of 137 patients.

4. The overall completion rate of the START forms by the treatment team members was 71%: 83% by psychiatrists, 70% by senior nurses, and 59% by social workers.

5. Although our small sample of women prevents us from reporting statistical differences, men did not appear to be more likely than women to have index offences for assault or violence (sex offences included; $n = 83$, 67.5% of men; $n = 7$, 46.7% of women) or murder ($n = 13$, 14.6% of men; $n = 2$, 13.3% of women).

6. The START has been modified since this study was initiated. It now uses two separate scales for strengths and risks. The instrument is coded in a manner consistent with the PCL-R (Hare, 2003) and the HCR-20 (Webster, Douglas, Eaves, & Hart, 1997; 0 = item is not evident, 1 = item is evident to some extent, 2 = item is present). One further difference between the version of the START used in the study and the published START is that evaluators provided Summary Risk Estimates (coded 0 = low, 1 = moderate, 2 = high) for just four (i.e., risk to others, self-harm, suicide, unauthorized leave) of the now seven START risk domains.

7. A total of 8 patients were excluded from follow-up: 4 patients (3 men, 1 woman) received Absolute Discharges and 4 patients (3 men, 1 woman) received Conditional Discharges to clinics outside the British Columbia lower mainland.

8. The likelihood of aggression against others, measured with the odds ratio statistic, was substantially higher among patients who engaged in self-harm. This was true of physical aggression (odds ratio [OR] = 7.81, 95% confidence interval [CI] = 1.42–42.83) and sexual aggression (OR = 5.13, 95% CI = .29–90.70) but the low base rate prevents us from identifying significant relationships (i.e., the CIs contain one and, therefore, cannot be assumed to represent a valid significant difference).

REFERENCES

Apter, A., Kotler, M., Sevy, S., Plutchik, R., Brown, S. L., Foster, H., et al. (1991). Correlates of risk of suicide in violent and nonviolent psychiatric patients. *American Journal of Psychiatry, 148,* 883–887.

Ash, D., Galletly, C., Haynes, J., & Braben, P. (2003). Violence, self-harm, victimisation and homelessness in patients admitted to an acute inpatient unit in South Australia. *International Journal of Social Psychiatry, 49,* 112–118.

Augimeri, L. K., Koegl, C. J., Webster, C. D., & Levene, K. S. (2001). *Early Assessment Risk List for Boys (EARL-20B), Version 2.* Toronto, Canada: Earlscourt Child Family Centre.

Beck, A. T., Weissman, A., Lester, D., & Trexler, L. (1974). The measurement of pessimism: The hopelessness scale. *Journal of Clinical Psychology, 42,* 861–865.

Borum, R., Bartel, P., & Forth, A. (2003). *Manual for the Structured Assessment of Violence Risk in Youth (SAVRY), Version 1.1.* Tampa: University of South Florida, Louis de la Parte Florida Mental Health Institute.

Brekke, J. S., Prindle, C., Bae, S. W., & Long, J. D. (2001). Risks for individuals with schizophrenia who are living in the community. *Psychiatric Services, 52,* 1358–1366.

Brown, G. K., Beck, A. T., Steer, R. A., & Grisham, J. R. (2000). Risk factors for suicide in psychiatric outpatients: A 20-year prospective study. *Journal of Consulting and Clinical Psychology, 68,* 371–377.

Daffern, M., & Howells, K. (2002). Psychiatric inpatient aggression: A review of structural and functional assessment approaches. *Aggression & Violent Behavior, 7,* 477–497.

Davies, S. (2001). Assaults and threats on psychiatrists. *Psychological Bulletin, 25,* 89–91.

Douglas, K. S., Guy, L., & Weir, J. (2005). *HCR-20 violence risk assessment scheme: Overview and annotated bibliography.* Available: www.violence-risk.com. Accessed April 19, 2007.

Douglas, K. S., Ogloff, J. R. P., & Hart, S. D. (2003). Evaluation of a model of violence risk assessment among forensic psychiatric patients. *Psychiatric Services, 54,* 1372–1379.

Edens, J., Poythress, N., & Lilienfeld, S. (1999). Identifying inmates at risk for disciplinary infractions: A comparison of two measures of psychopathy. *Behavioral Sciences and the Law, 17,* 435–443.

Ehmann, T. S., Smith, G. N., Yamamoto, A., McCarthy, N., Ross, D., Au, T., et al. (2001). Violence in treatment resistant psychotic inpatients. *Journal of Nervous & Mental Disease, 189,* 716–721.

Fava, M. (1990). "Anger attacks": Possible variants of panic and major depressive disorders. *American Journal of Psychiatry, 147,* 867–890.

Ferguson, C. J., Averill, P. M., Rhoades, H., Rocha, D., Gruber, N. P., & Gummattira, P. (2005). Social isolation, impulsivity, and depression as predictors of aggression in psychiatric inpatient population. *Psychiatric Quarterly, 76,* 123–137.

Flannery, R. B., Hanson, M. A., & Penk, W. E. (1994). Risk factors for psychiatric inpatient assaults on staff. *Journal of Mental Health Administration, 21,* 24–31.

Goldsmith, S. J., Fyer, M. R., & Frances, A. J. (1990). Personality and suicide. In S. J. Blumenthal & D. J. Kupfer (Eds.), *Suicide over the life cycle: Risk factors, assessment, and treatment of suicidal patients* (pp. 155–176). Washington, DC: American Psychiatric Association.

Gray, N. S., Hill, C., McGleish, A., Timmons, D., MacCulloch, M. J., & Snowden, R. J. (2003). Prediction of violence and self-harm in mentally disordered offenders: A prospective study of the efficacy of HCR-20, PCL-R, and psychiatric symptomatology. *Journal of Consulting and Clinical Psychology, 71,* 443–451.

Gray, N. S., Snowden, R. J., & MacCulloch, S. (2004). Relative efficacy of criminological, clinical, and personality measures of future risk of offending in mentally disordered offenders: A comparative study of HCR-20, PCL:SV, and OGRS. *Journal of Consulting & Clinical Psychology, 72,* 523–530.

Grevatt, M., Thomas-Peter, B., & Hughes, G. (2004). Violence, mental disorder and risk assessment: Can structured clinical assessments predict the short-term risk of inpatient violence? *Journal of Forensic Psychiatry and Psychology, 15,* 278–292.

Gunstone, S. (2003). Risk assessment and management of patients with self-neglect: A "grey area" for mental health workers. *Journal of Psychiatric and Mental Health Nursing, 10,* 287–296.

Hare, R. D. (1991). *The Hare Psychopathy Checklist—Revised.* Toronto, Canada: Multi-Health Systems.

Hare, R. D. (2003). *Hare Psychopathy Checklist—Revised (PCL-R): 2nd edition.* Toronto, Canada: Multi-Health Systems.

Harris, E. C., & Barraclough, B. (1997). Suicide as an outcome for mental disorders: A meta-analysis. *British Journal of Psychiatry, 170,* 205–228.

Hart, S. D., Cox, D. N., & Hare, R. D. (1995). *Manual for the Psychopathy Checklist: Screening Version (PCL:SV).* Toronto, Canada: Multi-Health Systems.

Hart, S. D. (1998). The role of psychopathy in assessing risk for violence: Conceptual and methodological issues. *Legal and Criminological Psychology, 3,* 121–137.

Hart, S. D., Kropp, P. R., & Laws, D. (2003). *The Risk for Sexual Violence Protocol.* Vancouver, Canada: Mental Health, Law, and Policy Institute, Simon Fraser University.

Hill, C. D., Rogers, R., & Bickford, M. E. (1996). Predicting aggressive and socially disruptive behavior in a maximum security forensic psychiatric hospital. *Journal of Forensic Sciences, 41,* 56–59.

Hillbrand, M. (1992). Self-directed and other-directed aggressive behavior in a forensic sample. *Suicide & Life-Threatening Behavior, 22,* 333–340.

Hillbrand, M. (1995). Aggression against self and aggression against others in violent psychiatric patients. *Journal of Consulting & Clinical Psychology, 63,* 668–671.

Hillbrand, M. (2001). Homicide-suicide and other forms of co-occurring aggression against self and against others. *Professional Psychology: Research & Practice, 32,* 626–635.

Hillbrand, M., Foster, H. G., & Hirt , M. (1988). Variables associated with violence in a forensic population. *Journal of Interpersonal Violence, 3,* 371–380.

Hunter, M., & Carmel, H. (1992). The cost of staff injuries from inpatient violence. *Hospital and Community Psychiatry, 43,* 586–588.

Korn, M. L., Botsis, A. J., & Kotler, M. (1992). The Suicide and Aggression Survey: A semistructured instrument for the measurement of suicidality and aggression. *Comprehensive Psychiatry, 33,* 359–365.

Korn, M. L., Putchik, R., & Van Praag, H. M. (1997). Panic-associated suicidal and aggressive ideation and behavior. *Journal of Psychiatric Research, 31,* 481–487.

Kropp, P. R., Hart, S. D., Webster, C. D., & Eaves, D. (1999). *Manual for the Spousal Assault Risk Assessment Guide* (3rd ed.). Toronto, Canada: Multi-Health Systems.

Levene, K. S., Augimeri, L. K., Pepler, D. J., Walsh, M. M., Webster, C. D., & Koegl, C. J. (2001). *Early Assessment Risk List for Girls (EARL-21G), Version 1: Consultation edition.* Toronto, Canada: Earlscourt Child Family Centre.

Lewinsohn, P. M., Rohde, P., & Seeley, J. R. (1994). Psychosocial risk factors for future adolescent suicide attempts. *Journal of Consulting & Clinical Psychology, 62,* 297–305.

Links, P. S., Gould, B., & Ratnayake, R. (2003). Assessing suicidal youth with antisocial, borderline, or narcissistic personality disorder. *Canadian Journal of Psychiatry, 48,* 301–310.

Mann, J. J., Waternaux, C., Haas, G. L., & Malone, K. M. (1999). Toward a clinical model of suicidal behaviour in psychiatric patients. *American Journal of Psychiatry, 156,* 181–189.

Marzuk, P. M., Tardiff, K., & Hirsch, C. S. (1992). The epidemiology of murder-suicide. *Journal of the American Medical Association, 267,* 3179–3183.

McNiel, D. E., Gregory, A. L., & Lam, J. N. (2003). Utility of decision support tools for assessing acute risk of violence. *Journal of Consulting & Clinical Psychology, 71,* 945–953.

Melton, G., Petrila, J., Poythress, N., & Slobogin, C. (1997). *Psychological evaluations for the court.* New York: Guilford.

Monahan, J., Steadman, H., Silver, E., Appelbaum, P., Robbins, P., Mulvey, E., et al. (2001). *Rethinking risk assessment: The MacArthur study of mental disorder and violence.* New York: Oxford University Press.

Mossman, D. (1994). Assessing predictions of violence: Being accurate about accuracy. *Journal of Consulting and Clinical Psychology, 62,* 783–792.

Nicholls, T. L., Ogloff, J. R. P., & Douglas, K. S. (2004). Assessing risk for violence among female and male civil psychiatric patients: The HCR-20, PCL:SV, and McNiel & Binder's VSC. *Behavioral Sciences and the Law, 22,* 127–158.

Nicholls, T. L., Roesch, R., Olley, M., Ogloff, J. R. P., & Hemphill, J. (2005). *Jail Screening Assessment Tool (JSAT): A guide for conducting mental health screening in jails and pretrial centres.* Burnaby, Canada: Mental Health, Law, and Policy Institute, Simon Fraser University.

Nikolova, M., Carignan, N., Moscovitz, N., & Demers, L. (2004). The psychogeriatric and risk behavior assessment scale (PARBAS): A new measure for use with older adults living in the community. *Archives of Gerontology & Geriatrics, 39,* 187–200.

Novaco, R. W., & Renwick, S. J. (1998). Anger predictors of the assaultiveness of forensic hospital patients. In E. Sanavio (Ed.), *Behavior and cognitive therapy today. Essays in honor of Hans J. Eysenck* (pp. 199–208). Oxford, UK: Elsevier Science.

Overall, J. E., & Gorham, D. R. (1962). The Brief Psychiatric Rating Scale. *Psychological Reports, 10,* 799–812.

Plutchik, R. (1995). Outward and inward directed aggressiveness: The interaction between violence and suicidality. *Pharmacopsychiatry, 28,* 47–57.

Polvi, N. H. (1997). Assessing risk of suicide in correctional settings. In C. D. Webster & M. A. Jackson (Eds.), *Impulsivity: New directions in research and clinical practice* (pp. 278–301). New York: Guildford.

Quinsey, V. L., Harris, G. T., Rice, M. E., & Cormier, A. C. (1998). *Violent offenders: Appraising and managing risk*. Washington, DC: American Psychological Association.

Rice, M. (1997). Violent offender research and implications for the criminal justice system. *American Psychologist, 32*, 414–423.

Rice, M., & Harris, G. T. (1997). The treatment of mentally disordered offenders. *Psychology, Public Policy and Law, 3*, 126–183.

Serper, M. R., Goldberg, B. R., Herman, K. G., Richarme, D., Chou, J., Dill, C. A., et al. (2005). Predictors of aggression on the psychiatric inpatient service. *Comprehensive Psychiatry, 46*, 121–127.

Seto, M. C., Harris, G., & Rice, M. E. (2004). The criminogenic, clinical, and social problems of forensic and civil psychiatric patients. *Law and Human Behavior, 28*, 577–586.

Skeem, J. L., & Mulvey, E. P. (2001). Psychopathy and community violence among civil psychiatric patients: Results from the MacArthur Violence Risk Assessment Study. *Journal of Consulting & Clinical Psychology, 69*, 358–374.

Skeem, J. L., Shubert, C., Stowman, S., Beeson, S., Mulvey, E., Gardner, W., et al. (2005). Gender and risk assessment accuracy: Underestimating women's violence potential. *Law and Human Behavior, 29*, 173–186.

Stälenheim, E. G. (2001). Relationships between attempted suicide, temperamental vulnerability, and violent criminality in a Swedish forensic psychiatric population. *European Psychiatry, 16*, 386–394.

Swanson, J. W., Holzer, C. E., Ganju, V. K., & Jono, R. T. (1990). Violence and psychiatric disorder in the community: Evidence from the epidemiologic catchment area surveys. *Hospital and Community Psychiatry, 41*, 761–770.

Swets, J. A. (1986). Indices of discrimination or diagnostic accuracy: Their ROCs and implied models. *Psychological Bulletin, 99*, 100–117.

Tardiff, K., & Sweillam, A. (1980). Assault, suicide and mental illness. *Archives of General Psychiatry, 37*, 164–169.

Timmerman, I. G. H., Vastenburgh, N. C., & Emmelkamp, P. M. G. (2001). The Forensic Inpatient Observation Scale (FIOS): Development, reliability and validity. *Criminal Behaviour and Mental Health, 11*, 144–162.

Vaughan, P. J., Pullen, N., & Kelly, M. (2000). Services for mentally disordered offenders in community psychiatry teams. *Journal of Forensic Psychiatry, 11*, 571–586.

Warm, A., Murray, C., & Fox, J. (2003). Why do people self-harm? *Psychology, Health & Medicine, 8*, 71–79.

Webster, C. D., Douglas, K. S., Eaves, D., & Hart, S. D. (1997). *HCR-20: Assessing risk for violence. Version 2*. Burnaby, Canada: Mental Health, Law, & Policy Institute, Simon Fraser University.

Webster, C. D., Martin, M. L., Brink, J., Nicholls, T. L., & Middleton, C. (2004). *Manual for the Short Term Assessment of Risk and Treatability (START). Version 1.0, Consultation edition*. St. Joseph's Healthcare, Hamilton, Ontario, Canada, and Forensic Psychiatric Services Commission, Port Coquitlam, British Columbia, Canada.

Webster, C. D., Martin, M. L., Dassinger, C., Brink, J., Nicholls, T. L., & Desmarais, S. L. (in press). *Short Term Assessment of Risk and Treatability (START) workbook. Version 1.1*. St. Joseph's Healthcare Hamilton, Ontario, Canada, and Forensic Psychiatric Services Commission, Port Coquitlam, British Columbia, Canada.

Webster, C. D., Nicholls, T. L., Martin, M. L., Desmarais, S. L., & Brink, J. (in press). Short-Term Assessment of Risk and Treatability (START): The case for a new violence risk structured professional judgment scheme. *Behavioral Science and Law*.

Yudofsky, S. C., Silver, J. M., Jackson, W., Endicott, J., & Williams, D. (1986). The Overt Aggression Scale for the objective rating of verbal and physical aggression. *American Journal of Psychiatry, 143*, 35–39.

IV

The Actuarial versus Clinical Controversy

Section IV

Introduction

The tension between the actuarial and clinical perspectives on violence risk assessment has already emerged in the first three sections of this collection. Some authors have found it somewhat surprising that a few pieces of easy-to-gather demographic information can have appreciable statistical power to predict violence and related outcomes, at least over the long term. Others have suggested that overemphasizing historical, relatively static factors can work against the release of high-scoring patients. Once patients are deemed to be "high risk," some clinicians and decision makers find it difficult to reframe such pessimistic forecasts. Their pessimism may hold despite sometimes dramatic changes in the patients' circumstances.

The actuarial versus clinical prediction controversy has stimulated research over the past 20 or more years. This debate alone has increased the numbers of both scientifically oriented and clinical writings in the field. As well, it has galvanized research into many related areas (e.g., sex offending, spousal assault, workplace violence) to which risk assessment paradigms have been applied (see Figure 1 in Chapter 4; and Lewis & Webster, 2004). Yet at times, the positive effects of this controversy are eclipsed by acrimonious and destructive debates (e.g., Ægisdóttir et al., 2006) in which leading proponents of the two contrasting views fail to realize that they are addressing different scientific and professional challenges. Those who explore the function of static variables in both retrospective and prospective studies are interested in prediction accuracy usually over a period of years; those who offer opinion or make decisions about violence and related risks in the present or limited future try to provide comprehensive assessments that meet current professional and ethical standards. Their goals being different, it is hardly surprising that one approach cannot nullify the other. What is important is which kinds of data are used for which kinds of purposes at which stages of assessment and treatment.

After attending one such "clinical versus actuarial" debate a few years ago, we, the editors of this collection, were left with the sense that each side's point of view was expressed in such extreme ways that the exercise had done more harm than good. The actuarially inclined proponents had become ever more strident, the practising clinicians ever more dismissive. We wondered, if neither of these positions deserves supremacy, what does? The answer seemed obvious: the pertinent law. All violence risk assessments have to be conducted within their particular legal frameworks. Risk assessments conducted for one purpose may have little usefulness or pertinence when applied to another.

Our perspective, later published in an article (by **Christopher D. Webster**, **Stephen J. Hucker** and **Hy Bloom**) reproduced in this section as Chapter 15, was that some laws are surprisingly specific about how clinical risk evaluations should be conducted (e.g., which information is proper to include, which information must be left out and, more importantly, which legal standard or test is to be applied in conducting the risk assessment). For example, Canada's Criminal Code confers continuing jurisdiction over an accused person found not criminally responsible for an act due to mental disorder on the appropriate provincial or territorial review board, until the person no longer represents a "significant threat" to the public's safety. Actuarial and structured professional judgment (SPJ) schemes almost invariably play a role in informing the decision-making process, but neither camp has created a protocol specific to the legal test that courts and review boards must abide by, nor have such guides or protocols been created precisely for the clientele, situation, variables or temporal considerations that these tribunals must deal with. The law seems to be the obvious starting point for risk evaluations. So while clinicians should consider actuarial information, SPJ schemes and well-grounded clinical and research observations, they should also refresh their memories of the pertinent statute and case law.

Many years ago, Bruce Ennis and Thomas Litwack wrote an article, subtitled "Flipping Coins in the Courtroom" (1974), arguing that mental health professionals are too inaccurate in their predictions of violence to be taken seriously. Nearly 30 years later, **Thomas R. Litwack** (Chapter 16) posited a different idea in an article included here, this time giving preference to clinical rather than actuarial methods as a means to predict violence. He counters Quinsey et al. (1998, 2006), who asserted provocatively— and to Litwack's mind preposterously—that "What we are advising is not the addition of actuarial methods to existing practices, but rather the complete replacement of existing practice with actuarial methods" (2006, page 197).

Litwack's chapter is included in this collection not only because it informs the actuarial-versus-clinical debate, but because it contains a great deal of conceptual information and simple logic about violence risk assessment and management. He points out, for example, that clinicians who lack training and expertise in risk assessment (recognizing that clinicians' abilities in this area vary dramatically) may be advised to rely solely on the kinds of information captured by a VRAG-type of assessment. He also advises against simply gathering as much information as possible when making assessments, since this material will be irrelevant in certain instances. Assessors should rely instead on a few variables with demonstrated strength. He also points out that actuarial schemes are validated against outcome criteria set by researchers. Researchers are mainly interested in establishing overall prediction accuracy and are not responsible for outcomes on a case-by-case basis. In contrast, clinicians, being accountable for day-to-day decisions affecting people's lives, focus primarily on issues related to managing violence and other risks. Since their purposes are so different, it is hardly surprising that statisticians and clinicians often find themselves at cross-purposes.[1]

Litwack reminds his readers that "at least in the courtroom, it may well be unethical to definitively claim more predictive power for an actuarial assessment scheme, or for clinical assessments, than is justified by actual research results" (page 311). He concludes that there tends to be a fair amount of unnecessary guesswork involved in contemporary clinical violence assessments, even when they are based on the HCR-20 or similar guides. Yet he also sees no reason to presume that actuarial methods are superior.[2]

Joel A. Dvoskin and **Kirk Heilbrun** (Chapter 17) remind us that "the scientific goal of prediction and the legal goal of decision-making in individual cases are rarely the same" (page 318). They caution legal decision makers not to "overvalue the applicability (legally, the 'relevance') as well as the scientific support (legally, the 'reliability') of the actuarial tool that is used" (page 318). Dvoskin and Heilbrun stress the importance of managing violence risk factors, of finding ways to evaluate the effects of interventions and of isolating protective factors. They caution, as do other authors in this collection, against over-reliance on actuarial scores as a basis for decision making. Without sufficient information to complete either an actuarial or an SPJ clinical assessment, there is the danger that the assessor may make decisions based on "inaccurate proxies such as the severity of the current offense" (page 320).[3]

The authors offer a model for returning people who have been violent to the community. They stress the importance of people being integrated into the community in small, graded steps and of their demonstrating that they have acquired the necessary skills at each stage. As to the "big debate" about the relative superiority of actuarial methods over clinical ones, they conclude, sensibly enough, that "it depends." If the court, wanting to follow the pertinent law, is looking for a long-range prediction, an actuarial estimate is probably appropriate. But if the court wants to receive advice from experts as to how violence in the individual case might be reduced or properly managed in the hospital or community, mental health and correctional professionals should use their practical experience to recommend ways to achieve the clinical or correctional end.

The much-cited paper by **John Monahan** and **Henry J. Steadman** (Chapter 18) makes a clever analogy between forecasting the weather and predicting violence. The authors describe how long-range weather forecasts, though containing inevitable error, are like actuarial predictions of violence risks: they enable citizens to make informed choices about how to manage their activities over the foreseeable future. But the astute person also takes into account the specific, *local* weather forecast, since circumstances close to home (e.g., elevation, proximity to the sea) may increase or decrease the likelihood of bad weather (e.g., desert conditions will yield small seasonal variations). This is similar to a clinical evaluation of risk that involves a multi-dimensional assessment of the person at a particular time in a particular set of circumstances. The analogy, though simple, is apt. It suggests that there is a place for both actuarial and clinical prediction. The one provides a general weather picture that may need to be modified by the other to account for particular local circumstances.

NOTES

1. In 1985, Webster (one of the editors of this collection) reported on a prediction-outcome study involving some 600 offenders with a mental disorder (Menzies et al., 1985). In the study, researchers merely asked clinicians to rate "dangerousness" on a low/medium/high scale. In a later twist, the research group extended, somewhat arbitrarily, the length of the follow-up interval from two to six years. Clinicians were likely disadvantaged at the outset by not being told what precise behaviours they were expected to predict or over what length of time.
2. Glancy (2006) has recently pointed to the "unreliability of actuarial schemes in real-life practice" (p. 274). He argues that "[g]uided clinical assessments are effective because they take into account the factors that have been suggested to correlate with recidivism and apply them to a specific individual and specific circumstances" (p. 274).
3. Readers will recall from Chapter 1 that Scott, too, cautions against over-relying on the features of the index offence.

REFERENCES

Ægisdóttir, S., Spengler, P.M. & White, M.J. (2006). Should I pack my umbrella? Clinical versus statistical prediction of mental health decisions. *The Counselling Psychologist, 34*, 410–419.

Ennis, B.J. & Litwack, T.R. (1974). Psychiatry and the presumption of expertise: Flipping coins in the courtroom. *California Law Review, 62*, 693–752.

Glancy, G.D. (2006). Caveat usare: Actuarial schemes in real life. *Journal of the American Academy of Psychiatry and the Law, 34*, 272–275.

Lewis, A.N.O. & Webster, C.D. (2004). General instruments for risk assessment. *Current Opinions in Psychiatry, 17*, 401–406.

Menzies, R.J., Webster, C.D. & Sepejak, D.S. (1985). Hitting the forensic sound barrier: Predictions of dangerousness in a pre-trial clinic. In C.D. Webster, M.H. Ben-Aron & S.J. Hucker (Eds.), *Dangerousness: Probability and Prediction, Psychiatry and Public Policy*. New York: Cambridge University Press.

Quinsey, V.L., Harris, G.T., Rice, M.E. & Cormier, C. (1998). *Violent Offenders: Appraising and Managing Risk*. Washington, DC: American Psychological Association.

Quinsey, V.L., Harris, G.T., Rice, M.E. & Cormier, C. (2006). *Violent offenders: Appraising and Managing Risk* (2nd ed.). Washington, DC: American Psychological Association.

15

Transcending the Actuarial versus Clinical Polemic in Assessing Risk for Violence

CHRISTOPHER D. WEBSTER, STEPHEN J. HUCKER AND HY BLOOM

ABSTRACT: *Much energy has been expended over recent years in debating the relative merits of actuarial versus clinical approaches to violence risk prediction. Although it has gradually become apparent that scores based on more or less static factors obtainable from the record do indeed associate with outcome violence over years of follow-up, there is no reason to suppose that, at least potentially, dynamic variables do not hold as much or more promise when it comes to projections over weeks or months. Clinicians involved in release decision-making might wish to consider the following, in order of importance: (a) the legal framework within which the decision is being made, (b) the thoroughness with which scientific methods have been applied to the particular case at issue, (c) the precision of the individualized statement of violence risk being offered, (d) the steps which could be taken to reduce that risk, and (e) if available, the individual's violence risk assessment score in relation to already amassed pertinent statistical data.*

Large controversies pervade the mental health and criminological disciplines periodically (Webster, 1990). It was argued some time ago that psychotherapy does not work, that its results overall do not improve on spontaneous recovery (Eysenck, 1952). Eventually, this idea faded away with the general recognition that psychotherapies of various kinds

Reprinted with permission. Criminal Justice and Behavior, 29 *(5), 659–665.* © *2002 American Association for Correctional Psychology.*

under various conditions can be shown to be effective (Cordess, 2001). Similarly, the notion that nothing works in correctional rehabilitation (Martinson, 1974) has lately been swamped by an impressive array of studies demonstrating the opposite (e.g., Ashford, Sales, & Reid, 2001; Hollin, 2001; Loeber & Farrington, 2001). These controversies are not without positive influences, as they customarily have a galvanizing effect on a field of study. They demand that evidence be produced to dispel a pronouncement. Because, though, no study on its own can ever be crucial, or rarely even strongly persuasive, it takes a long time, as Kuhn (1962) earlier told us, for a mistaken idea to give way.

It is perhaps odd that the polemic, or great debate (Dvoskin & Heilbrun, 2001), continues to rage around actuarial versus clinical prediction as it relates to risk assessment affecting mental patients and persons accused or convicted of criminally violent offences. Some legislators have seemingly been so impressed with the power of actuarial projections of risk that they have embodied the procedures into law (Witt, DelRusso, Oppenheim, & Ferguson, 1997).[1] On the other side, there have been many who have stood against such ventures (e.g., Stone, 1985). Some researchers call on the literature on actuarial versus clinical prediction generally as it applies to a wide range of tasks and settings, the weight of which they consider to favor the former at the expense of the latter, to argue against overreliance on clinical judgment in framing opinions about risk (e.g. Quinsey, Harris, Rice, & Cormier, 1998). But of course, readers will realize that the opposite point of view is also being articulated (e.g., Litwack, 2001).

The position we take here is straightforward: Both clinical and actuarial projections are important when it comes to assessing the individual case around issues of future violence. This becomes apparent routinely when members of review boards and tribunals have to reach decisions periodically about the award of precise kinds of freedoms and the institution of supervisory arrangements. In this practical circumstance, it seems absurd to say that actuarial considerations should carry the day, or vice versa. The question, surely, in such a context is which kinds of information should be taken into account at which stages of the release or detention process. Previous rubrics, such as allowing the clinical projections to be varied upward or downward by no more than 10% from the actuarial base (see Webster, Harris, Rice, Cormier, & Quinsey, 1994), now seem ill founded (Quinsey et al., 1998).[2]

In what follows, we have reviewed this integration issue from the perspective of board decision making.[3] Boards normally include mental health professionals, lawyers, judges, and, often, members of the public. Information is presented to them. There is usually a lengthy written account with recommendations, and often the board itself has an opportunity to examine the individual who appears before it. It has perhaps become fairly customary in North America for such boards to receive statistical projections of risk as well as clinical opinions (e.g., Nuffield, 1982). Judicial officers and boards are charged with the necessary and difficult task of distilling substantial amounts of information. Reports and other documents often contain highly divergent opinions from a variety of sources. It is hard to make decisions that balance public safety concerns, individual rights and freedoms, and the therapeutic, rehabilitative, and other requirements of the subject of the risk assessment. Obviously, board members tend to be highly reliant upon the assessments provided to them. This, then, raises the questions of what a competently executed assessment should look like from the perspective of the adjudicating board. Put another way, what criteria should a risk assessment meet? We now suggest five, it is hoped, sensible criteria and arrange them in what seems to be the best order of importance.

1. The assessment should show an understanding of the applicable legal framework. It should be evident from the materials submitted that the clinician knows the pertinent law and has situated the report within it. Very probably, accuracy of information provided to boards by clinicians depends on such mental health professionals' appreciation of the legal context (Heilbrun, 1997). It is, of course, essential that evaluators demonstrate that they are perfectly clear about the purpose of the risk assessment. Although, obviously, this will not extend to an expectation of sophisticated discourse on statutes or cases, it should nonetheless be evident that the assessor is fully aware of the provisions within which the board is required to operate. This will be done without any attempt to assume responsibilities that properly belong to the board, the court, or the tribunal. Generally speaking, then, the assessment should be conducted in a manner that respects the law. The content of mental health reports should be legally relevant.

2. The mental health or correctional risk assessment must be evidence based (Lehman & Steinwachs, 1998). By this we mean that the investigation must have been conducted and presented in a scientific manner.[4] It must be apparent that the assessor has a thorough grounding in the case at hand. No reasonable effort will have been spared to unearth information (Dietz, 1985). Additional data will have been added as the investigation proceeds. The circumstances for assessment will have been conducive to creating a comprehensive review. Information will have been sorted into fact, presumption, and conjecture, and all of it will have been evaluated critically. Limitations in the knowledge base will have been taken into account and acknowledged. A theory will often have been developed to take account of occurrences and incidents that otherwise might be inexplicable to those not versed in the mental health disciplines. The eventual report will be presented to decision makers in a logical and concise manner. In our view, properly done, this is an example of inductive science generalized to other like cases (Medawar, 1967). It contrasts to a deductive science that generalizes from the group to the individual. Although the inductive approach may have to defer to deductive science in terms of its verifiability according to commonly accepted normative-statistical procedural rules, it may gain the ascendancy when it comes to actual applicability to the case at hand. Our main point is that clinical-inductive science is not less than statistical-deductive science. By expecting a high level of rigor in the course of inductive exercises, the board will make it clear that there is here no invitation to resort to the unbridled use of clinical intuition.

3. The risk assessment will ordinarily contain an individualized statement of risk. This individualized statement about risk will be specific to the case at hand and it will be as precise as possible. It will explain conditions under which risk may be modified or eliminated, stipulate risk-enhancing circumstances, indicate likely victims, and limit the

time frame of the projection appropriately (i.e., to a week, a month, a year, 5 years, etc.). Some indication of the probability of occurrence will be offered, if only in terms of low, moderate, or high. Presenting such an opinion will in rare cases be virtually unnecessary. Sometimes, the incidents in the past were so serious that the board, understandably, has repeatedly over the years expressed its utter reluctance to grant release. Extended effort making projections in such cases would seem misplaced. An acceptable or even positive risk profile, whether actuarial or clinical, or both, may not, in these instances, have the power to displace concern stemming from the heinous nature of the past event, however unlikely to occur.[5]

4. An ideal evaluation before the board will suggest what steps could now be taken in the particular case to reduce or attenuate risk of further violence. This information has obvious usefulness to the board, which only rarely deals with simple decisions such as accept-reject or detain-release. Properly marshaled reports not only offer practical solutions to "What now?" questions but allow the assessing clinicians to rearticulate their views about the major risk factors seemingly at play. Because risk of violence is probably tied quite as much to circumstances and situations as to personalities and psychological states (Mischel, 1968), it is helpful for board members to try to figure out what, conceivably, might be done to reduce risk to acceptable levels in this instance.

5. With assessment in the individual case settled, so far as possible, it may sometimes be wise and even necessary to compare the specific case at hand with data amassed from statistically driven studies. It seems almost certain that this is the way of the future (see Monahan et al., 2001, who say explicitly that as multiple multivariate predictive models evolve, "clinicians will need to have computer support available," p. 143). To us, this is a fifth-level criterion. It is less important than the previous four for several reasons: (a) Finding clear, published samples typical of the particular individual under consideration is usually difficult (see Hirschmann, 1996); (b) risk factors beyond the obvious ones tend to have limited statistical power (Monahan et al., 2001); (c) little is known about how these factors interact to promote specific kinds of violence; (d) collecting normative data over the long term requires much time and effort and, as a result, the predictor variables not infrequently have a dated quality by the time the eventual data are analyzed and published; and (e) the results of actuarial assessments have to be presented to review boards very carefully (i.e., there is little point in appending such written analyses if no specialized scientist is on hand to interpret them correctly). We do not deny the importance of actuarial data or say that these do not play a useful role in many instances, but at present and likely for the foreseeable future it would seem highly unwise for decision-making boards to abrogate their responsibilities through overdependence on probability tables that from a scientific point of view remain in need of further development and refinement.[6] Monahan et al. (2001) seem to have stated the priorities the right way round when they said, "This reliance on clinical judgment—aided by empirical understanding of risk factors for violence and their interactions—reflects, and in our view should reflect, the standard of care at this juncture in the field's development" (pp. 134–135).

NOTES

1. This draws attention to the fact that decision making about risk is a high-stakes endeavor. It calls up public safety issues and concerns around freedom and stigmatization, to name just a few.

2. In an earlier publication, Webster, Harris, Rice, Cormier, and Quinsey (1994) argued that the Violence Appraised Risk Assessment Guide (VRAG) score should first be established. That score established, we suggested to clinicians that they might find it appropriate to vary the VRAG probability estimate, but not more than 10% in either direction. Later, Quinsey, Harris, Rice and Cormier (1998) realized that this is likely not the best course of action. The actuarial prediction is the actuarial prediction. It derives its meaning from statistical analysis. If an assessor wishes to offer an overall estimate of violence potential in the particular case, he or she must stipulate how that estimate was reached.

3. As Canadian authors, we are conscious of the fact that in the United States there is a general tendency to rely on judicial rulings (though the Oregon Review Board, which deals with insanity acquittees, has several parallels to the Canadian board system). And, in any event, most of what we have to say here has direct applicability to courtroom testimony, appearances before parole boards, and the like.

4. These general rules do not change much over time. One of us (Webster), 20 years ago in 1980 listed them as follows: (a) clear assumptions, (b) logical connection, (c) proper use of the existing evidence, (d) clarity of exposition, (e) a degree of sophistication that does justice to the problem, (f) a methodological strategy appropriate to the task, (g) data collected by some generally agreed-upon rules, (h) findings that have real theoretical and intellectual interest, (i) results that can be generalized but that are not overextended, (j) predictive power, (k) practical importance, and (l) novelty. Recently, Krause, Howard, and Lutz (1998) have made the point that researchers should *always* report specifically on change in the individual clinical case as well as on aggregate data.

5. It is perhaps worth nothing that in suggesting that such extreme cases are tantamount to irrelevant from a scientific risk assessment perspective, it can be argued that a switch has been made from the concept of "fluid" risk to "categorized" risk (see Brown, 2000). Fluid risk is grounded in scientific, logical thinking; categorical risk is based in moral and political opinion.

6. It is worth noting parenthetically that study of actual practice in one review board appeared to indicate that its members did not allow themselves to be much influenced by actuarial data available to them (Hilton & Simmons, 2001). What caught their interest was the opinion of the senior clinician.

REFERENCES

Ashford, J. B., Sales, B. D., & Reid, W. H. (Eds.). (2001). *Treating adult and juvenile offenders with special needs.* Washington, DC: American Psychological Association.

Brown, M. (2000). Calculations of risk in contemporary penal practice. In M. Brown & J. Pratt (Eds.), *Dangerous offenders: Punishment and social order* (pp. 93–108). London: Routledge.

Cordess, C. (2001). Forensic psychotherapy. In C. Hollin (Ed.), *Handbook of offender assessment and treatment* (pp. 309–329). Chichester, UK: Wiley.

Dietz, P. E. (1985). Hypothetical criteria for the prediction of individual criminality. In C. D. Webster, M. H. Ben-Aron, & S. J. Hucker (Eds.), *Dangerousness: Probability and prediction, psychiatry and public policy* (pp. 87–102). New York: Cambridge University Press.

Dvoskin, J. A., & Heilbrun, K. (2001). Risk assessment and release decision-making: Toward resolving the great debate. *The Journal of the American Academy of Psychiatry and the Law, 29,* 6–10.

Eysenck, H. J. (1952). The effects of psychotherapy: An evaluation. *Journal of Consulting Psychology, 16,* 319–324.

Heilbrun, K. (1997). Prediction versus management models relevant to risk assessment: The importance of legal decision-making context. *Law and Human Behavior, 21,* 347–359.

Hilton, N. Z., & Simmons, J. L. (2001). The influence of actuarial risk assessment in clinical judgments and tribunal decisions about mentally disordered offenders in maximum security. *Law and Human Behavior, 25,* 393–408.

Hirschmann, D. (1996). Parole and the dangerous offender. In N.Walker (Ed.), *Dangerous people* (pp. 137–153). London: Blackstone.

Hollin, C. R. (Ed.). (2001). *Handbook of offender assessment and treatment.* Chichester, UK: Wiley.

Krause, M. S., Howard, K. I., & Lutz, W. (1998). Exploring individual change. *Journal of Consulting and Clinical Psychology, 66,* 838–845.

Kuhn, T. S. (1962). *The structure of scientific revolutions.* Chicago: University of Chicago Press.

Lehman, A. F., & Steinwachs, D. M. (1998). At issue: Translating research into practice: The schizophrenia Patient Outcomes Research Team (PORT) treatment recommendations. *Schizophrenia Bulletin, 24,* 1–10.

Litwack, T. R. (2001) Actuarial versus clinical assessments of dangerousness. *Psychology, Public Policy and Law, 7,* 409–443.

Loeber, R., & Farrington, D. P. (Eds.). (2001). *Child delinquents: Development, interventions, and service needs.* Thousand Oaks, CA: Sage.

Martinson, R. (1974). What works? Questions and answers about prison reform. *The Public Interest, 35,* 22–54.

Medawar, P. B. (1967). *The art of the soluble.* London: Methuen.

Mischel, W. (1968). *Personality and assessment.* New York: Wiley.

Monahan, J., Steadman, H. J., Silver, E., Appelbaum, P. S., Robbins, P. C., Mulvey, E. P., et al. (2001). *Rethinking risk assessment: The Macarthur study of mental disorder and violence.* New York: Oxford University Press.

Nuffield, J. (1982). *Parole decision-making in Canada: Research towards decision guidelines.* Ottawa: Ministry of Supplies and Services, Canada.

Quinsey, V. L., Harris, G. T., Rice, M. E., & Cormier, C. A. (1998). *Violent offenders: Appraising and managing risk.* Washington, DC: American Psychological Association.

Stone, A. A. (1985). The new legal standard of dangerousness: Fair in theory, unfair in practice. In C. D. Webster, M. H. Ben-Aron, & S. H. Hucker (Eds.), *Dangerousness: Probability and prediction, psychiatry and public policy* (pp. 13–24). New York: Cambridge University Press.

Webster, C. D. (1980). The old torments: How to defeat the colloquium speaker (or toward good theory and research in experimental-clinical psychology). *Canadian Psychologist, 21,* 90–92.

Webster, C.D. (1990). Prediction of dangerousness polemic. *Canadian Journal of Criminology, 32,* 191–196.

Webster, C. D., Harris, G. T., Rice, M. E., Cormier, C., & Quinsey, V. L. (1994). *The violence prediction scheme: Assessing dangerousness in high risk men.* Toronto, Canada: University of Toronto, Centre of Criminology.

Witt, P. H., DelRusso, J., Oppenheim, J., & Ferguson, G. (1997). Sex offender risk assessment and the law. *Journal of Psychiatry and Law, 24,* 343–378.

16

Actuarial versus Clinical Assessments of Dangerousness

THOMAS R. LITWACK

ABSTRACT: *In their book,* Violent Offenders, *V. L. Quinsey, G. T. Harris, M. E. Rice, and C. A. Cormier (1999) proposed the "complete replacement" of clinical assessments of dangerousness with actuarial methods, such as the Violence Risk Appraisal Guide (VRAG). In this article, the author argues that (a) research to date has not demonstrated that actuarial methods of risk assessment are superior to clinical methods; (b) because most clinical determinations of dangerousness are not "predictions" of violence, as well as for other reasons, it is very difficult to meaningfully compare clinical and actuarial assessments of dangerousness; and (c) even the best researched and validated actuarial tool for assessing dangerousness to date, the VRAG, has not yet been validated in a manner that would make it appropriate for use in determining when individuals should be confined on the grounds of their dangerousness. Therefore, although clinicians who engage in risk assessments certainly should be knowledgeable about arguably relevant actuarial assessment schemes and other assessment guides (e.g., the HCR-20), it is premature, at best, to replace clinical risk assessments with actuarial assessments.*

Reprinted with permission. The official citation that should be used in referencing this material is Litwack, T.R. (2001). Actuarial versus clinical assessments of dangerousness. Psychology, Public Policy, and Law, 7 (2), 409–443. © 2001 by the *American Psychological Association Inc.*

A longstanding controversy exists within the field of psychology over the relative merits of actuarial (or statistical) versus clinical predictions. Within the field of dangerousness risk assessment, this controversy was heightened in 1999 by the American Psychological Association's publication of the book *Violent Offenders: Appraising and Managing Risk* by Quinsey, Harris, Rice and Cormier. In this book, the authors argued explicitly and strongly for the "complete replacement" of clinical assessments of dangerousness with actuarial methods. To be precise, they stated: "What we are advising is not the addition of actuarial methods to existing practice, but rather the complete replacement of existing practice with actuarial methods" (p. 171).

This article addresses the position taken by those authors regarding the relative merits of actuarial versus clinical assessments of dangerousness and, more generally, the increasingly widespread academic view that actuarial assessments of dangerousness are superior to clinical assessments. Today, one routinely finds statements in the literature suggesting that actuarial assessments of dangerousness have proven to be superior to clinical assessments, or at least, to unstructured clinical assessments (Douglas, Cox, & Webster, 1999, p. 156; Gottfredson, 1987; Loza & Dhaliwal, 1997; Monahan, 1981, p. 97; Ward & Dockerill, 1999, p. 126). However, in their revised textbook, Melton, Petrila, Poythress, and Slobogin (1997) concluded from their review of the literature that "[t]he bottom line is that the research has *not* delivered an actuarial equation suitable for clinical application in the area of violence prediction" (p. 285, italics added). Thus, the issue has definitely been joined.

Of some historical interest, in *Violent Offenders* Quinsey et al. (1999) recognized (on p. 171) that their current, extreme, position is a reversal of a more modest position that the authors took only 4 years earlier when, together with Webster, they published the *Violence Prediction Scheme* (Webster, Harris, Rice, Cormier, & Quinsey, 1994), in which they proposed integrating actuarial assessments with clinical considerations to allow for a more comprehensive assessment of dangerousness than by actuarial tools alone. Although the *Violence Prediction Scheme* emphasized actuarial prediction— when relevant and validated actuarial schemes were available—and although, even then, the authors recommended that clinical considerations should not change actuarial predictions by more than 10%, the authors then concluded that

> [if] adjustments [to actuarial assessments] are made conservatively and only because of factors that a clinician believes, on good evidence, to be related to the likelihood of violent recidivism in an individual case, predictive accuracy may be optimized (p. 57)

Even in 1997, Harris and Rice wrote that "clinicians may [legitimately] adjust actuarial predictions based on . . . unique aspects of an individual case" (p. 1171).

In this article, I review some basic historical and conceptual issues regarding the actuarial versus clinical debate and then examine the research literature on actuarial versus clinical assessments of dangerousness, to arrive at four primary conclusions:

1. Although it may be true that actuarial predictions have been demonstrated to

be superior to clinical predictions for a fairly wide range of prediction tasks, that is not the case for assessments of dangerousness.

2. Assessments of dangerousness are inherently different from many other predictive tasks, and they are different in ways that make it very difficult to meaningfully compare clinical and actuarial assessments.

3. If actuarial instruments, or structured assessment guides, are to be used in the fairest and most effective manner, they must be validated in a far more precise manner than has occurred to date. However, even the best studied and validated actuarial tool for assessing dangerousness, the Violence Risk Appraisal Guide (VRAG; Quinsey et al., 1999) has not been demonstrated as suitable for practical purposes in many instances, or to be superior to clinical assessments.

4. Therefore, it is premature to substitute actuarial for clinical assessments of dangerousness.

Before addressing these points, a basic historical observation is that the history of academic analyses of clinical assessments of dangerousness has long been characterized by a "rush to judgment," or more precisely, by a rush to negative judgment, without sufficient efforts to make a fair review of the clinical enterprise. In 1969 for example, Dershowitz, then known best as the coauthor of one of the first textbooks in psychiatry and the law, concluded, after reviewing the literature, that

> for every correct psychiatric prediction of violence there are numerous erroneous predictions. That is, among every group of inmates presently confined on the basis of psychiatric predictions of violence, there are *only a few* who . . . would actually engage in violence if released. (p. 47, italics added).

Unless all inmates predicted by psychiatrists to be violent were released wholesale, it is hard to see how anyone could reach such a conclusion. Nevertheless, just such a conclusion was reached.

Other examples abound. In 1978, a task force of the American Psychological Association on the role of psychology in the criminal justice system concluded:

> It does appear from reading the research that the validity of psycho-logical predictions of dangerous behavior, at least in the sentencing and release situation . . . , is extremely poor, so poor that one could oppose their use on the strictly empirical grounds that psychologists are not professionally competent to make such judgments. (American Psychological Association, 1978, p. 1110)

In addition, in an *amicus curie* brief filed with the Supreme Court of the United States in the 1983 case of *Barefoot v. Estelle*, the American Psychiatric Association claimed, according to Justice Blackmun, "that psychiatrists simply have no expertise in predicting long-term future dangerousness" (463 U.S. at 921) and that "two out of three predictions of long-term violence made by psychiatrists are wrong" (ibid at 920), a claim that was (and is) without any actual empirical support (Litwack & Schlesinger, 1987, pp. 207–209, 227–230: 1999, pp. 172–177).

Assessments of dangerousness by mental health professionals were viewed somewhat more positively, or at least more openly, after the publication of Monahan's monograph in 1981, in which he concluded that *we know very little about how accurately violent behavior may be predicted under many circumstances*" (p. 37; italics in original). Yet, only 3 years later, Monahan (1984) wrote that studies had "demonstrated that clinical predictions of violent behavior among institutionalized mentally disordered people are accurate at best one-third of the time" and that

> more studies concluding that psychiatrists and psychologists are relatively inaccurate clinical predictors of whether mentally disordered offenders who have been institutionalized for lengthy periods of time will offend once more are not needed. There are so many nails now in that coffin that I propose we declare the issue officially dead. (p. 13)

Such a position would render assessments of dangerousness of institutionalized insanity acquitees untenable (and unethical).

Now, as noted above, it is frequently claimed, often as if it were hardly worth discussing, that actuarial assessments of dangerousness have proven to be superior to clinical assessments. However, the actual picture that emerges from the research is far more complex. In addition, apart from their relative merits vis-a-vis clinical assessments, far more is currently claimed regarding the utility of actuarial tools for assessing dangerousness than is merited by actual research findings. Thus, once again, we have a rush to judgment in the field, although in this instance, perhaps, it is a rush to positive judgment.

Before addressing the research, however, certain basic conceptual and definitional issues must be addressed. Initially, and for the purposes of this article, *actuarial assessments* are assessments based on supposedly validated relationships between measurable predictor and outcome variables and ultimately determined by fixed, or mechanical, and explicit rules. The terms *fixed* or *mechanical* are preferred to the term *mathematical* simply because assessments using decision trees are mechanical but not mathematical. Steadman et al. (2000) have argued that the use of decision trees in dangerousness assessments has major advantages over the use of regression equations. Conversely, *clinical assessments* are viewed here as assessments ultimately determined by human judgment (beyond a human judgment to rely solely on a particular actuarial instrument), although good clinical practice may well entail, or even require, considering the results of an appropriate actuarial assessment, relevant base-rate data, or both (Davison, 1997, p. 203; Litwack & Schlesinger, 1999, pp. 202–204; Melton et al., 1997, pp. 284–285; Monahan, 1981, pp. 49, 59–62; Monahan et al., 2000). (The *base rate* of violence for a given group is the proportion of people in that group who would commit violence under specified circumstances within a given period of time [Monahan, 1981, pp. 49, 59]).

A different, but equally important, definitional issue concerns the distinction between clinical and actuarial variables (as opposed to assessment processes). This article defines actuarial and clinical variables somewhat differently than Douglas, Cox, and Webster (1999) did in their thorough review article, "Violence Risk Assessment: Science and Practice." There, although it was fully recognized that actuarial assessments may take clinical variables into account and that clinical assessments may take actuarial variables into account (Monahan, 1981, pp. 95–97), *actuarial* variables were defined as variables that are "static or historical" whereas *clinical* variables were defined as "dynamic factors that can change" (p. 155). It may be more meaningful, however, to define actuarial variables as variables that can be measured with little, if any, human judgment and clinical variables as personality factors or variables that require the use of human judgment to measure. For example, a person's weight can change dramatically but requires no clinical skill to measure. Conversely, a person's degree of psychopathy, even if relatively fixed, can only be measured through some degree of human education and judgment or a psychological test. At the least, it is a complex variable that cannot be easily measured (unlike age or arrest data from available records).

This is not an unimportant matter of definition. In a 1998 review of the recidivism prediction literature, Bonta, Law, and Hanson concluded: "clinical variables and clinical judgments contribute minimally in the prediction of recidivism" (p. 137). However, to arrive at that conclusion, which is so disparaging of the entire clinical enterprise, they had to claim that "a personality constellation of impulsiveness and thrill seeking," (p. 137) although admittedly important prognostic factors, were not clinical variables. If impulsiveness and thrill seeking are not clinical variables, what are?

It is also important to take note of the fact that, just as good clinical practice may well entail the consideration of actuarial data, modern actuarial instruments of assessing dangerousness often rely crucially on the clinical assessment of clinical variables (even if those assessments lead to a numerical score). For example, as is discussed below, the most important component of a VRAG rating is the subject's score on the Psychopathy Checklist—Revised (PCL-R; Hare, 1991), a score that measures a personality variable, which requires clinical judgment to obtain (even when the score is obtained from file data), and a score that is best obtained when a proper interview is part of the assessment process (Hart & Hare, 1997a, 1997b). Similarly, Monahan et al. (2000) and Steadman et al. (2000) have reported the development of actuarial (decision tree) instruments for assessing dangerousness that rely heavily on reviewing, in the first case, the participant's violent fantasies and psychiatric diagnosis (whether the participant exhibits schizophrenia) and, in the second case, whether the participant exhibits psychopathy and the participant's degree of "symptom activation."

Grove and Meehl titled their generally powerful and articulate 1996 review of the literature "Comparative Efficiency of Informal (Subjective, Impressionistic) and Formal (Mechanical, Algorithmic) Prediction Procedures: The Clinical—Statistical Controversy." Although there is no doubt that clinicians often make subjective, impressionistic, or intuitive judgments, it is questionable whether clinical judgments, particularly clinical assessments of dangerousness, are properly defined solely or primarily in those terms.

Synonyms for *subjective* are "arbitrary," "biased," "partial," "partisan," and "prejudiced." Many clinicians rightfully bridle at these characterizations of their assessments, particularly their assessments of dangerousness. Indeed, many experienced forensic clinicians argue that none of their assessments are subjective or impressionistic. Their ultimate judgment, they may concede, may well be wrong by some criteria; however, they argue, in each case they consider credible amounts of concrete data and follow a logical process of reasoning that, often, has to be detailed in formal reports for the courts and the patient's attorney. This hardly amounts to, or allows for, judgments that are merely arbitrary or based solely on intuition (Litwack & Schlesinger, 1999, pp. 195–202).

It is true, many clinicians will readily admit, that there are occasions when their intuition leads them to make further inquiries of a patient or of collateral witnesses or sources and that those intuition-based inquiries lead to the discovery of important, if not critical, information related to their assessment. However, they would argue, the information ultimately obtained is nonetheless concrete and apparently relevant information. Moreover, many experienced forensic clinicians argue that when they conduct dangerousness assessments they consider the factors recommended for consideration by structured assessment guides, such as the HCR-20 (Douglas, Cox, & Webster, 1999; Webster, Douglas, Eaves, & Hart, 1997); that they prepare for their assessments by first considering, to the extent possible, their patient's history; and that they are then guided in their assessments by that particular history (Litwack & Schlesinger, 1999, pp. 196, 198). Thus, even if they do not formally rely on an explicit assessment guide, many clinicians would argue that their assessments are, nevertheless, structured rather than unstructured. In short, as Holt (1970), Meehl's most persistent critic over the years, has observed: "Disciplined analytical judgment is generally better than global, diffuse judgment; but it is not any the less clinical" (p. 348).

On the other hand, it must be recognized that clinicians sometimes do make subjective (or at least uneducated, uninformed, or unthoughtful) judgments in the area of risk assessment (as well as other areas), and this should be considered when comparing actuarial versus clinical assessments. One argument in favor of relying solely on actuarial assessments is that even if some clinicians can do better (by some criteria) than the best available actuarial assessment instrument(s), given the range of skills of clinicians, fewer errors will be made, in total, if clinical assessment is eschewed in favor of actuarial assessment. Although this argument can be confirmed only by empirical investigation, it has logical force.

Moreover, it must also be noted that many arguments that are made in favor of clinical assessment, though seemingly logical on the surface, may in fact be wrong. For example, even though clinicians may believe, with apparent logic, that the best assessments can only be made when all seemingly relevant information is considered, it may well be the case that, with the exception of extreme cases (e.g., a patient who is delusional and paranoid but who has no history of violence but is stating intentions to harm an available alleged persecutor), considering information other than that required for the actuarial assessment may decrease assessment validity. Thus, although I argue for the proposition that all of those concerned with the field of dangerousness assessment should keep an open mind regarding how dangerousness assessments can and should best be conducted in the future, this call for open mindeness applies to clinicians as well as the advocates of actuarial assessments. At the least, even when recognizing the severe limitations of actuarial methods that have been noted by others (e.g., Buchanan, 1999; Melton et al., 1997) and that are discussed herein, clinicians should consider the possibility that applying appropriate actuarial or structured assessment tools to risk assessments will at least ensure that certain relevant factors will be considered, even if the scores derived from using those tools are not regarded as definitive.

With these considerations in mind, there are three points to be made regarding the research literature concerning clinical versus actuarial assessments of dangerousness.

I. Although Clinicians Should Take Actuarial Estimates of Dangerousness Into Serious Account When Relevant and Meaningful Actuarial Data Are Available, There Is Little Actual Empirical Support for the Proposition That Actuarial Assessments of Dangerousness Are Superior to Clinical Assessments, At Least in Many Circumstances, and, in Actuality, There Is Empirical Evidence to the Contrary

The authors of *Violent Offenders* claimed that "an overwhelming amount of research demonstrates that actuarial prediction systems are more valid than clinical judgments, *especially in the case of the prediction of violence*" (Quinsey et al., 1999, pp. 44–45; italics added). In fact, however, very few studies have directly compared clinical versus actuarial assessments of dangerousness regarding the same subject populations, and the actual results of these studies are very mixed. A survey of the literature through 1999 (i.e., through the end of the 20th century) yielded eight such studies published in academic journals. How was this survey conducted?

Initially, the 1996 review article by Grove and Meehl referred to a then unpublished meta-analysis of "Clinical Versus Mechanical Prediction" (Grove, Zald, Lebow, Snitz, & Nelson, 1995), which, supposedly, surveyed and listed all relevant studies to date. The meta-analysis was obtained and scrutinized for citations to articles dealing specifically with assessments of dangerousness. (A version of the meta-analysis has now been published. See Grove, Zald, Lebow, Snitz, & Nelson, 2000.) The references in two recent meta-analyses of assessments of dangerousness, Bonta et al. (1998) and Mossman (1994), were similarly scrutinized for articles that directly compared actuarial versus clinical assessments. Finally, a *PsycINFO* search was conducted using a variety of combinations of terms, including combinations (in article titles) of *clinical, actuarial,* and *statistical.*

Mossman's valuable 1994 article, "Assessing Predictions of Violence: Being Accurate About Accuracy," is often cited to support the claim that actuarial assessments of danger-ousness have proven to be more accurate than clinical assessments. Using "receiver [or relative] operating characteristic" (ROC) analyses (Quinsey et al., 1999, pp. 50–54), Mossman reanalyzed "58 data sets from 44 published studies of violence prediction" (p. 793). He found that "[t]aken together, these data strongly suggest that mental health professionals' violence predictions are substantially more accurate than chance" (p. 793). He also concluded, however, that the "average AUC [area under the curve] of discriminant functions (or 'actuarial methods') . . . evaluated using cross-validation groups is greater than the average for clinical prediction" (p. 789). Although Mossman went on to add that "these differences are explained by the relative accuracies of long-term (≥ 1 year) predictions of each type; the average accuracy of validation-fit discriminant functions covering less than 1 year [being] comparable to the average for clinical predictions" (p. 789), the former statement has been used to support the anticlinical position. The fact, however, is that, with or without the meta-analysis, different assessment techniques that may have been applied to very different populations, with very different outcome criteria, cannot be conclusively compared (Klein, 2000). Rather, clinical and actuarial assessment techniques can only truly be tested against one another when they are applied to the same populations with the same outcome criteria (among other factors, some of which are discussed later). Moreover, Mossman's meta-analysis considered none of the studies (discussed below) that actually compared clinical with actuarial assessments of long-term dangerousness regarding the same subject population.

In his review, Mossman (1994) reviewed six published studies of long-term (≥ 1 year) clinical assessments of dangerousness: Cocozza and Steadman (1976); Kozol, Boucher, and Garofalo (1972); Mullen and Reinehr (1982); Sepejak, Menzies, Webster, and Jensen (1983); Steadman (1977); and Webster et al. (1984). However, apart from the fact that these studies did not directly compare actuarial versus clinical assessments, the studies have serious methodological problems (discussed at length by Litwack & Schlesinger, 1987) and address unrepresentative situations. Therefore, it is impossible to draw firm or even meaningful conclusions from these studies regarding the general (much less the current) validity of clinical assessments of dangerousness, or the relative validity of clinical versus actuarially based assessments of long-term dangerousness.

In brief, Cocozza and Steadman (1976, 1978) studied clinical predictions of intrainstitutional violence, rather than of violence in the community, where the patients' known history of violence had occurred. Kozol et al. (1972) studied the recidivism rate of offenders released from confinement against clinical advice. Although only one third of that sample was discovered to have recidivated, the patients released against clinical advice were not at all a representative sample of all patients deemed dangerous by the clinicians, and they were not predicted to be violent in any event. Rather, they were simply not recommended for release (Litwack & Schlesinger, 1999, pp. 175–177).

Mullen and Reinehr (1982) asked staff members to rate hospitalized forensic patients as dangerous or not dangerous. Eleven percent of the patients deemed dangerous were ultimately rearrested versus 7% of those judged not dangerous. However, the judgments of dangerousness were not prerelease judgments of dangerousness in the community or formal assessments in any way. Rather, after each patient in the study had been on the ward for at least 1 month, the relevant staff members were simply asked to make a global "simple dichotomous judgment" (p. 225) as to whether the patient was dangerous.

Sepejak et al. (1983) and Webster et al. (1984) similarly (and simply) compared global ratings of dangerousness by clinicians in a "brief assessment unit" of a forensic service with related outcomes over a 2-year period. Ratings of dangerousness were significantly (if modestly) correlated with outcomes in both studies. The crucial point, however, is that the clinical examinations were very brief and the clinicians were actually more concerned with making short-term assessments of dangerousness rather than long-term assessments (and determinations of immediate dangerousness may have led to interventions that reduced future dangerousness). Steadman (1977) did not study the validity of prerelease assessments of dangerousness at all. He found only that offenders deemed "defective delinquents" and given special treatment (and lengthier incarcerations) recidivated at a lower rate than various comparison groups.

It should also be noted that in their review of the literature, Melton et al. (1997) cited two studies, another study by Cocozza and Steadman (1974) and one by Thornberry and Jacoby (1979), which supposedly showed some "meager" advantage for actuarial assessments (p. 285). However, as discussed by Litwack and Schlesinger (1999, pp. 177–178), these studies, regarding the notorious Baxstrom and Dixon patients, respectively, examined the validity of administrative decisions that were not clinical assessments in any meaningful sense of the term.

In short, comparisons of actuarial assessments with supposed clinical judgments that are far removed from actual, representative, clinical judgments are relatively meaningless. This is even more so the case when the clinical assessments concern different patient populations than the actuarial assessments. Therefore, Mossman's (1994) meta-analysis and the similar meta-analysis by Bonta et al. (1998) cannot be taken as evidence for the superiority of actuarial assessments of dangerousness. What of the eight actual comparative studies? They are considered below individually in chronological order.

1. In what appears to be the first published study of supposedly actuarial versus clinical assessments of dangerousness, Glaser (1955, 1962) found that a scheme for classifying parolees "by a prediction score derived from seven separate factors" (1962, p. 246) predicted parole violations (or lack thereof) better than unstructured clinical predictions (by a psychiatrist or sociologist) following an interview. The factors involved in the prediction score included a "subjective case study evaluation" of the parolees' "social development pattern" prior to incarceration (which was converted into a numerical score), ratings of the parolees' prior criminal record, ratings of their "use of prison time," and other factors (1962, p. 245).

However, although they had the possible advantage of interviewing the parole applicants, it is not at all clear from this report whether the clinicians had available to them the bulk of the information on which the actuarial scheme was based, such as information regarding the parole applicants' prior adjustment in the community, for example, or, equally important, the time to consider that information. Indeed, Glaser (1955) noted that one of the four sociologists, whose predictions were particularly poor, "had to commute between two institutions and carry a heavy case load during a personnel shortage" (p. 285). Moreover, the numerical predictive scheme was not cross-validated and the offenders were assessed between 1940 and 1949, long before there was any meaningful literature on factors that could be used to guide clinical assessments. And the offender population of this study was a rather narrowly defined one, "young and improvable" inmates (Glaser, 1955, p. 283), rather than a traditional psychiatric population for which specifically psychiatric judgments might be more applicable (although psychiatric reviews, per se, were sought in certain cases). Thus, although this early study did and does raise the issue of whether structured assessments of dangerousness (leading to an actuarial score) might be superior to unstructured clinical assessments, given the important, even crucial, clinical input into the actuarial scores and the lack of clear evidence that the practicing clinicians were able to consider all the information used to derive the prediction scores, this study provides, at best, only very limited support for the notion that actuarial assessments of dangerousness are superior to clinical assessments (even regarding the limited circumstances of parole determinations; cf. Study 3, below).

2. The next study of clinical versus actuarial assessments of dangerousness, and one relied upon by Grove et al. (1995) for their meta-analysis, is a 1968 study by Smith and Lanyon. They compared the accuracy of predictions of parole violations or non-violations through a base expectancy table that focused on the number of past court referrals, the seriousness of the most recent offense, the age of first court appearance, and school status, with predictions based solely on Minnesota Multiphasic Personality Inventory (MMPI; Hathaway & McKinley, 1983) results. In other words, they compared the predictive power of history with clinical judgments that were made without the benefit of history or interview data. Not surprisingly, the predictions made through the base expectancy table were better than chance predictions, and the judgments that were based on the MMPI were not; or, in the authors' words, "the future behavior of legal offenders is better predicted from their previous behavior than from personality test data" (Smith & Lanyon, 1968, p. 57).

It can be stipulated that assessments of dangerousness that are based on past behavior will be superior to assessments of dangerousness that are based on MMPI results alone. However, despite the claim of Smith and Lanyon (1968) that their study was another example of "actuarial prediction . . . [being] superior to clinical prediction" (p. 57), in actual practice clinicians would rarely, if ever, rely solely on the MMPI to perform risk assessments. Therefore, this study does not meaningfully compare clinical with actuarial assessments. Indeed, as Meehl (1986) himself has stressed, the issue is whether actuarial assessments can outperform clinical assessments when clinicians can consider the data used by the actuarial assessment scheme.

3. The third study is a 1983 study by Holland, Holt, Levi, and Beckett, titled "Comparison and Combination of Clinical and Statistical Prediction of Recidivism Among Adult Offenders." In this study, clinical prediction outperformed statistical prediction. Three hundred and forty-three male offenders were referred for presentence reviews by the clinical staff, who could review case files and discuss cases with each other. One hundred and ninety-eight of these offenders were released and followed up with. Of the 198, 175 were recommended for release by the staff and 23 were not. The

offenders were also rated on the Salient Factor Scale (Gottfredson, Wilkins, & Hoffman, 1978), described by the authors as " . . . a recidivism expectancy measure that was developed after extensive . . . research as a decisionmaking tool for the U.S. Parole Commission. It consists of nine criminal history and social stability items [which] . . . are typical of those that are contained in the recidivism literature" (p. 205).

The results showed that the Salient Factor Scale predicted arrests of any type, even those for nonviolent acts that did not result in conviction or incarceration, somewhat better than the staff assessments. However, regarding those outcomes that mattered most—arrest and conviction for a violent offense—the correlation between staff recommendations and recidivism was superior to that of the actuarial assessment. It is also noteworthy that of the 23 released offenders recommended for retention by the staff, 8 (35%) were rearrested, convicted, and incarcerated for a violent offense, whereas of the 175 offenders the staff recommended for probation, only 14 (8%) were convicted of violent offense during the study period (of whom 12 were incarcerated). As is discussed below, the fact that 15 of the 23 released offenders (65%) were not later convicted of a violent offense does not mean that clinical assessments of dangerousness were wrong two thirds of the time. The important point to note for now, however, is that the clinical assessments clearly distinguished between a more and less dangerous group of offenders.

4. The next study, by Wormith and Goldstone (1984) was titled "The Clinical and Statistical Prediction of Recidivism." A sample of 222 male offenders was chosen from a cohort of 508 Canadian federal offenders who had been released from prison, either on parole (without intensive supervision) or under mandatory supervision, and whose community placement had either been terminated successfully (by expiration of the warrant) or unsuccessfully (by a return to prison). Retrospectively, the offenders were given a Recidivism Prediction Score (RPS) that was based on a previously constructed and validated scale that focused on "a wide range of [weighted] categorical variables of the traditional legal and demographic nature" (p. 12), such as most recent offense, age of first conviction as an adult, academic achievement, previous employment, and marital status.

Offenders were placed into one of five prognostic categories on the basis of their RPS scores (very good, good, fair, fair/poor, or poor), and the community outcomes were compared with both the clinical decision (to grant parole or to require supervision) and with the RPS prognosis. The RPS did fare somewhat better, at least on the surface, than the parole judgments. Seventy-one percent of the paroled patients succeeded, compared with 76% of the offenders in the very good-fair prognostic categories. Similarly, "the incidence of false negatives made according to Board decisions (. . . 12.6%) was slightly higher than would have occurred using the RPS scheme (. . . 11.7%)" (p. 20). That is, 28 of the 98 participants who were paroled recidivated compared with 26 of the 94 offenders who were placed in the better RPS prognostic categories. Further, 51% of the not-paroled offenders apparently succeeded despite clinical qualms, whereas only 41% of the offenders in the two poorest RPS prognostic categories succeeded (manifesting a seemingly lower rate of false positives for the RPS scheme).

These are hardly substantial differences. To the extent that the differences did favor, however slightly, the actuarial scheme, Wormith and Goldstone (1984) admirably provided four reasons why this might be so that argue against negative conclusions about the clinical judgments: (a) Parole boards understandably defer outright release of murderers (even when it is recognized that their recidivism potential is low) because of the seriousness of their crimes (thus raising the false-negative rate among the released offenders and the false-positive rate among supervised offenders); (b) some offenders are released by parole boards despite considerable qualms because it is believed those offenders "deserve a chance" (p. 20); (c) "there is no guarantee that those successfully released on mandatory supervision [i.e., seemingly false positives] would have been equally successful on parole" (p. 20); and (d) parole boards may understandably wish to err on the side of having false negatives rather than false positives.

Thus, nothing in Wormith and Goldstone's (1984) study supports a claim of the superiority of actuarial over clinical assessments. Moreover, although not replicated in a subsequent study by the authors (reported in the same article), it was found in their study that parole board decisions independently added to the accurate prediction of outcome when RPS scores were controlled for. That is, in one of Wormith and Goldstone's studies, "the parole board's decision added a significant and independent contribution to the accurate prediction of offenders' recidivism" (p. 21). For example, 63% of offenders in the two poorest RPS prognostic categories succeeded when they were nevertheless paroled, whereas only 37% of such offenders who were not paroled succeeded, even though they were presumably under stricter supervision. (In the subsequent study, just referred to, it was found that the overall accuracy rate of what the authors called "legal-demographic" versus "subjective" predictions of recidivism was almost identical.)

5. Quinsey and Maguire (1986) determined the factors that experienced forensic clinicians use to classify patients in a maximum security psychiatric institutions as dangerous and compared those factors with the ones that were in fact associated with reoffending, over a period of at least 11 years, in a group of patients who had been released from the same institution. The clinicians based their judgments primarily on the seriousness of the admitting offense and the frequency of assaultive behavior within the institution. Overall, however, the factors used by clinicians to assess dangerousness did not predict violence in the released patients. The most important variables associated with dangerous outcome were, indeed, the seriousness of the admitting offense but also a history of economic crime, a criminal as opposed to a civil commitment, young age, and the number of previous correctional confinements. All but the first factor were not significantly used by the clinicians in making their assessments. In-hospital assaultiveness, to which the clinicians did give significant weight, had no relationship to postrelease offending.

Quinsey and Maguire (1986) concluded that "[t]he results of this study offer . . . despair at current practice. . . . The failure of the judgment model to predict the outcome of a new sample [is] a source of serious concern. . . ." (p. 168). However, and in addition to the crucial fact that their study (and the supposed superiority of the outcome model) was not cross-validated, their results do not, in fact, justify such a pessimistic conclusion about clinical judgments. As Quinsey and Maguire recognized (pp. 148–149), the outcome sample was not truly representative of the judgment sample. After all, they were patients who were released. Thus, they must have differed, clinically, in very significant ways from the patients who were not released, presumably including the nature of their dangerousness.

Indeed, the released patients had on average three times as many previous correctional confinements as the not-released sample and were far less likely to have committed a homicide ($Ms = 0.02$ for the released group and 0.27 for the judgment group) and far more likely to have a history of economic offenses. In short, the released outcome group appears to have been composed, to a significant degree, of chronic offenders. As Quinsey and Maguire (1986) observed, "[t]he picture of a dangerous releasee is that of a young man who has committed both serious crimes against the person and property crimes and who is *not* a typical psychiatric patient" (p. 165; italics added). It is hardly surprising, therefore, that different factors predicted their recidivism than clinicians would use to assess dangerousness in a group of offenders who were more substantially and classically psychotic.

Similarly, the fact that in-hospital assaultiveness did not correlate with post-release criminality in the outcome sample does not mean that it would, or should, mean as little in reviewing patients who are more psychotic. Moreover, in actual practice, clinicians in secure facilities may give great weight to in-hospital assaultiveness when assessing dangerousness, because their immediate task is to determine if their patients should be transferred to a less secure facility, rather than to determine how the patients will do in the community, eventually, on their release. In-hospital assaultiveness is, on the surface, highly relevant to determining whether a patient will be violent in another facility in the near future (even if it is not related to patients' dangerousness in the community after they are eventually released).

Quinsey and Maguire (1986) did find that a judgment model alone derived from patients who were psychotic could not predict the dangerousness of the small number ($n = 28$) of psychotic outcome patients. However, they did not report any data differentiating the psychotic outcome patients from the outcome patients with personality disorders. Therefore, it must be assumed that the psychotic outcome patients did not differ from the nonpsychotic outcome patients on such crucial variables as their history of economic crime, their prior numbers of criminal confinements, and their (relative lack) of history of committing a homicide, but that they did differ significantly from the psychotic judgment patients in these regards.

Another very important consideration, which is discussed below, concerns the meaning of a clinical rating of *dangerousness*. A clinical determination that a patient is dangerous does not necessarily indicate a judgment that the patient is likely to act violently if released. Rather, it may simply represent judgment that the patient poses a serious risk of causing significant harm, and the greater the harm the patient may potentially cause, the less the chances of causing that harm need be for a patient to be deemed dangerous.

Thus, for example, a patient who was perceived as presenting one chance in three of committing a homicide in the foreseeable future, if released, would certainly be viewed by most clinicians (and most other people) as being highly dangerous, and more dangerous, all in all, than a person who posed a 75% chance of committing a nonviolent theft. Not surprisingly, nor incorrectly, therefore, the clinicians in Quinsey and Maguire's (1986) study apparently gave far more importance to a history of homicide than to a history of economic crimes in their assessments of overall dangerousness, even though a history of economic crimes was predictive of recidivism among the released patients.

In summary, the factors that are most predictive of recidivism in a population of chronic offenders (e.g., young age and multiple imprisonments) may not be the factors that are most relevant to assessing dangerousness in psychotic murderers. Thus, the fact that the variables that best predicted recidivism in the released outcome sample were not the factors focused on by the clinicians in making most of their determinations of dangerousness does not negate the possibility that the clinicians in this study were focusing on the most important considerations regarding the patients who were not released (Litwack, Kirschner, & Wack, 1993, pp. 251–252; Litwack & Schlesinger, 1999, p. 184). Accordingly, and especially because the outcome model derived here was not cross-validated, this study does not provide support for the contention that actuarial assessments of dangerousness are superior to clinical assessments.

6. The issue of cross-validation or, rather, the lack thereof, plays a particularly important role in considering the next study, titled "Two Models for Predicting Recidivism" by Hassin (1986; a study that, for some reason, is rarely cited in the literature although, superficially, it is very supportive of actuarial assessments).

In 1978, on the occasion of the 30th birthday of the State of Israel, special pardon boards were established to examine prisoners' files and to recommend, in appropriate cases, the granting of pardons, early release, or reductions in sentences. For the purposes of the study, prisoners deemed by the boards as deserving a lightening of their sentence, as well as those deemed deserving of a pardon or outright release, were considered to have been clinically classified as offenders at low risk for recidivism. Those offenders not deemed worthy of more lenient treatment were deemed to have been clinically classified as at high risk for recidivism. During the study period, 167 offenders deemed worthy of more lenient treatment by the Boards were released and 455 prisoners whose sentences were left unchanged by the Boards were nevertheless released by some other method. Each of these offenders were followed up for some time to determine whether they recidivated.

The information presented to the Boards included 31 variables, of which 14 were sociodemographic, 12 were criminal, and 5 were connected with the release process itself. Hassin (1986) determined statistically which of these variables played the greatest role in the boards' determinations. The 3 variables that most strongly guided the Boards' decisions were the length of the current prison term, with either a life sentence or a sentence of up to 1 year most likely to lead to leniency and a sentence of 4–8 years most likely to lead to an unchanged sentence; the lack of prior imprisonments; and a positive recommendation from a social worker. Hassin also statistically determined which of the 31 variables were in fact most related to recidivism and found that those variables were quite different. The 3 most powerful predictive variables were young age at first offense, young age on release, and being unmarried.

Moreover, Hassin (1986) derived a "Discriminant Analysis Programme" that was based on the statistical analysis of how the 31 variables correlated with recidivism and compared the rates of recidivism resulting from the Boards' recommendations with the rates of recidivism resulting from the programs' recommendations. Not surprisingly, because the program was perfectly fit to the study population, the computer program outperformed the Boards by a ratio of 1.4 to 1. (That is, in Hassin's words, "[t]he Boards err[ed] 1.4 times as often as the computer" [p. 282].) However, given the extremely unusual nature of the sample population in this study, the unusual nature and circumstances of the review procedure, and, especially, the lack of cross-validation of the statistical program (and its comparison with clinical judgment) with another more representative sample, no firm conclusions can be reasonably drawn from this study about the relative merits of clinical versus actuarial assessments. Moreover, because the Boards' decisions were not based on any interviews, this study is largely irrelevant to clinical assessments of dangerousness, especially clinical assessments of dangerousness of more traditionally "forensic" populations that are based, in part, on interviews.

7. A 1988 study of clinical versus actuarial assessments of dangerousness regarding convicted sex offenders (Hall, 1988) claimed to provide evidence for the superiority for actuarial methods and suggested that clinicians should take careful note of available actuarial data when assessing dangerousness in such a population to help avoid false negatives (i.e., to avoid mistakenly viewing as safe for release offenders who are, in fact, still dangerous).

Three hundred and forty-two male sexual offenders treated in a state hospital (for a mean of 20 months) were reviewed for safety to be released to the community by a committee of psychiatrists and psychologists, "ostensibly based on the patient's . . . [response to] . . . a guided self-help peer confrontational treatment program" (Hall, 1988, p. 773). Patients who were found to be dangerous were usually sentenced to prison (for a mean of 9 months) but were ultimately released and followed up for 5 years to determine whether they had been rearrested for (a) sexual offenses against adults; (b) sexual offenses against children; (c) nonsexual violent offenses; or (d) nonsexual, nonviolent offenses. The total sample was split randomly into two nearly equal subsamples. The clinical assessments during hospitalization for one subsample were compared with a linear combination of actuarial predictors (age, prior offenses, IQ, and MMPI data) for the other subsample to determine their relative predictive accuracy.

Hall (1988) summarized his view of the results of this study as follows:

> . . . Discriminant analyses suggested that a linear combination of
> actuarial variables [prior offenses, age, and MMPI data, but not IQ

scores] was significantly predictive of sexual reoffenses against adults and of nonsexual violent and nonviolent reoffending. However, clinical judgment was not significantly predictive of recidivism, nor were actuarial or clinical variables predictive of sexual reoffending against children. (p. 773)

The actuarial scheme was superior to clinical judgments in identifying recidivists in this study. Combining the four categories of recidivism, 56% (41/73) of the actual recidivists were identified by the clinicians, whereas the actuarial predictors correctly classified 71% (66/93) of the recidivists. However, these differences, though significant, were not great and the actuarial scheme derived in this study was not cross-validated. (It should be noted, however, that in this study actuarial predictors did far better than clinicians in identifying sexual reoffenders against adults: 87% [13/15] vs. 50% [6/12].)

Moreover, although the actuarial scheme appeared to outperform the clinicians in predicting nonreoffenders for each (re)offense category, these results, and thus the overall comparisons of the clinical and actuarial predictions in this study, are meaningless because the clinicians and the actuarial schemes were not making comparable predictions. The clinicians were predicting for each patient whether any significant recidivism of any type would occur (i.e., whether the patient was "safe . . . to be at large" [Hall, 1988, p. 773]). The actuarial scheme made separate predictions for each of the four possible reoffense categories.

For example, Hall (1988) reported that " . . . clinical prediction correctly classified . . . 53% of the subjects who did not reoffend sexually against adults (predicted nonre-offenders = 86, actual non-reoffenders = 163). . . . The actuarial predictors correctly classified 93% of the nonreoffenders [sexually against adults] (predicted non-reoffenders = 129, actual nonreoffenders = 139)" (p. 774). But the actuarial predictors in this instance predicted which offenders would not reoffend sexually against adults (including, presumably, all offenders with no history of offending sexually against adults), whereas many (and presumably most) of the nonreoffenders who were predicted to reoffend by the clinicians (163 - 86 = 77) were predicted not to reoffend sexually against adults, but to reoffend in any significant way. Thus, although the above result, as reported, suggests that actuarial predictions did outlandishly better than clinicians in identifying offenders who would not reoffend by committing sexual offenses against adults (93% vs. 53%), in fact there were no clinical predictions of "safe for sexual offenses against adults" for the actuarial predictions to be compared with.

Moreover, Hall's (1988) conclusion that "clinical judgment was not significantly predictive of recidivism" (p. 773) in this study is simply incorrect. Regarding the assessments the clinicians did make, whether the patient was safe for release, they did differentiate, significantly, between recidivists and nonrecidivists. Fifty percent (41/82) of the patients viewed as unsafe for release by the clinicians recidivated (after some additional time period of confinement and, perhaps, treatment), whereas only 35% (32/93) of the patients viewed as safe for release recidivated, $\chi^2(1, 175) = 4.35, p < .05$.

8. Gardner, Lidz, Mulvey, and Shaw (1996a) compared actuarial and emergency

psychiatric assessments of future dangerousness for their accuracy in predicting any community violence versus serious community violence after the patient's release. Actuarial predictions had lower rates of false-positive and false-negative errors than the clinical assessments for any violence. The actuarial predictors, however, were not superior to clinical judgments in predicting serious violence, which is the issue of practical concern.

Even more important, data regarding three of the most important variables in the actuarial prediction equation were collected from patients who were not in the emergency room but who were in the community after being discharged from the hospital. These variables were the patient's score on the hostility subscale of the Brief Symptom Inventory (BSI; Derogatis & Melisaratos, 1983), the patient's recent history of drug abuse, and the patient's recent history of violence. Gardner, Lidz, Mulvey, and Shaw (1996a) reported that a simple decision tree that relied on these three variables and age less than 18 predicted future violence as well as a regression-based method using those and other variables. However, it is questionable, at best, whether the data required for the decision tree could be validly and reliably collected in the emergency room, given the patients' clinical conditions, and other practical considerations, at that time. At the very least, therefore, it has not been demonstrated by these studies that actuarial methods are superior to clinical methods in determining which patients evaluated in psychiatric emergency rooms should be hospitalized involuntarily at that time (see also Litwack & Schlesinger, 1999, pp. 179–180). To the contrary, because the clinicians in Gardner et al.'s study did as well as the actuarial predictors in predicting future serious violence (the only truly important relevant variable) and because, almost certainly, the necessary actuarial data would not have been nearly as valid if collected in the emergency room (if they could have been collected there at all), to date there is every reason to suppose that clinicians are at least equal to actuarial methods in determining short-term serious dangerousness—the only decision (regarding danger-ousness) that is actually called for—regarding individuals brought for evaluation to psychiatric emergency rooms. (Recall that Mossman's [1994] meta-analysis found no superiority for actuarial methods over clinical methods regarding short-term predictions of violence.)

In sum, it appears that the actual, direct evidence does not support a preference for actuarial over clinical assessments of dangerousness (or vice versa). Upon analysis, two studies (Hall, 1988; Hassin, 1986) may be said to favor actuarial assessments, but they were not cross-validated. Two studies (Gardner et al., 1996a, 1996b; Holland et al., 1983) may be said to lean in favor of clinical assessments. Three studies (Quinsey & Maguire, 1986; Smith & Lanyon, 1968; Wormith & Goldstone, 1984) produced inconclusive or meaningless results. And one study (Glaser, 1955, 1962) appears to be a study of structured versus unstructured (and perhaps rushed) clinical assessments more than a study of actuarial versus clinical assessments. Thus, despite claims or beliefs to the contrary, it is not the case that a large number of meaningful studies show at least some, and overall a significant, advantage for actuarial assessments (thereby establishing convergent validity for actuarial assessments) or that there is one relatively definitive study that favors actuarial assessments. Accordingly, it seems that much more research is needed to determine the relative merits of clinical versus actuarial assessments of dangerous [*sic*] and that such research should be conducted in as meaningful a manner as possible. To do so, however, will require taking into account certain fairly unique features regarding clinical assessments of dangerousness.

II. Assessments of Dangerousness Are Inherently Different From Many Other Predictive Tasks, and in Ways That Make It Very Difficult to Meaningfully Compare Clinical With Actuarial Assessments of Dangerousness

It is beyond the scope of this article to address the many arguments that have been raised in favor of and against both actuarial and clinical assessments (see, e.g., Buchanan, 1999; Einhorn, 1986; Evjen, 1962; Faust, 1997; Gottfredson & Gottfredson, 1988b; Groth-Marnat, 2000; Grove & Meehl, 1996; Grubin, 1997; Halleck, 1987; Holt, 1970, 1986; Karon, 2000; Kleinmuntz, 1990; Marchese, 1992: Murphy & Davidshofer, 1988; Poythress, 1992; Sarbin, 1986). It is also beyond the scope of this article to address the thesis of Meehl (1986) and his followers that at least most types of predictive activities made by human beings, including supposedly expert human beings, can be more accurately made, and, therefore, should be made, by actuarial methods. Even if Meehl's thesis is true for most predictive tasks, it may not be true of assessments of dangerousness, as the nature of dangerousness risk assessments is such that it is unusually difficult to arrive at actuarial equations that are truly suitable to many dangerousness assessment tasks or to meaningfully compare actuarial and clinical assessments of dangerousness.

To begin with, validated actuarial predictive equations simply cannot be developed regarding the dangerousness of many of those forensic patients who elicit the most serious clinical concern for the simple reason that these patients, be they emergency room reviewees or hospitalized insanity acquittees, will generally not be released as long as they are deemed dangerous (by clinicians, judges, or both). Therefore, one cannot validate, or cross-validate, meaningful actuarial predictive schemes regarding such patients or compare the predictive accuracy of these schemes with those of clinical judgments.

Second, and most important, in comparing actuarial with clinical assessments of dangerousness, it must be remembered (if truly meaningful research is to be done in this area) that clinical assessments of dangerousness are not predictions of violence. More precisely, a clinical (or judicial) determination that a patient should be confined is not necessarily, or even usually, a prediction that the patient will be violent (to self or others) if not confined. Rather, it is a judgment that the patient poses a sufficient risk of sufficient harm (to self or others) within a particular future time span to justify the confinement at issue (Litwack, 1996; Litwack & Schlesinger, 1999, pp. 177, 191–194; Schopp & Quattrocchi, 1995; cf. Janus & Meehl, 1997). Thus, frequently, patients are correctly deemed dangerous by clinicians (or judges) even when those patients are viewed as less than likely to commit violence because the risk that the patient will commit serious violence is simply too great to tolerate.

How is research going to take this fact into account? Imagine, for example, that clinicians seek to retain 100 insanity acquittees, each of whom is perceived as posing a 33% chance of attempting a murder if released. Also imagine that these individuals are nevertheless released and that one third attempt a murder. Were the clinicians 33% right or 100% right? From one point of view, they were 100% right. They may have recognized that each of these 100 patients had psychological vulnerabilities that put them at serious risk for attempting murder but that whether any of them would in fact attempt murder would depend on unforeseeable environmental or psychosocial events. Viewed in that way, the clinicians would have been 100% right. Thus, in reviewing clinical judgments, and in comparing them to actuarial judgments, the exact nature of the clinical judgment must be taken into account and a clinical determination of dangerousness that is not a prediction of violence cannot properly be viewed as such.

The degree of certainty of clinical judgments must also be considered. In the literature on clinical versus actuarial assessments in general, the confidence of clinicians is not strongly related to accuracy, if at all (McNiel, Sandberg, & Binder, 1998), but it may be regarding clinical assessments of dangerousness. In the one study to date to directly address the issue, McNiel et al. found that clinicians' confidence regarding their assessments of dangerousness was strongly correlated with accuracy. ("When clinicians had a high degree of confidence, their evaluations of risk of violence were strongly associated with whether or not patients became violent." p. 655)

This study concerned assessments of psychiatric patients' short-term, in-hospital risk of violence. Thus, it remains to be demonstrated that confident clinical assessments of long-term dangerousness in the community are equally, or at least significantly, correlated with accuracy. Still, to be truly meaningful, studies comparing actuarial versus clinical assessments of dangerousness should not only compare relevant actuarial schemes with clinical assessments in general but with those clinical assessments that were made with reasonable degrees of confidence. After all, even if, in general, actuarial assessments were superior to clinical assessments, if those clinical assessments made with confidence were shown to be superior to actuarial assessments then, in actual practice, confident clinical assessments should be relied on above actuarial assessments.

In addition, actuarial assessments of dangerousness are often compared with individual clinical assessments. However, in a variety of real-world contexts (e.g., the assessment of insanity acquitees) the ultimate clinical assessment is made by clinical teams, and the judgment of clinical teams may be more accurate, by certain criteria, than the judgment of individual clinicians. For example, Fuller and Cowan (1999) found that clinical teams fairly accurately assessed the risk that forensic patients posed to hospital staff and stated that their results "caution against uncritical substitution of multi-disciplinary clinical opinion by actuarial methods in advance of evidence that the latter perform better in any given context" (p. 286). Thus, when the real-world clinical judgment is a team judgment, any proposed actuarial assessment scheme must be compared with the judgment of the clinical teams to determine which procedure should be used in actual practice (taking into account any necessary cost-benefit analysis).

Another crucial point is that clinical assessments of dangerousness typically consider the seriousness of possible harm at issue, whereas actuarial assessments often do not. This point is addressed in more detail in the following section. Suffice it to point out for now that any meaningful comparison of actuarial versus clinical schemes for assessing dangerousness must take into account, not only the percentage of correct predictions under each scheme but also the totality of harm that will be caused by false negatives under each scheme and the degree of injury to false positives under each scheme (in relation to the cost of false negatives; Gottfredson & Gottfredson, 1988a).

Imagine again, for example, that in a certain forensic facility there are 100 insanity acquittees who had committed a murder and who are deemed dangerous by clinicians. An actuarial scheme deems 50 of the acquittees to be dangerous and 50 to be safe to be released. All 100 are released and 34 commit another murder. Of the 50 patients deemed dangerous by the actuarial scheme, 24 committed murder. Of the 50 patients deemed nondangerous by the actuarial scheme, 10 committed murder. If the clinical determinations are viewed as predictions, the actuarial scheme made more correct predictions (64% correct vs. 34% correct). However, which mode of prediction would one want to rely on in the future?

To sum up the general point that assessments of dangerousness are different from many other predictive assessments, it may be useful to point out some of the difficulties that would be involved in studying clinical versus actuarial assessments of dangerousness that might not be involved in studying a more common type of predictive assessment: for example, clinical versus actuarial assessments of school success. In the latter case, at least hypothetically, for 1 year, from the pool of applicants, applicants could be randomly admitted and then followed to allow for the determination of actuarial predictors of success and failure (without risking serious physical harm to anyone). Then, for a subsequent class, a representative sample of clinically predicted succeeders and actuarially predicted succeeders (and even another random sample of applicants) could be admitted and followed (again without risking physical harm to anyone) to determine the relative degrees of accuracy of each of the assessment methods. Moreover, predictions can be made and success determined on a simple dichotomous basis (passing or not passing a certain percentage of courses), and there is no weighing of risks that needs to be taken into account (although, in fact, a lack of diversity might be a cost of using the actuarial scheme). None of these advantages apply to studying clinical versus actuarial assessments of dangerousness.

Additionally, Hart (1998) has pointed out that *risk assessment* is "the process of evaluating individuals to (1) characterize the likelihood they will commit acts of violence *and* (2) develop interventions to manage or reduce that likelihood" (p. 122, italics added; see also Heilbrun, 1997). Even if actuarial assessments were clearly superior to clinical assessments regarding the first of these tasks, clinical assessments of dangerousness might still be necessary to effectuate the second. Actuarial assessments, and certainly numerical risk scores (e.g., VRAG scores), may provide little if any guidance to service providers regarding which treatment options or service settings would be most effective for particular potentially dangerous individuals (Glasser, 1996; Wack,

1993) or which "dynamic" variables should be the focus of treatment (Hanson & Harris, 2000). Indeed, the authors of *Violent Offenders* (Quinsey et al., 1999) observed that "[t]hrough cognitive (providing insight into the 'how' and 'why' of their behavior) and behavioral (providing actual experiences of mastery and success) means, a relapse prevention approach teaches offenders new ways of coping that may allow them to break the cycle before they relapse completely" (p. 217). In addition, actuarial assessments may be less sensitive than clinical assessments to changing conditions and protective factors (Rogers, 2000).

III. If Actuarial Dangerousness Assessment Instruments, or Even Structured Assessment Tools Such as the HCR-20 and the PCL-R, Are to Be Most Usefully and Fairly Used, They Will Have to Be Validated in a More Precise Manner Than Is Currently the Case

In *Violent Offenders,* Quinsey et al. (1999) devote considerable attention to the development and supposed utility of the VRAG, which the authors claimed to be "an actuarial instrument that predicted violent recidivism for serious offenders in general" (p. 144). The VRAG was developed by the authors by following up, for 7 (and later 10) years, 618 men who had been released from secure confinement, if only to be transferred to a minimum security psychiatric hospital, and determining the degree to which 50 "independent or predictor variables" (p. 143) obtained from file data related to violent recidivism. Many of the men were released from correctional institutions and some from psychiatric hospitals, but all had been deemed "mentally disordered" at the time of the arrest that led to their prerelease confinement. The authors found that 12 of the 50 studied predictor variables were significantly and independently related to violent recidivism. The best predictor was the offender's score (from file data) on the Psychopathy Checklist—Revised (PCL-R; Hare, 1991), followed by the degree of "elementary school maladjustment." More important, after developing a means for obtaining a total VRAG score that was based on a weighted rating of the significant predictor variables, the authors found through a series of studies that VRAG scores correlated very significantly with recidivism in their studied populations.

Many problems with the VRAG (and, more generally, with *Violent Offenders;* Quinsey et al., 1999) have been identified by Hart (1999). For the moment, however, I focus on one issue: the practical utility (or lack thereof) of the VRAG. The basic VRAG score is used to determine the risk for any violent recidivism, even a single simple assault, over a 7-year (or 10-year) period. The authors of the VRAG did cite evidence (see, e.g., Rice & Harris, 1995) that the VRAG is equally predictive of serious reoffending as well as reoffending over shorter periods of time (e.g., 3.5 years). However, there are two problems with that claim. First, the authors of the VRAG considered more than one assault causing bodily harm (i.e., two simple assaults), as well as more serious crimes, to be indicative of serious violence. Second, and more important, although it may be true that the VRAG predicts the relative risk of serious violence, or violence over a 3.5–year period, as well as the risk of any violence, the absolute risk of serious violence predicted by any relatively high VRAG score appears to be very significantly below the predicted risk of any violence.

The authors of the VRAG provided very precise data regarding the "probability of [any] violent recidivism" after 7 or 10 years of opportunity "as a function of nine equal sized VRAG categories" (Quinsey et al., 1999, p. 240). However, no such data were provided regarding the probability of serious violence, or violence within shorter time periods of opportunity. On the other hand, Rice and Harris (1995, pp. 741, 743) and Quinsey, Rice, and Harris (1995, p. 96) did provide evidence that for their study populations (including, in the latter case, a population of sex offenders), the base rate for serious violence, or for any violent recidivism after 3.5 years of opportunity, is substantially less than it is for any violence over 7 or 10 years of opportunity (cf. Grann, Belfrage, & Tengström, 2000, who found that the VRAG "predicted violent re-convictions within 2 years from release or discharge significantly better than random . . ." [p. 107]). It may still be the case that very high VRAG scorers have a very high rate of serious recidivism, in absolute terms, even within a few years after release. In terms of the actuarial versus clinical debate, however, the question is: Would not these very high VRAG scorers be deemed equally dangerous by clinicians?

Thus, even if it is true, as the authors of *Violent Offenders* (Quinsey et al., 1999) claimed, that "the VRAG score [is] positively related to the probability of at least one violent reoffense, to the severity of the reoffenses that occurred, and to the speed with which violent reoffenses occurred" (pp. 149–151), the fundamental question remains whether VRAG scores (if they can validly be applied to a particular offender or group of offenders at all) can sufficiently assess the absolute risk an offender poses of committing a sufficiently serious offense within a sufficiently short period of time (if released) to justify that offender's continued retention. That is, even if the VRAG very accurately predicts the relative risks of recidivism posed by various members of a group of previous offenders, there is still the issue of its ability to predict absolute risk well enough to justify continued detention on the basis of a VRAG score. Even an almost 100% probability that an offender, if released, will commit a simple assault within the next 10 years would not justify that offender's continued retention by any reasonable cost-benefit analysis. Thus, to date, even for the population from whom it was developed, it is highly questionable whether VRAG scores can be used to predict the severity and imminence, as well as the likelihood, of recidivism with sufficient precision to properly justify retention decisions.

In *Jones v. United States* (1983), the U.S. Supreme Court ruled that a finding of dangerousness that was sufficient to justify the confinement of an insanity acquittee who was mentally ill did not require a finding that the acquittee had committed, or was at serious risk to commit, a violent act. Rather, the Court held, "proof that a person committed a non-violent crime against property" (463 U.S. at 365), in this case attempting to steal a jacket from a department store, justified a (rebuttable) presumption that the acquittee was dangerous. And the Court went on, in a footnote, to point out how nonviolent crimes such as theft "frequently may result in violence . . ." (Footnote 14). In the same footnote, however, the Court also noted that "the *relative* 'dangerousness' of a particular individual, of course, should be a consideration at the release hearing" (italics added).

Thus, in certain contexts, a sufficient risk of a simple assault, or even a nonviolent crime, may, constitutionally, constitute dangerousness warranting confinement, or some other intrusive governmental action. It should also be noted that recent court decisions have admitted testimony regarding the risk of future violence posed by sex offenders according to their VRAG scores without any analysis of the seriousness of potential violence indicated by those scores (see, e.g., *In re Dean*, 2000; *In re Kienitz*, 1999; *In re Thorell*, 2000). Moreover, in *Doe v. Poritz* (1995), the Supreme Court of New Jersey ruled that in determining the level of community notification that was justified upon a sex offender's release from confinement, "the [absolute] probability of reoffense on the part of moderate- or high-risk offenders is not the issue . . . but rather the relatively greater risk of reoffense compared either to the low-risk or the moderate risk offender class" (622 A.2d at 384), making the use of VRAG scores more tenable in such instances.

It is beyond the scope of this article to critically analyze these court decisions or to address the question of specifically what degrees of likelihood and seriousness of potential future violence (or nonviolent criminal activity), within what possible time frame(s), would justify the continued confinement of, for example, convicted sex offenders whose sentences have expired (Campbell, 2000; Janus & Meehl, 1997; *Kansas v. Hendricks*, 1997), insanity acquittees (cf. Litwack, 1996), or ordinary civil committees (Litwack & Schlesinger, 1999, pp. 193–194). The point, however, is that the absolute as well as the relative dangerousness of such individuals should be an important consideration in determining whether their continued confinement is justified and that the precise meaning of, for example, a VRAG score (in terms of the degree of potential violence that it actually predicts) should be clearly spelled out to, and clearly understood and analyzed by, any court considering such scores as a basis for decisions affecting the liberty of individuals.

However, the VRAG does appear to be a very useful aid in determining when offenders who have been mentally disordered are sufficiently safe to be at least transferred from secure to more permissive institutions. Low scorers on the VRAG who were released from secure confinement—though perhaps only to a less secure institution— have a very low rate of recidivism for any violence after 10 years at risk. Therefore, it seems fair to conclude that offenders in secure detention who have a history of mental disorder and who score low on the VRAG are safe to be released from secure confinement unless there are clear (and clearly articulable) contraindications (although they may still require nonsecure hospitalization or intensive supervision).

According to Quinsey et al., 1999, their participants were considered to be at risk for recidivism if they had been "released to the community, a minimum security psychiatric hospital, or a halfway house" (p. 145); and "most" of their subjects were "institutionalized" following their release from secure confinement (p. 142). Therefore, that a mentally disordered offender confined in a secure institution has a low VRAG score does not indicate that it is safe to release the offender to the community (as opposed to a minimum-security psychiatric hospital). On the other hand, it is reasonable to suppose that if high VRAG scorers who were confined in nonsecure hospitals following their release from secure confinement had been released directly into the community (even with supervision, and almost certainly without it), their rate of recidivism would have been significantly higher than those obtained to date. Therefore, the absolute predictive power of high VRAG scores might be substantially greater for recidivism (including serious recidivism) in the community than has been established for recidivism whether in the community or in minimum-security institutions.

The problem of meaningfully validating dangerousness assessment instruments is also illustrated by recent research using what is perhaps the most widely applicable tool for structuring clinical assessments of dangerousness, the HCR-20 (Webster et al., 1997), a 20-item risk assessment guide that entails scoring 10 historical items, 5 clinical items, and 5 risk-management items from 0 to 2 each, yielding a total score from 0 to 40. Although the HCR-20 is intended to guide clinical assessments rather than determine ultimate risk assessments, research has related HCR-20 subscale and total scores to subsequent violence (for recent reviews, see Douglas et al., 1999; Douglas, Ogloff, Nicholls, & Grant, 1999). For example, Douglas, Ogloff et al. (1999) compared HCR-20 scores with recidivism after nearly 2 years subsequent to release for 193 former civil committees who had been released following requested release hearings. They found that HCR-20 scores obtained from file data were significantly related to any future violence (including threatening behavior), physical violence (including nonharmful attacks on persons), and subsequent criminal violence. Therefore, they concluded that "[t]his study demonstrates the validity of the HCR-20 for assessing the risk of post-hospital violence of civilly committed psychiatric patients" (p. 926), that "the HCR-20 is a strong predictor of violence in a civil psychiatric sample" (p. 927), and that "[t]he present research can be applied to the clinical practice of violence risk assessment and management" (p. 927).

Although the HCR-20 was shown to be a good predictor of relative recidivism in this sample, a question remains: How good was it as an absolute predictor, and, therefore, how useful was it for actual decision making? In making civil commitment decisions, for example, is it useful to know the risk that a patient will commit any type of violence, even of the most minor variety, within the next 2 years? In this study, "any" violence included *nonphysical* violence, which was defined to include "threats to harm a person, verbal attacks, and threatening or 'fear-inducing' behavior . . ." (Douglas, Ogloff, et al., 1999, p. 921). Would even a near certainty that a civilly committed patient, if released, would threaten someone over the next 2 years justify that person's continued hospitalization indefinitely?

The HCR-20 scores also predicted the relative risk of physical and criminal violence, but once again similar problems appear to emerge. For example, although patients who scored in the highest (≥ 27) range on the HCR-20 were 17 times as likely to commit criminal violence within nearly 2 years after release as patients who scored below 19, still only 35% of scorers in the ≥ 27 range were found to have committed criminal violence during the follow-up period. In making civil commitment decisions, how useful would it be to know that a patient posed a 35% chance of committing some (possibly relatively minor) criminal violence within the next 2 years if not detained? That is, even relatively high odds ratios may not be very meaningful if the comparison is with a very low incidence of violence.

Similarly, although 45% of the patients in the highest reported HCR-20 category committed physical violence in the 2-year follow-up period (compared with 4% in the lowest [0–14] HCR-20 category), the physical violence category included nonharmful, noncriminal "attacks on a person" (Douglas, Ogloff, et al., 1999, p. 921). Once again, the issue becomes whether such information is truly useful for civil commitment decisions. Indeed, because the recidivism rates referred to posttreatment recidivism, how useful are even low HCR-20 scores for making initial (e.g., emergency) civil commitment decisions? However, these results do suggest that, posttreatment for acute psychiatric disturbances, low HCR-20 scores, like low VRAG scores, are indicative of a low risk for recidivism, at least within certain circumstances (Grann et al., 2000). Thus, although the authors' overall discussion of their results in this study was quite judicious and thoughtful, is their conclusion that this research "can be applied to the clinical practice of violence risk assessment and management" (Douglas, Ogloff et al., 1999, p. 927) truly justified (except, perhaps, regarding low HCR-20 scorers posttreatment)?

This study also yielded the result that the HCR-20 predicted any violence better than the Psychopathy Checklist: Screening Version (PCL:SV; Hart, Cox, & Hare, 1995), thereby leading the Douglas et al. (1999) to conclude that "the HCR-20 added incremental validity to the PCL:SV" (p. 917). However, the HCR-20 did not perform better than the PCL:SV in predicting criminal violence. Therefore, because the PCL:SV may be far easier, and quicker, to score than the HCR-20, it remains questionable which instrument would "win" a cost-benefit analysis regarding their use in aiding civil commitment decisions.

The point, then, is simply this: Leaving aside the dilemma of how to best, and most fairly, compare clinical and actuarial (or score related) judgments—and given the development of instruments such as the HCR-20, actuarial assessments should be compared now with structured as well as unstructured clinical assessments (Kropp & Hart, 2000)—it is imperative that dangerousness assessment instruments, whether the VRAG, the PCL-R (Hart, 1998), or the HCR-20 or its counterparts (Webster & Jackson, 1997), be validated according to the most meaningful outcome criteria obtainable (Silver, Smith, & Banks, 2000, p. 760). For example, in validating an assessment instrument for use in civil commitment determinations, what is the best outcome measure for determining the validity of the instrument? A workable standard would not be any kind of violence at any time in the future. Rather, a proper measure would be sufficiently serious violence occurring sufficiently soon in the future that, had it been foreseen, would have justified continued commitment.

Admittedly, research would have to be done to determine what combinations of likelihood, immediacy, and seriousness of recidivism would justify a continuation of the particular confinement(s) at issue in the minds of most clinicians and judges. There is no doubt there would be significantly differing viewpoints among concerned professionals. Nevertheless, in all likelihood, composite criteria could be obtained and assessment scores could be matched to outcomes by those criteria. The problem would remain that the assessment instrument(s) could only be tested on released patients. At least regarding those released patients, however, the degree to which assessment scores meaningfully predicted (known) significant recidivism could be obtained.

Moreover, if assessment scores were meaningfully related to recidivism, it would then be instructive to compare the scores of the retained patients with those of the released patients. If there were retained patients who had scores seemingly predictive of low recidivism, it would be instructive to see whether there were clinical data or rationales that apparently (and logically) justified the retention decisions. Regarding the released patients, if the rates of recidivism according to assessment scores are to be compared with clinical risk assessments, at least those comparisons would be made according to outcome criteria that were the focus (if necessarily the composite focus) of clinical judgments. On the other hand, unless actuarial prediction schemes are validated according to outcome criteria that are equivalent to the possible or suspected outcomes focused on by clinicians in making their judgments, no meaningful comparisons between the two types of assessments can be made. Furthermore, unless actuarial schemes are validated according to outcome criteria that are meaningful for clinical or judicial decision making, those schemes have no proven practical use. As Buchanan (1999) stated,

> Two conditions have to be fulfilled if the general psychiatrist is to be helped by a mathematical formula. First, [the psychiatrist] needs to have available . . . research conducted using outcome measures similar to the one with which [the psychiatrist] is concerned, over a relevant time span that used, as independent variables, information that is available. . . . Secondly, [the psychiatrist] needs to know that research is relevant to [the] patient [being assessed]. (p. 469; see also Faust [1997], p. 349; but cf. Grove & Meehl [1996], pp. 301–303)

There seems to be no good reason why the process of improving validation cannot begin with currently available data sets. For example, the existing VRAG data could be reanalyzed using more meaningful outcome criteria. (Indeed, Quinsey et al., 1999, have written that they are "considering more sophisticated ways of measuring outcome that include both time at risk before recidivism and severity and number of new offenses" [p. 168].) And, indeed, how can researchers who stress that professionals should make risk assessments in the most scientifically valid way obtainable do otherwise than validate their predictive schemes in the most meaningful way possible?

IV. Addressing the Arguments in *Violent Offenders*

In Chapter 9 of *Violent Offenders* (Quinsey et al., 1999), titled "Fifteen Arguments Against Actuarial Risk Appraisal" and subtitled "Arguments Against Using the VRAG," the authors stated 15 arguments that have "been presented . . . as a serious ground for the rejection of actuarial methods of risk appraisal" (pp. 172–173). The authors then responded to each argument to support their contention that "there is enough evidence of the right kind to warrant the replacement of clinical prediction of violence by actuarial instruments" (p. 172).

In what follows, the first 10 arguments against actuarial assessments listed by Quinsey et al. (1999) are repeated (indented in italics), followed by an abbreviated (but hopefully accurate) version of the authors' response in favor of actuarial assessments (indented in roman type), followed by a response to their response (unindented). The point of this exercise is to further question the contention of *Violent Offenders* that the time has come for the "complete replacement" (p. 171) of clinical assessments of dangerousness with actuarial instruments. (Arguments 11–15 are more concerned with the ethics or professional implications of using actuarial methods of risk assessments than with the relative validity of actuarial versus clinical methods.)

> *Argument 1. This research was conducted in . . . Canada . . . on [mentally disordered] offenders. It does not apply to the population I have to deal with, or at least we do not know whether or not it applies. Thus I must use clinical judgment. (p. 173)*

> The evidence is very strong that the VRAG would work as well . . . with those offenders who have committed relatively serious offenses . . . because of the way we used cross-validation in its construction. For example, we checked to ensure that it worked as well with those patients who were only remanded for [psychiatric] assessment and who were later convicted as with those who remained for psychiatric treatment. . . . (p. 173)

First, the VRAG was never compared directly with clinical assessments for their relative degrees of accuracy (according to ideal outcome criteria or to any other criteria). Therefore, no definitive conclusions can be reached about the relative merits of the VRAG and even unstructured (much less structured, or confident, or team-based) clinical judgments. Moreover, even if the VRAG has fairly wide applicability, its validity has never been tested for populations such as insanity acquittees who are not released by clinicians or judges, or civil psychiatric patients.

> *Argument 2. This approach predicts only trivial violence. . . . (p. 174)*

> . . . [V]iolent recidivism included charges of murder, manslaughter, sexual assault, wounding, assault causing bodily harm, simple assault, kidnapping, armed robbery (but not simple robbery), pointing a firearm (but not simply

uttering threats), and acts that could have resulted in such charges [were the subject not hospitalized at the time]. . . . The actuarial instrument predicted serious violence (e.g., more severe than a single assault) just as well as violence in general. (p. 174)

The VRAG predicted serious violence as well as violence in general only in the sense that VRAG scores predicted the relative incidence of serious violence as well as the relative incidence of general violence. However, no data have been provided by the authors of the VRAG that would allow an assessor, or a judge, to determine the absolute risk of truly serious violence (i.e., beyond simple assaults) within specified periods of time for a given VRAG score.

Argument 3. This actuarial system is not accurate enough (has too many false positives, or has too low a correlation, or accounts for too small a proportion of the variance) to be used to make such important decisions. (p. 176)

. . . [D]emonstrably less accurate methods of risk appraisal are widely used instead. . . . [T]he only ethical course of action is to use the most accurate system available, even if it is imperfect. (p. 176)

Actuarial assessments of dangerousness have not, in fact, been proven to be superior to clinical assessments across assessment domains. In fact, some studies (e.g., Gardner et al., 1996a, 1996b; Holland et al., 1983) arguably favored clinical assessment (at least regarding certain assessments). Again, the VRAG has never been directly compared with clinical assessments regarding the same population (but see Grann et al., 2000, for a comparison of the VRAG with the historical part of the HCR-20). Moreover, the costs of doing an actuarial assessment must be considered in determining whether it should substitute for simpler or quicker, even if somewhat less accurate, methods of assessment in a given context.

Argument 4. More accurate systems to predict violent recidivism have already been developed. Using [physiological] variables . . . is the way to tell who's going to be violent. [And t]his actuarial method does not incorporate situational variables. (p. 176)

. . . Eventually, research is likely to result in improvements in our actuarial methods. . . . Such improvements might include physiological measures . . . or situational variables. . . . Realistically [however], clinical judgement will not supersede statistical methods. (pp. 176–177)

There are no validated statistical methods for assessing dangerousness in certain situations (e.g., emergency civil commitment decisions) that have been proven superior to clinical assessments in those situations. There is no evidence that actuarial assessments are superior to structured clinical assessments using modern assessment aids (such as the HCR-20), and recent evidence (Kropp & Hart, 2000) exists showing that structured clinical assessments can add to the validity of actuarial assessments.

> *Argument 5. . . . I do not understand statistics and I am uncomfortable using something I do not understand . . . so I will stick with what I do understand—my own clinical judgment. (p. 177)*

> . . . One does not have to defend the statistics or research to be able to use it. . . . [T]he actuarial risk appraisal works—patients identified as high risk actually exhibit rates of violent recidivism that are much, much greater than those exhibited by patients identified as low risk. (p. 177)

It is true that once one learns to score the PCL-R (an essentially clinical task that does not require the use of statistics), one can also derive a VRAG score by following the instructions in *Violent Offenders* and using simple mathematics. However, using *Violent Offenders* alone, one could only state the probability of any violent recidivism over 7 or 10 years. No data are provided for, as an example, the probability of serious violent recidivism over 3 years (but cf. Gratin et al., 2000).

> *Argument 6. This system is based solely on a person's history and only on a very few aspects of his history. . . . The actuarial score is just one piece of information I will include in my much more comprehensive assessment. (p. 177)*

> [In large part, [*Violent Offenders*] focuses on this objection. In short, there is good evidence that clinicians' appraisals of patients' current clinical conditions are unrelated to recidivism. With regard to static, historical variables, more is not necessarily better. . . . [I]t is now clear that the "getting to know" individuals that occurs in typical interviews does not improve the prediction of behavior in any domain (violent recidivism, academic attainment, job performance, etc.). (pp. 177–178)

Apart from the lack of specific citations offered to support this conclusion (at least regarding violent recidivism), it is simply not true. Recent research, including research by Quinsey, Coleman, Jones, and Altrows (1997); Strand, Belfrage, Fransson, and Levander (1999); Belfrage, Fransson, and Strand (2000); Hanson and Harris (2000); Kropp and Hart (2000); Appelbaum, Robbins, and Monahan (2000); Monahan et al. (2000); Steadman et al. 2000, and other research cited by Douglas, Cox, and Webster (1999) and Litwack and Schlesinger (1999, p. 190), indicates that considering current clinical conditions (especially regarding the presence of heightened anger or violent fantasies) can be an important contribution to assessments of dangerousness, as can assessments of an individual's degree of psychopathy (Hemphill, Templeman, Wong, & Hare, 1998; cf. Grann et al., 2000, pp. 109–110).

Argument 7. Based on my clinical experience . . . the instrument does not work nearly as well with psychotic individuals. Moreover, I have tried it on two serial murderers and they did not get very high scores, so it obviously does not work in all cases. (p. 178)

The data do not support the tempering, modification, or adjusting of actuarial estimates with clinical opinions. To the extent that unaided clinical opinions are blended with actuarial estimates, the result is . . . very likely to be less accurate than actuarial estimates alone. . . . It is presently unknown how well the VRAG (or anything else) could predict the recidivism of . . . serial murderers. . . . The only appropriate test of the validity of any method (actuarial or clinical) is a systematic and formal empirical evaluation. (p. 178)

It may be true that, in other areas, where very well-developed and validated actuarial predictive schemes can be applied, adjusting of actuarial estimates with clinical opinions may lessen overall predictive validity. However, that has not been shown to be the case regarding assessments of dangerousness. Indeed, as already noted, recent evidence suggests that at least structured clinical judgment can "outperform . . . decisions made using an actuarial method when the two were compared directly" (Kropp & Hart, 2000, p. 114). And if it is unknown how well the VRAG could predict the recidivism of serial murderers, how, exactly, should judgments about the future dangerousness of such individuals be made if and when they have to be made (e.g., if a serial murderer was found to be not guilty by reason of insanity)? Should the serial murderer be released if he obtained a fairly low VRAG score? If not, why not?

Argument 8. This patient says there are mistakes in his actuarial risk appraisal. He says he had no behavior problems in school. . . . He says the score on the Psychopathy Checklist is wrong. . . . How am I going to prove any of this one way or the other? A clinical appraisal is preferable because it would not depend on "facts" to be argued about—it is based on impressions. (p. 178)

Without question, the quality of any decision can only be as good as the information on which it is based. Whether they use our actuarial risk appraisal system or not, clinicians . . . make poor decisions with many errors when they rely on inaccurate, irrelevant, or vague information about offenders. The only way to improve decision making is with the right kind of accurate information about offenders. (pp. 178–179)

It can be granted that risk assessments that are based on the best information available will, on the whole, be better than assessments based on impressions. But few, if any, clinical risk assessments are based on impressions alone. Just as the possibility that there may sometimes be errors in the information on which an actuarial assessment is based is no reason to reject a particular actuarial scheme, or actuarial schemes in general, the possibility that some clinicians may sometimes rely too much on impressions is no reason to reject clinical assessments outright.

Argument 9. Actuarial methods . . . require consent. What if a patient refuses to consent to this exercise? . . . Because I do not necessarily need information from other sources to use my clinical judgment, I will just appraise his risk with that—then I . . . do not need his consent. (p. 179)

. . . For individuals who are under the control of the criminal justice system . . . no legal or ethical impediments prevent legally constituted authorities from gathering information relevant to risk. [In Canada], [f]or hospital patients, the patient's permission is not required to gather information. . . . [A]ctuarial risk appraisals of the sort [described in *Violent Offenders*] are based on a reorganization of existing clinical information. . . . (pp. 179–180)

Sufficient information to score the VRAG either will be available or it will not be. That there may be difficulties in obtaining necessary information is, admittedly, no reason to reject actuarial methods outright (although the time and other costs required to perform any type of assessment should be considered in any cost-benefit analysis of the relative merits of various assessment techniques). Conversely, however, the mere fact that the information necessary for an actuarial risk assessment is available does not provide a basis for preferring an actuarial assessment.

Argument 10. Each human being is unique and cannot be reduced to a number. It is morally wrong to do so. It is illegal or unethical to use group data to make statements about individuals. . . . (p. 180)

How unique people are is largely an empirical question. . . . [R]esearch clearly shows that some personal characteristics are consistently and strongly associated with future violent behavior. . . . People routinely use information about groups to make individual decisions. . . . [T]he use of an actuarial instrument to assess risk of violent recidivism is based on exactly the same reasoning. . . . (pp. 180–181)

Even if it is not unethical to use actuarial approaches to risk assessment, this in no way establishes their superiority over clinical assessments. In addition, at least in the courtroom, it may well be unethical to definitively claim more predictive power for an actuarial assessment scheme, or for clinical assessments, than is justified by actual research results. It is incumbent on all professionals concerned with assessments of dangerousness, whether through research or practice, to address this consequential subject as open mindedly as is possible and as objectively as is practicable.

CONCLUSION

It is hard to imagine that the day will ever come when actuarial assessments of dangerousness can properly and completely substitute for clinical assessments. That is because actuarial predictors cannot be validated regarding those subsets of supposedly dangerous individuals who are confined (e.g., emergency civil committees) or not released (e.g., supposedly dangerous insanity acquittees) on the basis of decisions by clinicians or judges. Moreover, as of yet, actuarial schemes for assessing dangerousness have not been proven to be generally superior to clinical assessments.

However, it is easy to imagine that in time, various actuarial assessment schemes will be developed and validated in a manner that significantly assists many dangerousness assessment tasks. Already it appears that some fairly objective measures of psychopathy, such as the PCL-R or the PCL-SV (Hart, 1998; Heilbrun, 1996), can enhance a variety of dangerousness risk assessments, as can structured assessment guides such as the HCR-20 and its progeny (Douglas, Cox, & Webster, 1999; Kropp & Hart, 2000). However, to be of maximal (or, perhaps, even minimal) value, actuarial assessment schemes will have to be tested and validated in terms of outcome variables and criteria that are truly relevant and meaningful to ultimate decision makers.

On the other hand, Krauss and Sales (1999) have argued that for a clinician's assessment testimony to truly qualify as expert testimony, the clinician should be aware of relevant research in his or her field, and if the clinician decides that such research does and should not dictate the results of his or her assessment, he or she should be able to explain clearly and knowledgeably why the seemingly relevant research should not be determinative. If one applies these principles to dangerousness assessments, clinicians doing risk assessments to which the VRAG, for example, would arguably apply should at least be knowledgeable about the VRAG. If the clinicians choose not to use the VRAG as part of their assessment(s), and if they claim expert status for courtroom purposes, the clinicians should be able to rationally articulate why they believe the VRAG was inapplicable to their case(s). At the least, it appears, as actuarial schemes and structured assessment guides for assessing dangerousness become better developed and validated, clinicians engaging in risk assessments have a professional responsibility to be aware of the advantages and limitations of using such risk assessment tools (Campbell, 2000; Litwack, 1993).

REFERENCES

American Psychological Association. (1978). Report of the task force on the role of psychology in the criminal justice system. *American Psychologist, 33,* 1099–1113.

Appelbaum, P. S., Robbins, P. C., & Monahan, J. (2000). Violence and delusions: Data from the MacArthur violence risk assessment study. *American Journal of Psychiatry, 157,* 566–572.

Barefoot v. Estelle, 463 U.S. 880 (1983).

Belfrage, H., Fransson, G., & Strand, S. (2000). Prediction of violence using the HCR-20: A prospective study in two maximum-security correctional institutions. *Journal of Forensic Psychiatry, 11,* 167–175.

Bonta, J., Law, M., & Hanson, K. (1998). The prediction of criminal and violent recidivism among mentally disordered offenders: A meta-analysis. *Psychological Bulletin, 123,* 123–142.

Buchanan, A. (1999). Risk and dangerousness. *Psychological Medicine, 29,* 465–473.

Campbell, T. W. (2000). Sexual predator evaluations and phrenology: Considering issues of evidentiary reliability. *Behavioral Sciences and the Law, 18,* 111–130.

Cocozza, J. J., & Steadman, H. J. (1974). Some refinements in the measurement and prediction of dangerous behavior. *American Journal of Psychiatry, 131,* 1012–1014.

Cocozza, J. J., & Steadman, H. J. (1976). The failure of psychiatric predictions of dangerousness: Clear and convincing evidence. *Rutgers Law Review, 29,* 1084–1101.

Cocozza, J. J., & Steadman, H. J. (1978). Prediction in psychiatry: An example of misplaced confidence in experts. *Social Problems, 25,* 265–276.

Davison, S. (1997). Risk assessment and management—a busy practitioner's perspective. *International Review of Psychiatry, 9,* 201–206.

Derogatis, L. R., & Melisaratos, N. (1983). The Brief Symptom Inventory: An introductory report. *Psychological Medicine, 13,* 595–605.

Dershowitz, A. (1969, February). The psychiatrist's power in civil commitment. *Psychology Today, 2,* 43–47.

Doe v. Poritz, 142, J. J. 1; 662 A. 2d 367 (1995).

Douglas, K. S., Cox, D. N., & Webster, C. D. (1999). Violence risk assessment: Science and practice. *Legal and Criminological Psychology, 4,* 149–184.

Douglas, K. S., Ogloff, J. R. P., Nicholls, T. L., & Grant, I. (1999). Assessing risk for violence among psychiatric patients: The HCR-20 violence risk assessment scheme and the Psychopathy Checklist: Screening version. *Journal of Consulting and Clinical Psychology, 67,* 917–930.

Einhorn, H. J. (1986). Accepting error to make less error. *Journal of Personality Assessment, 50,* 387–395.

Evjen, V. H. (1962). Current thinking on parole prediction tables. *Crime and Delinquency, 8,* 215–238.

Faust, D. (1997). Of science, meta-science, and clinical practice: The generalization of a generalization to a particular. *Journal of Personality Assessment, 68,* 331–354.

Fuller, J., & Cowan, J. (1999). Risk assessment in a multi-disciplinary forensic setting: Clinical judgement revisited. *Journal of Forensic Psychiatry, 10,* 276–289.

Gardner, W., Lidz, C. W., Mulvey, E. P., & Shaw, E. C. (1996a). Clinical versus actuarial predictions of violence in patients with mental illness. *Journal of Consulting and Clinical Psychology, 64,* 602–609.

Gardner, W., Lidz, C. W., Mulvey, E. P., & Shaw, E. C. (1996b). A comparison of actuarial methods for identifying repetitively violent patients with mental illness. *Law and Human Behavior, 20* (1), 35–48.

Glaser, D. (1955). The efficacy of alternative approaches to parole prediction. *American Sociological Review, 20,* 283–287.

Glaser, D. (1962). Prediction tables as accounting devices for judges and parole boards. *Crime and Delinquency, 8,* 239–258.

Glasser, M. (1996). The management of dangerousness: The psychoanalytic contribution. *Journal of Forensic Psychiatry, 7,* 271–283.

Gottfredson, D. M., Wilkins, L. T., & Hoffman, P. B. (1978). *Guidelines for parole and sentencing.* Lexington, MA: Lexington Books.

Gottfredson, S. D. (1987). Statistical and actuarial considerations. In F. N. Dutile & C. H. Foust (Eds.), *The prediction of criminal violence* (pp. 71–81). Springfield, IL: Charles C Thomas.

Gottfredson, S. D., & Gottfredson, D. M. (1988a). Stakes and risks in the prediction of violent criminal behavior. *Violence and Victims, 3,* 247–262.

Gottfredson, S. D., & Gottfredson, D. M. (1988b). Violence prediction methods: Statistical and clinical strategies. *Violence and Victims, 3,* 303–324.

Grann, M., Belfrage, H., & Tengström, A. (2000). Actuarial assessment of risk for violence: Predictive validity of the VRAG and the historical part of the HCR-20. *Criminal Justice and Behavior, 27,* 97–114.

Groth-Marnat, G. (2000). Visions of clinical assessment: Then, now, and a brief history of the future. *Journal of Clinical Psychology, 56,* 349–365.

Grove, W. M., & Meehl, P. E. (1996). Comparative efficiency of informal (subjective, impressionistic) and formal (mechanical, algorithmic) prediction procedures: The clinical-statistical controversy. *Psychology, Public Policy, and Law, 2,* 293–323.

Grove, W. M., Zald, D. H., Lebow, B. S., Snitz, B. E., & Nelson, C. (1995). *Clinical vs. mechanical prediction: A meta-analysis.* Unpublished manuscript.

Grove, W. M., Zald, D. H., Lebow, B. S., Snitz, B. E., & Nelson, C. (2000). Clinical versus mechanical prediction: A meta-analysis. *Psychological Assessment, 12,* 19–30.

Grubin, D. (1997). Predictors of risk in serious sex offenders. *British Journal of Psychiatry, 178* (Suppl. 32), 17–21.

Hall, G. C. N. (1988). Criminal behavior as a function of clinical and actuarial variables in a sexual offender population. *Journal of Consulting and Clinical Psychology, 56,* 773–775.

Halleck, S. (1987). Clinical applicability for prediction. In F. N. Dutile & C. H. Foust (Eds.), *The prediction of criminal violence* (pp. 83–91). Springfield, IL: Charles C Thomas.

Hanson, R. K., & Harris, A. J. R. (2000). Where should we intervene? Dynamic predictors of sexual offense recidivism. *Criminal Justice and Behavior, 27,* 6–35.

Hare, R. D. (1991). *Manual for the Hare Psychopathy Checklist—Revised.* Toronto, Canada: Multi Health Systems.

Harris, G. T., & Rice, M. E. (1997). Risk appraisal and management of violent behavior. *Psychiatric Services, 48,* 1168–1176.

Hart, S. D. (1998). The role of psychopathy in assessing risk for violence: Conceptual and methodological issues. *Legal and Criminological Psychology, 3,* 121–137.

Hart, S. D. (1999). Assessing violence risk: Thoughts and second thoughts. *Contemporary Psychology, 44,* 486–487.

Hart, S. D., Cox, D., & Hare, R. D. (1995). *The Hare Psychopathy Checklist: Screening Version (PCL:SV).* Toronto, Canada: Multi Health Systems.

Hart, S. D. & Hare, R. D. (1997a). The association between psychopathy and narcissism: Theoretical views and empirical evidence. In E. Ronningstam (Ed.), *Disorders of narcissism: Theoretical, empirical, and clinical applications* (pp. 415–436). Washington, DC: American Psychiatric Press.

Hart, S. D., & Hare, R. D. (1997b). Psychopathy: Assessment and association with criminal conduct. In D. M. Stoff, J. Brieling, & J. Maser (Eds.), *Handbook of antisocial behavior* (pp. 22–35). New York: Wiley.

Hassin, Y. (1986). Two models for predicting recidivism: Clinical versus statistical—another view. *British Journal of Criminology, 26,* 270–286.

Hathaway, S. R., & McKinley, J. C. (1983). *Minnesota Multiphasic Personality Inventory: Manual for administration and scoring.* New York: Psychological Corporation.

Heilbrun, A. B. (1996). *Criminal dangerousness and the risk of violence.* Lanham, MD: University Press of America.

Heilbrun, K. (1997). Prediction versus management models relevant to risk assessment: The importance of legal decision-making context. *Law and Human Behavior, 21,* 347–359.

Hemphill, J. F., Templeman, R., Wong, S., & Hare, R. D. (1998). Psychopathy and crime: Recidivism and criminal careers. In D. J. Cooke, A. E. Forth, & R. D. Hare (Eds.), *Psychopathy: Theory, research and implications for society* (pp. 375–399). Dordrecht, the Netherlands: Kluwer Academic.

Holland, T. R., Holt, N., Levi, M., & Beckett, G. E. (1983). Comparison and combination of clinical and statistical predictions of recidivism among adult offenders. *Journal of Applied Psychology, 68,* 203–211.

Holt, R. R. (1970). Yet another look at clinical and statistical prediction: Or is clinical psychology worthwhile? *American Psychologist, 25,* 337–349.

Holt, R. R. (1986). Clinical and statistical prediction: A retrospective and would-be integrative perspective. *Journal of Personality Assessment, 50,* 376–386.

In re Dean. 2000 Wash. App. LEXIS 811 (2000).

In re Kienitz. 227 Wis. 2d 423; 597 N.W. 2d 712 (1999).

In re Thorell. 99 Wn. App. 1041 (2000).

Janus, E. S., & Meehl, P. E. (1997). Assessing the legal standard for predictions of dangerousness in sex offender commitment proceedings. *Psychology, Public Policy, and Law, 3,* 33–64.

Jones v. United States. 463 U.S. 354 (1983).

Kansas v. Hendricks. 117 S. Ct. 2072 (1997).

Karon, B. P. (2000). The clinical interpretation of the Thematic Apperception Test, Rorschach, and other clinical data: A reexamination of statistical versus clinical prediction. *Professional Psychology: Research and Practice, 31,* 230–233.

Klein, D. F. (2000). Flawed meta-analysis comparing psychotherapy with pharmacotherapy. *American Journal of Psychiatry, 157,* 1204–1211.

Kleinmuntz, B. (1990). Why we still use our heads instead of formulas: Toward an integrative approach. *Psychological Bulletin, 107,* 296–310.

Kozol, H. L., Boucher, R. J., & Garofalo, R. F. (1972). The diagnosis and treatment of dangerousness. *Crime and Delinquency, 12,* 371–392.

Krauss, D. A., & Sales, B. D. (1999). The problem of "helpfulness" in applying Daubert to expert testimony: Child custody determinations in family law as an exemplar. *Psychology, Public Policy, and Law, 5,* 78–99.

Kropp, P. R., & Hart, S. D. (2000). The spousal assault risk assessment (SARA) guide: Reliability and validity in adult male offenders. *Law and Human Behavior, 24,* 101–118.

Litwack, T. R. (1993). On the ethics of dangerousness assessments. *Law and Human Behavior, 17,* 479–482.

Litwack, T. R. (1996). "Dangerous" patients: A survey of one forensic facility and review of the issue. *Aggression and Violent Behavior, 1,* 97–122.

Litwack, T. R., Kirschner, S. M., & Wack, R. C. (1993). The assessment of dangerousness and predictions of violence: Recent research and future prospects. *Psychiatric Quarterly, 64,* 245–273.

Litwack, T. R., & Schlesinger, L. B. (1987). Assessing and predicting violence: Research, law, and applications. In I. B. Weiner & A. K. Hess (Eds.), *Handbook of forensic psychology* (pp. 205–257). New York: Wiley.

Litwack, T. R., & Schlesinger, L. B. (1999). Dangerousness risk assessments: Research, legal and clinical considerations. In A. K. Hess & I. B. Weiner (Eds.), *Handbook of forensic psychology* (2nd ed., pp. 171–217). New York: Wiley.

Loza, W., & Dhaliwal, G. K. (1997). Psychometric evaluation of the Risk Appraisal Guide (RAG): A tool for assessing violent recidivism. *Journal of Interpersonal Violence, 12,* 779–793.

Marchese, M. C. (1992). Clinical versus actuarial prediction: A review of the literature. *Perceptual and Motor Skills, 75,* 583–594.

McNiel, D. E., Sandberg, D. A., & Binder, R. L. (1998). The relationship between confidence and accuracy in clinical assessments of psychiatric patients' potential for violence. *Law and Human Behavior, 22,* 655–669.

Meehl, L. P. (1986). Causes and effects of my disturbing little book. *Journal of Personality Assessment, 50,* 370–375.

Melton, G. B., Petrila, J., Poythress, N. G., & Slobogin, C. (1997). *Psychological evaluations for the courts* (2nd ed.). New York: Guilford Press.

Monahan, J. (1981). *Predicting violent behavior: An assessment of clinical techniques.* Beverly Hills, CA: Sage.

Monahan, J. (1984). The prediction of violent behavior: Toward a second generation of theory and policy. *American Journal of Psychiatry, 141,* 10–15.

Monahan, J., Steadman, H. J., Appelbaum, P. S., Robbins, P. C., Mulvey, E. P., Silver, E., Roth, L. H., & Grisso, T. (2000). Developing a clinically useful actuarial tool for assessing violence risk. *British Journal of Psychiatry, 176,* 312–319.

Mossman, D. (1994). Assessing predictions of violence: Being accurate about accuracy. *Journal of Consulting and Clinical Psychology, 62,* 783–792.

Mullen, J. M., & Reinehr, R. C. (1982). Predicting dangerousness of maximum security forensic mental patients. *Journal of Psychiatry & Law, 10,* 223–231.

Murphy, K. R., & Davidshofer, C. O. (1988). *Psychological testing: Principles and applications.* Englewood Cliffs, NJ: Prentice Hall.

Poythress, N. (1992). Expert testimony on violence and dangerousness: Roles for mental health professionals. *Forensic Reports, 5,* 135–150.

Quinsey, V. L., Coleman, G., Jones, B., & Altrows, I. F. (1997). Proximal antecedents of eloping and reoffending among supervised mentally disordered offenders. *Journal of Interpersonal Violence, 12,* 794–813.

Quinsey, V. L., Harris, G. T., Rice, M. E., & Cormier, C. A. (1999). *Violent offenders: Appraising and managing risk.* Washington, DC: American Psychological Association.

Quinsey, V. L., & Maguire, A. (1986). Maximum security psychiatric patients: Actuarial and clinical predictions of dangerousness. *Journal of Interpersonal Violence, 1,* 143–171.

Quinsey, V. L., Rice, M. E., & Harris, G. T. (1995). Actuarial prediction of sexual recidivism. *Journal of Interpersonal Violence, 10,* 85–105.

Rice, M. E., & Harris, G. T. (1995). Violent recidivism: Assessing predictive accuracy. *Journal of Consulting and Clinical Psychology, 63,* 737–748.

Rogers, R. (2000). The uncritical acceptance of risk assessment in forensic practice. *Law and Human*

Behavior, 24, 595–605.

Sarbin, T. R. (1986). Prediction and clinical inference. *Journal of Personality Assessment, 50,* 362–369.

Schopp, R. F., & Quattrocchi, M. R. (1995). Predicting the present: Expert testimony and civil commitment. *Behavioral Sciences and the Law, 13,* 159–181.

Sepejak, D., Menzies, R. J., Webster, C. D., & Jensen, F. A. S. (1983). Clinical predictions of dangerousness: Two-year follow-up of 406 pre-trial forensic cases. *Bulletin of the American Academy of Psychiatry and the Law, 11,* 171–181.

Silver, E., Smith, W. R., & Banks, S. (2000). Constructing actuarial devices for predicting recidivism: A comparison of methods. *Criminal Justice and Behavior, 27,* 733–764.

Smith, J., & Lanyon, R. I. (1968). Prediction of juvenile probation violators. *Journal of Consulting and Clinical Psychology, 32,* 54–58.

Steadman, H. J. (1977). A new look at recidivism among Patuxent inmates. *Bulletin of the American Academy of Psychiatry and the Law, 5,* 200–209.

Steadman, H. J., Silver, E., Monahan, J., Appelbaum, P. S., Robbins, P. C., Mulvey, E. P., Grisso, T., Roth, L. H., & Banks, S. (2000). A classification tree approach to the development of actuarial violence risk assessment tools. *Law and Human Behavior, 24,* 83–100.

Strand, S., Belfrage, H., Fransson, G., & Levander, S. (1999). Clinical and risk management factors in risk prediction of mentally disordered offenders—more important than historical data? A retrospective study of 40 mentally disordered offenders assessed with the HCR-20 violence risk assessment scheme. *Legal and Criminological Psychology, 4,* 67–76.

Thornberry, T. P., & Jacoby, J. E. (1979). *The criminally insane: A community follow-up of mentally ill offenders.* Chicago: University of Chicago Press.

Wack, R. C. (1993). The ongoing risk assessment in the treatment of forensic patients on conditional release status. *Psychiatric Quarterly, 64,* 275–293.

Ward, A., & Dockerill, J. (1999). The predictive accuracy of the violent offender treatment program assessment scale. *Criminal Justice and Behavior, 26,* 125–140.

Webster, C. D., Douglas, K. S., Eaves, D., & Hart, S. D. (1997). *The HCR-20 scheme: The assessment of dangerousness and risk (version 2).* Burnaby, Canada: Mental Health, Law, and Policy Institute, Simon Fraser University.

Webster, C. D., Harris, G. T., Rice, M. E., Cormier, C., & Quinsey, V. L. (1994). *The violence prediction scheme: Assessing dangerousness in high risk men.* Toronto, Ontario, Canada: University of Toronto.

Webster, C. D., & Jackson, M. A. (1997). *Impulsivity: Perspectives, principles, and practice.* New York: Guilford Press.

Webster, C. D., Sepejak, D. S., Menzies, R. J., Slomen, D. J., Jensen, F. A. S., & Butler, B. T. (1984). The reliability and validity of dangerous behavior predictions. *Bulletin of the American Academy of Psychiatry and the Law, 12,* 41–50.

Wormith, S. J., & Goldstone, C. W. (1984). The clinical and statistical prediction of recidivism. *Criminal Justice and Behavior, 11,* 3–34.

17

Risk Assessment and Release Decision-Making: Toward Resolving the Great Debate

JOEL A. DVOSKIN AND KIRK HEILBRUN

Currently, there is a vigorous debate in the professional literature about the relative merits of clinical versus actuarial prediction of violent behavior in the broader context of risk assessment. In this editorial, we argue that the forced choice between these two models is unnecessary and we propose a model for incorporating both types of decision-making in the real world of forensic and correctional release.

The origins of this debate are not new, and they must be framed in the context of a larger debate about clinical versus actuarial judgment. As early as 1954, Paul Meehl[1] (and later, Meehl and colleagues[2,3]) argued for the general superiority of actuarial approaches in circumstances in which the predictors and formula are available, validation research has been done, and the task involves maximizing the accuracy of the prediction. However, they noted there is a problem when the necessary predictors and validation research are not available or prediction is not the goal.

Quinsey et al.[4] argued strenuously that however accuracy is measured, "pure" actuarial tools yield superior predictions. Indeed, when clinical judgments (overrides) are incorporated into these actuarial predictions, their accuracy is said to "decrease." Steven Hart,[5] on the other hand, while supporting the utility of actuarial predictors as part of the puzzle, suggests that the limitations of actuarial prediction and the varied contexts in which risk assessment is performed mandate a meaningful role for clinical judgments.

Reprinted with permission. The Journal of the American Academy of Psychiatry and the Law, 29, 6–10. © 2001 American Academy of Psychiatry and the Law.

Indeed, actuarial predictive schemes appear to be more accurate in predicting recidivism for groups of subjects who have characteristics consistent with the populations for whom each scheme was validated. However, the scientific goal of prediction and the legal goal of decision-making in individual cases are rarely the same. For example, a predictive tool that yields accuracy rates significantly above chance might have tremendous value scientifically (or in a casino). However, because of the extreme consequences of each erroneous judgment in the legal system, that same tool might be less useful in a criminal justice context. Of course, the use of an actuarial tool would still yield more accurate predictions than clinical judgment—but for what, over what period of time, under what circumstances, and in light of what interventions? These are questions that behavioral science eventually may answer, but the research base is not yet adequate to address these and similar questions. Without explicit acknowledgment of the limits as well as the strengths of actuarial prediction in forensic contexts, there is the danger that the decision-maker will overvalue the applicability (legally, the "relevance") as well as the scientific support (legally, the "reliability") of the actuarial tool that is used.

Public mental health systems have to make real-life decisions about whether, when, and how to release psychiatric patients who have previously committed acts of violence. Important questions include the following. (1) Has the mental health system done everything it can reasonably do while the person is hospitalized to reduce subsequent violence risk in the community? (2) Has the system developed a good plan for living in the community that incorporates and builds on the hospital's interventions? (3) Are there mechanisms for early detection of problems before they develop into violence? (4) Is all this enough? (Often, this last question is left to a judge; ideally, it would *always* be left to a judge or quasi-legal decision-maker.) To answer these questions for individuals such as hospitalized insanity acquittees, or Hendricks-committed sexual offenders and incarcerated offenders, release decision-making should consider both an individual's risk of future violent behavior, the extent to which such risk has been altered through intervention, and the extent to which such risk can be altered after release by the conditions of the release itself; that is, the conditions applicable in the community.

To date, actuarial schemes rely almost entirely on static risk factors such as demographic and historical factors. With the exception of age (which for some of us changes all too predictably), these factors typically do not change; nor do they reflect changes that result from treatment or other interventions.

Of course, if the only decision were the release itself, it would be difficult to argue against using a purely actuarial approach. The only relevant outcome would be the accuracy of the prediction. Sometimes, this has been the case. At one time, many forensic mental health systems used "all-or-nothing" prediction schemes in making release decisions. In Virginia, for example, before the early 1980s, insanity acquittees were housed in the state's maximum-security hospital until it was decided (i.e., predicted) that they could be returned safely to the community, at which point they were simply and summarily released. Similarly, even today many overstretched parole systems make all-or-nothing release decisions with few if any individualized conditions; even for those conditions that are imposed, parole officers often are unable to scrutinize compliance.

PREDICTION VERSUS RISK MANAGEMENT

There is an important difference between prediction of violent behavior and risk management/risk reduction. The decision of which strategy (prediction versus management) to adopt is crucial for a number of very practical reasons. First, whether a system focuses on prediction or management of risk has important implications for the kinds of risk factors that are considered. Second, this decision (prediction versus risk management) largely determines the kinds of interventions that the system will implement as it seeks to affect the lives of the people for whom it bears some responsibility.

Fortunately, long ago, most forensic mental health systems throughout the United States abandoned the all-or-nothing (i.e., solely predictive) approach to releases. Indeed, one of the few points of general agreement in this area is that the safest way to return someone from confinement to freedom is in carefully managed increments of decreased structure and increased freedom. Thus, release decisions have ceased to be all or nothing, and, fortunately, there is no need to choose between actuarial tools and clinical judgment.

Decision-making under this model should draw a distinction between three aspects of risk: likelihood (i.e., probability), imminence, and severity of outcome. Systematic consideration must be given to individuals considered in each of these ways and incorporating *a priori* risk and risk reduction status. Individuals with high *a priori* risk, for example, should be considered very conservatively and treated intensively while incarcerated, as well as monitored intensively if released. The combination of high likelihood of risk, coupled with either high imminence or high severity, would constitute reasonable grounds for rejecting a release request. When release is considered, there should be a contingent element to the decision; factors such as the level of monitoring, case management services, housing, social support, work, and treatment services (with anticipated adherence) should be considered as they relate to the conditional aspects of such decision-making.

The development of risk reduction strategies can be guided by at least two approaches. One approach uses empirical data obtained using effectiveness and efficacy designs in research on the impact of programs on risk reduction.[4] A second approach involves considering the dynamic, risk-relevant needs and deficits of an individual and delivering a series of "modular" interventions targeted at addressing each deficit.[6]

There appears to be a role for guided clinical judgment using either approach. Such judgment would be used in ratings made directly from the intervention, such as participation and progress in risk-relevant interventions and the assessment of the extent to which deficits have been reduced or protective factors enhanced through such interventions. Progress in risk reduction also can be monitored through information obtained from other sources as well. Using a "demonstration model," some populations can be checked for progress using data obtained from a variety of hospital sources (e.g., job, ward behavior, off-unit behavior). This is true particularly when institutional behavior is clearly relevant to violence risk, but less so with populations in which institutional behavior is less relevant to specialized kinds of outcomes (such as those who sexually abuse children). Other valuable "demonstration" data likewise can be obtained from an individual's performance under a graduated series of less restrictive (but still monitored) conditions on the hospital grounds and in the course of community visits.

Thus, most forensic systems have adopted what we will call a risk management approach to the release of once violent patients. However, while prediction has ceased to be the only goal of such decisions, predictive tools remain an important source of information in the development of case-specific management plans.

Under the risk management approach, an individual's risk may be seen as changing over time and in response to interventions, as contrasted with the single, unchanging risk estimate yielded under the prediction model by actuarial tools that use static (unchangeable through planned intervention) risk factors. Common sense dictates somewhat different treatment and decision-making for higher risk individuals; the public will (and ought to) demand that more intensive intervention be delivered to those individuals who pose the greatest risk to public safety, if those individuals are to be released to the community. This requires some fair and accurate mechanism for deciding which patients are "high risk" or assigning a relative level of *a priori* risk that will influence their release planning. In some cases, there may not be an applicable prediction tool available to assess the person's *a priori* risk. When such tools have not been developed for a particular population, then an alternative may be the use of strong actuarial variables that have demonstrated value in violence prediction across a variety of populations. The factors included in such measures typically are static and based heavily on the person's history of previous violence and other kinds of antisocial behavior. Alternatively, systems may rely on potentially inaccurate proxies such as the severity of the current offense. However, even when empirically based, static risk factors typically do not reflect the impact of interventions. Thus, for hospitalized or incarcerated subjects, static risk appraisal is unlikely to be significantly changed by the course of their confinement.

To interpret the static risk level yielded by an actuarial tool as evidence that an individual's risk level never changes is scientifically unsupported for two reasons. First, the instruments themselves were never intended to reflect changes in risk status over time and in response to interventions. Second, clinical studies of risk reduction efforts, especially for high-risk individuals, are in their infancy. Further, the assumption that risk level never changes would be enormously problematic for the legal goal of individualized decision-making. We cannot accurately gauge the impact of violence risk reduction interventions until we have studied them systematically. During the last decade, the field has made very significant scientific advances in violence prediction and virtually none in the scientific study of violence risk reduction. The next challenge for the medical and behavioral sciences in the area of violence risk appraisal is to develop an accurate way of measuring those aspects of violence risk that change, particularly when we know something about the individual's *a priori* risk. (Some risk tools, such as the HCR-20[7] and the LSI-R,[8] measure both static and potentially changeable aspects of risk; using either would facilitate research in measuring the impact of risk reduction interventions.) When this has been accomplished, the resulting tool will have broader applicability in forensic release decision-making contexts, partly because the conclusion "once high risk, always high risk" will be less automatic and better informed by data.

With such a tool, a forensic clinician could make a more accurate prediction/ classification regarding future risk and specifically consider and target the individual's dynamic risk and protective factors for intervention planning and decision-making. It would not be helpful to use clinical judgment to replace or even modify the score or level yielded by the actuarial part of the tool. However, we should contextualize this score or level. We can explain it, describing both its strengths and limitations. We can indicate that if the court wants to hear our best attempt at a prediction, we must go with the score (assuming it's applicable—another part of the contextualizing). However, we can assert that risk also depends on a number of considerations and explain what those considerations are—information that can be obtained through individualized clinical assessment.

For example, the MacArthur Iterative Classification Tree (ICT),[9] when ready for use, will yield a three-way risk classification—above, at, or below base rate, with the base rate described. Suppose the individual is classified as above base rate. Is there further information that should be considered regarding whether violence will occur? Examples might include access to a victim, the availability of a weapon, the presence of a job, the nature of the living situation, or the intensity of the monitoring. Are protective factors present, such as treatment involvement or a good reason not to be violent? Providing this information would not change the ICT classification of the individual as above base rate in risk for serious violence over the next year, but it would put it into a clearer context.

RISK COMMUNICATION

The prediction versus risk management decision also will affect the ways in which clinicians and systems of care communicate levels of risk to each other and to other relevant actors in the community. *A priori* risk (a classification or probability estimate of an individual's likelihood of future violent behavior, based largely on stable factors) is best measured using an actuarial measure such as the Violence Risk Appraisal Guide[4] or the Iterative Classification Tree.[10] The value in using such measures presumes that the necessary data have been collected and the actuarial formula for the prediction developed and validated.

The communication of risk should reflect, integrate, and convey the decision-making rationale and outcome in an understandable way, using nontechnical language. It also should reflect what we know about the language used to communicate the results of our predictive efforts.[11,12] In addition, it is important to communicate the results of risk assessment in a way that is consistent with what has been done. If a predictive tool has been used, then the most consistent form of communication would involve a conclusion that an individual is "high versus moderate versus low" risk, or is "x percent likely to commit y acts over z period of time." On the other hand, risk reduction approaches are better communicated by describing the applicable risk factors and the risk reduction intervention strategies for each, a form that is consistently referred by clinicians across a variety of disciplines.[13] Risk communication is a particularly important component of the larger assessment process; even risk assessment that is relevant, empirically supported, and applicable to the individual may be useless if the results are not understood by the decision-maker.

CONCLUSIONS

The safest way to return someone from confinement to freedom is in increments of decreased structure and increased freedom. As likelihood, severity, and imminence of predicted violent behavior increase, the patient should be required to negotiate a greater number of increments, each of which is thus smaller, and there should be a more demanding threshold used to define successful completion of each increment. The increments themselves should each include demonstration of skill acquisition that is related to specific risk factors that emerge from careful clinical study of the patient's history.

Forensic release decision-making should distinguish between three aspects of risk: probability, imminence, and severity of outcome. Severity is best defined by prior violence to date, including the current charges; probability is best defined by actuarial models; and imminence is defined by the pattern of violence in the person's prior career, as well as their statements, plans, target availability, and life circumstances.

These goals can be advanced through the continued development of empirically driven risk assessment procedures. Our view about the debate between actuarial and clinical approaches in this area can be captured in the same phrase we find useful in responding to a judge or attorney who asks whether an individual is dangerous: It "depends." If the court is interested, entirely or in part, on the best available prediction of violence risk, then one should rely on an applicable actuarial tool. If the court wants to know how an individual's violence risk might be reduced through hospital or community interventions, then one should provide a strategy that encompasses interventions addressing potentially changeable violence risk factors in a specific case or recommend interventions that have empirically demonstrated risk reduction value.

The field has carefully studied violence prediction but understudied violence intervention effectiveness. If we are to become better able to address the full range of a court's questions about an individual's violence risk, we must remedy this deficit in the coming decade. Until we do, we can answer some predictive questions when there is applicable research and an appropriate tool but should not make specific predictions where there is not. We also must exercise caution in responding to risk reduction questions, indicating that we can determine from some sources what would be helpful in reducing risk while acknowledging that the field has not yet systematically studied the area.

REFERENCES

1. Meehl P: Clinical versus statistical prediction: a theoretical analysis and review of the evidence. Minneapolis: University of Minnesota Press, 1954
2. Dawes R, Faust D, Meehl P: Clinical versus actuarial judgment. Science 243:1668–74, 1989
3. Grove W, Meehl P: Comparative efficiency of informal (subjective, impressionistic) and formal (mechanical, algorithmic) prediction procedures: the clinical-statistical controversy. Psychol Public Policy Law 2:293–323, 1996
4. Quinsey VL, Harris GT, Rice ME, Cormier CA: Violent offenders: appraising and managing risk. Washington, DC: American Psychological Association Press, 1998
5. Hart SD: The role of psychopathy in assessing risk for violence: conceptual and methodological issues. Legal Criminol Psychol 3:123–40, 1998
6. Heilbrun K, Nezu C, Kenney M, Chung S, Wasserman A: Sexual offending: linking assessment, intervention, and decision-making. Psychol Public Policy Law 4:138–72, 1998
7. Webster C, Douglas K, Eaves D, Hart S: HCR-20: Assessing Risk for Violence (Version 2). Burnaby, BC, Canada: Mental Health, Law, and Policy Institute, Simon Fraser University, 1997
8. Andrews D, Bonta J: Level of Service Inventory–Revised. Toronto: Multi-Health Systems, 1995
9. Monahan J, Steadman HJ, Appelbaum P, et al: Developing a clinically useful actuarial tool for assessing violence risk. Br J Psychiatry, in press
10. Harris GT, Rice ME, Quinsey VL: Violent recidivism of mentally disordered offenders: the development of a statistical prediction instrument. Crim Just Behav 20:315–35,1993
11. Heilbrun K, Dvoskin J, Hart S, McNiel D: Violence risk communication: implications for research, policy, and practice. Health Risk Soc 1:91–106,1999
12. Slovic P, Monahan J, MacGregor D: Violence risk assessment and risk communication: the effects of using actual cases, providing instruction, and employing probability versus frequency formats. Law Hum Behav 24:271–96, 2000
13. Heilbrun K, O'Neill M, Strohman L, Bowman Q, Philipson J: Expert approaches to communicating violence risk. Law Hum Behav 24:137–48, 2000

18

Violent Storms and Violent People: How Meteorology Can Inform Risk Communication in Mental Health Law

JOHN MONAHAN AND HENRY J. STEADMAN

ABSTRACT: *Meteorology is often thought of as a field with highly developed techniques for forecasting rare and severe events. Risk assessment of another type of rare and severe event—violence to others—occurs in mental health law. The analogy between these two forms of risk assessment is explored in this article. How meteorologists go about assessing the risk of harmful weather is described. Implications from the meteorological analogy are drawn for one aspect of violence prediction that is routinely ignored in mental health law: the communication of risk "forecasts."*

Never was waves nor wind more violent.

— Shakespeare, *Pericles*

In its landmark report, *Improving Risk Communication* (1989), the National Research Council's Committee on Risk Perception and Communication pointed out weather forecasters as exemplary risk assessors: "When they predict a 70 percent chance of rain, there is measurable precipitation just about 70 percent of the time" (p. 46). The Committee

Reprinted with permission. The official citation that should be used in referencing this material is Monahan, J. & Steadman, H.J. (1996). Violent storms and violent people: How meteorology can inform risk communication in mental health law. American Psychologist 2003, 51 (9), 931–938. © 2003 by the American Psychological Association Inc.

listed five reasons why weather forecasters are so good at what they do:

1. Frequent practice: Weather forecasters "make numerous forecasts of the same kind" (p. 46).
2. Base-rate information: "Extensive statistical data are available on the average probability of the events they are estimating" (p. 46).
3. Actuarial support: Weather forecasters "receive computer-generated predictions for specific periods prior to making their forecasts" (p. 46).
4. Availability of feedback: "A readily verifiable criterion event allows for quick and unambiguous knowledge of results" (p. 46).
5. Educational programs. The weather forecasting profession "admits its imprecision and the need for training" (pp. 46–47).

At first glance, these meteorological assessments of the risk of harmful weather may seem to bear only semantic similarity to psychological and psychiatric assessments of the risk of harmful behavior—assessments that play a pivotal role in mental health law (Monahan & Shah, 1989). Yet there are indications that the conditions identified by the National Research Council as underlying the success of meteorologists as risk assessors of weather are coming to characterize, to an increasing degree, the task of mental health professionals in assessing risk of violence:

1. Frequent practice: Violent patients now make up a large and growing portion of the caseload of the public mental health system (Appelbaum, 1988). One recent study of three acute-care mental hospitals reported that 37% of all admissions had been physically violent within the two months prior to hospitalization (Steadman et al., 1994).
2. Base-rate information: Statistical information on the base rates of violence among given types of civil patients (Lidz, Mulvey, & Gardner, 1993) and forensic patients (Webster, Harris, Rice, Cormier, & Quinsey, 1994) has become available for the first time.
3. Actuarial support: Actuarial data to anchor clinical risk assessments have been reported both for inpatient violence (McNiel & Binder, 1994) and for violence in the open community (Harris, Rice, & Quinsey, 1993).
4. Availability of feedback: With drastically shortened lengths of hospital stays and the rise of outpatient commitment (Swartz et al., 1995) and other forms of supervised community treatment (Dennis & Monahan, 1996), the occurrence of violence in the community is much better documented than in the past.
5. Educational programs: Both training materials (Appelbaum & Gutheil, 1991; Monahan, 1993) and training programs in the risk assessment of violence are readily available throughout the mental health professions.

In this article, we propose that risk assessment in mental health law can learn some important things from risk assessment in meteorology. Thinking of violence prediction as analogous to weather prediction has a number of heuristic implications for mental health law. For example, the temporal specificity of weather forecasts suggests the need for shorter term and more frequently updated risk assessments of violence. And the contextual specificity of weather forecasts, which are limited to a given forecast area, suggests the importance of context in behavioral prediction. The implication we wish to draw out here, however, does not have to do with the formation of risk assessments themselves, but with how risk forecasts, once arrived at, are communicated to those who need to know them (see Murphy & Daan, 1985; Murphy & Winkler, 1987, 1992).

We first pursue the analogy between meteorology and mental health law in greater depth. We then describe how meteorologists go about assessing the risk of harmful weather. Finally, implications from meteorology are drawn for one aspect of violence prediction that is routinely ignored in mental health law: the communication of risk "forecasts."

THE METEOROLOGICAL ANALOGY

The first meaning *Merriam-Webster's Dictionary* (1977) gives for the term *analogy* is an "inference that if two or more things agree with one another in some respects, they will probably agree in others" (p. 41). But do violence and the weather "agree" with one another in any meaningful respect? Contrasting violence and the weather—pointing out ways in which the two "disagree" at the concrete level—certainly takes little imagination. Substantively, violence is a human activity that is subject to poorly known laws of psychology, sociology, and biology (Reiss & Roth, 1993). Weather is an atmospheric or oceanographic activity that is subject to better known laws of physical science (Ahrens, 1991). Humans who commit harm are moral agents, and notions of intent, blame, responsibility, excuse, and justification are invoked to describe them. Even storms that cause great devastation (e.g., "killer hurricanes") do not respond to moral censure or legal deterrence. Recall the parody: "A law was made a distant moon ago here. July and August cannot be too hot. And there's a legal limit to the snow here, in Camelot" (Lerner, 1962, pp. 32–33).

But a moment's reflection reveals that the "agreements" at the conceptual level between how meteorologists and how psychologists and psychiatrists actually assess risk are also striking and relevant. In both domains of risk assessment:
(a) Someone credentialed as a professional
(b) assesses risk factors derived from past experience or from theories and
(c) processes these risk factors with the aid of explicit or implicit prediction models.
(d) The professional then constructs a likelihood estimate (or "forecast") of the event of interest occurring, and, finally,
(e) the professional issues a risk communication containing this forecast to various audiences of relevant decision makers.

Why do these five parallels make us think that learning something about meteorology will be useful to researchers, and ultimately to practitioners, in mental health law? There are several reasons.

First, the prediction of weather events[1] provides a simplified and, therefore, clarifying model for the prediction of violent events (Faigman, 1989, p. 1047). Because weather events lack moral agency, they can serve to illustrate the technology of risk assessment in its purest and most schematized form. The fact that principles of thermo-dynamics and fluid mechanics are so much better understood than principles of sociology, psychology, and biology means that weather prediction can serve as an ideal case illustration of what risk assessment in mental health law would look like if we really knew what we were doing (Monahan & Steadman, 1994). Predicting the weather is easy compared with predicting violence, and taking easy examples is a good way to start thinking through a difficult topic.

Second, meteorologists have an enormous amount of experience with the generic concepts and techniques of risk assessment. Although there may be an increasing concern with violence in the practice of psychology and psychiatry, the experience of most mental health professionals with forecasting violence (except for those employed in forensic facilities) is not acquired on a daily basis. However, with weather events being forecast throughout the day—or throughout the hour—every day by meteorologists, a vast store of experience in forecasting weather events has been accumulated. It would be surprising indeed if some of the concepts and techniques that meteorologists have found useful in managing their risk assessment tasks would not be portable to less experienced uses of risk assessment in other areas—one of these areas being mental health law.

Finally, risk assessment in meteorology is much better understood and accepted by policymakers and the general public than risk assessment in mental health law. To the extent that some of the concepts taken for granted in meteorology would be usefully applied to mental health law, drawing the analogy between risk assessment of violence and the risk assessment of the weather may be a powerful device for communicating with decision makers (e.g., judges and hospital staff) and the general public (Chess, Salomone, Hance, & Saville, 1995).

METEOROLOGY: CONCEPTS AND PROCEDURES

Meteorology is "the study of the atmosphere and its phenomena" (Ahrens, 1991, p. 13). Much of meteorology is concerned with understanding ordinary, day-to-day weather events, such as rain, wind, and clouds. Another subdiscipline of the field, and the one of most direct relevance here, is concerned with estimating the risk of certain hazards, such as tornadoes, hurricanes, and heavy rains, that pose a threat to life or property. Murphy (1991) referred to these hazards as "rare and severe [weather] events" (RSEs; p. 302). To assist in assessing these risks, governmental agencies around the world routinely collect information on variables (e.g., barometric pressure, wind speeds, and cloud formation) that are known to be predictors of one or another of these hazards. This information is analyzed by regression-based computer programs that incorporate models of the association between patterns of these predictors and the occurrence of given hazards in the past. These programs yield *objective predictions* (sometimes called *statistical* or *numerical predictions*) of various weather events. These objective predictions are given at regular periods to meteorologists in local areas. These meteorologists then modify the objective predictions in light of predictors that they believe were not adequately accounted for in the computer model, or in response to new information that has become available since the objective prediction was formulated. A *subjective prediction* is then publicly issued, and this risk message is referred to as the *forecast*.

Three aspects of forecasts are of central importance: The forecast is issued only for a specified valid period of time; the forecast is issued only for a specified forecast area; and the forecast always mentions, in addition to specifying the nature of the hazard in question (e.g., tornado, etc.), the degree of certainty about the occurrence of the hazard. Sometimes this uncertainty is expressed in probabilistic terms, such as a 40% chance of precipitation, and sometimes it is expressed in categorical terms, as in hurricane "watches" and "warnings" (see below). In whatever manner it is expressed, the forecast then becomes information that a wide variety of users can take into account, depending on how a particular user balances the monetary and nonmonetary costs of precautionary measures and the losses that would ensue if the event occurred—often referred to as the user's *cost-loss function*. One important category of users is *emergency managers,* officials responsible for taking public precautions such as evacuating the population of an area in response to a large-scale hazard (e.g., a hurricane). These officials have formalized their cost-loss function into critical action thresholds for given precautions (see, in general, Mileti & Fitzpatrick, 1991, 1992). For example, when the forecast includes a hurricane warning, there are standard policies that automatically trigger a series of steps to minimize the exposure of the affected population to harm.

The system that provides the comprehensive data from which all forecasts are generated is operated, in the United States, by the National Weather Service (NWS), a division of the National Oceanic and Atmospheric Administration within the Department of Commerce. Worldwide, over 10,000 land-based stations and hundreds of ships collect weather information daily at six-hour intervals. In addition, many satellites, radiosondes (weather balloons), aircraft, and trained volunteers ("spotters") make observations throughout the day (Ahrens, 1991). The gathering of information from all these sources is coordinated by the World Meteorological Organization, a United Nations agency. The information is sent to one of several World Meteorological Centers. For the United States, the information is analyzed at the National Meteorological Center in Camp Springs, Maryland, and then sent electronically to one of 53 regional Weather Service Forecast offices. These offices prepare regional forecasts. These regional forecasts are made more specific at 249 Weather Service offices, which adapt the regional forecasts to local conditions. These local NWS forecasts are communicated to the general public by being read verbatim by many radio and television announcers (or printed in newspapers). Other radio and television stations hire their own meteorologists to make "private" forecasts (such as "Accuweather"), but even these forecasts are based on NWS data and analyses. As described by Murphy and Brown (1984, p. 371),

> Weather forecasters in the U.S. are charged with the responsibility of preparing the official forecasts disseminated to the general public and specific users. In formulating these forecasts, the forecasters aggregate

information from many different sources, including the output of numerical and statistical models as well as observational data. The aggregation process and the process of determining the form and content of the official forecasts varies greatly from forecaster to forecaster and from occasion to occasion for each forecaster.

THE METEOROLOGICAL ANALOGY AND
MENTAL HEALTH LAW: RISK COMMUNICATION

Before 1965, the NWS issued risk messages for common weather events, such as precipitation, in dichotomous terms (sometimes called *deterministic predictions*—for example, "It will/will not rain today." On occasion, those deterministic predictions were qualitatively hedged, as in "it is likely/not likely to rain today." Beginning in 1965, however, the NWS began issuing risk messages for common weather events in probabilistic terms—for example, "There is a 40% chance of rain today." Surveys indicated that although there was some resistance among users to the introduction of probabilistic precipitation forecasting, the general public not only quickly adapted to it, but soon came to prefer probabilistic prediction—by a ratio of two or three to one (Murphy, 1991)—to the deterministic or qualitatively hedged statements that had previously been the staple of the NWS.

For weather events more rare and more severe than precipitation (i.e., thunderstorms, tornadoes, hurricanes, high winds, flash floods, heavy snow, and winter storms), however, the NWS has, since the 1950s, provided risk estimates in categorical form (Wernley, personal communication, May 1994). The NWS did not abandon the use of categorical risk messages for severe weather events in 1965, when it switched to probabilistic prediction for more common events such as rain. Although the categories that are used vary somewhat from one type of severe weather event to another (e.g., *advisories* are issued when inconvenient, but not life-threatening, weather events are anticipated: *small craft cautionary statements* are given when there is a risk of a tropical cyclone), in general, three categories are still used by the NWS to describe the risk of a severe weather event.

Category 1: *No message.* From the absence of any NWS risk message, one can infer that the Service does not assess risk for the weather event in question to be appreciably above base rate.

Category 2: *Watches.* This category indicates a significantly higher than base-rate likelihood of a life-threatening weather event occurring in a given area. A NWS risk message headed *hurricane watch*, for example, is "an announcement that hurricane conditions pose a possible threat to a specified coastal area within 36 hours" (National Weather Service, 1993a, p. 33).

Category 3: *Warnings.* This category represents the highest likelihood of a life-threatening weather event. A NWS risk message headed *flash flood warning,* for example, "means that a flash flood has been reported or is imminent" (National Weather Service, 1991, p. 4). A hurricane warning is issued "when hurricane conditions are expected in a specified coastal area in 24 hours or less" (National Weather Service, 1991, p. 4).

Some warnings are conditional. In the case of tornado warnings, for example, the relevant NWS publication (1993b) states that "if a tornado warning is issued for your area and the sky becomes threatening, move to your pre-designated place of safety" (p. 6). Presumably, if a tornado warning is issued but the sky does not become threatening, no action is indicated (see Mulvey & Lidz, 1995, on "conditional" violence prediction).

The NWS categorical messages for severe weather events do more than communicate information about risk levels. Each category integrates a *descriptive statement* of current risk (i.e., a forecast) with two kinds of *prescriptive statements,* one about the need for additional information and another about risk management strategies. *A watch* message, in addition to informing the public that an intermediate risk of a negative weather event is present, is accompanied by a recommendation that people carefully monitor the situation and prepare for action. For example, NWS publications exhort the reader: "When a flash flood watch is issued, be alert to flash flooding and be ready to evacuate on a moment's notice" (p. 4). More prescriptive advice is given in hurricane watches, including "frequently monitor radio . . . for official bulletins of the storm's progress," "fuel and service family vehicles," "check food and water supplies," and "stock up on extra batteries" (p. 34). Likewise, a *warning* message, in addition to informing users that a high risk of a serious weather event is present, is joined with a recommendation for immediate action to prevent harm. For example, when it issues a flash flood warning, the NWS advises people to "act quickly to save yourself. You may have only seconds! Go to higher ground" (National Weather Service, 1992, p. 10). For hurricane warnings, people are told to "stay home, if sturdy and on high ground . . . Stay indoors on the downwind side of house away from windows. Leave mobile homes" (National Weather Service, 1991, p. 4).

The use of categorical risk messages by the NWS is by no means generally accepted in the meteorological community. Some leading meteorologists have argued cogently that categorical risk messages necessarily convey less information about risk than probabilistic risk messages, because they are less precise and because it is unclear what cut-off scores separate each of the categories. In addition, the values of the decision maker are unknown to the forecaster and may well vary across decision makers (Alexandridis & Krzysztofowicz, 1985). In other words, all of the criticisms made about dichotomous risk messages ("it will rain," "it will not rain") also apply to multilevel risk messages (e.g., *no message, watch,* and *warning*). As Alan Murphy (1991, p. 304) stated, in terms as applicable to violence forecasting as to weather forecasting, when categorical risk messages are offered, "Uncertainty is ignored and, in effect, the forecaster 'becomes' the decision maker, a role for which he/she generally is not well-equipped."

Why does the NWS choose to offer probabilistic risk messages for common weather events (e.g., precipitation) and categorical risk messages for rare ones (e.g., tornadoes)?

The answer appears to lie in the NWS's skepticism about the competence of users—particularly the general public—to optimally process information about low probability events (Hughes, 1980). For example, 72 hours before landfall, the maximum probability of hurricane conditions at any given coastal location does not exceed .10 (Baker, 1984b). It can be argued—with much support from psychological research (e.g., Slovic, 1987)—that people will either overvalue or undervalue such relatively small probabilities, with potentially catastrophic consequences for their decision making.

Little research exists to help resolve this choice between probabilistic and categorical risk messages. Baker (1984a), in one of the few studies in this area, investigated people's stated intentions to evacuate their homes in response to various risk messages. He compared official risk management statements (no statement, official advice to evacuate, and official order to evacuate) with and without probability-of-hurricane statements appended. He found that stated intention to evacuate was strongly influenced by the categorical risk statement and less affected by the probability figures. People used probabilities primarily in a comparative or ordinal sense: If the probability of a hurricane hitting their area was appreciably higher than the probability of a hurricane hitting adjacent areas, people would tend to evacuate. If the probability of the hurricane hitting their area was appreciably lower than it hitting adjacent areas, they would tend not to evacuate. These results were independent of what the absolute values of the probabilities were.

Among many others, we have long recommended that mental health professionals communicate risk assessments of violence in probabilistic terms (Monahan & Wexler, 1978; Steadman, 1987). We believe that as predictions become more valid, they will become more likely to be expressed as probabilities. Our own ongoing research assumes probabilistic risk communication as one of its primary goals (Steadman et al., 1994, p. 297). But the meteorological analogy forces us to rethink this long held and taken-for-granted assumption and to ask the following question: Is communicating a risk estimate of a rare and severe behavioral event such as violence sufficiently analogous to communicating a risk estimate of a rare and severe weather event such as a tornado that categorical rather than probabilistic risk messages should be preferred in mental health law, as they are in weather prediction?[2]

As with categorical risk communication in meteorology, there is no research that would directly answer this question. What would categorical risk messages in mental health law look like? Three things about categorical risk communication should be kept in mind. First, there is no necessity that the categorical communication format be segmented into three levels (although the strategy must have at least three levels or we are back to dichotomous statements of *dangerous* or *not dangerous*), and there is certainly no necessity that the category labels be the same as those used by the NWS (*no message*, *watch*, and *warning*). Indeed, it has been recently suggested that the NWS itself change both the number of risk categories and the labels applied to them. The NWS is considering a move to a four-category format in light of highly favorable experience using a four-category approach on the children's television workshop program, *Sesame Street* (with the category labels being *no message*, *Ready*, *Set*, and *Go!*; Wernley, personal communication, May 1994).

Second, a risk communication strategy that integrated descriptive risk estimates with prescriptive statements about (a) the need for additional information gathering and (b) recommended risk management strategies would have to be carefully tailored to the specific clinical or legal context in which the relevant decision makers ("users") are likely to be found (Maibach & Holtgrave, 1995). A probability of violence that would qualify for the highest risk category in a civil hospital may be determined not to qualify for the highest risk category in a forensic hospital. Just as the NWS prescriptions for additional information gathering and for risk management activities differ for hurricanes and for tornadoes, there could be no "generic," context-independent risk messages for violence. Information gathering and risk management activities appropriate in an outpatient setting may be different than those appropriate in a hospital. Decisions to be made by clinicians, for example, the decision to issue an escorted or an unescorted grounds pass, present different issues than decisions to be made by judges (e.g., the decision to involuntarily commit a person as *dangerous to others*). Each type of decision has its own "critical threshold for action" (Wernly, 1994, p. 17), and the categories by which risk is communicated must be relevant to these thresholds.

Third, there is no reason why categorical and probabilistic formats could not be combined in a single risk message (see Wallsten, Budescu, Zwick, & Kemp, 1993). The use of multiple risk formats might aid comprehension. One could issue a categorical risk message and add "this means that the patient is believed to have an X likelihood of being violent over Y period of time" (or, better, "of being violent to the following people," or "under the following conditions"). Alternatively, a categorical risk message could be joined with a frequentist, rather than a probabilist, statement (Gigerenzer, 1994), as in "this means that of every X patients with this person's salient characteristics and in this context, Y have been found to be violent over Z period of time."

With these points in mind,[3] consider the following hypothetical illustration of categorical risk messages:

Category 1: *Low violence risk.* Few risk factors are present. No further inquiry into violence risk or special preventive actions are indicated (e.g., a 60-year-old depressed man with no violence history and no threats of violence).

Category 2: *Moderate violence risk.* Several risk factors are present. Gather additional information and monitor the individual more closely than usual (e.g., a 25-year-old woman who is abusing alcohol, with a history of assault, but without a recent violent act or threat).

Category 3: *High violence risk.* A number of key risk factors are present. Give priority to gathering additional information and close patient monitoring. Make preparations for preventive action should the situation deteriorate (e.g., a 30-year-old woman who is using illegal drugs, with a history of assault, and with vague recent threats).

Category 4: *Very high violence risk.* Many key risk factors are present. Enough information is available to make a decision. Take preventive action now (e.g., intensive case management or treatment, voluntary or involuntary hospitalization, and warning the potential victim; e.g., a 35-year-old man who is using illegal drugs, is noncompliant with psychotropic medication, has a history of recent serious violence, is threatening his wife, and has just bought a gun).

An excellent example of how categorical risk communications can work in practice is provided by the United States Secret Service (USSS; Steadman, 1991). As part of its protective intelligence mission, the USSS is responsible for investigating and assessing threats and inappropriate behavior against their *protectees* (i.e., persons whom the Service is authorized to protect). What the USSS has developed is a risk assessment and risk management system that relies on a wide variety of factors, many of which are quantified. However, for the purpose of decision making about risk management, the individual cases are put into one of three categories, with no attempts at further refinement.

In 1987, the USSS implemented a three-tiered Case Classification System (CCS) to structure both the conduct of its investigations and the reports of these investigations. The intent of the system was to match investigative resources and staff to the seriousness and complexity of the case (i.e., the subject or subjects being investigated) and to provide a format whereby investigative agents have significant input in terms of assigning a proper priority to cases being investigated.

The new system resulted in all investigations being categorized as Class 1, Class 2, or Class 3 on the basis of how comprehensive an investigation was needed and the estimated level of threat posed to protectees of the USSS by the subject. The level of threat was determined by the findings of the investigating case agent, with input from agents in the Intelligence Division at USSS headquarters.

Persons categorized as *Class 1* are those for whom initial investigation clearly demonstrates that they present no danger to persons under USSS protection. Persons in *Class 2* also do not appear to present a danger to USSS protectees, but this determination is made only after a more extensive investigation than occurred for Class 1 cases. *Class 3* cases are those that are determined to present a significant danger to persons under USSS protection.

The CCS process begins with a reported threat or an identified "direction of interest" (e.g., a person who is reported to have excessive and inappropriate interest in a protectee or in assassinations of public figures). The sequence is shown in Figure 1.

Class 1 and Class 2 investigations terminate with the case being closed because there is insufficient risk to protectees to warrant case management (i.e., periodic checks with persons incarcerated or hospitalized, interviews with persons who are unconfined, or other appropriate monitoring). Class 3 cases are evaluated as posing sufficient risk to protectees that continuing case management is required until a person no longer is deemed to present serious concern. To maintain Class 3 status for cases that no longer warrant that high level of management wastes resources that could better be used for new investigations or for managing other Class 3 cases. Every additional incident that brings a previously classified person back to USSS attention results in a case being reopened and a new investigation being conducted.

FIGURE 1
Secret Service Case Classification System

A second example of categorical risk communication, this one tailored to violence among patients in maximum security forensic facilities, has recently been reported by Webster et al. (1994). To communicate empirically derived estimates of risk, these clinician-researchers partitioned their sample into nine categories that were based on the participants' likelihoods of violence. The authors provided an illustration of how risk is communicated to decision makers by including a report written on a "Mr. Moore." The concluding paragraph in the report reads as follows:

> Based on his score on a risk appraisal instrument constructed from the variables discussed above, Mr. Moore's category for risk of violent recidivism is the *third highest* of nine categories. Among mentally disordered offenders in the studies described above, less than *nine percent* obtained *higher* scores and approximately *fifty-five percent* in that category reoffended violently within an average of seven years after release. (p. 80)

Note that the report combines categorical risk communication ("third highest of nine categories") with statements of both absolute ("fifty-five percent") and relative likelihood ("less than nine percent obtained higher scores").

Finally, it is worth recalling in regard to communicating risk of violence to others that categorical risk communication has for many years been standard operating procedure when violence to self has been at issue. As stated by Maris, Berman, and Maltsberger (1992, p. 662):

> Almost every hospital has a policy and procedural manual in which various types of actual or probable self-destructive behaviors are linked to two or three levels of precautions. Suicide watches vary from 24-hour (i.e., "constant") within-arms'-reach, one-to-one supervision (for acute suicide probability, often based on a prior explicit suicide attempt) to 15-, 30- or 60-minute logged observations.

CONCLUSION

Even people intrigued by the meteorological analogy in mental health law often mention one objection to pursuing its implications in areas such as risk communication: Despite the conceptual agreements between what meteorologists and what psychologists and psychiatrists do in assessing risk, the state of the art of risk assessment in meteorology is so much more advanced than the state of the art of risk assessment in psychology and psychiatry that the analogy lacks force. This would be an important objection, if it were true.

As amazing as it may seem, however, the superiority of meteorologists over psychologists and psychiatrists as risk assessors is more apparent than real in all but very short-term predictions. The National Research Council (1989) was accurate in stating, "When they [meteorologists] predict a 70 percent chance of rain, there is measurable precipitation just about 70 percent of the time" (p. 46). What was not said, however, is that this impressive degree of predictive validity can be achieved only when the lead time is 12–24 hours (see, e.g., Murphy & Winkler, 1992). The accuracy of weather forecasts "falls off rapidly" (Ahrens, 1991, p: 382) when they are made more than three days in advance (Ahrens, 1991, p. 382) and "tends to be swamped by chaos beyond six days or so" (Ken, 1994, p. 1940). It was not until January of 1995, for example, that the NWS even attempted to forecast rain more than 90 days in advance, and these new long-lead climate outlooks are limited to a simple four-level categorical statement: *above median precipitation, below median precipitation, normal precipitation,* and *insufficient skill to make a valid estimate of precipitation.* Courts have held psychologists and psychiatrists liable for inaccurately assessing risk of violence when the violence in question did not transpire until many months after the clinician had made the prediction (Monahan, 1993). It is not clear that meteorologists can do any better in making long-lead predictions of the weather than clinicians can in making long-lead predictions of violence.

Ultimately, the goal of a warning system in mental health law is the same as the goal of a warning system in meteorology: "to maximize the number of people who take appropriate and timely actions for the safety of life and property. All warning systems start with detection of the event and end with getting out of harm's way" (Wernly, 1994, p. 12). Both the production of risk estimates and the construction of risk communications demand careful, creative research. Until now, much attention has been paid to producing valid risk estimates, but none to constructing effective risk communications. What Murphy (1993, p. 286) observed about weather forecasts, however, is equally applicable to forecasts of violence: "Forecasts possess no intrinsic value. They acquire value through their ability to influence the decisions made by users of the forecasts." Understanding how best to communicate assessments of risk is as important to mental health law as improving the validity of those assessments themselves.

NOTES

1. It may be useful to distinguish *weather*—the "condition of the atmosphere at any particular time and place" (Ahrens, 1991, p. 564)—from *climate*. *Climate* is "average weather," or "the accumulation of daily and seasonal weather events over a long period of time" (Ahrens, 1991, p. 12). For example, the weather in Seattle today may be sunny, but the climate of Seattle at given times of year is rainy. Climate therefore may be thought of as the meteorological "personality" or set of relatively enduring meteorological "traits" of a given area, in distinction to more specific and behavioral weather "events," such as rain or snow in the area on a certain date.

2. There may be two additional reasons to question whether clinical risk estimates of violence are best expressed in probabilistic form. First, much anecdotal evidence suggests that clinicians, unlike meteorologists, are distinctly uncomfortable in generating risk assessments in the form of explicit probabilities, not just in communicating risk assessments in probabilistic form. Given the substantively modest (though statistically significant) validity of clinical predictions of violence over a six-month period that the best recent research has revealed (Lidz et al., 1993), clinicians may find it both pretentious and potentially misleading to produce risk assessments along a 100-point probability scale. Second, a recent study (Slovic & Monahan, 1995) suggests that this discomfort may be warranted. Experienced forensic clinicians were shown vignettes describing mental patients and were asked to judge the probability that the patient would harm someone. Judged probability was strongly dependent on the form of the response scale the clinicians were given, suggesting that probability was not represented consistently and quantitatively in the clinicians' minds. For example, one response scale for expressing the probability of harm went from 0% to 100% in 10% increments. Another response scale went from "less than 1 chance in 1,000" to "greater than 40%." Clinicians' judgments about the probability of violence were much higher using the first response scale than using the second (see, in general, Fischhoff, 1994, 1995; Teigen and Brun, 1995; Tversky & Kochler, 1994).

3. The political issue of who decides the number of risk categories and the category labels and the prescriptions for information-gathering and risk management that accompany each category must also be confronted. In light of legitimate concerns such as those of Murphy (1991) that categorical risk assessment conflates scientific questions (i.e., probability estimates) with questions of social values (i.e., the choice of cutoff scores distinguishing categories), we believe that it is essential that the ultimate users of risk communications about violence (e.g., judges and other policy makers) be centrally involved from the beginning in developing any categorical risk communication scheme.

REFERENCES

Ahrens. C. (1991). *Meteorology today: An introduction to weather* (4th ed.). St Paul, MN: West Publishing Company.

Alexandridis. M., & Krzysztofowicz. R. (1985). Decision models for categorical and probabilistic weather forecasts. *Applied Mathematics and Computation, 17*, 241–266.

Appelbaum, P. (1988). The new preventive detention: Psychiatry's problematic responsibility for the control of violence. *American Journal of Psychiatry, 145*, 779–785.

Appelbaum, P., & Gutheil, T. (1991). *Clinical handbook of psychiatry and the law* (2nd ed.). Baltimore: Williams and Wilkins.

Baker, J. (1984a). *Public responses in Hurricane Alicia: Probabilities and the people of Galveston.* Tallahassee, FL: Environmental Hazards Center. Florida State University.

Baker, J. (1984b). *Public responses to hurricane probability forecasts* (National Oceanic and Atmospheric Administration Tech. Memorandum No. NWS FCST 29). Washington, DC: U.S. Department of Commerce.

Chess, C., Salomone, K., Hance, B., & Saville, A. (1995). Results of a national symposium on risk communication: Next steps for government agencies. *Risk Analysis, 15*, 115–125.

Dennis, D., & Monahan, J. (1996). *Coercion and aggressive community treatment: A new frontier in mental health law.* New York: Plenum.

Faigman, D. (1989). To have and have not: Assessing the value of social science to the law as science and policy. *Emory Law Journal, 38*, 1005–1095.

Fischhoff, B. (1994). What forecasts (seem to) mean. *International Journal of Forecasting, 10*, 387–403.

Fischhoff, B. (1995). Risk perception and communication unplugged: Twenty years of process. *Risk Analysis, 15*, 137–145.

Gigerenzer, G. (1994). Why the distinction between single-event probabilities and frequencies is important for psychology and vice versa. In G. Wright & P. Ayton (Eds.). *Subjective probability* (pp.129–161). New York: Wiley.

Harris, G., Rice, M., & Quinsey, V. (1993). Violent recidivism of mentally disordered offenders: The development of a statistical prediction instrument. *Criminal Justice and Behavior, 20*, 315–335.

Hughes, L. (1980). *Probability forecasting: Reasons, procedures, problems* (National Oceanic and Atmospheric Administration Tech. Memorandum No. NWS FCST 24). Washington, DC: U.S. Department of Commerce.

Kerr, R. (1994). Official forecasts pushed out to a year ahead. *Science, 266*, 1940–1941.

Lerner, A. (1962). *Camelot.* New York: Chappell Music.

Lidz. C., Mulvey. E., & Gardner, W. (1993). The accuracy of predictions of violence to others. *Journal of the American Medical Association, 269*, 1007–1011.

Maibach, E., & Holtgrave. D. (1995). Advances in public health communication. *Annual Review of Public Health, 16*, 219–238.

Maris, R., Berman, A., & Maltsberger, J. (1992). What have we learned about suicide assessment and prediction? In R. Maris, A. Berman, J. Maltsberger, & R. Yufit (Eds.). *Assessment and prediction of suicide* (pp. 640–672). New York: Guilford Press.

Merriam-Webster's new collegiate dictionary. (1977), Springfield. MA: Merriam-Webster.

McNiel, D., & Binder, R. (1994). Screening for inpatient violence: Validation of an actuarial tool. *Law and Human Behavior, 18*. 579–586.

Mileti, D., & Fitzpatrick, C. (1991). Communication of public risk: Its theory and its application. *Sociological Practice Review, 2*, 20–28.

Mileti, D., & Fitzpatrick, C. (1992). The causal sequence of risk communication in the Parkfield earthquake prediction experiment. *Risk Analysis, 12*, 393–400.

Monahan, J. (1993). Limiting therapist exposure to *Tarasoff* liability: Guidelines for risk containment. *American Psychologist, 48*, 242– 250.

Monahan, J., & Shah, S. (1989). Dangerousness and commitment of the mentally disordered in the United States. *Schizophrenia Bulletin, 15*, 541–553.

Monahan, J., & Steadman, H. (1994). Toward the rejuvenation of risk research. In J. Monahan & H. Steadman (Eds.). *Violence and mental disorder: Developments in risk assessment* (pp. 1–17). Chicago: University of Chicago Press.

Monahan, J., & Wexler, D. (1978). A definite maybe: Proof and probability in civil commitment. *Law and Human Behavior, 2*, 37–42.

Mulvey, E., & Lidz, C. (1995). Conditional prediction: A model for research on dangerousness to others in a new era. *International Journal of Law and Psychiatry, 18*, 129–143.

Murphy, A. (1991). Probabilities, odds, and forecasts of rare events. *Weather and Forecasting, 6*, 302–307.

Murphy, A. (1993). What is a good forecast? An essay on the nature of goodness in weather forecasting. *Weather and Forecasting, 8*, 281–293.

Murphy, A., & Brown, B. (1984). A comparative evaluation of objective and subjective weather forecasts in the United States. *Journal of Forecasting, 3*, 269–393.

Murphy, A., & Daan, H. (1985). Forecast evaluation. In A. Murphy & R. Katz (Eds.). *Probability, statistics, and decision making in the atmospheric sciences* (pp. 379–437). Boulder, CO: Westview Press.

Murphy, A., & Winkler, R. (1987). A general framework for forecast verification. *Monthly Weather Review, 115*, 1330–1338.

Murphy, A., & Winkler, R. (1992). Diagnostic verification of probability forecasts. *International Journal of Forecasting, 7*, 435–455.

National Research Council. (1989). *Improving risk communication.* Washington. DC: National Academy Press.

National Weather Service. (1991). *Storm surge and hurricane safety.* Washington. DC: U.S. Department of Commerce.

National Weather Service. (1992). *Flash floods and floods: The awesome power.* Washington, DC: U.S. Department of Commerce.

National Weather Service. (l993a). *Hurricane: A familiarization booklet.* Washington. DC: U.S. Department of Commerce.

National Weather Service (1993b). *Tornadoes: Nature's most violent storms.* Washington. DC: U.S. Department of Commerce.

Reiss. A., & Roth, J. (1993). *Understanding and preventing violence.* Washington, DC: National Academy Press.

Slovic, P. (1987). Perception of risk. *Science, 236,* 280–285.

Slovic, P., & Monahan, J. (1995). Danger and coercion: A study of risk perception and decision making in mental health law. *Law and Human Behavior, 19,* 49–65.

Steadman, H. (1987). How well can we predict violence for adults? In F. Dutile & C. Foust (Eds.). *The prediction of criminal violence* (pp. 5–16). Springfield, IL: Charles C Thomas.

Steadman, H. (1991). *Research to strengthen the Case Classification System of the United States Secret Service.* Delmar, NY: Policy Research Associates.

Steadman, H., Monahan, J., Appelbaum, P., Grisso, T., Mulvey, E., Roth, L., Robbins, P., & Klassen, D. (1994). Designing a new generation of risk assessment research. In J. Monahan & H. Steadman (Eds.). *Violence and mental disorder: Developments in risk assessment* (pp. 297–318). Chicago: University of Chicago Press.

Swartz, M., Burns, B., Hiday, V., George, L., Swanson, J., & Wagner, H. (1995). New directions in research on outpatient commitment. *Psychiatric Services, 46,* 381–385.

Teigen, K., & Brun, W. (1995). Yes, but it is uncertain: Direction and communicative intention of verbal probabilistic terms. *Acta Psychologica, 88,* 233–258.

Tversky, A., & Koehler, J. (1994). Support theory: A nonextensional representation of subjective probability. *Psychological Review, 101,* 547–567.

Wallsten, T., Budescu, D., Zwick, R., & Kemp, S. (1993). Preferences and reasons for communicating probabilistic information in verbal or numerical terms. *Bulletin of the Psychonomic Society, 31,* 135–138.

Webster, C., Harris, G., Rice, M., Cormier, C., & Quinsey, V. (1994). *The violence prediction scheme: Assessing dangerousness in high risk men.* Toronto, Ontario, Canada: Centre of Criminology, University of Toronto.

Wernly, D. (1994). *The rules of meteorologists and hydrologists in disaster preparedness* (World Meteorological Organization Tech. Doc. No. 598). Geneva, Switzerland: World Meteorological Association.

V

Decision Making

Section V

Introduction

When interdisciplinary colleagues work together in a team, we generally assume that they will make decisions that are relatively free of bias and that the simple act of discussion will promote homogeneity in opinion. Yet it is not always easy to create teams that are well led and free of offensive control practices (e.g., see Burns, 2004). Vernon Quinsey was one of the first researchers to point out that teams do not necessarily "add value" to decision making.

Vernon L. Quinsey and **Anne Maguire** (Chapter 19) examined 200 consecutive male remands at the maximum secure facility for men in Penetanguishene, Ontario. All 200 cases were reviewed by an interdisciplinary team consisting of psychiatrists, psychologists and other staff members who had attended at least 60 case conferences. After extensive discussion, staff members would complete a Remand Assessment Questionnaire. This questionnaire invited the staff participants to identify what kinds of treatment were needed in each particular case. They were asked to rate the likely effectiveness of various treatment alternatives, ranging from medication to electroconvulsive therapy to milieu therapy to psychoanalysis. What was striking was the lack of agreement among respondents. Although the participants agreed moderately on "dangerousness" (i.e., the likelihood of people behaving dangerously in the institution or upon release), they disagreed markedly on the treatability of the people remanded for assessment. The only area in which they agreed on likely treatment effectiveness was in the use of phenothiazines, the largest class of antipsychotic drugs; however, Quinsey and Maguire worried that the participants' apparent agreement about medication was misleading, as physicians tend to vary in the dosage levels they prescribe.

While this study was completed in 1984, at the height of the "nothing works" controversy (Martinson, 1974), it is still noteworthy that, generally, results from the questionnaire pointed to marked pessimism about the efficacy of any and all treatments. The staff participants in the study seemed to believe that the offenders with a major mental disorder had a chance of responding to medication but that those with a personality disorder were unlikely to benefit from any treatment.

Denis Murphy's essay (Chapter 20) is based on his observations working within institutions that treat people with violent behaviour. Using a "socio-anthropological" approach, he reminds us that working with people who are aggressive requires "notions such as courage and calmness when facing danger, which are not part of the usual vocabulary of risk assessment" (page 365). Murphy's approach, as well as being socio-anthropological, can also be characterized as a psychodynamic exploration of the complexities of group processes on a stressful forensic psychiatric unit. He describes how the various mental health, correctional and criminological staff members on these units can be sorely tried by the work and by patients who can be extraordinarily difficult to understand and help (see Adler, 1972). And he discusses how these circumstances can affect the team's functioning.

Murphy also points to the "powerful emotional forces" sometimes at play when difficult, dangerous situations have to be addressed. In keeping with the findings from Quinsey and Maguire's study in this section, Murphy points out that tension can arise when the leader comes to a conclusion "without much reference to the views of the group" (page 369). In his view, the modern approach is now to share decisions within an interdisciplinary or multi-agency group rather than decisions being made by one person in authority—even though this requires that time and energy be spent in debate. Murphy makes an important point, one often overlooked or underacknowledged: that the essential prerequisite for assessing and managing violence risk is to create a humane environment that has the appropriate therapeutic conditions. The task of risk assessment and management is a human endeavour, and cannot be entirely circumscribed by legal and scientific considerations.

Murphy emphasizes that day-to-day work in this medium is complex and fraught with difficult interpersonal and group dynamics. While clinicians are bound to be the objects of transference and to experience countertransference themselves, Murphy argues that these psychodynamic phenomena can increase clinicians' clinical acuity. He argues in favour of "collective judgment" a view that is consistent with contemporary opinion on evidence-based best practices.

At least some inaccuracy in assessors' abilities to predict violence may be due to their lack of confidence in rating various risk factors. Conceivably, evaluators are sometimes asked to undertake assessments without having the right amounts and types of information to make a judgment. **Kevin S. Douglas** and **James R. P. Ogloff** (Chapter 21) suggest that if this is true, we could conclude, erroneously, that clinicians lack the capacity to complete the prediction task. This issue was examined with 100 civil psychiatric patients. As well as completing the HCR-20 from clinical files, trained raters also indicated how confident they were in their ratings. Eventually, the HCR-20 results—both in terms of overall ratings of low, moderate or high risk and in total risk scores (out of 40)—were linked to actual outcome. The findings show a positive relationship between confidence and accuracy. This effect was strong not only with the clinical (C) items of the HCR-20 but even with the "actuarial," more or less static, historical (H) factors (which, being scored from people's files, might have been expected to be immune from the "confidence effect").

Like Douglas and Ogloff, **Jennifer Skeem**, **Edward Mulvey** and **Charles Lidz** (Chapter 22) explore the limits of clinical ability in predicting violence and how this ability can be enhanced. Whereas Douglas and Ogloff concentrate on confidence as the key variable of interest, the Skeem group argues that, at least in theory, it should be possible to raise accuracy levels by allowing for the possibility of "contextualized" predictions of violence. In other words, clinicians should be given the opportunity in individual cases to adjust their predictions by considering the variables that they deem dominant (e.g., substance use problems, non-adherence to medication, lack of inter-personal skills).

In this particular study, the authors concentrate on the effects of alcohol-related predictions—a variable selected because it is so common among people who have been violent. By obtaining records of drinking and records of violence among some 700 people, mental health professionals, working in a large, university-based emergency department, were able to identify the patients who became violent when they were drinking and to contrast them with those who did not become violent. The researchers didn't find the connection between drinking and violence that they had anticipated. In fact, knowing about alcohol use did not help to predict violence beyond considering it as a risk factor in the abstract. Rather, it helped only to give insight into the typical drinking behaviour of people deemed to be at high risk for violence. The authors comment: "[T]hus clinicians' predictions of alcohol-related violence may be more descriptive of the typical drinking behavior of a group considered to be at high risk for violence than predictive of violent incidents during which patients are drinking" (page 402).

The results are thus somewhat disappointing. It would have been encouraging to be able to demonstrate that, at least to an extent, clinicians can forecast which people will be at increased risk for violence due to drinking. But so many people in the sample behaved violently who had *not* been drinking that any actual effect was extremely marginal. Some comfort is derived from the fact that clinicians were considering an important risk factor, alcohol abuse. The paper is included in this text not so much because it adds new substantive knowledge but because it helps point future researchers toward creating the kinds of multifactor models that are likely needed for the real-life testing of clinical acumen. It could be, for example, that clinicians would fare better were they able to construct a "full" model for violence prediction for indi-vidual cases—a model that would allow them to consider the interactions among a few seemingly pertinent critical factors.

N. Zoe Hilton and **Janet L. Simmons** (Chapter 23) from the Penetanguishene facility explored how decisions are actually made at the tribunal level. They point out that, in 1992, the Violence Risk Assessment Guide (VRAG) first became admissible evidence in the Ontario Review Board's decision-making process. They wanted to find out the extent to which actual VRAG forecasts were influential in board decision making. The results of their research, based on the study of 187 men facing this tribunal, clearly showed that the availability of a VRAG score had negligible influence on board decisions. Any effect of VRAG scores was overpowered by the opinion of clinicians, especially the testimony provided at hearings by the senior professional.

The authors found in their statistical modelling that clinicians' testimony was influenced by four main factors: institutional management problems; psychotropic medication and success in applying it; criminal history prior to the index offence; and attractiveness (as rated by research assistants from photographs). Clinicians were more likely to recommend the release of those deemed "attractive" and to recommend detention in maximum security for those deemed less attractive. Since VRAG scores did not correlate with recommendations for detention, the researchers concluded that senior clinicians were not much influenced by this actuarial score. In their article, Hilton and Simmons express surprise at the small influence of the VRAG. They wonder why the board would be so swayed by clinical opinion and so little influenced by the demonstrated predictive capacity of a well-established, locally developed device. They comment at some length on their finding that a variable such as physical attractiveness, which might be predicted to be more or less irrelevant, was apparently given appreciable weight by the presiding clinician, and by the team as a whole.

It may be naive to think that a newly introduced technology in violence risk assessment, one that had not yet been fully substantiated by the scientific or clinical community, should be so influential as to virtually make the decision for the tribunal. To our knowledge, there is no appellate court in Canada that has accepted a score derived from an actuarial (or any other) risk appraisal device as determinative of the ultimate question a court or tribunal must decide (e.g., Is the person a dangerous offender? Is he or she a significant threat to the safety of the public?). Clinicians and decision makers should avail themselves of *all* scientific and other technological advances shown to be useful in the field. Courts and tribunals must also take a penetrating look at what is involved in making decisions and the ways in which they are and are not influenced by expert opinions. Decision makers at tribunals do, of course, recognize that their decisions about the risk people pose to the public have far-reaching effects on these people's freedom.

Hilton and Simmons should be commended for tackling important but difficult research. It is imperative to know what risk variables link to what outcomes, but it is also vital to find out how variables are actually weighted in the course of day-to-day decision making by courts, boards and tribunals. As already noted, their finding that clinicians tended to recommend release for clients who were relatively attractive warrants more detailed study. This bias, which has been noted in vignette studies on attractiveness (e.g., Esses & Webster, 1988), has important implications for clinical practice. Clearly, violence risk should not be attributed to people based merely on unsubstantiated considerations.

REFERENCES

Adler, G. (1972). Helplessness in the helpers. *British Journal of Medical Psychology, 45*, 315–326.

Burns, T. (2004). *Community Mental Health Teams: A Guide to Current Practices.* Oxford: Oxford University Press.

Esses, V.M. & Webster, C.D. (1988). Physical attractiveness, dangerousness, and the Canadian Criminal Code. *Journal of Applied Social Psychology, 18*, 1017–1031.

Martinson, R. (1974). What works? Questions and answers about prison reform. *Public Interest, 35*, 22–54.

19

Offenders Remanded for a Psychiatric Examination: Perceived Treatability and Disposition

VERNON L. QUINSEY AND ANNE MAGUIRE

One of the great debates in criminology and psychiatry is whether criminals should be viewed as mental health problems or whether they should be viewed as "bad." Philosophical considerations aside, the question often becomes a practical one of whether or not offenders are modifiable or "treatable" using methods developed in psychiatric institutions. Some serious offenders, of course, do appear to suffer from severe "mental disorders" and, in Ontario, these have been treated primarily in the Oak Ridge maximum security Division of the Penetanguishene Mental Health Centre which is part of the Ontario Ministry of Health.

Men who have been charged with an offence are sometimes remanded by the courts to a psychiatric facility in order to determine whether they should enter the correctional or mental health system. This decision is based upon a number of considerations: whether (a) the person is fit to stand trial, (b) he was insane at the time of the offence, (c) he is dangerous to others, and (d) he is treatable in a psychiatric institution. A recent Ontario study (Webster, Menzies, & Jackson, 1982) indicated that all of these questions were of considerable interest to provincial court judges. Psychiatrists and psychologists provide advice on these matters to the court which makes the final decision.

Several points should be made about the foregoing description. In law, resolution of the first two issues determine whether the offender enters the health or correctional system. However, determination of the second two issues can importantly modify the

Reprinted from International Journal of Law and Psychiatry, 6 *(2), 193–205.* © *1983, with permission from Elsevier.*

offender's disposition. For example, if the offender is viewed as not dangerous and as mentally ill, the charges may be dropped and he can be certified under the Mental Health Act of Ontario and admitted to a regional psychiatric facility. If the offender is viewed as treatable but culpable, he can be sentenced but receive a recommendation that he be treated in a mental health facility. In fact, even if the offender is sentenced without such a recommendation, he can later be transferred to a mental hospital by agreement between Oak Ridge and either the provincial or federal correctional systems. There has been continuing criticism of this system and various recommendations for change. The Law Reform Commission of Canada (1975), for example, has advocated Hospital Order legislation which would allow the hospital and a convicted offender to negotiate the admission and course of treatment. In addition, Schiffer (1982) has critically discussed these issues from a legal perspective in some detail.

A number of important questions are raised by the process of determining the disposition of mentally disordered offenders, such as, whether mental health professionals can offer expert advice concerning an offender's dangerousness or treatability. These questions are important because they involve large numbers of people (165 men were remanded to Oak Ridge alone in 1982), affect the length of confinement for men on indeterminate warrants, affect the length of sentence for those who are eligible for parole, and determine who has access to scarce psychiatric resources. We have studied psychiatric determinations of dangerousness extensively (Pruesse & Quinsey, 1977; Quinsey, 1975, 1979; Quinsey & Ambtman, 1978, 1979) but there have been few studies of the treatability of mentally ill offenders. How do forensic clinicians decide who gets treatment? Do the courts listen to their advice? Can clinicians predict which offenders will and will not benefit from treatment? These questions have received little empirical study despite their ethical and economic implications.

It should be noted in this connection that, in Canada, the provincial Ministries of Health and the courts have considerable leeway in what type of offenders are admitted to the mental health system. For example, a survey of persons found not guilty by reason of insanity or unfit for trial conducted in 1975 found that, in Ontario, the percentages of personality disorders and psychotics were 27 and 61, whereas, in Quebec, the percentages were 5 and 76, respectively (Quinsey & Boyd, 1977). Other characteristics of mentally ill offenders also varied widely across the provinces.

The purpose of this study is to examine assessments of the treatability of mentally disordered offenders and to determine which offender and offence variables are related to the outcome of these assessments and the extent to which the psychiatric reports are related to judicial decisions.

METHOD

Remands

Two hundred consecutive remands to the Oak Ridge Division of the Penetanguishene Mental Health Centre from July 1978 to September 1980 were studied. One hundred and ninety offenders were remanded by the court for a pretrial psychiatric assessment and ten for a posttrial assessment on the issue of sentencing. All subjects were male. The characteristics of the sample studied are shown in the first 10 rows of Table 1. In summary, Table 1 shows that the sample was composed of relatively young, poorly educated, primarily personality disordered men charged with serious offences.

Conference Participants

Each remand was conferenced by an interdisciplinary team. Because the individuals who attended each conference varied, only physicians, psychologists, and those attending 60 conferences or more were included for analysis; only those attending more than 60 conferences were used in analyses of interclinician agreement. This sampling method included those who most frequently attended and those most likely to give courtroom testimony. Four psychiatrists attended 196, 91, 6, and 3 conferences, respectively; four psychologists attended 173, 11, 10, and 5; two social work assistants attended 126 and 93; one attendant attended 120; two social workers attended 95 and 68; one nurse attended 67; and three physicians attended 16, 5, and 1 conference, respectively.

Measures

Conference

Each conference participant filled out a Remand Assessment Questionnaire during or immediately after the conference; thus, the ratings were usually completed after extensive group discussion. The first question read, "What type of post-trial treatment(s) would benefit this remand's clinical status, if any? For each type of treatment which is relevant to the remand's clinical status, how much improvement would he be likely to make during a 2-year (or less) period? Assume all are equally available. The goals of treatment would include reducing the probability of recidivism and a reduction in psychiatric symptomatology." After each treatment type there was a box marked "irrelevant" and a nine point scale labelled "expected amount of improvement" ranging from 1 (*slight*) to 5 (*moderate*) to 9 (*great*). The treatment types were: phenothiazine medication, ECT, antiepileptic drugs, milieu therapy, ward token economy, aversion therapy, social skills or assertion training, vocational training, psychoanalysis, group therapy, individual counselling, passage of time, correctional placement, minor tranquillizers, marital counselling, intensive encounter groups, defence disrupting drugs, and other.

Six 9-point rating scales followed, which measured (a) how much insight the remand had into the nature of his illness, (b) how genuinely motivated he was for treatment, (c) how dangerous to others he was, (d) how psychotic he was, (e) how personality disordered he was, and (f) given the optimal treatment program, how much improvement he was likely to make in a 2-year period. Item F was the measure of general treatability.

The final question was "Assuming that the remand committed the alleged offence, what disposition of this case would you make if the decision were left to you?" Nine alternatives followed: probation with or without out-patient treatment, correctional

TABLE 1

Characteristics of Sample and Recommended Dispositions

VARIABLE	DIAGNOSIS[1]			TOTAL (INCLUDES 7 OTHERS)
	PERSONALITY DISORDER	PSYCHOSIS	RETARDATION	
1. Number	118	60	15	200
2. Mean age on admission (S.D.)	26.65 (9.37)	31.10 (9.86)	28.73 (9.59)	28.45 (10.07)
3. Mean highest grade completed (S.D.)	9.03 (2.26)	9.88 (2.47)	4.67 (3.05)	9.01 (2.71)
4. Percent any college or university	13	30	0	17
5. Percent ever married	45	40	0	41
6. Percent no occupation	54	65	80	59
7. Percent previous corrections	41 (N = 116)	23	40	35 (N = 198)
8. Percent previous psychiatric hospitalizations	49 (N = 116)	75 (N = 59)	67	58 (N = 197)
9. Percent previous Oak Ridge	16	32	40	22
10. Admission offence (percent)			N = 14	N = 199
a) Homicide	20	22	7	20
b) Nonsexual vs persons	31	28	7	29
c) Sexual	25	7	50	21
d) Property	8	8	14	8
e) Other	16	35	22	22
11. Conference recommendations (percent)	N = 117	N = 58	N = 13	N = 195
a) Treatment	37	97	85	58
b) Health stream	3	48	46	19
12. Letter recommendations (percent)				
a) Fit	98 (N = 100)	91 (N = 55)	91 (N = 11)	95 (N = 171)
b) Bail	9 (N = 115)	10 (N = 58)	14 (N = 14)	10 (N = 194)
c) Insanity Defence	4 (N = 80)	42 (N = 36)	15 (N = 7)	15 (N = 126)
d) Treatment	71 (N = 65)	98 (N = 51)	75 (N = 12)	83 (N = 134)
13. Court disposition (percent)				
a) NGRI WLG	6 (N = 117)	38 (N = 58)	7	15 (N = 197)
b) Correctional sentence	66 (N = 117)	21 (N = 58)	47	51 (N = 197)
c) Treatment	36 (N = 116)	74 (N = 57)	57 (N = 14)	49 (N = 194)
d) Health stream	6 (N = 106)	46 (N = 48)	7 (N = 14)	17 (N = 175)
14. Returned to Oak Ridge (percent)	12	45	27	23

1. Diagnosis is the primary diagnosis given by the attending psychiatrist at discharge or case conference. Previous hospitalizations excludes previous admissions to Oak Ridge and previous Oak Ridge admissions excludes admissions on the same charge. Homicide includes any offence which involved the killing of another person. Armed robbery was considered an offence against persons whereas robbery was included as a property offence. Ever married includes common-law arrangements. N's are inserted where there are missing (usually unknown) data.

placement with or without psychiatric treatment, return to Oak Ridge, community diversion without probation or treatment, community diversion without probation but with treatment, in-patient treatment in a minimum security psychiatric hospital, and other.

Letter to court

The psychiatrist in charge of each case invariably wrote a letter to the court describing his findings. This letter was sometimes supplemented by court testimony by the psychiatrist and/or the psychologist assigned to the case but this testimony was not part of our data set.

Each letter to the court was examined and it was determined if: bail was specifically recommended, recommended against, or not mentioned; the insanity defense was thought applicable (yes, no, no mention); the remand was thought to be dangerous; and, finally, if the prognosis was good, poor, uncertain, or not mentioned. The recommended disposition of the case was recorded: psychiatric treatment, return to Oak Ridge, return to community with some intervention, further assessment, or no treatment.

Disposition

The crown attorneys for each case were contacted by mail and/or phone to determine the disposition the court had made. The first followup data were gathered in December of 1980 and 90% of the material was complete in August of 1981; the remaining 10% was not obtained until May of 1982. The follow-up time was about 12 months for most remands (range 4–47 months). The verdict was determined (guilty, not guilty, warrant outstanding, not guilty by reason of insanity, unfit, or not finished in court). If the offender was found guilty, the sentence was recorded. It was also determined whether some recommendation for treatment was made by the court. As well, the Oak Ridge records were examined to find whether a remanded offender had been returned to Oak Ridge.

Analysis

Because different clinicians attended different conferences, the Remand Assessment Questionnaire data were handled in several different ways. For each rated variable, all analyses were performed on: the average response of all conference participants for each conference, the average of all psychiatrists and psychologists, and the individual responses of the psychologist and psychiatrist who attended the most conferences. Interrater agreement analyses (Pearson r's for rated variables and kappas for categorical variables) were computed for each pair of participants who attended 60 or more conferences based on the conferences that they had both attended.

All rated variables were intercorrelated. *Treatability* and *dangerousness* were each predicted from the demographic variables in Table 1 using stepwise multiple regression. This analysis involved 15 predictors, 5 of which were continuous and the remainder dichotomous. Stepwise regression equations were used to predict both dangerousness and treatability from the six 9-point scales on the Remand Assessment Questionnaire.

The files and letters to the court of 40 randomly selected remands were examined by two raters who independently coded the information used in this study. Agreement indices were satisfactory for all variables coded (the correlations and kappas were all above .70, most in the .85 to 1.0 range, and all percent agreements were above 70, mostly in the nineties).

RESULTS

Conference Data

Nine clinicians attended 60 or more conferences. For ratings of the treatability of each remand, the interclinician correlations varied from .04 to .75 with an average of .43 (SD = .12). For the dangerousness ratings, the correlations ranged from .19 to .71 and averaged .53 (SD = .16). Disposition was divided into six categories: probation, corrections, Oak Ridge, community diversion, in-patient, and other. Interclinician kappas for disposition ranged from .15 to .70 and averaged .44 (SD = .12).

The means of and intercorrelations among the six rated variables of the Remand Assessment Questionnaire for all raters are shown in Table 2. As a group, the remands were seen as rather dangerous and personality disordered but not as good treatment candidates. The *motivation* and *insight* items were very highly correlated and appeared to be measuring the same phenomenon. The agreement on degree of psychosis and degree of personality disorder was high. For example, the ratings of the psychiatrist and psychologist who attended the most conferences correlated .83 ($n = 163$) for psychosis and .69 ($n = 163$) for degree of personality disorder.

A stepwise regression analysis based on all raters showed that expected improvement was best predicted by rated degree of personality disorder and by perceived motivation for treatment. The addition of the other variables did not add any predictive power. With the first 2 variables r was .81 and only rose to .83 with all variables. A similar finding was obtained in predicting dangerousness. The first variable entered was degree of personality disorder and the second was degree of psychosis; no other variables were important; a multiple r of .58 was obtained with 4 variables (.56 with the first two).

Perceived treatability (average of all raters) was also predicted by the demographic and clinical variables in Table 1. A multiple r of .71 was obtained but only three variables contributed more than 4% change in the variance accounted for. In order of declining importance, these were a diagnosis of personality disorder ($r = -.59$) number of previous correctional placements ($r = -.35$), and a diagnosis of retardation ($r = -.02$). Perceived dangerousness (average of all raters) was predicted by an offence involving homicide ($r = .35$), a property offence ($r = -.33$), and number of previous correctional placements ($r = .23$). The overall r was .60 and the r obtained with the first 3 variables was .52, with no other variables adding more than 4% of the variance.

Specific treatment type ratings were examined for the nine clinicians who attended 60 or more conferences. Relatively few treatments were judged to be more than moderately effective: phenothiazines (in 18% of the cases), passage of time (16%), corrections

TABLE 2

Averages and Intercorrelations for Rated Variables (Average of All Raters)

	MEAN	S.D.	DANGEROUSNESS	PERSONALITY DISORDER	PSYCHOSIS	MOTIVATION	INSIGHT
1. Expected improvement	3.06	1.24	−.29	−.71	.55	.63	.57
2. Dangerousness	5.24	1.58		.46	.02	−.07	−.13
3. Personality disorder	5.13	1.61			−.55	−.38	−.37
4. Psychosis	2.31	1.77				.27	.13
5. Motivation	2.33	1.18					.86
6. Insight	2.58	1.15					

(12%), vocational training (11%), social skills (10%), group therapy (8%), and individual counselling (9%). In fact, most of the treatment types were judged to be irrelevant most of the time. Averaging over all raters, minor tranquilizers and psychoanalysis were judged to be irrelevant in over 90% of the cases. Corrections, individual counselling, and the passage of time were the most frequently advocated (being judged irrelevant in between 49% and 56% of the cases). There were marked individual differences in clinicians' pessimism about treatment. At the extremes, the attendant participant thought that, on average, each treatment was irrelevant 94% of the time; at the optimistic end, a psychologist and a nurse believed the treatments to be irrelevant 68% of the time.

To examine the issue of interclinician agreement on specific treatments, the ratings of each possible pair among the nine clinicians were correlated with each other on each of the treatment type variables using data from the conferences they both attended. Average interclinician correlations were obtained by weighting each interclinician correlation by the number of conferences on which it was based. These averages are shown in Table 3. As can be seen in Table 3, only judgments of the degree of improvement to be expected with phenothiazines showed good inter-judge congruence.

Before the finding of poor agreement on treatment type efficacy can be accepted, several alternative interpretations of the data must be excluded. Because most treatments were not seen as particularly beneficial, it might be argued that the correlations were low because of a restriction of range artifact. As can be seen in Table 3, however, a comparison of the two most optimistic clinicians (a psychologist and a nurse) indicated only modest improvement in agreement. Similarly, ratings of those remands who were diagnosed as psychotic and hence who would most likely be considered to be treatable yielded lower rates of agreement (Table 3). A further argument could be that the poor agreement simply reflected differences in experience or training among the clinicians. This interpretation does not appear valid: The most "senior" pair of raters both in terms of responsibility for the majority of the cases and the largest number of conferences attended (a psychiatrist and psychologist) did not show appreciably higher levels of agreement than those found when pooling over all raters: the pair of psychiatrists who attended more than 60 conferences similarly showed no higher level of agreement.

TABLE 3

Interrater Agreement on Expected Degree of Improvement

TREATMENT MODALITY	CORRELATIONS POOLED OVER 1711 OBSERVATIONS	MOST OPTIMISTIC PAIR ($n = 51$)	MOST SENIOR PAIR[1] ($n = 149$)	POOLED CORRELATIONS FOR PSYCHOTICS ONLY ($n = 544$)
1. Phenothiazines	.728	.833	.868	.439
2. Aversion Therapy	.326	.487	.343	.096
3. Group Therapy	.238	.243	.244	.246
4. Correctional Placement	.220	.217	.231	.210
5. Social Skills or Assertion	.167	.302	.224	.147
6. Milieu Therapy	.143	.180	.463	.048
7. Passage of Time	.112	.153	.165	.064
8. Token Economy	.098	.653	.099	.053
9. Vocational Training	.095	.188	.145	.175
10. Individual Counselling	.090	.053	.185	.060

1. Includes only remands diagnosed as personality disordered or psychotic.

A further possible objection to these agreement data is that the treatments, with the exception of phenothiazines, were ill specified and the poor agreement simply reflects the vagueness of the categories. Several factors make this an implausible interpretation: (a) each of the treatments listed, excluding psychoanalysis and marital therapy, has existed within Oak Ridge in a well defined program structure; (b) the treatment types listed are those which are in fact recommended for offenders; and (c) combining the treatment types into broader categories did not improve agreement. This latter analysis involved combining the treatment types into three categories: somatic (phenothiazines, ECT, antiepileptic medication, and minor tranquilizers), psychotherapeutic (milieu therapy, group therapy, counselling, encounter groups, and marital therapy), and behavioral (aversion therapy, token economy, and social skill). The psychologist and psychiatrist who had attended the most conferences (the senior pair of raters) were used in this analysis; for each conference which they both attended it was determined whether all of the treatments within a category were marked *irrelevant*. If such was the case, the category was scored as irrelevant and not otherwise. Percent agreements for the irrelevancy of treatment categories for personality disorders ($n = 99$) was 82% (somatic), 39% (psychotherapeutic), and 42% (behavioral). For psychotics, the percent agreements were 61% (somatic), 35% (psychotherapeutic), and 49% (behavioral). The corresponding kappas were low (ranging from −.041 to .355). Thus there was poor agreement even with the broadened categories and liberal scoring system.

The final alternative explanation of these findings to be considered is that the specific treatment types were marked at random because the raters did not attend to or understand the task. The specific treatment type data did, however, appear to be lawful even though the clinicians did not agree. For example, the mean ratings for most treatment types were lower for personality disorders than for psychotics; especially in the case of phenothiazine effectiveness (and, of course. subjects did agree on this variable). Differences among clinicians which appeared in overall ratings of treatability were reflected in ratings of the effectiveness of individual treatment types. For example, the most senior pair of raters differed in their pessimism about overall treatability and, as expected, the more optimistic clinician was more optimistic about each of the specific treatment types. These differences were not always significant as, for example, with phenothiazine effectiveness, but were sometimes enormous. The largest involved the benefits of the passage of time (t for matched pairs, $[d. f. = 148] = 11.04, p < .001$, based on conferences of personality disordered or psychotic offenders which both attended).

In order to make the results more concrete, brief descriptions of the individual remands perceived as most and least dangerous and the remands perceived as most and least treatable are given below. The remand seen as most dangerous received the following average ratings by the entire conference team: insight (1), motivation (1), dangerousness (8.5), degree of psychosis (1), degree of personality disorder (7.2), and amount of expected improvement (1.5). This 25-year-old single man was charged with second degree murder; he had killed a man with a shotgun following a group fight outside of a tavern. His criminal career involved early breaking and entering charges and he received grade 10 in training school. He was later expelled from a vocational school for fighting with the teachers. He worked in construction and in the winter was employed as a tavern doorman. During his late teens and early twenties he was charged with assault, wounding with intent, obstructing police (3 times), failing to appear, attempted theft, and several liquor act offences.

The least dangerous remand received ratings of 3.4 (insight), 2.4 (motivation), 1.4 (dangerousness), 1.4 (degree of psychosis), 3.0 (degree of personality disorder), and 4.4 (expected improvement). This 18-year-old man was charged with theft, willful damage, and possession of a dangerous weapon. The incident involved the theft of a canoe, knocking over a motorcycle, and brandishing a stick at police officers. The offence had occurred some time before his appearance at Oak Ridge. Immediately after the offence, he had been put in a local jail where his "bizarre thought patterns" caused him to be sent to a psychiatric hospital from which he eloped and lived without further incident for several months. He had no previous record, appeared psychiatrically normal at Oak Ridge, and had been doing well at school during his elopment [sic].

The remand seen as most treatable received ratings of 3.1 (insight), 2.7 (motivation), 3.6 (dangerousness), 3.4 (degree of psychosis), 5.6 (degree of personality disorder), and 6.4 (expected improvement). He was a 36-year-old skilled laborer who was charged with assaulting a police officer after he resisted the policeman's attempt to move him out of a drinking lounge. He subsequently hit another patient in a regional psychiatric hospital to which he had been sent after breaking his bail conditions by drinking. He was sent to Oak Ridge after being arrested again and being assaultive in jail. This patient had had periodic attacks of mania over the past several years and had responded well to lithium.

FIGURE 1

Disposition of Offenders Remanded to Oak Ridge

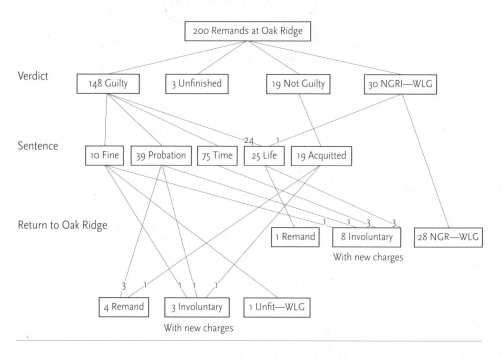

The remand seen as least treatable received average ratings of 1.3 (insight), 1.0 (motivation), 7.0 (dangerousness), 1.0 (degree of psychosis), 8.0 (degree of personality disorder), and 1.0 (expected improvement). He was an 18-year-old man charged with attempted murder of his 28-year-old girlfriend. He stabbed the victim with no warning or previous interaction as she lay in bed early in the morning. He stole her car and was apprehended by the police. While at Oak Ridge he denied stabbing her and couldn't understand why she had accused him. He claimed he had tried to phone for an ambulance after he found her stabbed but was all choked up and couldn't speak. His account of the crime, personal history, and complaints of various psychological symptoms (including amnesia and hallucinations) varied daily. His previous record included auto theft.

Letter to the Court

As shown in Table 1, the psychiatrist's letter to the court almost always indicated that the remand was fit for trial, usually indicated that the insanity defence was not applicable, seldom recommended bail, and suggested treatment about half of the time.

Court Disposition

The disposition and follow-up data are presented in Figure 1. As can be seen, 74% of the remands were found guilty and none unfit for trial. During the follow-up period,

TABLE 4

Agreement Between Psychiatrist's Letter to the Court and the Court Judgment on Section 16 and Treatment

		LETTER RECOMMENDATION		
		NGRI	NO NGRI	TOTAL
	NGRI	14	5	19
Court Judgment	No NGRI	5	91	96
	Total	19	96	115

		LETTER RECOMMENDATION		
		TREATMENT	NO TREATMENT	TOTAL
	Treatment	63	28	91
Court Judgment	No Treatment	44	50	94
	Total	107	78	185

Note: Cases are included where the information was clear in both the letter and the court judgment

45 remands returned to Oak Ridge, 8 of these with new charges. It is of interest that nine of the remands who had been found guilty were returned to Oak Ridge without new charges. All WLGs were returned to Oak Ridge save two: one (not shown in the figure) who was admitted to a medium security facility and another who committed a new offence while on a WLG and was sentenced to prison. One person sentenced to life was remanded to Oak Ridge for a previous offence.

Relation Between the Psychiatrist's Letter and the Court Judgment

Table 4 shows the relation between the psychiatrist's letter to the court and the court judgment on whether the insanity defence was applicable and whether treatment should be tried. The court and letter showed high agreement as to the insanity defence [$\chi^2(1$ d. f.$) = 53.92$, p $< .0001$; Kappa $= .685$] but the amount of agreement on the treatment recommendation, although significant, was of small magnitude [$\chi^2(1$ d. f.$) = 9.53$, $p < .01$; Kappa $= .202$]. In this connection it should be noted that the primary questions of interest for the majority of remand assessments were fitness and the insanity defence. As well, it must be remembered that opposing psychiatric testimony on all issues was often presented in court.

DISCUSSION

The interclinician agreement on how dangerous the remanded patients were was moderate; this finding replicates our earlier studies on prediction (Quinsey, 1975; Quinsey & Ambtman, 1978, 1979). The clinicians agreed among themselves less about the remands' treatability. The variability among the correlations on both variables is rather disturbing. Similarly, the absolute magnitude and variability of the interclinician kappas for recommended disposition were not encouraging. The fact that these correlations were obtained after extensive discussion of the cases emphasizes the lack of precision in the judgments.

The data, however, become alarming when we consider type of treatment. Surprisingly, the interclinician agreement for recommended type of treatment was extremely low with the exception of the efficacy of phenothiazines. The agreement on the efficacy of phenothiazines is encouraging but must be tempered by the findings that there are marked discrepancies in psychiatrists' prescriptive policies for psychoactive drugs; individual psychiatrists have been found to disagree with each other about dose level and type of medication and to be inconsistent themselves on these issues (Gillis & Moran, 1981). Clearly, there is no consensus among clinicians even after a case has been discussed as to whether any particular treatment other than phenothiazines is relevant for a particular remand or as to how much he might benefit from a particular treatment. The implications of this finding for nondrug treatments are profound. If no consensus exists, how can an institution rationally organize a treatment program or assign patients to particular subprograms? Even more disturbing is the spectre of what a psychiatrist's or psychologist's testimony in court regarding treatment recommendations really means. Given the lack of agreement, it is at best an arbitrary pronouncement.

Because of the importance of this issue and the radical implications of our findings, replication is clearly called for. These data, however, cannot be dismissed lightly; Oak Ridge receives the most serious cases for psychiatric assessment in Ontario and the clinicians who participated in this study are among the most experienced anywhere. Moreover, Oak Ridge provides the bulk of treatment programming for men found not guilty by reason of insanity in Ontario. In addition, similar observations have appeared before. Greenland and Rosenblatt (1972) noted large discrepancies over the various Ontario hospitals in whether inpatient treatment was recommended for remanded offenders. In a study of remanded patients conducted at Oak Ridge 10 years ago, Quinsey (1975) found marked disagreements among staff in ratings of whether remands would benefit from treatment; specifically, attendant staff were much more pessimistic about treatment response than other staff categories (a pattern of data similar to that found in the present study). More recently, Webster, Menzies, and Jackson (1982) found that in their sample, psychiatrists disagreed among themselves concerning the treatability of remanded offenders. It is, of course, a separate question as to whether those who are recommended for treatment and receive it are, in fact, good treatment candidates. Bowden (1978) found that, among offenders remanded to Brixton prison in England, 13% were recommended for and received treatment but that 62% of these cases did not benefit from the treatment therapeutically.

Despite the poor agreement on treatability and on the relevancy of particular types of programs, it is clear that there is profound pessimism about treatment efficacy. This pessimism is most marked in connection with personality disordered offenders. In the prediction of treatability ratings from file data, diagnosis of personality disorder was highly and negatively correlated with treatability ratings. Rated degree of personality disorder was also highly related to low treatability ratings in the conference data. It appeared that the clinicians sorted the offenders into personality disordered and psychotic categories; the personality disordered offenders were seen as essentially untreatable and the psychotic offenders were thought to respond to phenothiazines. Although there are no convincing data one way or the other, it is common folklore that personality disordered offenders are untreatable. Given the psychiatric community's belief about such offenders, it is quite clear that few of them will in fact receive treatment.

Pervasive pessimism about treatability may well be responsible for the failure of forensic clinicians to routinely consider various treatment options in specific and concrete terms and to systematically gather data which would allow for treatment decisions to be made on rational grounds. It is important to realize that the issue of treatability is not necessarily related to that of diagnosis; in the present study, agreement on degree of personality disorder and psychosis was high but, nevertheless, the agreement on treatability was low.

Considering the lack of consensus regarding treatability, the posttrial "slippage" of offenders between the correctional and health streams may be a positive outcome. The amount of slippage was small in the present study but the follow-up time was only a year for most remands. This movement of offenders back and forth between health and corrections for various reasons has been documented by others (e.g. Webster, Menzies, & Jackson, 1982) and can be regarded as a real and important phenomenon. It may well be that treatment decisions are best made after the offender has been observed in a correctional or psychiatric setting for a period of time. With respect to mentally disordered offenders, it has been noted (Quinsey , 1979) that a verdict of not guilty by reason of insanity does not mean that a treatment for the "insanity" is currently available. A flexible arrangement whereby an offender and a psychiatric institution can negotiate the length and type of treatment appears very desirable. A similar arrangement would, of course, be desirable for those offenders found guilty and who want and need psychiatric treatment.

REFERENCES

Bowden, P. Men remanded into custody for medical reports: The outcome of the treatment recommendation. *British Journal of Psychiatry*, 1978, *132*, 320–331.

Gillis, J. S., & Moran, T. J. An analysis of drug decisions in a state psychiatric hospital. *Journal of Clinical Psychology*, 1981, *37*, 32–42.

Greenland, C., & Rosenblatt, E. Remands for psychiatric examination in Ontario, 1969–1970, *Canadian Psychiatric Association Journal*, 1972, *17*, 387–401.

Law Reform Commission of Canada. *The criminal process and mental disorder,* Working Paper 14. Ottawa: Information Canada, 1975.

Pruesse, M. G., & Quinsey, V. L. The dangerousness of patients released from maximum security: A replication. *Journal of Psychiatry and Law*, 1977, *5*. 293–299.

Quinsey, V. L. Psychiatric staff conferences of dangerous mentally disordered offenders. *Canadian Journal of Behavioural Science*, 1975, *7*, 60–69.

Quinsey, V. L. Assessments of the dangerousness of mental patients held in maximum security. *International Journal of Law and Psychiatry*, 1979, *2*, 389–406.

Quinsey, V. L., & Ambtman, R. Psychiatric assessments of the dangerousness of mentally ill offenders. *Crime and Justice*, 1978, 6, 249–257.

Quinsey, V. L., & Ambtman, R. Variables affecting psychiatrists' and teachers' assessments of the dangerousness of mentally ill offenders. *Journal of Consulting and Clinical Psychology*, 1979, 47, 353–362.

Quinsey, V. L., & Boyd, B. A. An assessment of the characteristics and dangerousness of patients held on warrants of the lieutenant governor. *Crime and Justice*, 1977, 4, 269–274.

Schiffer, M. E. *Psychiatry behind bars: A legal perspective.* Toronto: Butterworths, 1982.

Webster, C. D., Menzies, R. J., & Jackson, M. A. *Clinical assessment before trial: Legal issues and mental disorder.* Toronto: Butterworths, 1982.

20

Risk Assessment as Collective Clinical Judgement

DENIS MURPHY

ABSTRACT

INTRODUCTION: *Risk assessment occupies an increasingly important position in psychiatry. This paper contends that collective judgement is the optimal method of assessing risk.*

THE MEANING OF RISK: *Risk has a dual meaning: emotional and judgemental.*

RISKS FACED BY STAFF: *Assaults, threats and survival anxiety.*

THE EFFECTS OF DANGER ON THE GROUP: *Staff wariness and resistance, attribution of blame.*

THE AMBIGUOUS TASK: *For a group to function well it must have a clear task. Custodial roles can lead to ambiguity.*

THE EMOTIONS OF LARGER GROUPS: *Externally directed hostility, internal homogenization of views.*

SOCIAL DEFENCES: *Rituals can develop in forensic institutions, as well as militarism.*

ANTI-THERAPEUTIC CULTURE: *Sadism may develop where a marked power differential develops.*

THE ROLE OF THE LEADER: *Danger intensifies the feelings about leaders, perhaps idealization, perhaps disaffection. Leaders and others need to agree on risk assessment or fragmentation will occur.*

THE MODIFICATION OF RISK: *The assessment of risk may modify it. Mutual hostility must be reduced. Dialogue and understanding are needed.*

Reprinted with permission. Criminal Behaviour and Mental Health, 12, *169–178.* © *2002 Whurr Publishers Ltd.*

A CLIMATE FOR RISK ASSESSMENT: *The environment should be less authoritarian and more democratic, so that patients can join a group and internalize its values. Reflective space is also required.*

CONCLUSIONS: *Risk assessment is best described in terms of human endeavour, not in the language of scientific measurement.*

INTRODUCTION

Risk assessment occupies an increasingly important position in psychiatry. There is debate about the relative merits of clinical and actuarial approaches. This paper supports the clinical approach and contends that collective judgement is the optimal method of assessing risk. This is consistent with the current emphasis on multidisciplinary and multi-agency cooperation.

It is suggested here that a collective approach to risk is more likely to produce a balanced view because of the tendency of individual opinion to be flawed or biased. Collective judgement can also be distorted. The aim of the paper is to examine the group processes in organizations that assess risk and to describe how assessment can be distorted. It also attempts to elucidate those factors that are helpful in achieving a balanced collective view of the risk.

While drawing on the relevant literature and influenced by psychodynamic theory the paper is based on the author's experience as a participant observer in forensic psychiatry. This socioanthropological approach is common in the study of organizations where more structured methodologies are difficult to apply. There is a selective emphasis here on the staff group but of course the patient group will have its own dynamics.

THE MEANING OF RISK

The concept of risk assessment is confused by ambiguity in the meaning of the word "risk": it has a dual meaning. One meaning refers to the mathematical concept of "odds" or chances of an event happening. This actuarial meaning originated in the world of finance.

Mathematical approaches have not been very successful in predicting which individuals will reoffend but there is hope that refinements will remedy this. These approaches may be misleading: they may imply an ability to predict which cannot be achieved. Risk rating scales are described as "tools" with connotations of scientific preci-sion. Clinicians may worry that they have not found the correct formula. Of much more importance for the clinician, at present, is the other meaning of risk, which is danger.

To help illustrate the different meanings of "risk" an analogy from the fire service may be helpful. There is much useful information to be gained by studying why fires arise, in what sorts of buildings and how they spread. This statistical assessment of risk is used to prevent future fires. However, when an actual fire occurs, the role of statistics becomes less important. What is required is that firemen approach the fire and make an appraisal of the danger to enable them to manage it. Their judgement is all important. To assess the risk to other buildings and people they must put themselves "at risk" or "in danger." This introduces notions such as courage and calmness when facing danger, which are not part of the usual vocabulary of risk assessment.

Fortunately, the clinician does not usually meet danger alone but is supported by colleagues. For most risk assessment the patient becomes, for a time at least, part of a group of staff and often other patients. Personal encounter with a dangerous patient by a group of people is inevitably affected by powerful emotional forces.

THE RISKS FACED BY STAFF

Mentally disordered offenders can cause damage to the physical well-being of those who attempt to assess them. Hostage taking, riots and killings occur. Assaults and threats are commonplace. As well as these obvious dangers there are fears of contamination of mental well-being.

From the earliest times there were accounts of the dangers of close contact with malevolent men. Malevolence was thought to be transmitted by looking in an evil or envious way. The "evil eye" is a recurring theme. The philosopher Francis Bacon wrote in Tudor times that the envious gaze "emitteth some malign and poisonous spirit which taketh hold of the spirit of another." In modern times these transmitted and invasive noxious influences might be described in different terms such as "the replication of a pathological internal world," using mechanisms such as projection or projective identification.

The psychological consequence of exposure to danger has been termed "survival anxiety" (Nitsun, 1996). This can be described as the fear of physical attack with a corresponding anxiety about injury or death or fear of psychological damage. This latter fear of contagion seems to be common and is fuelled by the observation that certain patients seem to evoke intense reactions in staff. Those with personality disorder interfere with our feelings, often leading us to feel intruded upon and evoking a hostile and rejecting response from us both as individuals and as a group (Hinshelwood, 1999).

There is a danger that the group's ability to think and reflect on its experiences may be impaired by the proximity of very disturbed individuals. Many writers in the psychoanalytical tradition have drawn attention to this phenomenon (de Mare, 1991).

There are other less direct dangers. Staff may be blamed, often quite unreasonably, for the actions of those they are assessing. There is the risk of professional and personal disgrace.

THE EFFECTS OF DANGER ON THE GROUP

Those who visit prisons and forensic psychiatric hospitals can probably describe an "atmosphere" in those places where criminals are detained. It is like a heaviness or seriousness or tension reflecting the burden felt by those who operate the law (Zilboorg, 1955). It has been described as a paranoid atmosphere (Gilligan, 1992). This atmosphere can be regarded as arising from danger. There is much black humour but this can be understood as a defiance of the danger and horror.

Patients, especially new ones, are treated with wariness. There is often resistance, overt or tacit, to the introduction of a new patient. There are many ways by which staff can seek to avoid contact with potentially dangerous patients. Attempts are made to shift responsibility to other services such as the prisons. Management can try to deny the problems and fail to provide proper facilities. Unions can mobilize to blacklist undesirable patients. There are lengthy assessment procedures that sometimes seem like delaying tactics. In parallel with formal procedures there are many ways in which the group can express its foreboding before admission and its anger afterwards if the patient turns out to be difficult or too dangerous.

Those members of staff who have played most part in the admission of the patient are blamed for adverse happenings. This blame is usually expressed in subtle and informal ways but is nonetheless a potent deterrent to admitting anyone unsuitable. Referral meetings in forensic services tend to be clouded with suspicion that others are trying to "dump" unsuitable cases. In recent years, since the closure of large psychiatric hospitals, there have been insufficient hospital places for disturbed and violent patients, resulting in even greater reluctance to cater for the needs at these patients. The hidden agenda of the staff group is to protect itself from too much pain and horror.

THE AMBIGUOUS TASK

For a group to function well it must have a clearly defined task. Work entails risk, and understanding the task is a prerequisite to meeting the risk and transforming it into a challenge or an opportunity. In forensic psychiatry there is often ambiguity about the task, leading to an increased risk of confusion and malfunction. In the past the task was seen as primarily custodial. This is no longer true. Society has decided that if suitable treatment is administered many mentally disordered offenders can be released within quite short periods of time.

There are increasing demands that secure hospitals become more therapeutic (Ashworth Enquiry, 1992). There are also frequent demands for less leniency. Conflict between the task definitions makes effective performance of tasks difficult. Low morale and high stress can result. Similar consequences arise when the primary task of assessing and managing risk is so difficult as to be impossible or overwhelming. Sometimes the risk cannot be ascertained with much confidence because of the inability or unwillingness of some patients to share or explore their internal world. There is often uncertainty about whether a patient is primarily criminal or mentally ill.

The ambiguity of the task is likely to arouse anxiety and other unpleasant emotions such as feelings of inadequacy and shame. Also feelings of irritation and helplessness may arise when outside agencies intervene in a way that is seen as unhelpful.

THE EMOTIONS OF LARGE GROUPS

It may be useful to compare the group processes of forensic organizations with those of large groups or crowds (Turquet, 1975). There seem to be some central similarities even though in forensic institutions the processes are obscured or controlled by social structuring and well-organized task performance.

Violent and primitive emotions may emerge in large groups which may be very difficult for the individual to resist: the effects of mob violence are well known. The concept of group regression is of importance: this is some backward movement from an assumed norm (Kernberg, 1988). Danger precipitates such regression.

Large groups often erect an external enemy where outer-directed hostility contributes to cohesion within the group. The vehemence of criticism of outsiders in forensic units can be striking. There is a tendency to homogenization among staff and group solidarity is highly valued. This loss of personal identity is compensated for by the shared omnipotence of all its members. Violence by staff to patients is not uncommon. This reflects the need to denigrate any external reality that interferes with the group illusion of omnipotence.

The organization seems to provide a conscience in place of that of the individual by offering to absolve guilt in exchange for loyalty, leaving open the possibility of actions that would be condemned in the wider society. This seems to be the mechanism of many of the scandals that occur in forensic settings.

SOCIAL DEFENCES

To deal with the anxiety generated by danger, groups develop and deploy a set of social defences which distort the group's capacity to accomplish its primary task. These group defences fall into three categories: basic assumptions, covert coalitions and organizational ritual (Hirschhorn, 1992). Only a brief discussion of these mechanisms is possible here.

Basic assumptions were described by W.R. Bion (1961). They concern small groups. When the task seems too arduous the group may take refuge in a variety of reactions such as a panic-like state (fight and flight), dependent inactivity or sexualization. In forensic settings the mood of groups may seem inappropriate to the task in hand.

Covert coalition refers to situations where, due to anxiety, family dynamics of earlier life are projected onto colleagues, reproducing the original constellation within the family.

The word ritual, applied to the group under consideration, is used to describe a procedure or practice that takes on a life of its own, which is more related to the anxiety induced by the risk than to efficient performance of the task. Menzies (1961) in her classic study analysed nursing practices in a general hospital. She suggested that many procedures and routines were practised mainly to control the anxiety of nursing staff.

The use of ritual to deal with the anxiety of killing or fear of being killed is well described by Dixon (1988). He points to many practices in the army, such as excessive cleaning, ordering and controlling, which do not serve much purpose in furthering the army's main task of engaging the enemy in battle. He suggests that their main purpose is to deal with anxiety.

In some forensic psychiatric settings there can be rituals with militaristic connotations. In some high security hospitals staff wear uniforms. Those in authority are often called "Sir" in a way that is unusual outside the hospital. Reports have criticized the degree of regimentation in these hospitals. The enquiry into Ashworth Hospital (1992), having acknowledged the importance of security, described "a regime of petty rules" and said "what remains a frustration is the extent to which it constitutes an overwhelming and at times unjust and unexplained barrier placed deliberately in the path of progressive initiatives." These rituals can have a dual purpose: warding off staff anxiety and furthering control over the patients.

ANTI-THERAPEUTIC CULTURE

As a defence against danger a culture can develop which is inimical to therapeutic work. Zimbardo (1972) with his prison simulation experiment showed how easily sadistic features entered into a situation where a power differential existed between two groups. A sense of superiority by one group can easily lead to the other being ill-treated or humiliated. The victimization of set offenders within the prison system provides an example.

Dehumanization is a mechanism whereby one group deals with the dangers presented by another group. This involves the use of words and concepts which suggest that members of the other group are not to be accorded the same respect as members of one's own group. In psychiatry "scientific" classifications can be used in such a way as to unduly simplify or even belittle the complexity of patients' problems.

THE ROLE OF THE LEADER

Feelings about leaders become more intense when there is danger (Kernberg, 1998). This is probably because during the course of evolution the survival of the group depended on the quality of the leadership. There is a tendency to blame the leadership for any malfunctioning of the organization, which makes forensic work difficult because the intensity of the blame is often so great.

Kernberg, however, makes the point that the leadership does not always deserve the blame. Even competent leaders may experience major difficulties. The nature of the task may at times be overwhelming and the leader may be blamed. All members of the organization can be expected to have feelings about leaders which can be described as transferential perceptions. These will have an influence on group processes and may trigger off and amplify reactions in the leader.

The cumulative effect of all these transferential perceptions is a tendency to produce idealization of the leader (Kernberg, 1998), although its counterparts, disappointment and disaffection, will emerge if major problems arise. Under certain circumstances the group pressures from either inside or outside the organization are so great that the leader seems like a prisoner of the group atmosphere.

There are pressures on the leader either to become more authoritarian or to relinquish his/her authority, letting chaos reign. The limits of patience and empathy will be tested.

This inevitable tension will affect risk assessment: the leader may come to a conclusion about risk without much reference to the views of the group. This was more common in former times. The expectation now is that a multidisciplinary or multi-agency group will share decisions about risk. On the principle of "two heads are better than one" a fuller and more rounded assessment is obtained. This is at the cost, however, of increased time and mental energy expended in debate.

Whatever the formal processes for deciding on risk, serious trouble will ensue if the views on risk of the leader greatly or persistently diverge from those of the group. Fragmentation of the group may occur.

Some individual must have a final say and represent the views of the group to the outside world. The principles of cabinet government seem to be relevant: there is internal debate and toleration of disagreement but when finally an "official" view is presented there is collective responsibility for this.

THE MODIFICATION OF RISK

The assessment of danger may serve to modify it. First, it is necessary to construct a group that is large enough and strong enough to contain the destructive forces while the assessment continues. The notion of the group as a container was described by Bion. It has its origin in the military idea of containing an attack and for our purpose it describes well the process of absorbing and defusing the large amounts of aggression that are directed into it.

Dangerous psychiatric patients come to the group surrounded by negative emotions. Dr Johnson said: "He who injures one threatens many." The patient enters the group under a cloud of suspicion. All the feelings of antagonism towards the patient could be described as hostility. This is a word that many professionals would not readily admit to. Of course most staff maintain an attitude of professional interest and concern but beneath that often lie feelings of suspicion and disapproval of an unknown and anti-social person. The patient him/herself may well experience hatred towards those whom he/she may perceive as oppressors or gaolers.

The hoped for results of assessment and treatment (which are often inseparable) is a reduction in, or transformation of, this hostility. It is hoped that the patient will come to trust the group and that the group will come to understand how the individual came to commit his/her crime. It is hoped that this mutual understanding can become the basis of a proposal that the patient can once again take part in ordinary life.

The group will employ a variety of approaches to mental disorder but most important is the attempt to provide understanding of the danger—for the patient, the staff group and for the outside world.

The process whereby this happens can be described as dialogue. This indicates a solidarity among the members expressed in a form of associative conversing. It of course includes the patient. It is akin to a political process and factions may develop for or against the patient. It is through this dialogue that hatred is transformed into understanding. De Mare (De Mare et al., 1991) has written about the process by which hatred in large groups is transformed into the drive that mobilizes dialogue. De Mare says "dialogue is one continuous process of reflected experiences. It is a commentary, by which 'the sap of reason quenches the fire of passion.'"

Dialogue enables a shared knowledge of the patient to be built up. It happens during formal and informal meetings. Fed into the process are formal assessments, ex-cathedra statements, many different and divergent opinions, arguments, gossip, scraps of conversation, representations from outside individuals and agencies. They address the same questions. Why did he do it? What is he really like? Will he do it again? These are often difficult to answer.

Given time to evolve, the group can become a sensitive and informed thinking apparatus. The hierarchical structure and professional divisions of the group become less important. With forensic psychiatry patients there is a tendency for attitudes to become polarized between paranoia and idealization. Dialogue is able to heal this split.

It must not be thought that the maintenance of the process of dialogue is easy. It has to take place within the maelstrom of emotions within the group described above. Dialogue can break down, leading to fragmentation, mob emotions and scapegoating. A culture must be created in which dialogue can flourish.

A CLIMATE FOR RISK ASSESSMENT

James Gilligan (1996) said "A humane environment is an absolute prerequisite for the healing of violent men." It is the responsibility of the managers of the organization to create therapeutic conditions for both assessment and treatment. Given that the needs of security are paramount, attempts should be made to make the group less authoritarian and more democratic in its style. This enables the patient to feel sympathetic to the group and makes it likely that he/she will accept more readily the information it gives and internalize the values it promotes. It enables the group to know the patient better. A distinction should be made between "knowing about" a person and the personal knowledge gained by acquaintance with him/her (Stapley, 1996). A new group is formed of the "risky" patient(s) and the staff. The patient may feel that he/she has been granted some respect by the staff that may have been denied him/her earlier in life.

It is essential that, in spite of the pressures of primitive aggression, space can be found to allow the process of dialogue to continue and for the organization to be able to make mature judgements. Hinshelwood (1994) draws attention to the importance of "the reflective space" when he says that free-floating discussion and dialogue have to be won against the attacks of primitive aggression. Analogous to the individual's need to reflect on his/her experience, the group has a similar need.

CONCLUSIONS

Those who come close to mentally disordered people who have done unpleasant things are exposed to noxious forces. These dangers, both real and imagined, evoke powerful and sometimes primitive group responses. The process or assessment can be derailed by group forces that swirl around the organization. Enduring, understanding and sometimes combating these forces is a heavy burden but is the main work of forensic psychiatry. Forensic clinicians are experts on danger. In their encounter with it the best weapons are the group processes of debate, dialogue and reflection. These processes are not easy and require high levels of personal qualities such as courage, maturity, perseverance and knowledge.

Risk assessment is best described in terms of human endeavour, not in the language of scientific measurement. After all, danger is encountered in other spheres such as politics, the military or the law and there it is clearer that the complexities of danger are best appraised by collective judgement.

REFERENCES

Ashworth Enquiry (1992) *Report of the Committee of Enquiry about Ashworth Hospital.* London: HMSO.

Bion W (1961) *Experiences in Groups.* New York: Basic Books.

De Mare P, Piper R, Thompson S (1991) *Koinonia. From Hate through Dialogue, to Culture in the Large Group.* London: Karnac Books.

Dixon N (1979) *On the Psychology of Military Incompetence.* London: Futura.

Gilligan J (1996) *Violence: Our Deadly Epidemic and Its Causes.* New York: Grosset/Putnam.

Hinshelwood R (1994) Attacks on the reflective space: containing primitive emotional states. In Schermer V, Pines M, eds. *Ring of Fire. Primitive Affects and Object Relations in Group Psychotherapy.* London: Routledge, pp. 86–106.

Hinshelwood R (1999) The difficult patient. The role of 'scientific psychiatry' in understanding patients with chronic schizophrenia or severe personality disorder. *British Journal of Psychiatry* 174, 187–190.

Hirschhorn L (1992) *The Workplace Within. Psychodynamics of Organizational Life.* Cambridge, MA: MIT Press.

Kernberg O (1998) *Ideology, Conflict and Leadership in Groups and Organizations.* New Haven, CT: Yale University Press.

Menzies I (1961) *The Functioning of Social Systems as a Defence against Anxiety. A Report on a Study of the Nursing Service of a General Hospital.* London: Tavistock.

Nitsun M (1996) *The Anti-Group. Destructive Forces in the Group and their Creative Potential.* London: Routledge.

Stapley L (1996) *The Personality of the Organisation. A Psychodynamic Explanation of Culture and Change.* London: Free Association Books.

Turquet P (1915) Threats to identity in the large group. In Kreeger L; ed. *The Large Group: Dynamics and Therapy.* London: Constable, pp. 87–144.

Zilboorg G (1955) *The Psychology of the Criminal Act and Punishment.* London; Hogarth Press.

Zimbardo P (1972) Pathology of imprisonment. *Trans-Action* 9 (April): 4–8.

21

The Impact of Confidence on the Accuracy of Structured Professional and Actuarial Violence Risk Judgments in a Sample of Forensic Psychiatric Patients

KEVIN S. DOUGLAS AND JAMES R. P. OGLOFF

ABSTRACT: *Some previous research indicates that confidence affects the accuracy of probabilistic clinical ratings of risk for violence among civil psychiatric inpatients. The current study investigated the impact of confidence on actuarial and structured professional risk assessments, in a forensic psychiatric population, using community violence as the outcome criteria. Raters completed the HCR-20 violence risk assessment scheme for a sample of 100 forensic psychiatric patients. Results showed that accuracy of both actuarial judgments (HCR-20 total scores) and structured professional judgments (of low, moderate, and high risk) were substantially more accurate when raters were more confident about their judgments. Findings suggest that confidence of ratings should be studied as a potentially important mediator of structured professional and actuarial risk judgments.*

KEYWORDS: *violence risk assessment; prediction; violence; confidence; clinical judgment.*

Research on the clinical and actuarial prediction of violence by persons with mental illness has produced numerous advances in recent years. In the past, the prevailing position was that accurate predictions of violence were not attainable (Ennis & Litwack, 1974). Contemporary reviews have been more promising (Borum, 1996; Douglas & Webster, 1999; Otto, 2000). A good deal of research has been devoted to

Reprinted with kind permission of Springer Science and Business Media. Law and Human Behavior, 27 (6), 573–587. © 2003 *American Psychology-Law Society/Division 41 of the American Psychology Association.*

understanding the factors that might increase accuracy, including risk factors that might be predictive of future violence (Douglas & Webster, 1999; Monahan & Steadman, 1994; Otto, 2000); whether risk assessment scales or measures are feasible (Augimeri, Koegl, Webster, & Levene, 2001; Boer, Hart, Kropp, & Webster, 1997; Borum, Bartel, & Forth, 2001; Kropp, Hart, Webster, & Eaves, 1999; Monahan et al., 2001; Quinsey, Harris, Rice, & Cormier, 1998; Webster, Douglas, Eaves, & Hart, 1997); and aspects of decision-making itself that might affect accuracy, such as whether clinicians attend to cues that actually relate to violence (Werner, Rose, & Yesavage, 1983).

Along the lines of the latter investigations, some research has been devoted to exploring conditions under which predictions of violence are more accurate or less accurate. A relatively understudied construct in this regard is the *confidence* with which risk judgments are made. McNiel, Sandberg, and Binder (1998) had 78 physicians rate the risk of violence among 317 patients over 7 days, using a scale of 0% (very low risk) to 100% (very high risk). They reported that these clinical probabilistic assessments of risk that were made more confidently were more accurate than those made less confidently. Logistic regression analyses demonstrated that (1) clinical predictions of violence were significantly associated with later violence, and (2) level of confidence (low, moderate, or high) moderated this relationship such that prediction accuracy was highest in the high confidence group, moderate in the medium confidence group, and lowest (nonsignificant) in the low confidence group. Analyses using receiver operating characteristic (ROC) procedures showed an area under the curve (AUC) value of .73, which is at least of moderate strength.[1] However, this value varied greatly across low, moderate, and high confidence levels—.52, .67, and .97, respectively. In a study by Rabinowitz and Garelik-Wyler (1999), however, the authors reported no relationship between accuracy and confidence. This latter study suffered from overall low predictive accuracy, and fairly small cell sizes after defining three subgroups based on confidence ($ns = 41, 27, 11$).

Why might confidence be related to the predictive accuracy of risk judgments? Some commentators in other contexts, such as eyewitness identification (Yarmey, 1979), for example, have stated that confidence and accuracy are *inversely* related. Researchers have observed that physicians' accuracy is unrelated to confidence, and that more experienced physicians are more confident but no more accurate than more junior physicians (Dawson et al., 1993). Commentators have suggested the same might hold true in violence risk assessment (Faust & Ziskin, 1988).

However, as explained by McNiel et al. (1998), this issue has received little empirical attention in the area of violence risk assessment, in which there might be reasons to expect that some relationship does in fact exist. Further, subsequent reviews in the eyewitness identification field, including meta-analyses, report positive and moderate correlations between confidence and accuracy of positive identifications (Sporer, Penrod, Read, & Cutler, 1995; Stephenson, 1984), providing some indication that a confidence–accuracy relationship, if even moderate, might exist under certain circumstances even in these other areas.

Arkes (2001) has suggested that one of the main causes of overconfidence (and hence of a lack of relationship between confidence and accuracy) is the tendency to search for data that confirm one's judgment. Procedures that structure an assessment, then, might not contribute to this overconfidence bias because they provide evidence for and against decisions of high risk, and permit the consideration of alternative outcomes, another procedure that serves to further reduce the bias (Arkes, 2001). In other areas as well, such as weather forecasting or the game of bridge, a relationship has been observed between confidence and accuracy, primarily because of the opportunity in these contexts for immediate feedback (Arkes, 2001).

It should be noted, however, that the confidence–accuracy issue within the context of violence risk assessment is somewhat different than how the issue has been defined and studied in other contexts. For instance, confidence is often defined as the estimated probability of some event occurring. Overconfidence happens when the estimated probability exceeds the actual occurrence. In risk assessment terms, this is akin to false positives—lower rates of violence than were predicted to occur. However, another approach to confidence, and the one taken in the present paper, is to treat probability or risk estimates and confidence judgments separately. In this way, a person can be rated to be high risk but with low or moderate confidence in the judgment, or a person could be rated to be low risk, but with high confidence.

The research by McNiel et al. (1998) showed that confidence impacted the accuracy of clinical judgments about risk for violence. Clinical judgment, however, has been criticized as being particularly susceptible to extraneous influences (Borum, Otto, & Golding, 1993; Grove & Meehl, 1996). A question that arises, then, is whether confidence would affect more structured types of risk judgments. On the one hand, structured approaches might present disconfirming data or at least alternative views on the issue, and hence mitigate the overconfidence bias, resulting in a relationship between confidence and accuracy. However, structured approaches arguably could also mitigate the influence of extraneous sources of variance in prediction, and hence reduce the effect of confidence on accuracy. These competing hypotheses are tested in the present research.

McNiel et al. (1998) employed a relatively unstructured prediction paradigm. Although the prediction format was standardized (0–100%), the assessment procedure itself, including which risk factors to consider, was not. The common alternative of traditional clinical prediction is actuarial prediction. A third approach—structured professional judgment (SPJ)—has emerged in recent years in response to alleged shortcomings of both traditional clinical and actuarial prediction (Hart, 1998; 2001a, 2001b; Kropp & Hart, 2000; Otto, 2000). As reviewed below, both the actuarial and SPJ approaches to risk assessment differ from the traditional clinical approach in that they are more structured, explicit, and guided. It would be of interest to investigate whether the construct of confidence has the same impact on these two models of risk assessment, or if it is limited to a method of prediction that is less well defined and structured.

The present research, then, will evaluate the validity generalization of the construct of confidence to (a) two different models of risk assessment (structured professional judgment and actuarial), among (b) forensic psychiatric rather than civil psychiatric patients, concerning (c) postrelease community violence rather than institutional violence (d) over a substantially longer time period than was possible in the McNiel et al. (1998) study.

METHOD

Participants included 100 forensic psychiatric patients who had been detained in a secure forensic facility in western North America. All patients had been found to be not criminally responsible of criminal offenses, and were discharged by a review board. These 100 patients represent almost all patients who had been discharged in 1996–1997. There were actually 116 patients who had been discharged, but 16 were not included in the sample so as to leave some patients for training purposes. This sample is described in detail elsewhere (Douglas, Ogloff, & Hart, in press). Characteristics are presented in Table 1.

TABLE 1
Descriptive Information on Sample

CHARACTERISTIC	n OR $\dot{M}$ (% OR SD)
Age at admission (years)	35.30 (9.84)
Number with children	30 (30.3%)
Single	67 (67.0%)
Completed high school	40 (40.0%)
Unemployed	93 (93.0%)
Juvenile criminal record	32 (34.4%)
Age at first charge	16 (16.2%)
Past violent charge	91 (91.9%)
Past violent conviction	48 (48.5%)
Violent index offense	79 (79.0%)
Child psychiatric treatment	6 (6.1%)
Juvenile psychiatric treatment	26 (26.3%)
Adult psychiatric treatment	95 (96.0%)
Previous inpatient treatment	83 (83.0%)
Admission diagnosis (primary)	
Schizophrenia	72 (73.5%)
Mood	18 (18.4%)
Substance	5 (5.1%)
Other	3 (3.1%)
Admission personality disorder	24 (24.0%)

Note: $N = 100$.

Procedure

Data were collected from files. Two raters coded the clinical–legal files of the 100 participants. These files are detailed and often voluminous, containing social, psychological, psychiatric, medical, criminal, and legal reports and information. Raters were blind to outcome. Each of the raters completed 75 clinical files, with an overlap of 50% of all files to permit interrater reliability analyses. Because data were collected archivally, there were no consent procedures. Research using forensic patients indicates that file-only ratings of the primary measure used in this study (the HCR-20 violence risk assessment scheme, described below) are closely related to ratings completed by using both files and interviews (Vincent et al., 2001).

Raters were graduate students in clinical psychology who underwent a thorough, multiday training procedure that involved both didactic and applied procedures. Raters were informed about risk assessment generally, and the study measures specifically. This information included a review of the nature and purpose of the HCR-20, its content, and its intended use. Raters read the HCR-20 manual as part of this training. In addition, raters were assigned several key readings on risk assessment and the HCR-20. Training cases were provided that were based on three actual HCR-20 forensic assessments that had been court-ordered. Scores were reviewed and discussed between the raters and the trainer (who had conducted the original assessments). Then, raters independently completed five HCR-20 protocols based on the actual files that were to be used for the research but that were excluded from the sample for training purposes.

Measures

HCR-20 Violence Risk Assessment Scheme

The HCR-20 (Webster et al., 1997) is a violence risk assessment scheme. It contains 20 risk factors, each scored 0, 1, or 2, that are dispersed across three subscales— Historical (10 items), Clinical (5 items), and Risk Management (5 items). The HCR- 20 is not a self-report scale, but a clinician-rated instrument meant to structure violence risk assessments. It requires users to produce final summary risk ratings of low, moderate, and high risk. These are considered "structured clinical or professional judgments." They are "structured" because they are based on a consideration of a standardized set of operationally defined risk factors. Users also are provided some guidance in the manual in terms of linking their final risk ratings to expected necessary levels of risk management or intervention required to prevent violence.

Research and commentary is accumulating on the HCR-20 (for book reviews, see Arbisi, 2003; Buchanan, 2001; Cooper, 2003; Mossman, 2000; Witt, 2000). In general, it shows that the HCR-20 and its scales can be rated reliably and tend to be related to violence among forensic psychiatric patients, civil psychiatric patients, and correctional offenders (for reviews, see Douglas & Webster, 1999; Otto, 2000). In the present sample, interrater reliability was conducted on 50 of 100 cases. Results are discussed at length elsewhere (Douglas et al., in press). Intraclass correlation coefficients (ICC_1) were good for the total scale (.85), H scale (.90; individual item range = .41 to 1.0), and C scale (.79; range = .34 to .69), and moderate at best for the R scale (.47; range = .01 to .54). Interrater reliability of the structured clinical risk judgments of low, moderate, and high risk were "good" to "substantial" (ICC_1 = 61; ICC_2 = :76) using practical descriptors (Cicchetti & Sparrow, 1981; Landis & Koch, 1977).

Actuarial versus Structured Clinical Judgments

The terms "actuarial" and "clinical" are used here in the way that Meehl (1954) and colleagues (Grove & Meehl, 1996; Grove, Zald, Lebow, Snitz, & Nelson, 2000) have suggested—in terms of the method of combining factors to make a decision. The actuarial prediction procedure has been described as "a formal method" that "uses an equation, a formula, a graph, or an actuarial table to arrive at a probability, or expected value, of some outcome" (Grove & Meehl, 1996, p. 294). It also has been described as mechanical and algorithmic (Grove & Meehl, 1996), and "well specified" and "100% reproducible" (Grove et al., 2000, p. 19). In the present study, actuarial predictions were simply the scores obtained by summing the HCR-20 items, a procedure that has been shown to be as valid—if not more so—than different weighting strategies (Grann & Långström, in press).

The *traditional* clinical prediction procedure, on the other hand, has been described as an "informal, 'in the head,' impressionistic, subjective conclusion, reached (somehow) by a human clinical judge" (Grove & Meehl, 1996, p. 294). By definition, traditional clinical prediction is a process involving no constraints or guidelines for the evaluator. Decisions are made with considerable clinical discretion and are usually justified according to the qualifications and experience of the person making them. The approach has been widely criticized for lacking reliability, validity, and accountability (Grove et al., 2000; Grove & Meehl, 1996; Litwack & Schlesinger, 1999).

A model of decision making called the "Structured Professional Judgment" (SPJ) model of risk assessment has emerged in recent years (Hart, 1998; 2001a, 2001b; see also Douglas & Kropp, 2002; Otto, 2000), and has produced a number of measures (Augimeri et al., 2001; Boer et al., 1997; Borum et al., 2001; Kropp et al., 1999; Laws, 2000; Webster et al., 1997) and reviews (for book reviews, see Arbisi, 2003; Buchanan, 2001; Cooper, 2003; Mossman, 2000; Witt, 2000; for research reviews, see Dolan & Doyle, 2000; Douglas, 2002; Douglas & Webster, 1999; Otto, 2000). This model produces final risk judgments of low, moderate, and high risk to be made after consideration of a standard set of operationally defined risk factors and the degree of intervention that they call for in the present case. We used this decision—low, moderate, or high risk—as the decision index from the SPJ model, based on the HCR-20 violence risk assessment scheme (Webster et al., 1997). This decision has sometimes been referred to as a "structured clinical judgment" (Hart, 1998) or a structured professional judgment (Douglas & Kropp, 2002).

Confidence Ratings

Raters provided ratings of the confidence of their HCR-20 judgments on a scale ranging from 1 to 10. The definition of confidence provided to raters was as follows: "The rater has a feeling of certainty or reliance or trust about the correctness of the rating." For the purposes of analyses, a median split was performed to form two confidence groups, defined as low (scoring at or below the median) and high (scoring above the median).

Outcome Variables

Violence was coded from criminal records and hospital readmission records, the latter of which often include collateral reports of patient behavior in the community. The definition used in the HCR-20 manual was adopted for this research—"actual, attempted, or threatened harm to a person or persons" (p. 24). This intentionally broad definition permits the coding of less and more serious forms of violence. For the present research, violence was divided into physical violence, requiring physical contact by the perpetrator or use of a weapon, and nonphysical violence, which included verbal threats and fear-inducing behavior. This categorization has been used in several recent published risk assessment studies (Douglas, Ogloff, Nicholls, & Grant, 1999; McNiel & Binder, 1994). Two other categories were created—"any violence" and "criminal violence." The former category is simply an omnibus category that includes all violence. The latter category indicates the violence that led to criminal justice system involvement (arrests or convictions).

Analyses

Univariate analyses included point biserial correlations between predictors and violence, with violence being coded dichotomously, and predictors being either continuous or categorical. Although point biserial correlations were used to facilitate comparisons with other published risk assessment studies, they are susceptible to base rates of the criterion variable that deviate from .50. As such, receiver operating characteristic analyses also were used, as they are much less sensitive to base rate problems (Mossman, 1994; Mossman & Somoza, 1991), as described earlier.

Cox proportional hazards analysis also was used for multivariate analyses. This semiparametric procedure does not model the shape of the hazard function, but does model whether predictors (which can be dichotomous, categorical, or continuous) independently impact the hazard function. This method is useful because it takes time and uneven follow-up periods into account (Luke & Homan, 1998).

RESULTS

The Influence of Confidence on Structured Professional Judgments

First, univariate analyses (point biserial correlations and receiver operating characteristic analysis) were used to display the relationship between structured professional judgments of risk for violence across confidence groups. As shown in Table 2, there were substantial differences between sets of correlations and AUC values across the two groups. For the subset scoring *above* the median confidence level, effects were routinely large in magnitude and significant. For the subset scoring *at or below the median confidence* level, effects were consistently small and nonsignificant.

The analyses below are useful for different reasons: Correlational analyses provide

TABLE 2

Effect of Confidence on Accuracy of Structured Professional Risk Ratings

	CATEGORY OF VIOLENCE			
STRUCTURED RISK RATING	ANY	PHYSICAL	NONPHYSICAL	CRIMINAL
Point biserial correlations				
Confidence ≤ median (N = 65)	.14	.18	.10	.03
Confidence > median (N = 35)	.62***	.54***	.48**	.43**
Areas under ROC curve				
Confidence ≤ median (N = 65)	.58	.63	.58	.52
Confidence > Median (N = 35)	.86**	.82**	.82**	.84*

Note: N = 100. Risk categories = low, moderate, and high risk.
*p ≤ .05. **p ≤ .01. ***p ≤ .001.

a commonly used index of the strength of association, and hence permit comparisons to other published studies. However, these analyses are affected (attenuated) by base rates of the criterion variables that deviate from .50. ROC analysis does not suffer from this problem. As neither analysis controls for the time at risk, Cox regression analysis was used to provide a further evaluation of the role of confidence.

Analyses for the group scoring *at or below the median* were carried out first. Structured professional risk judgments were entered as the predictor variable, with "any violence" as the dependent measure. This produced a nonsignificant model fit, −2 Log Likelihood = 98.139, χ^2 (1, N = 65) = 2.117, p = .146; B = .748, SE = .520, Wald = 2.125, e^B = 2.134, p = .145. Second, this same Cox regression analysis was used with the subset scoring *above the median confidence level*. Despite the relatively low N (35) in this subgroup, a significant model was obtained, −2 Log Likelihood = 47.987, χ^2 (1, N = 100) = 12.782, p = .000; B = 2.187, SE = .677, Wald = 10.430, e^B = 8.907, p = .001. The hazard ratio from these analyses (e^B) showed that, in the high confidence group, there was a roughly ninefold increase in the hazard of violence occurring at each increased step of the predictor violence (i.e., between low and moderate, and also between moderate and high risk ratings). These findings parallel the point biserial and ROC analyses, controlling for time and uneven follow-up periods.

The Influence of Confidence on Actuarial Risk Judgments

In this section, a similar set of analyses was carried out. The main difference is that three actuarial judgments were used, rather than the single structured professional judgments. This stems from the fact that the HCR-20 has three subscales, and each was used as a predictor, rather than using the total scale score. Univariate analyses are presented first above. As shown in Table 3, the pattern of point biserial correlations and *AUC* values between low and high confidence groups mirrored those of the structured professional judgments. In the *low confidence* group, statistical effect sizes were routinely near-zero and nonsignificant, whereas the effects in the *high confidence* group were in general larger and statistically significant.

TABLE 3

Effect of Confidence on Accuracy of Actuarial Risk Ratings

	CATEGORY OF VIOLENCE			
HCR-20 ACTUARIAL RATING	ANY	PHYSICAL	NONPHYSICAL	CRIMINAL
Point biserial correlations				
Confidence ≤ median (N = 65)				
H Scale	.01	−.05	.09	−.06
C Scale	.12	.14	.05	.03
R Scale	−.11	−.12	−.07	−.06
Confidence > median (N = 35)				
H Scale	.41**	.40**	.33*	.28*
C Scale	.47**	.41**	.41**	.38**
R Scale	.22	.20	.15	.22
Areas under ROC curve				
Confidence ≤ median (N = 65)				
H Scale	.53	.53	.55	.49
C Scale	.57	.58	.57	.54
R Scale	.44	.40	.46	.48
Confidence > median (N = 35)				
H Scale	.77*	.76*	.76*	.72
C Scale	.82**	.79**	.82**	.85*
R Scale	.65	.64	.62	.73

Note: $N = 100$. Actuarial risk ratings are the sum of risk factors on the various HCR-20 scales.

*$p \leq .05$. **$p \leq .01$. ***$p \leq .001$.

Again, Cox regression was used to investigate the relationship between actuarial predictions and violence, controlling for uneven follow-up time periods. In this case, because there are three predictors, the analysis is multivariate. Analyses were conducted first for the *low confidence group*. "Any violence" was again used as the outcome criterion to maximize the base rate. All three scales were allowed to enter the model. This procedure produced a nonsignificant model fit, −2 Log Likelihood = 96.358, χ^2 (3, $N = 65$) = 3.951, $p = .267$. The betas (B) for the H, C, and R scales were .010, .279, and −.359, respectively; the e^B values were 1.010, 1.322, and 0.698; the Wald F was .009, 3.004, and 2.283. None of the scales was statistically significant, although the C scale was marginally significant ($p = .08$).

In the *high confidence group*, again despite the relatively low N, the three subscales produced a significant model fit, −2 Log Likelihood = 54.354, χ^2 (3, $N = 35$) = 7.068, $p = .008$. Having used a forward entry procedure, only the C scale was significantly related to violence, $B = .437$, $e^B = 1.548$, Wald $F = 6.206$ ($p = .013$). The H scale was marginally significant ($p = .06$). The main point is that the overall model was significant, where it was not for the subgroup that scored at or below the median confidence level. The hazard ratio (e^B) of 1.548 indicates a 55% increase in the probability of violence occurring at each increased level of the predictor, in this case the C scale (i.e., between 0 and 1, 1 and 2, ..., 9 and 10). This is a five- to sixfold increase in the hazard of violence from a score of 0 to a score of 10 on the C scale.

Differential Variance as a Potential Explanation for Findings

In principle, it is possible that the present findings were an artifact of differences in variability of the predictors between the low and high confidence groups. That is, raters might have been more confident when HCR-20 scores were either very high or very low, and less confident for cases with intermediate scores. If this were the case, there would be restricted range in the low confidence group, and much greater variability in the high confidence group. This alone could account for findings. To test this possibility, we compared indices of variability for the low and high confidence groups. In general, there was little if any evidence that this was the case—all indices of variability, both for scale scores and final risk ratings, were highly comparable between low and high confidence groups.

For instance, comparing the low and high confidence groups (low/high), standard deviations for the H, C, R, and final risk scores were, respectively, 2.86/2.66, 1.99/2.11, 1.45/1.48, and 0.57/0.64. Range of scores (minimum–maximum) also were similar for H, C, and R scales, respectively, in low and high confidence groups (low/high), as follows: 6–19/9–19, 0–10/0–9, 3–9/2–9. Finally, the final decisions of low, moderate, and high risk were distributed similarly across low and high confidence groups. Proportions of judgments at low, moderate, and high risk in the low and high confidence groups were as follows (low/high): 24.6/20.0, 66.6/60.0, and 9.2/20.0.

DISCUSSION

This study investigated the impact of confidence of risk judgments on their relationship to violence. Previous research (McNiel et al., 1998) has shown that probabilistic clinical risk ratings of potential inpatient violence by civil psychiatric patients were influenced by the confidence of clinicians who made the judgments. This research sought to investigate whether the same effect would hold true using different—more structured—methods of risk assessment. There were competing hypotheses—that the use of structured methods would counter the overconfidence bias, leading to a closer correspondence between accuracy and confidence; or that use of structured methods would reduce extraneous influences (i.e., confidence) on predictive accuracy, and no correspondence between confidence and accuracy would be observed.

Results showed a strong relationship between confidence and accuracy. The relationship between the risk ratings, whether using actuarial or structured professional assessment models, and violence was much stronger in the high confidence group than in the low confidence group. This study thus extends the findings of McNiel et al. (1998) to (1) forensic rather than civil psychiatric patients, (2) with respect to postrelease community violence rather than inpatient violence, (3) using two different models of decision making (actuarial and structured professional judgment), and (4) over a longer time period than used by McNiel et al. (1998).

These findings are consistent with the debiasing effect of providing possible alternative judgments or possibly disconfirming evidence (Arkes, 2001). That is, in each case raters considered at least 20 risk factors. It is possible that in cases that otherwise would have been rated high (or low) risk, evidence (few/many risk factors) disconfirmed this initial judgment, and lowered confidence. However, it is important to return to a point made in the Introduction—that many accuracy–confidence studies in other contexts use different research paradigms, such that confidence is defined as the probability of an event occurring. In the present study, confidence ratings were theoretically orthogonal to accuracy ratings, such that a rater could specify high (low) risk, but low (high) confidence. As such, theoretical explanations from these other paradigms might not apply here.

There are other potential explanations of the findings. In the present research, although not reported, data were collected not only on confidence ratings but on ratings of the perceived *quality* of the information upon which risk factors and final risk decisions were based. The correlation between confidence and quality was very high (>.90), suggesting that the perceived quality of file, interview, and test material that comprises an assessment strongly influences confidence. This could mean either that (1) low quality information, which would tend to be of low reliability and trustworthiness, is the primary cause of both low confidence and the lack of association between judgments and outcome when confidence is low. If this were the case, then confidence itself would be more of a proxy than an actual determinant of accuracy. The key issue would be the completeness, comprehensiveness, and veracity of file and other assessment data.

Alternatively, perceived quality could be but one factor that influences confidence, rather than being the primary cause. In this case, confidence might be more independently related to accuracy, rather than being, in effect, an artifact of quality of assessment data. The search for other correlates and determinants of confidence might include certain patient factors (i.e., in the absence of strong violence risk factors, clinicians might have less confidence) or contextual factors (i.e., institutional resources devoted to risk assessment).

Perceived quality of assessment information determining confidence could account for why actuarial predictions, which are simply the sum of risk factors, a process involving no human judgment other than that required to rate the risk factors, were affected by confidence as much as structured professional judgments were (and as much as pure clinical predictions were in the research by McNiel et al., 1998). A feature of actuarial prediction that often is forwarded as a decided advantage is its imperviousness to human subjectivity, heuristics, and extraneous influences. In principle, confidence could be counted among the influences that actuarial prediction seeks to minimize. The present findings, however, indicated that the accuracy of the mere summed total of items (actuarial prediction), a task with little human subjectivity, was vulnerable to the impact of confidence. This would seem to indicate that confidence, in fact, is related to the quality of information. Lower quality of assessment information could affect the ratings of risk factors detrimentally, which in turn could affect their validity. If confidence was related to the accuracy of human decision-making independently of quality of assessment information, then the automatization of decisions that is attained through the use of actuarial procedures for combining risk factors should, in principle, reduce or eliminate the impact of confidence on accuracy. Such was not the case in the present data.

Future research should attempt to disentangle these competing explanations, as well as use other research procedures (actual clinicians). Studies could include experimental manipulations of potential determinants of confidence, such as an objective measure of the quality of assessment data, nature of patient characteristics, gravity of the potential outcome, as well as assessor characteristics. Regardless of the precise causal mechanism underlying the effect, there are important implications for clinical practice. Findings from the current research, as well as those of McNiel et al. (1998) suggest that when clinicians have completed a risk assessment, whether using actuarial, clinical, or SPJ methods, they perhaps should reevaluate their assessment material if they are not confident in the final decision. Reevaluation, collateral contacts, (dis)confirmation of information, and consultation with colleagues might be advisable.

Limitations

This research used a "retrospective follow-up" design rather than a truly prospective design, and relied solely on charts to code the HCR-20 and make risk decisions. These factors both could preclude optimal assessment procedures and hence result in the underestimation of validity findings. However, the major limiting factor concerns the number (two) and nature (graduate students) of raters. As such, this is best considered an analogue study that attempts to model and estimate actual clinical decision-making. This is an inherent limitation that cannot be redressed in the present study, but which readers can take into account in interpreting findings. Subsequent studies would benefit from using a greater number of raters with professional qualifications more closely representing decision-makers in actual applied settings.

However, there are several reasons to suspect a reasonable degree of generalizability. First, raters had clinical experience in the types of settings in which the HCR-20 is used (i.e., psychiatric and forensic settings). Second, the training procedure for the HCR-20 was as involved as HCR-20 training offered to clinicians in the community, if not more so. Third, as pointed out previously, Vincent et al. (2001) showed that research- and clinical-based HCR-20 scores bore a reasonably strong correspondence to one another. Fourth, there is a fair amount of evidence that judgments by persons with different amounts of experience do not to vary greatly (Andreason et al., 1982; Grove & Meehl, 1996). Fifth, the raters in the present study are typical of raters in many other HCR-20 studies, as well as in risk assessment studies more generally. Sixth, it was the HCR-20 *measure*, and not pure unstructured clinical judgment, that was the subject of study in the present research. That is, the HCR-20 requires several different types of judgment. Most apparent are the ratings or judgments of risk factors, and the rating or judgment of risk itself. In this way, it was the instrument and not the raters that was the primary unit of analysis. Finally, an attempt was made to ensure findings would be generalizable on the basis of *patients*. For this reason, nearly all persons in a cohort who had been released were included in the study. Increasing the number of raters could decrease the number of study participants (assuming equal resources available to complete the study), particularly if all raters provided judgments on all participants (which would be the ideal, fully nested design).

Despite all these reasons discussed above, it remains the case that the generalizability might have been somewhat greater by using a greater number of raters. One alternative to using two raters to rate a large number of patients would be to employ procedures from Generalizability Theory (GT—see Brennan, 2001; Cronbach, Gleser, Nanda, & Rajaratnam, 1972), and have pairs of raters each judge smaller groups of patients, as mentioned above. However, the primary strength of GT has been described as the ability to evaluate more than one facet or source of error in a single study (i.e., raters, occasions, racial interactions; Hoyt & Melby, 1999). In the present study, there was only one facet under investigation—error due to raters. Further, Hoyt and Melby (1999) reported that in single-facet GT studies, the generalizability coefficient (the index of generalizability or reliability in GT), is identical to reliability coefficients obtained under classical test theory.

In sum, then, while it is conceded that some degree of generalizability might have been sacrificed, it is concluded, based on the reasons outlined above, that the present results are reasonably generalizable to other settings in which the HCR-20 clinical judgments might be used. Of course, as with any line of research, this conclusion would be strengthened by subsequent research that produced similar findings, and weakened by research that reported dissimilar findings.

NOTES

1. Receiver operating characteristic (ROC) analyses are much less sensitive to base rate problems than are other types of statistical procedures, such as correlation (Mossman, 1994; Mossman & Somoza, 1991). They produce an index called the area under the curve (AUC) that is an index of the overall predictive accuracy of a predictive measure. Values range from 0 (perfect negative prediction) to .50 (chance) to 1.0 (perfect positive prediction). The value can be interpreted as the probability that a randomly chosen actually violent person will score higher on the predictive measure than a randomly chosen actually nonviolent person (Mossman & Somoza, 1991).

REFERENCES

Andreason, N. C., McDonald-Scott, P., Grove, W. M., Keller, M. D., Shapiro, R. W., & Hirschfeld, R. M. A. (1982). Assessment of reliability in multi-center collaborative research using a videotape approach. *American Journal of Psychiatry, 139*, 876–882.

Arbisi, P. A. (2003). Review of the HCR-20: Assessing risk for violence. In B. S. Plake, J. C. Impara, & R. A. Spies (Eds.), *The fifteenth mental measurements yearbook* [Electronic version]. Retrieved May 7, 2003, from the Buros Institute's Test Reviews Online website: http://www.unl.edu/buros

Arkes, H. R. (2001). Overconfidence in judgmental forecasting. In J. S. Armstrong (Ed.), *Forecasting principles handbook* (pp. 442–459). Norwell, MA: Kluwer.

Augimeri, L. K., Koegl, C. J., Webster, C. D., & Levene, K. S. (2001). *Early assessment risk list for boys (EARL-20B): Version 2*. Toronto, ON: Earlscourt Child and Family Centre.

Boer, D. P., Hart, S. D., Kropp, P. R., & Webster, C. D. (1997). *Manual for the sexual violence risk—20: Professional guidelines for assessing risk of sexual violence*. Vancouver, BC: British Columbia Institute Against Family Violence.

Borum, R. (1996). Improving the clinical practice of violence risk assessment: Technology, guidelines, and training. *American Psychologist, 51,* 945–956.

Borum, R., Bartel, P., & Forth, A. (2001). *Manual for the structured assessment for violence risk in youth (SAVRY): Consultation version*. Tampa, FL: Florida Mental Health Institute, University of South Florida.

Borum, R., Otto, R. K., & Golding, S. (1993). Improving clinical judgment and decision making in forensic evaluation. *Journal of Psychiatry and Law, 21,* 35–76.

Brennan, R. L. (2001). *Generalizability theory*. New York, NY: Springer.

Buchanan, A. (2001). [Review of the book, HCR-20: Assessing risk for violence, Version 2]. *Criminal Behaviour and Mental Health, 11,* S77–S89.

Cicchetti, D.V., & Sparrow, S.A. (1981). Developing criteria for establishing interrater reliability of specific items: Applications to assessment of adaptive behavior. *American Journal of Mental Deficiency, 86,* 127–137.

Cooper, C. (2003). Review of the HCR-20: Assessing risk for violence. In B. S. Plake, J. C. Impara, & R.A. Spies (Eds.), *The fifteenth mental measurements yearbook* [Electronic version]. Retrieved May 7, 2003, from the Buros Institute's Test Reviews Online website: http://www.unl.edu/buros

Cronbach, L. J., Gleser, G. C., Nanda, H., & Rajaratnam, N. (1972). *The dependability of behavioral measurements: Theory of generalizability for scores and profiles*. New York, NY: John Wiley & Sons.

Dawson, N. V., Conners, A. F., Speroff, T., Kemka, A., Shaw, P., & Arkes, H. R. (1993). Homodynamic assessment in managing the critically ill: Is physician confidence warranted? *Medical Decision Making, 13,* 258–266.

Dolan, M., & Doyle, M. (2000). Violence risk prediction: Clinical and actuarial measures and the role of the Psychopathy Checklist. *British Journal of Psychiatry, 177,* 303–311.

Douglas, K. S. (2002). *HCR-20 violence risk assessment scheme: Overview and annotated bibliography* [On-line]. Available from http://www.sfu.ca/psychology/groups/faculty/ hartviolink.htm

Douglas, K. S., & Kropp, P. R. (2002). A prevention-based paradigm for violence risk assessment: Clinical and research applications. *Criminal Justice and Behavior, 29,* 617–658.

Douglas, K. S., Ogloff, J. R. P., & Hart, S. D. (2003). *Evaluation of the structured professional judgment model of violence risk assessment among forensic psychiatric patients*. Psychiatric Services.

Douglas, K. S., Ogloff, J. R. P., Nicholls, T. L., & Grant, I. (1999). Assessing risk for violence among psychiatric patients: The HCR-20 violence risk assessment scheme and the Psychopathy Checklist: Screening version. *Journal of Consulting and Clinical Psychology, 67,* 917–930.

Douglas, K. S., & Webster, C. D. (1999). Predicting violence in mentally and personality disordered individuals. In R. Roesch, S. D. Hart, & J. R. P. Ogloff (Eds.), *Psychology and law: The state of the discipline* (pp. 175–239). New York: Plenum.

Ennis, B. J., & Litwack, T. R. (1974). Psychiatry and the presumption of expertise: Flipping coins in the courtroom. *California Law Review, 62,* 693–752.

Faust, D., & Ziskin, J. (1988). The expert witness in psychology and psychiatry. *Science, 241,* 31–35.

Grann, M., & Långström, N. (in press). Actuarial assessment of risk for violence: To weigh or not to weigh? *Criminal Justice and Behavior*.

Grove, W. M., & Meehl, P. E. (1996). Comparative efficiency of informal (subjective, impressionistic) and formal (mechanical, algorithmic) prediction procedures: The clinical-statistical controversy. *Psychology, Public Policy, and Law, 2,* 293–323.

Grove, W. M., Zald, D. H., Lebow, B. S., Snitz, B. E., & Nelson, C. (2000). Clinical versus mechanical prediction: A meta-analysis. *Psychological Assessment, 12,* 19–30.

Hart, S. D. (1998). The role of psychopathy in assessing risk for violence: Conceptual and methodological issues. *Legal and Criminological Psychology, 3,* 121–137.

Hart, S. D. (2001a). Assessing and managing violence risk. In K. S. Douglas, C. D. Webster, S. D. Hart, D. Eaves, & J. R. P. Ogloff (Eds.), *HCR-20 violence risk management companion guide* (pp. 13–25). Burnaby, BC: Mental Health Law and Policy Institute, Simon Fraser University.

Hart, S. D. (2001b). *Complexity, uncertainty, and the reconceptualization of risk assessment* [On-line]. Available from http://www.sfu.ca/psychology/groups/faculty/hart

Hoyt, W. T., & Melby, J. N. (1999). Dependability of measurement in counseling psychology: An introduction to generalizability theory. *Counseling Psychologist, 27,* 325–352.

Kropp, P. R., & Hart, S. D. (2000). The spousal assault risk assessment (SARA) guide: Reliability and validity in adult male offenders. *Law and Human Behavior, 24*, 101–118.

Kropp, P. R., Hart, S. D., Webster, C. D., & Eaves, D. (1999). *Manual for the spousal assault risk assessment guide* (3rd ed.). Toronto, ON: Multi-Health Systems.

Landis, J., & Koch, G. G. (1977). The measurement of observer agreement for categorical data. *Biometrics, 33,* 159–174.

Laws, R. (2000, November). *Risk for sexual violence protocol (RSVP): A new guide for assessment and management.* Symposium presented at the founding conference of the International Association of Forensic Mental Health Services, Vancouver, Canada.

Litwack, T. R., & Schlesinger, L. B. (1999). Dangerousness risk assessments: Research, legal and clinical considerations. In A. K. Hess & I. B. Weiner (Eds.), *Handbook of forensic psychology* (2nd ed., pp. 171–217). New York: Wiley.

Luke, D. A., & Homan, S. M. (1998). Time and change: Using survival analysis in clinical assessment and treatment evaluation. *Psychological Assessment, 10,* 360–378.

McNiel, D. E., & Binder, R. L. (1994). Screening for risk of inpatient violence: Validation of an actuarial tool. *Law and Human Behavior, 18,* 579–586.

McNiel, D. E., Sandberg, D. A., & Binder, R. L. (1998). The relationship between confidence and accuracy in clinical assessment of psychiatric patients' potential for violence. *Law and Human Behavior, 22,* 655–669.

Meehl, P. E. (1954). *Clinical versus statistical prediction.* Minneapolis, MN: University of Minnesota Press.

Monahan, J., & Steadman, H. J. (Eds.). (1994). *Violence and mental disorder: Developments in risk assessment.* Chicago, IL: University of Chicago Press.

Monahan, J., Steadman, H. J., Silver, E., Appelbaum, P. S., Robbins, P. C., Mulvey, E. P., et al. (2001). *Rethinking risk assessment: The MacArthur study of mental disorder and violence.* New York: Oxford University Press.

Mossman, D. (1994). Assessing predictions of violence: Being accurate about accuracy. *Journal of Consulting and Clinical Psychology, 62,* 783–792.

Mossman, D. (2000). Evaluating violence risk 'by the book': A review of HCR-20: Assessing risk for violence, Version 2 and The manual for the sexual violence risk—20. *Behavioral Sciences and the Law, 18,* 781–789.

Mossman, D., & Somoza, E. (1991). ROC curves, test accuracy, and the description of diagnostic tests. *Journal of Neuropsychiatry and Clinical Neurosciences, 3,* 330–333.

Otto, R. K. (2000). Assessing and managing violence risk in outpatient settings. *Journal of Clinical Psychology, 56,* 1239–1262.

Quinsey, V. L., Harris, G. T., Rice, G. T., & Cormier, C. A. (1998). *Violent offenders: Appraising and managing risk.* Washington, DC: American Psychological Association.

Rabinowitz, J., & Garelik-Wyler, R. (1999). Accuracy and confidence in clinical assessment of psychiatric inpatients risk of violence. *International Journal of Law and Psychiatry, 22,* 99–106.

Sporer, S. L., Penrod, S., Read, D., & Cutler, B. (1995). Choosing, confidence, and accuracy: A meta-analysis of the confidence-accuracy relation in eyewitness identification studies. *Psychological Bulletin, 118,* 315–327.

Stephenson, G. M. (1984). Accuracy and confidence in testimony: A critical review and some fresh evidence. In D. J. Muller, D. E. Blackman, & A. J. Chapman (Eds.), *Psychology and law* (pp. 229–248). New York: Wiley.

Vincent, G. M., Ross, D. J., Whittemore, K., Eaves, D., Hart, S. D., Ogloff, J. R. P., et al. (2001, April). *Using the HCR-20: File-based researcher ratings vs. file + interview-based clinician ratings.* Paper presented at the founding conference of the International Association of Forensic Mental Health Services, Vancouver, BC, Canada.

Webster, C. D., Douglas, K. S., Eaves, D., & Hart, S. D. (1997). *HCR-20: Assessing risk for violence* (Version 2). Burnaby, BC: Mental Health, Law, and Policy Institute, Simon Fraser University.

Werner, P. D., Rose, T. L., & Yesavage, J. A. (1983). Reliability, accuracy, and decision-making strategy in clinical predictions of imminent dangerousness. *Journal of Consulting and Clinical Psychology, 51,* 815–825.

Witt, P. H. (2000). A practitioner's view of risk assessment: The HCR-20 and SVR-20. *Behavioral Sciences and the Law, 18,* 791–798.

Yarmey, A. D. (1979). The psychology of eyewitness testimony. London, Macmillan.

22

Building Mental Health Professionals' Decisional Models into Tests of Predictive Validity: The Accuracy of Contextualized Predictions of Violence

JENNIFER L. SKEEM, EDWARD P. MULVEY, AND CHARLES W. LIDZ

ABSTRACT: *To safely manage potentially violent patients in the community, mental health professionals (MHPs) must assess when and under what conditions a patient may be involved in a violent act. This study applies a more ecologically sensitive approach than past research by building the conditions that MHPs believe make patient violence more likely into tests of their predictive validity. In specific, the accuracy of MHPs' predictions that patients were more likely to become violent when they consumed alcohol was assessed based on a sample of 714 patients. The results indicate that MHPs do not discriminate well between patients who are likely to become violent during periods in which they drink from those who are not. MHPs' predictions appear more descriptive of the drinking behavior of a high-risk group than predictive of alcohol-related violent incidents. Thus, even when their apparent decisional processes are considered in tests of accuracy, MHPs' predictions of violence are only moderately more accurate than chance. This paper analyzes the implications of these findings for risk assessment practice and for conducting further clinically relevant research.*

Reprinted with kind permission of Springer Science and Business Media. Law and Human Behavior, 24 (6), 607–628. © 2000 *American Psychology-Law Society/Division 41 of the American Psychology Association.*

INTRODUCTION

Estimating a patient's risk of violence toward others seems to be an inescapable part of clinical practice. Over two decades ago, Shah (1978) described at least 15 clinical and legal contexts that required mental health professionals (MHPs) to assess risk of violence. Most of these situations still confront clinicians today. In fact, despite abundant evidence of MHPs' only modest predictive accuracy (e.g., Lidz, Mulvey, & Gardner, 1993; Otto, 1992), the courts have increased the scope of legal issues that rely upon assessments of risk (e.g., *Kansas v. Hendricks*, 1997; see Melton, Petrila, Poythress, & Slobogin, 1997, for a review). MHPs must routinely assess risk to fulfill their legal duties to protect third parties from patients' potential violence (*Tarasoff v. Regents of the University of California*, 1976) or to decide whether a patient should be involuntarily hospitalized (see Parry, 1994, for a review of statutory requirements).

As systems of care have evolved toward more community-based services over the past two decades, the contours of the judgment task regarding violence potential have changed. Historically, a determination that a patient was likely to be violent resulted in hospitalization and potential long-term infringement of civil liberties. However, with deinstitutionalization (Lerman, 1981), the implementation of policies to treat patients in the least restrictive setting available (*Shelton v. Tucker*, 1960), and the institution of managed care systems (Mechanic, 1998; Petrila, 1995), the length of hospital stays has dropped dramatically (Narrow, Regier, Rae, Manderscheid, & Locke, 1993; Kiesler & Simkins, 1993). Violence-prone patients are increasingly being treated in less expensive community-based settings, often in intensive case management programs (e.g., Dvoskin & Steadman 1994; Slobogin, 1994). These changes have shifted the emphasis from constitutional issues associated with single, dichotomous predictions of danger-ousness as gateways to institutionalization, to liability issues associated with the ongoing responsibility to protect third parties while working with potentially violent patients in the community (Monahan, 1996). Currently, MHPs are responsible for assessing when and under what conditions a patient may commit a violent act and monitoring changes in those conditions in an attempt to prevent violence (Heilbrun, 1997; Steadman, et al., 1994; Webster, Douglas, Eaves, & Hart, 1997).

To produce information relevant to these new clinical realities, researchers must reconceptualize how they test predictive accuracy (Mulvey & Lidz, 1995). Research has focused almost exclusively on MHPs' simple, context-free predictions of violence. However, as explained below, operationalizing MHPs' judgments in either dichotomous ("predicted violent/not predicted violent") or scaled ("predicted likelihood of violence = 4.5/7) terms that are *divorced from context* fails to address the demands of managing violence in the community and widens the already entrenched divide between science and practice in risk assessment (Borum, 1996). This study attempts to apply a more ecologically sensitive approach to evaluating MHPs' risk assessments by considering the conditions that MHPs believe make patient violence more likely as necessary parts of their predictions.

A Conditional Model of Prediction

This study differs substantially from past research in that it tests the accuracy of clinical judgments while accounting for contextual factors that MHPs perceive as related to violence. Most prior research on clinical prediction of future violence has been guided by a cue-utilization model of human judgment (see Grisso, 1981, for a description). This model frames the task of predicting dangerousness as a clinical exercise in developing and applying a maximally predictive, context-free algorithm for combining individually based risk factors. This model is usually assumed even though a large body of research on clinical judgment strongly indicates that MHPs are not "consistent, cue-utilizing, rational problem solvers" (Mulvey & Lidz, 1995, p. 134; see also Meehl, 1954; Turk & Salovy, 1988), but are instead likely to assess risk in a more insightful manner, guided by cognitive heuristics and experience-based knowledge structures, such as prototypes, schemas, and scripts (see Garb, 1998, Chapter 7; Fiske, 1993; Schneider, 1991; for reviews; see also Borum, Otto, & Golding, 1993; Genero & Cantor, 1987). Moreover, the cue-utilization model assumes that behavior is largely independent of context, and it is therefore poorly suited to the current challenge of assessing risk in order effectively to manage potentially violent patients in the community. In short, a substantial body of research on MHPs' predictive accuracy appears to based on a model of clinical decision making that inadequately represents the actual nature and goals of MHPs' risk assessments.

Mulvey and Lidz (1995) proposed an alternative, conditional model of violence prediction. This approach is based partially on the authors' observation that emergency room MHPs seemed to develop contextualized judgments about violence that were guided by implicit schemas about how a patient's violence would unfold. According to this perspective,

> clinicians' predictions about the occurrence of violence are based upon an assessment of what particular type of violence the patient might commit and the circumstances under which it will be done. Clinicians do not generally view a patient as either being "dangerous" or "not dangerous," but instead see a patient as possibly doing some type of act (e.g., beating his mother) if certain situations either persist or present themselves (e.g., his mother keeps living with her present boyfriend) (p. 135).

These situations or "conditions" are key components of this model. Conditions include enduring features of the patient's life situation (e.g., being involved in a violent marriage), behavior patterns (e.g., medication noncompliance, substance abuse), or forseeable events or stressors (e.g., being evicted). The model's description of MHPs' predictions of violence as situationally dependent is consistent with the commentary of experts in the field (e.g., Heilbrun, 1997; Monahan, 1981; Steadman et al., 1993; Webster et al., 1997) as well as the empirical literature on clinical decision making reviewed above.

An appealing aspect of the conditional model is that it may permit a more refined examination of MHPs' predictive accuracy. As noted previously, most research has operationalized MHPs' predictions in simple terms. This research typically reveals a high false-positive rate, suggesting that MHPs tend erroneously to predict that a patient will be violent when in fact he or she is not (see Litwack & Schlesinger, 1999; Otto, 1992; for reviews). However, this false-positive rate may be inflated by the failure to account methodologically for the way in which MHPs actually assess risk. The position outlined above proposes that MHPs incorporate conditions in their predictions that directly affect the perceived likelihood of violence.

For example, an emergency room clinician may predict that a patient who recently stopped taking his medication and became isolative and paranoid is highly likely to assault his roommate, whom he believes is involved in a scheme to harm him. In a traditional cue-utilization study, this prediction would be operationalized as a context-free prediction that the patient is likely to be violent. However, assume that (1) the patient resumes taking medication that dampens his paranoia or (2) his roommate moves out of his apartment. At follow-up, the traditional study reflects only that the patient has not been violent and classifies the prediction as a false positive. If the prediction of violence had been characterized as contingent upon the patient's being noncompliant with medication and upon his having continued access to his roommate, however, the prediction would have been deemed correct. That is, the conditions that the clinician saw as necessary components of the violence were not present and the violence did not occur.

Incorporating MHPs' conditions into tests of predictive validity may not only reveal valid predictions that are "hidden" by binary tests, but may also shed light on the types of cases in which MHPs' predictions do or do not work well (Mulvey & Lidz, 1985, 1995). Several experts have long argued that MHPs' predictions may be highly accurate with particular types of cases, for example, those in which there is a known history of repeated violence (Litwack & Schlesinger, 1987, 1999). Aggregate data, however, sum over types of cases in which MHPs may be exceptionally good or poor at determining risk. One way of examining differential clinical accuracy would be to examine accuracy within subgroups of cases based on the conditions that MHPs see as strongly related to patient violence (e.g., noncompliance with medication, substance abuse, interpersonal difficulties).

Applying the Model to Alcohol-Related Predictions of Violence

The purpose of this study is to apply the model of conditional prediction to MHPs' risk assessments to determine whether doing so reveals higher rates of predictive accuracy than that found in past research. Because there is an exceedingly large number of case types or conditions available to test, we chose to begin by carefully applying the model to MHPs' predictions that some patients were more likely to be violent when they drank alcohol. This type of prediction was selected for three reasons. First, MHPs often believe that alcohol use plays a crucial role in patient violence. In the predictions examined here, clinicians and attending physicians cited drinking as a condition for violence in 62%

of the cases they predicted to be violent, making drinking the second most frequently listed condition related to violence, after psychiatric deterioration (listed in 72% of cases; Mulvey & Lidz, 1998).[1] Second, recent research consistently indicates that alcohol and other substance use dramatically increases patients' risk of violence (e.g., Hodgins, 1992; Rasanen et al., 1998; Swanson, Borum, Swartz, & Hiday, 1999; Swartz et al., 1998; Tiihonen, Isohanni, Raesaenen, Koiranen, & Moring, 1997). For example, in a community-based sample, Swanson, Holzer, Ganju, and Jono (1990) found that individuals with a serious mental disorder were 3 times more likely to commit a violent act than those without a mental disorder and mentally disordered individuals with a comorbid substance abuse disorder were 12 times more likely to do so. Third, comorbid major mental disorders and substance abuse disorders are prevalent, and may require relatively frequent and intensive mental health care services. Thus, the focus on alcohol use has much practical relevance since MHPs may often be faced with managing risk through affecting alcohol and drug use in a large number of patients in the community.

METHOD

Participants and General Procedure

Original Matched Sample

The original study is described in Lidz et al. (1993). The study was conducted at a large university-based hospital with responsibility for an urban catchment area. Over a 2-year period, researchers approached 2,452 patients between the ages of 14 and 65 years who had a permanent residence address within the catchment area; 1,948 (79%) consented to take part in the study. Although individuals who consented to the study were generally similar to those who refused, the former were more likely to be African American (39% vs. 32%) and young (40% vs. 27% less than 27 years old). This may reflect our payment of $40 for three 1-hr interviews, which was presumably more attractive to poorer patients.

Because the primary purpose of the original study was to test the simple accuracy of emergency room MHPs' predictions of future violence, participants were *matched pairs* of patients, one predicted to be violent and the other predicted not to be violent. The matching design was used (1) to prevent clinicians from obtaining high rates of predictive accuracy based on demographic (rather than clinical) differences between patients and (2) to use study resources efficiently by following a smaller patient sample. In the emergency department it was routine procedure for nurse-clinicians or junior residents ("clinicians") to interview patients in detail, then present the case to the attending psychiatrist ("attending"), who reinterviewed the patient. The clinician and attending would then meet and, on the basis of their interviews and any available collateral information, jointly determine a disposition. After a disposition was determined, researchers asked the clinician and attending independently to (a) indicate *whether they had any concern that the patient might be violent toward others in the next 6 months*, and, if so (b) *rate their degree of concern*, using a 5-point scale (1 = little concern for violence, to 5 = great concern for violence). In short, they were asked to forecast the patient's likelihood of violence over the next 6 months and rate their degree of concern about it. Clinicians and attendings' ratings were strongly correlated (r = .68). A total of 148 different clinicians and 67 different attending psychiatrists provided ratings for the sample examined here.

Clinicians' and attendings' raw ratings were summed to generate a score between 0 (both have no concern) and 10 (both have great concern) that reflected the "summed concern" of the professionals handling the case. These ratings were summed (1) to reflect the fact that clinicians and attending acted jointly as ER teams to process the case and determine the patient's disposition and (2) in an attempt to reduce error associated with a particular predictor's idiosyncrasies. Patients who received a summed concern rating of at least 3 (N = 564) were designated as predicted to be violent. The criterion of 3 was chosen after extensive pretesting and interviews with MHPs, who indicated that the lower ratings reflected minor concerns about violence. A comparison group was then selected from among the consenting patients who were judged *not* potentially violent or those who received a summed concern rating of 0 ("no concern"). They were selected to match the predicted violent group on age, gender, race, and whether they were admitted to the hospital.[2]

Predictions were operationalized categorically in this study to (1) reflect the original study design and database, which divided cases into predicted violent and predicted nonviolent cases, and (2) simplify the presentation of analyses, which make further distinctions among predicted violent cases based on the perceived effect of alcohol consumption on violence potential. As noted in Lidz et al. (1993), patients with high clinical ratings of summed concern (6–10) were no more likely to become violent than patients with lower ratings of summed concern (3–5). Thus, little meaningful information about violence potential is lost by transforming MHPs' ordinal violence predictions into dichotomous predictions.

Researchers followed these predicted and comparison patients in the community. Attempts were made to interview each patient and a collateral (i.e., someone named by the patient as likely to know what goes on in his or her life) three times over a 6-month follow-up period. In each interview, researchers gathered (1) detailed information about changes in multiple domains of the patient's life (e.g., social networks, drug and alcohol use, work, symptoms, treatment), and later (2) descriptions of violent incidents that might have occurred during the previous 2 months. Cases were included in the study if at least two community interviews with the patient or three interviews, including at least one with the patient, had occurred. Of the 564 patients predicted to be violent, 433 met this criterion,[3] but 76 of these could not be matched with a comparison case. The final sample used for analyses in prior tests of clinical accuracy reported from this study thus consisted of 357 matched pairs of patients.

Study Subgroup

The analyses reported here use a slightly different sample construction strategy, but built off of the originally reported sample of 714 matched patients. In this article, clinicians' and attendings' predictions that patients were likely to be violent were analyzed separately to permit consideration of the conditions that each professional deemed relevant to the predicted violence and to reduce problems with data dependence. The 357 cases that were jointly judged[4] as likely to become violent were broken down into 323 predictions of violence by clinicians and 310 predictions of violence by attendings (the numbers differ because there were not always 2 professionals assigned per case, and pairs of professionals did not always agree about patient dangerousness). The remaining 357 comparison cases were jointly judged *not* potentially violent. To simplify the presentation of results, this paper only reports analyses run on the 323 clinicians' predictions of violence. However, virtually identical results were obtained for the attendings' predictions, indicating that the conclusions reported here are not restricted to particular mental health disciplines.

Despite slight changes from the original matched pairs in the sample construction, there were no demographic differences between the cases predicted likely to be violent and comparison cases judged not potentially violent. For example, the cases that clinicians predicted to be violent did not differ from comparison cases in age, $t(677) = .67$, $p = .50$, gender, $\chi^2 (1, N = 679) = .095$, $p = .76$, race, $\chi^2 (1, N = 679) = .00$, $p = .98$, or whether or not they were admitted to the hospital, $\chi^2 (1, N = 679) = .71$, $p = .40$. The demographic characteristics and diagnoses among patients that clinicians predicted to be violent and comparison cases are presented in Table 1. In the table, however, cases are separated based on the nature of clinicians' predictions. The incidence of violence among these patients is presented below.

Operationalization of Alcohol-Related Predictions

While interviewing clinicians (and attendings) about their predictions that patients were likely to become violent, researchers asked them to indicate conditions for violence or "any changes in the patient's behavior pattern or life situation which might make the act more likely to occur." (Conditions for violence are not applicable in comparison cases, where both professionals had "no concern" that the patient would become violent.) After freely responding to this question, clinicians (and attendings) were asked whether particular conditions, such as alcohol use, medication noncompliance, and trouble in relationships, would make the violent act more likely to occur (e.g., "Do you believe that changes in the patient's alcohol use would make this act more likely to occur?"). If they volunteered or endorsed alcohol use as a condition for violence, researchers asked them to indicate "how likely this act is to occur during periods when the patient drank alcohol?" using a 10-point scale, where 0 = no chance and 10 = certain. They were asked to use the same scale to rate the baseline likelihood that the violent act would occur if none of the conditions endorsed were present (e.g., "How likely is the act

TABLE 1

Demographic and Diagnostic Characteristics of Potentially Violent and Comparison Groups

	PREDICTED TO BE VIOLENT: ALCOHOL INTENSIFIES LIKELIHOOD (%)	PREDICTED TO BE VIOLENT: ALCOHOL DOES *NOT* INTENSIFY LIKELIHOOD (%)	PREDICTED TO BE NONVIOLENT: COMPARISON GROUP (%)
Basic demographic			
Average age* (years [SD])	30 [10]	26 [11]	29 [11]
Gender (% male)	64	59	60
Race (% African American)	48	47	48
Hollingshead SES**			
Class I (highest)	1	5	4
Class II	8	11	16
Class III	14	10	12
Class IV	22	36	32
Class V (lowest)	55	38	36
Diagnosis***			
Schizophrenia	14	13	15
Affective	6	22	24
Substance abuse	56	19	30
Personality disorder	14	26	14
Other	10	20	17

*$p < .05$; **$p < .01$; ***$p < .001$.

to occur if none of the behaviors or life situations that contribute to the act's occurrence are present?").

For the purposes of these analyses, predictions of violence were deemed "alcohol-intensified" predictions of violence if (1) the clinician volunteered or endorsed alcohol use as a condition for violence and (2) their rating of the likelihood of violence if the patient used alcohol was at least 2 points greater than their rating of the patient's baseline likelihood of violence. The criterion of two points was set based on pretesting and suggestions that scale differences of 2–3 points were meaningful (see above). Because none of the predictions that included alcohol as a condition for violence had a baseline likelihood of violence greater than 8, this criterion was not subject to ceiling effects. Of clinicians' predictions of violence, 48% were classified as alcohol-intensified predictions of violence and 52% were deemed non-alcohol-intensified predictions of violence.

Measures of Patient Behavior

Alcohol Consumption

At each follow-up interview, patients were questioned about the amount and type of alcohol they had consumed during the 7 days prior to the interview (i.e., how many times they drank in the past week, and, for each day of the week on which they drank, how much beer, wine, and liquor they consumed). If they reported that the week prior to the interview was atypical of their drinking behavior, they were questioned in the same way about their typical consumption of alcohol per week during the preceding 2-month interval. Their typical rate of alcohol consumption during the follow-up interval was expressed in number of drinks per week. For the primary analyses reported below, these rates were classified into three categories based on the distribution of drinking in the sample: (1) no drinking (0 drinks per week), (2) light–moderate drinking (1–13 drinks/week), and (3) moderate–heavy drinking (over 13 drinks/week). It should be noted, however, that analyses produced similar results regardless of whether alcohol was operationalized as a continuous, dichotomous, or multicategory variable based on various thresholds.

Violence

Patient violence was measured based on information from patient and collateral interviews as well as state police records of arrest, county civil commitment records, county treatment usage records, and hospital medical charts. The vast majority of reports of violence, however, were obtained from patient and collateral interviews (Mulvey, Shaw, and Lidz, 1994). To elicit information about violent incidents, interviewers administered an expanded version of the Conflict Tactics Scale (Straus & Gelles, 1990), which assesses multiple categories of specific acts of aggression ranging from *pushing, grabbing, or shoving*, to *using a weapon* on someone (Lidz et al., 1993). For each follow-up period, a patient was judged to have been involved in a violent incident if the patient, collateral, or an official record reported that the patient had laid hands on another person with intent to harm him or her or had threatened someone with a weapon in hand. Verbal threats, incidents in which the patient was the victim of violence (e.g., the victim of a mugging) or did not engage in any retaliatory violent act, and parental discipline were excluded. Only violent incidents that occurred in the community (rather than closed treatment settings) were considered in these analyses. Patients' particular acts of violence and professionals' accuracy in predicting particular violent events are presented in Mulvey and Lidz (1998).

Measure of Drinking-Associated Violent Incidents for Supplementary Analyses

The *immediate* relationship between alcohol and violence was also directly measured for use in the *supplementary* analyses described below. For each follow-up period, when a violent incident occurred, interviewers asked patients and collaterals about the presence of numerous specific conditions at the time of the incident (e.g., medication use, drug and alcohol use, financial stressors, residence, symptoms). For example, they were asked whether alcohol use was involved in the incident.[5] When the patient had reportedly been drinking at the time of the incident, or earlier that day, the incident was coded as drinking-associated.

A Note About Terminology

In this article, the relationship between alcohol consumption and violence is assessed based on their cooccurrence within both short-term (i.e., 2 months) and immediate (i.e., 24 hr or less) time intervals. Discussion of the short-term relationship will refer to "violent incidents during periods of drinking," while discussion of the immediate relationship will refer to "alcohol-associated violent incidents." In a similar sense, predictions about whether or not a patient is more likely to become violent when drinking are, as a class, referred to as "alcohol-related predictions." They are specifically classified as "alcohol-intensified" or "non-alcohol-intensified."

RESULTS

Background Relationships

The central issue of this study is the accuracy of MHPs' identification of patients who are more likely to become violent during periods in which they drink. This issue was conceptualized as the joint product of three bivariate relationships that are important in themselves: (1) the overall accuracy of MHPs' predictions of whether a patient will become violent, (2) the association between patients' drinking and violence, and (3) the relationship between MHPs' alcohol-intensified predictions of violence and patients' drinking. A MHP's overall accuracy in predicting the occurrence of alcohol-related violence is dependent on the interplay among these three associations.

Accuracy of Simple Predictions of Violence

The overall rate of accuracy of clinicians' predictions of violence is shown in Table 2. In this table, clinicians' predictions of whether or not a patient would be violent are cross-tabulated with whether or not that patient had a report of a violent incident at *any* of the three intervals during the entire 6-month follow-up period. The data indicate that 55% of patients predicted to be violent had a violent incident, and only 36% of patients predicted to be nonviolent had a violent incident. Although these rates are based on a subsample of the full dataset, they are very similar to the rates reported for the full research sample (see Lidz et al., 1993). The relationship between predictions of violence and violent incidents was significant, $\chi^2(1, N = 679) = 23.71$, $p < .001$, but weak ($\phi = .19$).[6]

Although the data presented above are the best estimates of clinicians' overall predictive accuracy, Table 3 presents the rate of accuracy of clinicians' predictions of violence for the first follow-up interval (e.g., the initial 2-month period after the predictions were made). Table 3 is presented to complement the data described below, which also pertain to the first follow-up interval. We focus here on just the first follow-up interval for several reasons. First, a single follow-up period makes the most sense for testing the hypotheses of interest. The relationship of interest here is whether the clinician can

TABLE 2

Accuracy of Clinicians' Violence Predictions *across*
All Three Follow-Up Intervals

	NO VIOLENT INCIDENT	VIOLENT INCIDENT	TOTAL
Predicted to be violent	146	177	323
Predicted to be nonviolent	227	129	356
Total	373	306	679

Positive predictive power	58%
Negative predictive power	61%
Sensitivity	.55
Specificity	.64

detect periods when drinking and violence cooccur, and this is best tested by looking at the shortest time frame available in the dataset. It makes little sense to determine whether a patient's drinking this month is related to a violent incident 4–6 months later. Second, because the results were virtually identical no matter which of the follow-up intervals we examined (see below), a decision was made to present data from only one follow-up interval. Third, data from the first follow-up interval was most closely related in time to when the prediction was made.

In Table 3, clinicians' predictions of whether or not a patient would be violent are cross-tabulated with whether or not that patient had a violent incident during the first follow-up interval. The data indicate that 33% of those predicted to be violent had a violent incident during the first follow-up period compared to 20% of those predicted to be nonviolent. The relationship between predictions of violence and violent incidents within 2 months was significant, $\chi^2(1, N = 679) = 15.93, p < .001$, but weak ($\phi = 0.15$). (The phi coefficient is a special case of the correlation coefficient for dichotomous variables; Edwards, 1984.)

TABLE 3

Accuracy of Clinicians' Violence Predictions
at Follow-Up Interval 1

	NO VIOLENT INCIDENT	VIOLENT INCIDENT	TOTAL
Predicted to be violent	216	107	323
Predicted to be nonviolent	286	70	356
Total	502	177	679

Positive predictive power	60%
Negative predictive power	57%
Sensitivity	.33
Specificity	.80

TABLE 4

Simple Association of Patient's Alcohol Use and Violent Incidents *at Follow-Up Interval* 1

	NO VIOLENT INCIDENT	VIOLENT INCIDENT	TOTAL
Moderate–heavy drinking	48	24	72
Light–moderate drinking	165	81	246
Abstinent	290	72	362
Total	503	177	680

Relationship Between Drinking and Violence

The second relationship to consider is between alcohol use and violence. Table 4 presents a cross-tabulation of the patient's degree of alcohol use during the first, 2-month follow-up interval with whether or not the patient had a violent incident during that interval. The data indicate that 20% of patients who did not drink had a violent incident compared with 33% of patients who were light–moderate drinkers (up to 13 drinks per week) and 33% of patients who were moderate–heavy drinkers (over 13 drinks per week). The relationship between alcohol use and violent incidents was significant, $\chi^2(2, N = 680) = 15.16, p < .01$, but weak ($\phi = .15$).

Relationship Between Predictions of Violence and Drinking

The third and final relationship considered is the association between clinicians' alcohol-intensified predictions of violence and patients' alcohol use. Table 5 presents a cross-tabulation of clinicians' predictions of alcohol-related violence with patients' degree of alcohol use during the first, 2-month follow-up interval. The data indicate that 56% of the patients predicted more likely to be violent when drinking were drinking during the first follow-up period compared to only 36% of patients predicted likely to be violent regardless of drinking and 47% of patients predicted to be nonviolent. This relationship between clinicians' alcohol-related predictions of violence and patients' alcohol use was significant, $\chi^2(4, N = 679) = 23.02, p < .001$, but weak ($\phi = .18$).

Because this follow-up period was brief, the figures above underestimate the association of clinician's alcohol-related predictions of violence with patient's drinking. Thus, the relationship was examined again, taking into account whether or not patients drank at any point during the 6-month follow-up period. This analysis revealed that 71% of patients predicted more likely to be violent when drinking drank during the 6-month follow-up period compared to only 48% of patients predicted to be violent regardless of drinking and 60% of patients predicted to be nonviolent. This relationship was also significant, $\chi^2 (2, N = 679) = 17.62, p < .001$, but weak ($\phi = .16$). Whether drinking is considered on a short- or long-term basis, clinicians' predictions of alcohol-related violence are associated with patients' use of alcohol. In addition, the level of drinking among those predicted to become violent regardless of drinking is relatively low compared to those predicted to be nonviolent.

TABLE 5

Association of Clinicians' Alcohol-Related Predictions of Violence and Patient's Drinking *at Follow-Up Interval 1*

	ABSTINENT	LIGHT– MODERATE DRINKING	MODERATE– HEAVY DRINKING	TOTAL
Predicted to be violent: alcohol intensifies likelihood	68	57	29	154
Predicted to be violent: alcohol does *not* intensify likelihood	108	49	12	169
Predicted to be nonviolent	186	140	30	356
Total	362	246	71	679

Summary of Bivariate Relationships

In summary, these analyses indicate that (1) clinicians' predictions of whether or not a patient will become violent are associated with violent incidents, (2) patients are more likely to become violent during periods in which they drink, and (3) clinicians' alcohol-related predictions of violence are associated with patients' drinking. The next step is to determine how well clinicians discriminate among patients who are likely to become violent during periods in which they drink and those who are not.

Essential Issue: Identification of Patients Who Become Violent during Periods in Which They Drink

A hierarchical log-linear analysis was performed to assess the relationship among the three variables examined above, that is, among clinicians' alcohol-related predictions of violence, patients' degree of alcohol use, and whether or not the patient was violent during the first follow-up interval. Stepwise selection by simple backward deletion of effects produced a significant model, $LR(4) = 8.14$, $p = .09$, that fit the observed frequencies well (normed fit index $= .98$).[7] This model included all of the first-order effects and all of the two-way associations, or interactions, between (1) alcohol-related violence predictions and violent incidents, (2) alcohol use and violent incidents, and (3) alcohol-related violence predictions and alcohol use (see Table 6).

These results reflect the bivariate associations presented above. What is notable, however, is that the relationship of focus, that is, the three-way association among alcohol-related predictions of violence, patients' degree of alcohol use, and patient's violent incidents, was *not* significant, $\chi^2 (4) = 8.15$, $p = .09$. Despite the fact that there was adequate power to detect at least a medium effect (Cohen, 1988, 1992), the three-way association was deleted from the model. These results indicate that clinicians do *not* discriminate well between patients who are likely to become violent during periods in which they drink from those who are not.

TABLE 6

Main Effects and Two-Way Interactions Identified by
Hierarchical Loglinear Analysis

EFFECT	df	PARTIAL χ^2
Alcohol-related predictions × Violent incident at first round	2	17.51***
Alcohol use at first round × Violent incident at first round	2	16.93***
Alcohol-related predictions × Alcohol use at first round	4	22.96***
Alcohol-related predictions	2	105.15***
Alcohol use at first round	2	216.39***
Violent incident at first round	1	162.12***

***$p < .001$.

Table 7 shows the frequencies behind these results (it consolidates Tables 2–4). This table presents two notable comparisons. First, 33% of patients with alcohol-intensified predictions of violence became violent compared with 33% of patients with nonalcohol intensified predictions of violence and 20% of patients predicted to be nonviolent. Second, 24% of patients with alcohol-intensified predictions of violence had violent incidents during a 2-month period in which they drank compared to 18% of patients with *non*-alcohol-intensified predictions of violence and 11% of patients predicted to be nonviolent. However, as indicated by the results of the log-linear analysis, these differences do not indicate a significant increment in predictive accuracy attributable to the clinicians' designation of a case as one that is likely to involve alcohol-related violence. Instead, the data are best explained by a scenario in which (1) clinicians are moderately accurate in predicting who will have a violent incident, (2) clinicians tend to predict that patients who drink heavily are more likely to have violent incidents when drinking, and (3) patients who drink are more likely to have violent incidents. The group with alcohol-intensified predictions of violence drank more and was at greater risk for violence, but a substantial number of cases that were not expected to have drinking-related violence also did so. Thus, clinicians' predictions of alcohol-related violence may be more descriptive of the typical drinking behavior of a group considered to be at risk for violence than predictive of violent incidents during periods in which patients are drinking.

Replication of Basic Results across Data Subsets

The analyses reported above were completed on numerous subsamples of the data, applying different definitions of the variables of interest. The pattern of results reported above was found regardless of whether (1) data used were from followup interval one, two, or three (occurring 2, 4, and 6 months after the prediction, respectively), (2) clinicians or attending physicians made the predictions, (3) alcohol use was operationalized as a continuous, ordinal, or dichotomous variable, and (4) cases predicted *not* to be violent were included in analyses. Thus, the basic results are robust across follow-up intervals, clinical disciplines, and alternative modes of measurement and analyses.

TABLE 7

Association of Alcohol-Related Predictions of Violence, Alcohol Use, and Violent Incidents

	NO VIOLENT INCIDENT	VIOLENT INCIDENT	TOTAL
Predicted to be violent: alcohol intensifies likelihood ($N = 154$)			
Abstinent	54	14	68
Light–moderate drinking	32	25	57
Moderate–heavy drinking	17	12	29
Predicted to be violent: alcohol does *not* intensify likelihood ($N = 169$)			
Abstinent	82	26	108
Light–moderate drinking	27	22	49
Moderate–heavy drinking	4	8	12
Predicted to be nonviolent ($N = 356$)			
Abstinent	154	32	186
Light–moderate drinking	106	34	140
Moderate–heavy drinking	26	4	30
Total	502	177	679

Testing an Alternative Interpretation: How Accurately Do MHPs Predict *Drinking-Associated* Violence?

The results above assess the relationship between alcohol consumption and violence based on a 2-month time interval (i.e., is a patient more likely to be violent during a period in which they drink?). Although it would be inconsistent with the central structure of the data collection interview, it may be argued that MHPs intended for their alcohol-related predictions of violence to indicate whether or not a patient was more likely to be violent *at the time he or she was under the influence of alcohol rather than during a period in which he or she was drinking.*

This alternative interpretation was tested by using a multinomial logistic regression in which clinicians' alcohol-related predictions of violence were used to predict whether or not the patient was judged to have had a violent incident while under the influence of alcohol during the first follow-up round (i.e., drinking-associated incident, non-drinking-associated violence, or no incident). The typical rate of alcohol consumption (average number of drinks consumed) per week during the first follow-up round was used as a covariate for clinicians' alcohol-related predictions, given the relationship between these predictions and patients' alcohol use identified above. There was a good model fit (discrimination among groups) on the basis of the covariate alone, that is, patients' typical rate of alcohol consumption, $\chi^2(2) = 12.34$, $p < .01$. However, comparison of the log-likelihood ratios for models with and without clinicians' alcohol-related predictions did *not* indicate improvement with the addition of clinicians' predictions, $\chi^2(2) = 3.96$, $p = .13$. Thus, regardless of whether clinicians interpret alcohol use as a condition for violence based on its immediate effects or on the more enduring, but short-term effects of heavy drinking, they do not discriminate well between patients who are more likely to become violent when drinking (or during periods in which they drink) and those who are not.

Nonjudgment Predictors of Violence during Periods in Which Patients Were Drinking

Further analyses were completed to determine whether predictors other than clinical judgment were effective in discriminating patients who were violent during a period in which they drank from those who had no violent incidents during periods of drinking. A stepwise logistic regression analysis was conducted with violence during a period of drinking as the dependent measure and degree of alcohol consumption, presence or absence of alcohol-related diagnoses, primary clinical diagnosis (schizophrenia or affective disorder, affective disorder, substance abuse, personality disorder, and other), age, race, gender, and socioeconomic status included as independent variables. The results indicated that violence during periods of drinking was significantly associated only with age, $\chi^2(1, N = 299) = 14.88$, $p < .0001$. Individual bivariate comparisons across these variables confirmed that the groups were distinguishable only in that patients who drank and became violent were somewhat younger ($M = 26$ years, $SD = 10$) than those who drank without becoming violent ($M = 30$ years, $SD = 10$) ($t(316) = 3.72$, $p < .000$). However, the most potentially powerful predictor of "alcohol-related violence," i.e., the extent and nature of the patient's past drinking-related violence, was not systematically coded by study investigators and available for inclusion in the analyses. It should be noted that the MHPs in this study *did* have access to this predictor, as they were left free to assess violence potential in whatever form they wished. MHPs could easily have assessed the patient's history of (drinking-related) violence during interviews or record reviews if they believed this was relevant to the case.

DISCUSSION

This study is among the first systematically to test the accuracy of MHPs' contextualized predictions of violence. By taking into account how MHPs must actually assess risk in response to the modern demands of risk management, this study provides a test of accuracy that is both "fairer" and more ecologically relevant than prior studies of MHPs' binary judgments of the likelihood of future violence. Nevertheless, the results do not unveil predictive accuracy that was hidden by prior studies, at least with respect to the condition of alcohol use. Accounting for clinicians' judgments that patient violence is particularly likely if they consume alcohol does not significantly increase their basic predictive validity. Of patients with alcohol-intensified predictions of violence, 24% had violent incidents during periods in which they drank, but a majority (57%) of those who drank did not become violent during that period. Conversely, a substantial proportion of patients who clinicians did *not* expect to become violent during periods in which they drank did so, including 18% of patients with *non*-alcohol-intensified predictions of violence and 11% of patients predicted to be nonviolent. Moreover, even when the relationship between alcohol use and violence was assessed *directly*, clinicians' alcohol-related predictions of violence did not predict drinking-associated violent incidents.

The patients who clinicians believed were more likely to have violent incidents when drinking drank more heavily and were therefore at greater risk for violence. However, a substantial number of patients who clinicians did *not* expect to have drinking-related violent incidents also did so. These data indicate that even when MHPs' apparent decisional processes are "built in" to tests of accuracy, their predictions of violence are still only marginally more accurate than chance (Monahan & Steadman, 1994; Otto, 1992).

Implications for Clinical Practice: Description Versus Prediction in Risk Assessment

It certainly would be welcome news if MHPs showed increased acumen when evaluating patients with drinking problems. Comorbid mental and alcohol abuse disorders are prevalent and risk-enhancing conditions that demand intensive clinical resources. For example, according to data from the Epidemiologic Catchment Area survey, having a mental disorder more than doubles the risk of having an alcohol disorder and vice versa (Regier et al., 1990). Similarly, in the MacArthur Violence Risk Assessment study, approximately 40% of patients with mental disorders had alcohol or other drug abuse diagnoses (Steadman et al., 1998; see Menezes, Johnson, Thornicroft, & Marshall, 1996, for alcohol-specific rates). Given their increased vulnerability to poor compliance with treatment, exacerbation of symptomatology, repeated hospitalization, and violent behavior, these patients require effective, targeted, ongoing mental health services (Bartels, Drake, & Wallach, 1995; Bartels, Teague, Drake, & Clarke, 1993; Maynard & Cox, 1998; Osher & Drake, 1996; J. Smith & Hucker, 1994).

Given that it is probably not an artifact of the study design, MHPs' frequent identification of alcohol use as a condition for violence is encouraging. Experimenters asked clinicians if there were conditions under which a patient was more likely to be violent and, after recording conditions that clinicians freely listed, asked if several specific conditions might potentiate violence. Clinicians often freely volunteered the condition of alcohol use, suggesting that this condition was salient to them. This suggests that MHPs are aware of relevant assessment issues and attend to crucial risk factors and appropriate targets for ongoing risk management even if this information fails to have a marked effect on their predictive accuracy. At least given the context of this study, MHPs appear to act in accordance with experts' recommendations to consider the situationally dependent nature of violence (e.g., Heilbrun, 1997; Monahan, 1981; Steadman et al., 1993; Webster et al., 1997).

Nevertheless, MHPs' predictions of alcohol-related violence are arguably more *descriptive* of the typical drinking behavior of a high-risk group than they are *predictive* of violent incidents during periods of drinking. The greater a patient's typical alcohol consumption, the greater MHPs' perceived risk that drinking would lead to violence. Because alcohol consumption and violence risk are positively correlated, predicting that heavy drinkers are more likely to become violent when drinking is a logical, good bet. However, the effectiveness of this strategy is limited, and contributes little in the way of specialized knowledge to risk assessment. The relationship between drinking and violence is far from unity, indicating that a substantial number of patients can drink heavily without incident, whereas others who consume little or no alcohol become violent. Moreover, the strategy adds little or no expertise to lay beliefs about the relationship between drinking and violence. Substantial survey research on alcohol attitudes and expectancies reveals a widespread belief in Western cultures that alcohol plays a causal role in aggression and violence (e.g., Critchlow, 1986; Kidder & Cohn, 1979; Roizen, 1983; Sjoberg, 1998). In a survey of 994 residents of Ontario, Paglia and Room (1998) found that 78% believed that someone who "had a few drinks and felt its effects" was likely to become aggressive and violent, and 85% believed that someone who "got very drunk" was likely to do so.

MHPs may add expertise to the prediction process by going beyond identifying whether a salient risk factor such as heavy drinking is present specifically to assessing the *link* between that risk factor and violence potential for the individual patient (for substance-abuse related reviews, see Johns, 1997; J. Smith & Hucker, 1994; Swanson, 1993; Osher & Drake, 1996). By assessing a patient's behavioral patterns over time, an MHP can determine whether drinking is a real condition that makes "violence more likely when present, or prevents or significantly reduces the likelihood of violence when absent" (Mulvey & Lidz, 1995, p. 138). Based on the results presented here, MHPs do not appear to be systematically evaluating whether alcohol use actually increases patients' risk for future violence.

Implications for Conducting Clinically Relevant Research

This study's essential finding that contextualized predictions of violence are no more accurate than binary predictions casts some doubt on experts' arguments that more sensitive, carefully designed research, perhaps focused on particular types of cases,[8] will detect substantially better rates of predictive accuracy than those found in modern studies of short-term predictions of violence (Buchanan, 1997; Grisso & Appelbaum, 1992; Litwack & Schlesinger, 1987, 1999). This single study does not, however, settle the issue. The condition of alcohol use is merely one "ingredient" in MHPs' complex scripts or narratives for expected patient violence. Because MHPs' predictions involve multiple conditions ($M = 4$, $SD = 2$) as well as specifications about the nature, target, and location of the expected violence, one might reasonably argue that the issue of MHPs' selective predictive accuracy remains open.

However, three points suggest that it may not be much more than "ajar." First, although this study isolated the single condition of alcohol use, MHPs had to have believed that drinking actually increased the patient's violence potential in order for their predictions to qualify as alcohol-intensified. Thus, drinking-related predictions of violence should have contributed predictive power to basic binary predictions, but did not. Second, Mulvey and Lidz (1998) studied several conditions and multiple specifications about expected violence using a different methodology and found limited predictive accuracy, very similar to that revealed in this study (see footnote 1).

Third, although patient's rate of alcohol consumption was measured in this study based on self-report, this arguably did not introduce enough error to affect the basic results. In supplementary analyses, clinicians' alcohol-related predictions were not predictive of *alcohol-associated incidents*, which reflect patient and collateral reports of whether or not alcohol was involved in each violent incident. Even taking collateral reports into account about the use of alcohol during the incident did not alter the pattern of the results. In addition, although collateral informants were not asked to estimate the number of drinks a patient consumed per week (because most were unable validly to do so), collateral informants and patients showed "good" (Cicchetti & Sparrow, 1981) chance-corrected levels of agreement as to whether or not the patient had been drinking over a 2-month period (kappa = .62).

Nevertheless, future investigations using (a) community-based samples of MHPs and (b) methodologies that permit richer depictions of clinical judgment may produce different results. Relative to the emergency room MHPs studied in this research, MHPs who treat potentially violent patients on an ongoing basis in the community are likely to develop richer violence narratives that include more carefully articulated and accurate conditions for violence. MHPs who work in emergency rooms are accustomed to focusing on immediate crises and may be less well-equipped to make short-term, highly contextualized predictions of violence than MHPs who treat patients in the community. In addition, cognitive theories and methodology, such as prototype or narrative-based research, may be best suited for capturing the key dimensions of MHPs' predictions and assessing the extent to which they match the features of patients' violent events or "nonevents" (Ericsson & Simon, 1984; Pennington & Hastie, 1992; Skeem, 1999; V. L. Smith, 1991, 1993). Methods that have been used to describe MHPs' forensic assessments could also be extrapolated to study the type of data and instruments upon which MHPs rely to assess risk and the logic they use to link perceived risk factors to violence potential (Heilbrun & Collins, 1995; Skeem, Golding, Berge & Cohn, 1998). Such research may (1) promote more sensitive and informative investigations of predictive accuracy and (2) identify specific problems in decision-making processes and assessment practices to target for improvement. Such efforts still seem worthwhile despite the results of this investigation. As observed by Borum (1996), "despite a long history of clinical and research interest in, and criticism of, MHPs' ability to predict violence, there have been few efforts to develop or evaluate interventions to improve decision making in this area" (p. 495). Efforts to improve practice can only be mounted after we obtain a better understanding of it.

NOTES

1. Mulvey and Lidz (1998) tested the accuracy of clinicians' specifications about patient violence (e.g., expected nature, timing, and target) and conditions for violence (i.e., medication noncompliance, alcohol use, and drug use). However, because the latter analyses did not include nonviolent cases, they could not address the central issue of this article, that is, how well clinicians discriminate between patients who were and were not likely to respond violently when drinking.

2. Because of this matching design, the study group is not representative of patients who appear at an emergency room. These cases were selected in a manner that overrepresented both those emergency room patients whom clinicians thought might commit violence and individuals who had demographic characteristics associated with this judgment. Compared to the individuals who appeared in the emergency room during the recruitment period, the study group was younger (28.6 years vs. 32.2 years) and more likely to be African American (48% vs. 34%) and male (62% vs. 44%).

3. All of the six possible interviews (one patient and one collateral interview at each of three follow-up intervals) were gathered for 59% of the study group that we were able to follow, and 78% had at least four interviews.

4. Because the study design classified patients as "predicted likely to be violent" and "predicted nonviolent" based on the summed ratings of clinicians and attendings, it may be argued that these classifications do not reflect clinicians' independent judgments. This argument is countered by two points. First, as previously noted, the ratings of clinicians and attendings were strongly correlated ($r = .68$). Second, clinicians were later asked to independently rate, on a 10-point scale ($0 =$ no change; $10 =$ certain), the likelihood that a patient would become violent if the conditions that he or she specified were met. In 98.5% of the 323 predictions classified as "likely to be violent," clinicians rated the patient at a 3 or above on this 10-point scale, a threshold similar to that set for the summed rating that qualified the prediction as "likely to be violent" (see above). Thus, it is quite likely that those cases jointly classified as "likely to be violent" typically reflected clinicians' independent judgments.

5. Because subjects were asked about conditions for violence after reporting and describing a violent incident, expectancy effects and recall bias could partially explain any relationship between violent incidents and drinking in these supplementary analyses. These biases are much less likely to affect the primary analyses reported above.

6. In fact, the relationship between clinicians' predictions and violence may be somewhat weaker than this figure suggests because cases in which MHP teams had little concern about violence (i.e., additive concern = 1–2) were excluded from analyses.

7. The normed fit index (Bentler & Bonett, 1980) evaluates models by comparing the c2 value of the model obtained to the χ^2 value of the model of independence: NFI = $(\chi^2_{indep} - \chi^2_{model}) \div (\chi^2_{indep})$. Values above .90 indicate a "good-fitting model" (Tabachnik & Fidell, 1996, p. 749).

8. McNiel and Binder (1998) found that clinicians' predictions of inpatient violence were more likely to be accurate when clinicians were confident in these predictions. Further research is needed to determine whether clinicians are more confident and accurate in particular *types* of cases. Clinicians are likely to be more confident and accurate in predicting violence where a patient has a clear, repetitive history of serious violence. However, accurate predictions in clear-cut cases are *not* strong testaments to clinicians' predictive powers. Our study calls into question whether there are meaningful *types* of cases (e.g., substance abuse cases, medication noncompliance cases, psychiatric deterioration cases) in which clinicians are more accurate.

REFERENCES

Bartels, S. J., Drake, R. E., & Wallach, M. A. (1995). Long-term course of substance use disorders among patients with severe mental illness. *Psychiatric Services, 46*(3), 248–251.

Bartels, S. J., Teague, G. B., Drake, R. E., & Clark, R. E. (1993). Substance abuse in schizophrenia: Service utilization and costs. *Journal of Nervous and Mental Disease, 181*(4), 227–232.

Bentler, P. & Bonett, D. (1980). Significance tests and goodness of fit in the analysis of covariance structures. *Psychological Bulletin, 88,* 588–606.

Borum, R. (1996). Improving the clinical practice of violence risk assessment: Technology, guidelines, and training. *American Psychologist, 51,* 945–956.

Borum, R., Otto, R., & Golding, S. (1993). Improving clinical judgment and decision making in forensic evaluation. *Journal of Psychiatry and Law, 21,* 35–76.

Buchanan, A. (1997). The investigation of acting on delusions as a tool for risk assessment in the mentally disordered. *British Journal of Psychiatry, 170,* 12–16.

Cicchetti, D. & Sparrow, S. (1981). Developing criteria for establishing interrater reliability of specific items: Applications to assessment of adaptive behavior. *American Journal of Mental Deficiency, 86,* 127–137.

Cohen, J. (1988). *Statistical power analysis for the behavioral sciences* (2nd ed.). Hillsdale, NJ: Erlbaum.

Cohen, J. (1992). A power primer. *Psychological Bulletin, 112,* 155–159.

Critchlow, B. (1986). The powers of John Barleycorn: Beliefs about the effects of alcohol on social behavior. *American Psychologist, 41*(7), 751–764.

Dvoskin, J. A. & Steadman, H. J. (1994). Using intensive case management to reduce violence by mentally ill persons in the community. *Hospital and Community Psychiatry, 45,* 679–684.

Edwards, A. (1984). *An introduction to linear regression and correlation,* (2nd ed.). New York: Freeman.

Ericsson, K. & Simon, H. A. (1984). *Protocol analysis: Verbal reports as data.* Cambridge, MA: MIT Press.

Fiske, S. T. (1993). Social cognition and social perception. *Annual Review of Psychology, 44,* 155–194.

Garb, H. N. (1998). *Studying the clinician: Judgment research and psychological assessment.* Washington, DC: American Psychological Association.

Genero, N. & Cantor, N. (1987). Exemplar prototypes and clinical diagnosis: Toward a cognitive economy. *Journal of Social and Clinical Psychology, 5,* 59–86.

Grisso, T. (1981). Clinical assessment for legally-relevant decisions: Research recommendations. In S. Shah & B. Sales (Eds.), *Law and mental health: Major developments and research needs* (pp. 49–81). Washington, DC: National Institute of Mental Health.

Grisso, T. & Appelbaum, P. S. (1992). Is it unethical to offer predictions of future violence? *Law and Human Behavior, 16*(6), 621–633.

Heilbrun, K. (1997). Prediction versus management models relevant to risk assessment: The importance of legal decision-making context. *Law and Human Behavior, 21,* 347–359.

Heilbrun, K. & Collins, S. (1995). Evaluations of trial competency and mental state at time of offense: Report characteristics. *Professional Psychology: Research and Practice, 26*(1), 61–67.

Hodgins, S. (1992). Mental disorder, intellectual deficiency, and crime: Evidence from a birth cohort. *Archives of General Psychiatry, 49*(6), 476–483.

Johns, A. (1997). Substance misuse: A primary risk and a major problem of comorbidity. *International Review of Psychiatry, 9,* 233–241.

Kansas v. Hendricks. (1997). 4564. U.S.L.W. 65.

Kidder, L. & Cohn, E. (1979). Public views of crime and crime prevention. In I. Frieze, D. Bar-Tal, & J. Carroll (Eds.), *New approaches to social problems* (pp. 237–264). San Francisco: Jossey-Bass.

Kiesler, C. & Simkins, C. (1993). *The unnoticed majority in inpatient care.* New York: Plenum Press.

Lerman, D. (1981). *Deinstitutionalization: A cross-problem analysis.* Rockville, MD: Department of Health and Human Services.

Lidz, C. W., Mulvey, E. P., & Gardner, W. (1993). The accuracy of predictions of violence to others. *Journal of the American Medical Association, 269*(8), 1007–1011.

Litwack, T. R. & Schlesinger, L. B. (1987). Assessing and predicting violence: Research, law, and applications. In I. Weiner & A. Hess (Eds.), *Handbook of forensic psychology* (pp. 205–257). New York: Wiley.

Litwack, T. R. & Schlesinger, L. B. (1999). Dangerousness risk assessments: Research, legal, and clinical considerations. In A. Hess & I. Weiner (Eds.), *Handbook of forensic psychology* (pp. 171–217). New York: Wiley.

Maynard, C. & Cox, G. B. (1998). Psychiatric hospitalization of persons with dual diagnoses: Estimates from two national surveys. *Psychiatric Services, 49*(12), 1615–1617.

McNiel, D. & Binder, R. (1998). The relationship between confidence and accuracy in clinical assessment of psychiatric patients' potential for violence. *Law and Human Behavior, 23,* 655–669.

Mechanic, D. (Ed.). (1998). *Managed behavioral health care: Current realities and future potential.* San Francisco: Jossey-Bass.

Meehl, P. E. (1954). *Clinical vs. statistical prediction: A theoretical analysis and a review of the evidence.* Minneapolis, MN: University of Minnesota Press.

Melton, G. B., Petrila, J., Poythress, N. G., & Slobogin, C. (1997). *Psychological evaluations for the courts*: A handbook for mental health professionals and lawyers (2nd ed.). New York: Guilford Press.

Menezes, P. R., Johnson, S., Thornicroft, G., & Marshall, J. (1996). Drug and alcohol problems among individuals with severe mental illnesses in South London. *British Journal of Psychiatry, 168*(5), 612–619.

Monahan, J. (1981). *The clinical prediction of violent behavior*. Washington, DC: U.S. Government Printing Office.

Monahan, J. (1996). Violence prediction: The past twenty and the next twenty years. *Criminal Justice and Behavior, 23,* 107–120.

Monahan, J. & Steadman, H. J. E. (1994). *Violence and mental disorder*: Developments in risk assessment. Chicago: University of Illinois Press.

Mossman, D. (1994). Assessing predictions of violence: Being accurate about accuracy. *Journal of Consulting and Clinical Psychology, 62,* 783–792.

Mulvey, E. P. & Lidz, C. W. (1985). Back to basics: A critical analysis of dangerousness research in a new legal environment. *Law and Human Behavior, 9,* 209–219.

Mulvey, E. P. & Lidz, C. W. (1995). Conditional prediction: A model for research on dangerousness to others in a new era. *International Journal of Law and Psychiatry, 18,* 129–143.

Mulvey, E. P. & Lidz, C. W. (1998). Clinical prediction of violence as a conditional judgment. *Social Psychiatry and Psychiatric Epidemiology, 33*(Supplement 1), S107–S113.

Mulvey, E., Shaw, E., & Lidz, C. (1994). Why use multiple sources in research on patient violence in the community? *Patient Behavior and Mental Health, 4,* 253–258.

Narrow, W. E., Regier, D. A., Rae, D. S., & Manderscheid, R. W., & Locke, B. Z. (1993). Use of services by persons with mental and addictive disorders: Findings from the National Institute of Mental Health Epidemiologic Catchment Area Program. *Archives of General Psychiatry, 50*(2), 95–107.

Osher, F. C. & Drake, R. E. (1996). Reversing a history of unmet needs: Approaches to care for persons with co-occurring addictive and mental disorders. *American Journal of Orthopsychiatry, 66*(1), 4–11.

Otto, R. K. (1992). Prediction of dangerous behavior: A review and analysis of "second-generation" research. *Forensic Reports, 5,* 103–133.

Paglia, A. & Room, R. (1998). Alcohol and aggression: General population views about causation and responsibility. *Journal of Substance Abuse, 10,* 199–216.

Parry, J. W. (1994). Involuntary civil commitment in the 90s: A constitutional perspective. *Mental and Physical Disability Law Reporter, 18,* 320–336.

Pennington, N. & Hastie, R. (1992). Explaining the evidence: Tests of the Story Model for juror decision making. *Journal of Personality and Social Psychology, 62,* 189–206.

Petrila, J. (1995). Who will pay for involuntary civil commitment under capitated managed care? An emerging dilemma. *Psychiatric Services, 46,* 1045–1048.

Rasanen, P., Tiihonen, J., Isohanni, M., Rantakallio, P., Lehtonen, J., & Moring, J. (1998). Schizophrenia, alcohol abuse, and violent beavhior: A 26-year followup study of an unselected birth cohort. *Schizophrenia Bulletin, 24*(3), 437–441.

Regier, D. A., Farmer, M., Rae, D. S., Locke, B., Keith, S., Judd, L., & Goodwin, F. (1990). Comorbidity of mental disorders with alcohol and other drug abuse: Results from the Epidemiologic Catchment Area (ECA) study. *Journal of the American Medical Association, 264*(19), 2511–2518.

Regier, D. A., Narrow, W. E., Rae, D. S., & Manderscheid, R. W. (1993). The de facto US mental and addictive disorders service system: Epidemiologic Catchment Area prospective 1-year prevalence rates of disorders and services. *Archives of General Psychiatry, 50*(2), 85–94.

Roizen, R. (1983). Loosening up: General population views of the effects of alcohol. In R. Room & G. Collins (Eds.), *Alcohol and disinhibitions*: Nature and meaning of the link (pp. 236–275). Washington, DC: Government Printing Office.

Schneider, D. (1991). Social cognition. *Annual Review of Psychology, 42,* 527–561.

Shah, S. A. (1978). Dangerousness: A paradigm for exploring some issues in law and psychology. *American Psychologist, 33*(3), 224–238.

Shelton v. Tucker. (1960). 364. U.S. 479.

Sjoberg, L. (1998). Risk perception of alcohol consumption. *Alcoholism*: Clinical and Experimental Research, 22(7 Supplement), S277–S284.

Skeem, J. (1999). *Understanding juror decision making and bias in insanity defense cases: The role of lay conceptions and case-relevant attitudes.* Unpublished doctoral dissertation, University of Utah, Salt Lake City.

Skeem, J. L., Golding, S. L., Berge, G., & Cohn, N. B. (1998). Logic and reliability of evaluations of competence to stand trial. *Law and Human Behavior, 22,* 519–547.

Slobogin, C. (1994). Involuntary community treatment of people who are violent and mentally ill: A legal analysis. *Hospital and Community Psychiatry, 45,* 685–689.

Smith, J. & Hucker, S. (1994). Schizophrenia and substance abuse. *British Journal of Psychiatry, 165*(1), 13–21.

Smith, V. L. (1991). Prototypes in the courtroom: Lay representations of legal concepts. *Journal of Personality and Social Psychology, 61,* 857–872.

Smith, V. L. (1993). When prior knowledge and law collide: Helping jurors use the law. *Law and Human Behavior, 17,* 507–536.

Steadman, H. J., Monahan, J., Appelbaum, P. S., Grisso, T., Mulvey, E. P., Roth, L. H., Robbins, P. C., & Klasser, D. (1994). Designing a new generation of risk assessment research. In J. Monahan & H. J. Steadman (Eds.), *Violence and Mental Disorder* (pp. 297–318). Chicago: University of Illinois Press.

Steadman, H. J., Mulvey, E. P., Monahan, J., Robbins, P. C., Appelbaum, P. S., Grisso, T., Roth, L. H., & Silver, E. (1998). Violence by people discharged from acute psychiatric inpatient facilities and by others in the same neighborhoods. *Archives of General Psychiatry, 55,* 393–401.

Straus, M., & Gelles, R. (1990). *Physical violence in American families.* Brunswick, NJ: Transaction.

Swanson, J. W. (1993). Alcohol abuse, mental disorder, and violent behavior: An epidemiologic Inquiry. *Alcohol Health and Research World, 17,* 123–132.

Swanson, J., Borum, R., Swartz, M., & Hiday, V. (1999). Violent behavior preceding hospitalization among persons with severe mental illness. *Law and Human Behavior, 23*(2), 185–204.

Swanson, J. W., Holzer, C. E., Ganju, V. K., & Jono, R. T. (1990). Violence and psychiatric disorder in the community: Evidence from the Epidemiologic Catchment Area surveys. *Hospital and Community Psychiatry, 41*(7), 761–770.

Swartz, M. S., Swanson, J. W., Hiday, V. A., Borum, R., Wagner, H. R., & Burns, B. J. (1998). Violence and severe mental illness: The effects of substance abuse and nonadherence to medication. *American Journal of Psychiatry, 155,* 226–231.

Tabachnick, B. & Fidell, L. (1996). *Using multivariate statistics* (3rd ed.). New York: Harper Collins.

Tarasoff v. Regents of the University of California. (1976). 551. P 2d. 334.

Tiihonen, J., Isohanni, M., Raesaenen, P., Koiranen, M., & Moring, J. (1997). Specific major mental disorders and criminality: A 26-year prospective study of the 1996 Northern Finland Birth Cohort. *American Journal of Psychiatry, 154*(6), 840–845.

Turk, D. C. E. & Salovey, P. E. (1988). *Reasoning, inference, and judgment in clinical psychology.* New York: Free Press.

Webster, C. D., Douglas, K. S., Eaves, D., & Hart, S. D. (1997). Assessing risk of violence to others. In C. D. Webster & M. A. Jackson (Eds.), *Impulsivity: Theory, assessment and treatment* (pp. 251–277). New York: Guilford Press.

23

The Influence of Actuarial Risk Assessment in Clinical Judgments and Tribunal Decisions about Mentally Disordered Offenders in Maximum Security

N. ZOE HILTON AND JANET L. SIMMONS

ABSTRACT: *Research has shown that actuarial assessments of violence risk are consistently more accurate than unaided judgments by clinicians, and it has been suggested that the availability of actuarial instruments will improve forensic decision making. This study examined clinical judgments and autonomous review tribunal decisions to detain forensic patients in maximum security. Variables included the availability of an actuarial risk report at the time of decision making, patient characteristics and history, and clinical presentation over the previous year. Detained and transferred patients did not differ in their actuarial risk of violent recidivism. The best predictor of tribunal decision was the senior clinician's testimony. There was also no significant association between the actuarial risk score and clinicians' opinions. Whether the actuarial report was available at the time of decision making did not alter the statistical model of either clinical judgments or tribunal decisions. Implications for the use of actuarial risk assessment in forensic decision making are discussed.*

Research over the past several years has indicated that unaided clinical judgment can lead to better-than-chance predictions of violence among mentally disordered offenders (e.g., Fuller & Cowan, 1999; Gardner, Lidz, Mulvey, & Shaw, 1996; Monahan, 1996; Mossman, 1994). Clinicians appear to be better, though, at identifying patients who

Reprinted with kind permission of Springer Science and Business Media. Law and Human Behavior, 25 (4), 393–408. © 2001 *American Psychology-Law Society/Division 41 of the American Psychology Association.*

adjust poorly to the institutional setting than those who are at long-term risk of violence after release (e.g., Bjørkly, 1995; McNeil & Binder, 1994; Quinsey, 1979). The accuracy of clinicians making unaided judgments of even imminent risk, moreover, is limited by generally low reliability (e.g., McNiel, Sandberg, & Binder, 1998; Werner, Rose, & Yesavage, 1990) and by systematic errors. For example, clinicians tend to overemphasize the importance of a history of homicide compared with property offenses (Quinsey & Maguire, 1986) and of medication noncompliance (Mulvey & Lidz, 1998) compared with characteristics such as hostility (McNiel & Binder, 1994).

Another limitation of clinical judgment in risk assessment is that clinicians using only unaided clinical judgment can be subject to the same errors and biases as lay persons. Little difference in predictive accuracy has been found, for example, among judgments made by psychiatrists, judges, and untrained raters in several simulated and naturalistic studies (Green & Baglioni, 1997; Jackson, 1989; Quinsey & Ambtman, 1979; Quinsey & Cyr, 1986; Webster, Sepejak, Menzies, Slomen, Jensen, & Butler, 1984). In one study, psychiatrists and teachers used the same sources of information when judging dangerousness, weighted the information in the same way, and showed similarly low degrees of interrater reliability (Quinsey & Ambtman, 1979). Neither group made great use of clinical assessment information. Thus, it could be argued that clinicians cannot be considered "experts" in that they appear to use the same methods and heuristics as non "experts" when making unaided judgments. One variable associated with positive ratings on numerous judgments is physical attractiveness (e.g., Agnew, 1984; Eagly, Ashmore, Makhijani, & Longo, 1991; Herman, Zanna, & Higgins, 1986; Thornhill & Gangestad, 1993). Facial attractiveness was found to significantly influence judgments of likelihood of sexual recidivism in a simulation study (Esses & Webster, 1988; see also MacCoun, 1990) despite no evidence that attractiveness is actually related to risk. As an example of another source of bias, Peay (1981) reported that composition of a tribunal panel was a primary predictor of actual and simulated decisions to release patients.

The accumulation of research into violence and risk assessment has led to assertions that unaided clinical judgments are of little value (e.g., Dawes, 1994; Dawes, Faust & Meehl, 1989; Grove & Meehl, 1996; Janus & Meehl, 1997; Mullen & Reinehr, 1982; Rice & Harris, 1995). Although there is still interest in developing clinician friendly rating scales and mnemonic devices to aid clinical judgment (e.g., Webster, Douglas, Eaves, & Hart, 1997), the question of the relative predictive accuracy of clinical and actuarial risk assessment methods has been declared "a dead horse" (Monahan et al., 2001).

In a wide variety of medical and social science decisions, actuarial assessments consistently meet or surpass the accuracy of clinical assessments (e.g., Grove & Meehl, 1996). According to Dawes et al. (1989, p. 1668), in the clinical method, "the decision maker combines or processes information in his or her head," whereas the actuarial method eliminates human judgment, and "conclusions rest solely on empirically established relations between data and . . . the event of interest." Actuarial assessments are designed to make systematic use of what is known about a group (e.g., men with a history of violence) and apply that knowledge to individual members of the group. Several actuarial assessments have been developed for predicting violence (e.g., Hanson & Thornton,

2000; Harris, Rice, & Quinsey, 1993; Steadman et al., 2000). These instruments rely on historic information about the offender (e.g., childhood behavior, criminal history, clinical history). Some of these variables, such as diagnosis of schizophrenia or psychotic symptoms, are inversely associated with future violence despite clinicians' traditional belief in a positive association (e.g., Harris & Rice, 1997; Steadman et al., 2000).

To what extent are actuarial instruments and clinical judgments used in forensic decision making? Judicial decision making has been said to be essentially "rubber-stamping" the recommendations made by psychiatrists (Konečni & Ebbesen, 1984, p. 12), even though psychiatrists' recommendations are associated primarily with criminal history (Konečni, Mulcahy, & Ebbesen, 1980). Similarly, decisions by a provincial government to release its forensic patients were highly congruent with the original clinical team recommendations (Quinsey & Ambtman, 1978; see also Adams, Pitre, & Cieszkowski, 1997). Thus, clinical judgments were extremely influential in forensic decisions in past decades. Is the same true since the introduction of more accurate methods of risk assessment? More recently, clinician ratings of treatment gains were indeed strongly related to the granting of parole for convicted sex offenders despite the lack of association of such ratings with recidivism (Quinsey, Khanna, & Malcolm, 1998).

For mental health tribunals charged with making decisions about the release of mentally disordered offenders, the availability of actuarial assessment is a fairly new phenomenon and its use virtually unstudied. Taylor, Goldberg, Leese, Butwell and Reed (1999) observed that tribunals did not reliably use actuarial information in such decisions. Indeed, there is little agreement about how such information can be used to inform forensic decision making. The debate includes those who argue that risk assessment should be based entirely (e.g., Quinsey, Harris, Rice, & Cormier, 1998) or not at all (e.g, Litwack, 1993; Price, 1997) on actuarial methods. Others look with optimism to a combination of actuarial and clinical methods (e.g., Janus & Meehl, 1997; Monahan, 1996) and suggest that the next important direction for risk assessment research is the communication of risk information and the flow from risk assessment to effective risk management (Fuller & Cowan, 1999; Heilbrun, O'Neill, Strohman, Bowman, & Philipson, 2000; Monahan, 1996). Kropp and Hart (2000) expressed optimism that the availability of risk assessments will result in improved decision making and ultimately decreased recidivism rates.

Does providing an actuarial risk assessment report to clinicians and other decision makers increase their use of such information? How do judicial decision makers balance actuarial risk scores with nonactuarial testimony from clinicians? Do clinicians combine actuarial information with more idiosyncratic case information? The setting of this research allowed us to study not only decisions by an autonomous review tribunal, but also clinical opinions of multidisciplinary treatment teams independently of the tribunal and senior clinicians testifying at the tribunal, in cases for which actuarial assessments were reported on patient files and others for which these reports were not available.

THE SETTING

We examined decisions made about insanity acquittee or unfit patients held under maximum security (all male) in the Province of Ontario since 1992, when the tribunal Ontario Review Board became the decision-making body regarding such persons. The function of this tribunal is identical to others across Canada and essentially the same as mental health review tribunals found elsewhere (e.g., Taylor et al., 1999). The *Criminal Code of Canada* (Section 672.54) instructs review boards to base their annual decisions upon "the need to protect the public from dangerous persons, the mental condition of the accused, the reintegration of the accused into society, and the other needs of the accused." The tribunal may detain a patient in maximum security or a less secure hospital or discharge the patient, with or without conditions in each case. The tribunal quorum must include a chairperson (lawyer or judge), a psychiatrist, and one other member. Remaining panel members include additional lawyers or psychiatrists, psychologists, or lay members. In Ontario's maximum security facility, the patient's multidisciplinary clinical team meets prior to the hearing to discuss his suitability for release to another facility. Their collective recommendation is included in a written report that is read by the tribunal panel before the hearing. The tribunal hears evidence from a senior clinician in almost every case. The report also summarizes the patient's history, course in hospital, and actuarial risk assessment when available (described later).

The actuarial assessment provided to decision makers in this setting is the Violence Risk Appraisal Guide (VRAG) (Harris, Rice, & Quinsey, 1993; Quinsey, Harris, et al., 1998). The VRAG was constructed and initially cross-validated on men assessed in Oak Ridge, many of whom were subsequently convicted. It uses a weighted score of 12 items including demographic, childhood history, criminal history, and static psychiatric variables. The scoring is based on information obtained upon the first postindex offense admission to a custodial or psychiatric facility. Almost all of the VRAG construction sample was eventually at risk (i.e., not in a secure facility) during the followup period. Its predictive accuracy for violent recidivism, as measured by the area under the curve of the relative operating characteristic, ranged from .73 to .77, corresponding to a large effect size (Cohen's $d > 1.0$; Quinsey, Harris, et al., 1998). The ability of the VRAG to predict violent recidivism in both mentally disordered and convicted offenders has been borne out in a variety of replications (e.g., Barbaree & Seto, 1998; Bélanger & Earls, 1996; Hanson & Harris, 2000; Quinsey, Coleman, Jones, & Altrows, 1997; Rice & Harris, 1997). Even pronounced deviations from the published scoring criteria outperform clinical judgment (Grann, Belfrage, & Tengström, 2000; Polvi, 1999). Polvi (1999) also showed that clinical judgment does not account for variability in recidivism that is not also (and more powerfully) explained by the VRAG. For these reasons, we used VRAG score as an index of violence risk in this sample.

The VRAG was first deemed admissable evidence in a 1992 Ontario Review Board hearing. Beginning that same year, VRAG reports were completed by trained hospital staff and placed on patient files, so that by 1997 reports were available for 90% of patients shortly after admission. The VRAG report summarized the VRAG items and information associated with the VRAG score, based on information otherwise already documented throughout the file (and therefore available to clinicians and the tribunal with or without the VRAG report). The VRAG report also stated the percentile rank of the patients' score, the category of risk (out of nine categories), and the probability of violent recidivism within 7 or 10 years of release associated with that category (for sample reports see Quinsey, Harris, et al. 1998).

RESEARCH QUESTIONS

The aim of this study was not to examine the relative accuracy of actuarial and clinical risk assessments; rather, we used the VRAG score as an index of risk. We examined the extent to which tribunal decisions and clinical opinions were associated with actuarial risk or other variables, overall and as a function of whether the VRAG report was available to decision makers. Because clinicians have been shown to predict violence better than chance, we predicted a positive association of both the tribunal decision and clinical opinions with actuarial risk score; moreover, we predicted that these associations would be stronger when the VRAG report was on file at the time of the tribunal. Because research predating the availability of actuarial risk assessment indicates that clinicians consider variables that are unrelated or are inversely related to violent outcome, we anticipated that such variables would also be related to decisions and to clinical opinions in this study. To examine this, we recorded current clinical presentation (symptoms, behavior problems, life skills, mood, etc.) and criminal history including index offense severity. To account for some apparently irrelevant variables which have nevertheless been associated with forensic decision making in previous research, we recorded the professional composition of the tribunal panel and research assistants' ratings of patients' physical attractiveness. We predicted that actuarial risk scores would add significantly to multiple regression models of tribunal decisions and clinical opinions after such variables.

METHOD

Tribunal Cases

All cases were coded from files pertaining to patients detained in Oak Ridge other than for assessment, excluding involuntarily committed patients because they are not under the jurisdiction of the Ontario Review Board. Characteristics of patients in this facility have been described elsewhere (e.g., Quinsey, Harris, et al., 1998). Most have been charged with serious, usually violent, offenses. We examined one hearing held in 1992 or later (up to spring, 1999) for each patient. We excluded hearings at which the patient was found fit to stand trial and returned to court because the hearings did not concern release. Because of the high rate of hearings resulting in no change to the patients' status (cf. Taylor et al., 1999), we used a stratified sampling method to ensure that at least 30% of the sampled hearings resulted in release decisions. Variables coded for the present study were coded from files by research assistants and the second author, with a random 10% sample also independently coded by the first author. All variables reported in the analyses met interrater reliabilities of $r > .80$ or $\kappa > .70$.

Variables

Because the tribunal has a range of disposition options, including more than one level of security in between maximum and community release, tribunal decision was coded on a 5-point ordinal scale (0 – discharge, 1 – medium security with community access, 2 – medium security with no community access, 3 – medium security for temporary period other than for assessment, 4 – remain in maximum security). For some analyses, this variable was dichotomized at $0 - 2$ (*transfer*) and $3 - 4$ (*detain*). Recommendations made to the tribunal by the clinical team were coded on a 5-point scale (1 – unanimous to release from maximum security, 2 – majority for release, 3 – team split, 4 – majority for remain, 5 – unanimous to remain). Senior clinician testimony given at the hearing was coded on a similar scale (1 – recommends release, 2 – no explicit recommendation but testimony favors release, 3 – undecided, 4 – testimony favors remaining, 5 – recommends remaining). These variables were used as interval scales to reflect both direction and strength of decision. Psychotropic medication intended to treat a disorder of thought or mood, but not hormonal or other medications, were coded on a 5-point scale (1 – refused, 2 – not offered, 3 – complied inconsistently, 4 – complied with limited success, 5 – complied with satisfactory success). "Success" was based on statements made on the clinical file about the effect of medication upon the patient's symptoms. For some analyses, this variable was transformed into several dichotomies (i.e., offered vs. not offered, any success noted vs. not, compliance vs. any noncompliance).

Patient Characteristics

Physical attractiveness was rated before coding the file by raters who did not know the patient, on a scale of 1–10, using the file photograph (head and shoulders) most recent to the hearing. This photograph was sometimes more than a year old at the time of the hearing. No attempt was made to obtain tribunal panel members' perceptions of patient attractiveness or other characteristics. For 30 cases of recent hearings, raters familiar with the patients used the same scale to rate general attractiveness. The two ratings were correlated, $r(30) = .70$; only photograph ratings are reported later. IQ was coded as a full score from existing psychological reports in the file. Psychopathy was scored from file information according to the manual of the Psychopathy Checklist—Revised (Hare, 1991) by a rater with extensive experience and established reliability and validity in such scoring (Harris, Rice, & Quinsey, 1993). Status was coded as either unfit or insanity acquittee/not criminally responsible (NCR).

Patient History

Length of stay was calculated from the most recent admission up to the hearing date. Prior admissions included admissions to the maximum security facility or its associated regional psychiatric facility. The index offense (the charge(s) resulting in the finding of NCR or currently faced by the unfit patient) and preindex criminal histories including violent, nonviolent, and property offenses, were scored using the Cormier–Lang system for quantifying criminal history (Quinsey, Harris, et al., 1998). This score is the sum of weighted scores for each charge, ranging from 1 (*for mischief, forged check, etc.*) to 28 (*for homicide*) such that it quantifies the extent and severity of the criminal history. We also recorded whether the VRAG report was on the patient's file at the time of the hearing. The file report did not include the raw score but stated the risk level as one of nine categories of risk, the percentile rank, and the probability of violent recidivism (see sample report in Quinsey, Harris, et al., 1998).

The raw VRAG score was derived from a database of forensic patients in Ontario created subsequent to most of the decisions in this study (Rice, Harris, Cormier, Lang, Coleman, & Smith Krans, 1999). Thus, we were able to use VRAG score as an index of violence risk in cases in which the VRAG report either was or was not available to decision makers. A score of zero represents the mean risk for the construction sample of violent offenders, with positive and negative scores indicating higher and lower risk, respectively.

Clinical Presentation

Problems documented in the hospital file were coded for the year preceding the multidisciplinary team recommendation, or from admission to hearing when less than a year, using a 78-item problem checklist. This checklist was modified from a rating scale used in previous research in this setting and elsewhere, with problem categories yielded by previous analyses distinguishing patient clusters (e.g., Harris, Hilton, & Rice, 1993; Harris & Rice, 1990; Quinsey, Cyr, & Lavellee, 1988; Rice & Harris, 1988). The categories include institutional management problems (29 items, e.g., assaults, procriminal attitudes, rule-breaking, lying), active psychotic symptoms (12 items, e.g., hallucinatory behavior, grandiosity), life skills deficits (13 items, e.g., poor self-care, poor conversation skills), and other smaller scales concerning mood and behaviors noted in the institution (Table 1).

RESULTS

The stratified sampling biased tribunals in favor of those resulting in release decisions, but we included all patients with hearings meeting the research criteria, and examined one hearing per patient. In rare cases (under five), documentation was not available in our archives because the patient was transferred soon after the hearing. A sample of 187 hearings resulted. Tribunal panels consisted of various combinations of 69 tribunal panel members, not equally represented; multidisciplinary teams also included combinations of many clinicians from several disciplines; testimony was provided at the hearings by at least 10 different senior clinicians (some were not named in the tribunal report) including two representing 64% of cases.

Of the 187 tribunals, 66 (35.3%) resulted in decisions to transfer from maximum security, including 64 transfers to medium security (23.0% with community access, 11.2% without) and two discharges. Characteristics distinguishing detained and transferred patients are shown in Table 1. VRAG reports were on file at the time of the hearing in 119 cases (63.6%), and VRAG scores were obtained for 169 cases (90.4%) for this study. The availability of a VRAG report at the hearing was positively associated with patients' length of stay at that time, $r(184) = .25, p < .001$.

Tribunal Decision[1]

There was a strong, positive correlation of tribunal decision (5-point scale) with the senior clinician testimony at the tribunal, $r(167) = .84$, and with the multidisciplinary team recommendation, $r(173) = .78$, $ps < .001$. The two forms of clinical opinion were also strongly associated with each other, $r(154) = .84, p < .001$. Contrary to our prediction, there was no significant association of the VRAG score with the tribunal decision, $r(169) = .06$, the team recommendation, $r(160) = .01$, or the senior clinician testimony, $r(152) = -.02$, all ns. We had predicted these correlations would be more strongly positive when the VRAG was on file at the time of the hearing than when it was not; however, there were only very small, nonsignificant differences: tribunal decision, $r(114) = .07$ versus $r(55) = .03$; team recommendation, $r(114) = .02$ versus $r(46) = -.03$; clinician testimony, $r(106) = -.06$ versus $r(46) = .04$; for VRAG on-file and not on-file, respectively. Thus, detained and transferred patients did not differ significantly in their mean risk of violent recidivism as scored on the VRAG (Table 1), and having the VRAG on file at the time of the decision did not alter this result. In the few cases in which the tribunal made a decision contrary to the senior clinician testimony, transferred patients tended to have lower scores, although this difference was not statistically significant in this small sample, transferred $M= -4.44$ ($SD= 10.13$), detained $M = 6.29$ ($SD= 15.82$), $t(14) = 1.65, p < .12$.

To examine the variables associated with tribunal decision, we conducted separate stepwise regression analyses (α to enter = .05 and remove = .10) of patient characteristics and history, clinical presentation variables, clinical opinions, and tribunal variables. The surviving variables were entered into a final stepwise analysis. The most parsimonious model contained only senior clinician testimony, β and multiple $R = .84$, $R^2_a = .71$, $F(1, 165) = 396.55, p < .001$. When the VRAG report was available, a small but significant improvement over the testimony-only model was made with the addition of the VRAG score, $\beta = .11, R^2$ change = .01, $p = .05$. When no VRAG report was available at the time of decision-making, the statistical contribution of actuarial risk score was nil. Using binary logistic regression on the dichotomized tribunal decision, only senior clinician testimony made a significant contribution even when the VRAG was available; clinician testimony correctly classified 91.2% of decisions to detain versus transfer.

TABLE 1

Characteristics of Review Cases by Tribunal Decision

TRIBUNAL DECISION	DETAIN	TRANSFER	t OR χ^2	r VRAG SCORE
PATIENT CHARACTERISTICS				
Attractiveness	3.46 (2.04)	4.64 (2.03)	3.70***	
IQ	96.38 (16.11)	99.23 (17.09)		
Psychopathy scores	17.96 (9.12)	14.07 (7.76)	2.35*	.82***
Unfit to stand trial (%)	14.9	3.2	5.85*	
PATIENT HISTORY				
Length of stay (years)	4.02 (4.83)	3.17 (3.15)		.30**
Prior admissions	1.83 (2.00)	1.13 (1.35)	2.51**	.18*
Index offense score	16.69 (18.23)	16.28 (13.04)		
Preindex criminal history score	21.30 (25.40)	11.52 (15.25)	2.82**	.40***
VRAG score	3.13 (11.16)	1.55 (11.72)		—
CLINICAL PRESENTATION IN PAST YEAR				
Total problem score	13.29 (6.50)	10.71 (6.15)	2.62*	
Institutional management problems	5.53 (3.25)	3.92 (2.82)	3.31***	
Active psychotic symptoms	3.73 (2.72)	2.61 (2.19)	2.84**	−.18*
Life skills deficits	1.68 (1.67)	1.71 (1.59)		
Social withdrawal	1.38 (1.17)	1.55 (1.26)		−.31***
Depression/anxiety	.43 (.82)	.69 (.78)	2.06*	
PSYCHOTROPIC MEDICATION				
Offered	88.2	87.9		−.26***
Compliant[a]	67.3	82.8	4.49*	
Success noted[a]	66.7	86.2	7.35**	
CLINICAL OPINIONS (PERCENT RECOMMENDING TRANSFER)				
Senior clinician	7.4	86.2	115.25***	
Clinical team	8.3	80.3	99.21***	
TRIBUNAL (%)				
Patient counsel present	81.8	90.9		
Nonpsychiatrist clinician on board	21.5	17.7		
Layperson on review board	73.3	85.9	3.82*	
Female(s) on review board	53.8	55.4		
Senior clinician testimony cited	87.6	93.8		
VRAG on file	63.6	63.6		.21*

Note: Standard deviations in parentheses. Cell sizes range from 68 to 121 (detained) and 41 to 63 (transferred). Only statistically significant ($p < .05$ two-tailed) test statistics are shown.ˆ

a. Excludes those not offered medication.

*$p < .05$. **$p < .01$. ***$p < .001$.

Clinical Opinions

Because tribunal decision was so strongly related to clinical opinions, we conducted separate stepwise regression analyses of patient characteristics, history, and clinical presentation variables to obtain surviving variables for a final stepwise regression analysis of each clinical opinion. The variables in the final model of senior clinician testimony were, in order of entry: institutional management problems, $\beta = .22, p < .001$; psychotropic medication use and success (5-point scale), $\beta = -.31$, R^2 change = .07, $p < .01$; attractiveness, $\beta = -.23$, R^2 change = .06, $p < .01$; and preindex criminal history, $\beta = .16$, R^2 change = .02, $p < .05$. That is, patients with more institutional management problems, less medication compliance and success, lower attractiveness, and more serious preindex criminal history were more likely to be recommended for detention in maximum security. The model of multidisciplinary team recommendation was almost identical: institutional management problem score, $\beta = .20$, $p < .001$; psychotropic medication $\beta = -.31$, R^2 change = .07, $p < .001$; attractiveness $\beta = -.21$, R^2 change = .05, $p < .01$; and preindex criminal history score $\beta = .20$, R^2 change = .04, $p < .01$, model multiple $R = .51$, $R^2_a = .24$, $F(4, 151) = 11.66$, $p < .001$.

The VRAG score did not contribute to either of the clinical opinion models even when the VRAG report was available at the time of decision making, contrary to our prediction. In addition, when the VRAG report was available, criminal history no longer contributed to the model of senior clinician testimony, and the only surviving variables were psychotropic medication use and success, $\beta = -.36$, and attractiveness, $\beta = -.29$, R^2 change = .08, $p < .01$. Because of the importance of these two variables in the clinical opinion models, we examined them both more closely.

Medication

Most patients (88.1%) were offered psychotropic medication in the previous year; not surprisingly, then, predictors of clinical opinions among those offered medication were the same as those in the models for the entire sample. Among those offered medication, compliance and success were not significantly associated with VRAG score.

Attractiveness

Attractiveness was associated with team recommendations, $r(159) = -.23, p < .01$, and senior clinician testimony, $r(156) = -.26, p < .001$, such that more attractive patients were less likely to be detained. More attractive patients had worse index offenses, $r(174) = .23, p < .01$, fewer prior psychiatric admissions, $r(173) = -.19, p < .05$, and a lower total problem score, $r(173) = -.26, p < .001$ (especially in the categories of Life Skills Deficits, Active Psychotic Symptoms, and Institutional Management Problems). Also, attractiveness was inversely correlated with age such that younger patients were more attractive, $r(174) = -.20, p < .01$.

DISCUSSION

Findings and Implications

This study found that an autonomous tribunal's decisions to detain mentally disordered offenders in maximum security were best predicted by clinical opinions, particularly the senior clinician testimony given at the tribunal hearing. There was no significant correlation between the actuarial risk of violent recidivism and the tribunal decision or clinical opinions. Transferred patients did not have significantly lower actuarial risk scores than detained patients even when the actuarial risk report was available to decision makers. Clinicians' recommendations for release were predicted by psychotropic medication, patient physical attractiveness, institutional management problems, and criminal history. Consistent with our prediction, only one of these variables (criminal history) significantly correlated with the VRAG score, whereas being offered medication was inversely correlated. These findings overall indicate that, contrary to current optimism in the field, actuarial risk assessment had little influence on clinical judgments and tribunal decisions about mentally disordered offenders in this maximum security setting.

When the VRAG report was available, risk score made a small but significant contribution to a multiple regression model of tribunal decisions after accounting for clinical opinions. Thus, although the VRAG score was derived from information otherwise present in the patient file, only when the actuarial assessment results were available did the score make any statistical contribution to tribunal decisions. This suggests there is some value in providing the assessment report to decision makers. Unfortunately, this finding was not confirmed by a more conservative binary logistic regression of dichotomized decisions to detain versus transfer. Thus, it appears that detention of patients in maximum security was influenced little or not at all by the risk of reoffending.[2] Indeed, when the VRAG report was available, the model of senior clinician testimony included only medication (inversely related to risk) and attractiveness (unrelated to risk). This finding is consistent with the notion that clinicians try to offer the tribunal an opinion based on clinical information that is not already accounted for in the VRAG, a notion that we have heard expressed in clinical meetings (e.g., "The VRAG is just one part of the picture; we provide a different part"). Unfortunately, it appears that such opinions were unrelated to risk of violent recidivism.

Whether the patient was offered such medication in the previous year was unrelated to recommendations or release (but inversely to risk); however, compliance and success were positively related. Similarly, Quinsey and Ambtman (1978) reported that clinicians recommended for release more patients who were not receiving psychotropic medication at the time the recommendations were made. We speculate that clinicians attend not so much to the role of mental disorder (or lack thereof) as a predictor of violent recidivism, as to the successful treatment of mental disorder. This idea suggests that the traditional clinical role of symptom management has a predominant and deleterious influence on forensic decisions pertaining to risk of violence.

The finding that clinicians recommended more attractive patients for release is similar to that of simulation studies in which lay persons acquitted more attractive defendants (MacCoun, 1990) and rated unattractive sex offenders more likely to meet criteria for dangerousness (Esses & Webster, 1988). In our sample, attractiveness was unrelated to actuarial risk of future violence; however, lower attractiveness was associated with more psychiatric hospitalizations and more problems noted in the previous year, including psychotic symptoms. Perhaps less attractive patients were simply those whose psychotic disturbance rendered them both more disruptive and less likely to care for their physical appearance, and it was their disordered and disruptive behavior that led to the recommendation against transfer. It is also possible that attractiveness in itself created a more favorable impression, and more attractive patients were consequently better able to persuade clinicians to support their request for release (a large majority of these patients believe they should be released, Rice et al., 1999). This interpretation is consistent with psychological research on attractiveness, and with a possible construct of "likeability" to which both attractiveness and compliance might contribute. The links among attractiveness, psychiatric disorder, and other heuristic cues in forensic decision making warrant further study.

In this study, VRAG score was positively associated with the VRAG report being on the file at the time of the tribunal. Quinsey (1999) has stated that even a small tendency to detain more dangerous patients eventually leads to an accumulation of long stay high risk patients; indeed, the VRAG report of longer stay patients was more likely to be completed and on file in time for the tribunals. This confound might be attributable to the practical limitations of completing a time-consuming risk assessment. This confound might explain a positive association between VRAG report availability and conservative decisions. Yet, in cases where the VRAG report was on file, VRAG score was associated with other continuous (e.g., IQ, total problems score) and dichotomized (e.g., medications offered) variables, indicating that there was sufficient variability in VRAG scores when available to permit powerful tests of its effect.

This study required stratified sampling of hearings (but not patients), in order to predict transfer decisions within a conservative system yielding few transfers per year. An advantage of this method is that correlation coefficients are a better index of effect size as the base rate approaches 50%. A possible undesirable consequence of increasing the base rate of transfer decisions in order to detect effects, was that it might have artificially inflated some statistical associations detected. The magnitude of the coefficients obtained for the association of clinical judgments with variables such as institutional management problems, therefore, might be attenuated in replications using other sampling methods. Stratified sampling is unlikely to affect the type of associations observed; for example, were VRAG score truly associated with decision making, patients with lower scores would nevertheless have been more likely to appear among the hearings leading to transfer. Our conclusions about variables not associated with decisions are not affected by the sampling method.

We had hoped to examine nonmedical treatment, but statements about goals, attendance, and success of nonmedical treatment were often absent from files. A supplementary survey of clinical staff, intended to inform our variable definition, revealed little agreement on the activities that were considered to be "therapy." Such problems demonstrate the limits to reliability and validity of clinical assessment, and the need to improve accuracy in measuring and recording clinical information. This problem has been noted in previous research; the assessment of treatment potential and success has shown poor reliability and equivocal association with violent recidivism (e.g., Quinsey, Khanna, & Malcolm, 1998; Rogers & Webster, 1989; Seto & Barbaree, 1999).

Also, this study was conducted at a single, maximum security institution; however, the findings concerning clinical opinions are consistent with previous research suggesting that the results are generalizable to other jurisdictions.

Future Research

We studied only one tribunal decision per offender, so that long-stay patients would not unduly influence the results. In the future, though, examining more than one hearing for each patient would permit a study of the effects of changes in patient characteristics or other variables. Also, we studied the variables associated with tribunal decisions in a naturalistic study. A simulation study could experimentally manipulate the availability or content of clinical opinions, or the score on an actuarial risk assessment instrument, to test conditions that might affect how the two sources of information might be weighted by a tribunal panel. Ways of communicating actuarial risk information and the effect they have on decision making could also be examined experimentally.

We did not interview the decision makers or examine the transcript of the tribunal. Examining how tribunal panels attempt to assimilate the great deal of information they obtain from reports and *viva voce* evidence into a single decision might help explain the present findings. For example, in our experience of review board hearings, much time and attention is given to current clinical presentation, recent treatment progress, and *viva voce* evidence, rather than to written reports. There is little discussion of the actuarial assessment, yet there may be an earnest attempt to identify changes that might indicate a change in risk, an area in which empirical research is comparatively weak (e.g., Hanson, 1998). Research into the process of assessing risk has shed light on such variables as clinician confidence, conservatism, differing perceptions of criteria for risk, etc. (e.g., Lidz, Mulvey, Apperson, Evanczuk, & Shea, 1992; McNiel, et al., 1998). In the future, similar studies could examine how decision makers deliberate on actuarial risk assessment results and other sources of information, and how they justify each decision. Such research could inform the development of accurate yet clinician-friendly assessment tools.

Risk Assessment and Decision Making

This study suggests that decisions about release of mentally disordered offenders are made somewhat on the basis of successful treatment of disorder. Current research indicating the inverse association of clinical variables and future violence does not support the view that treating disorders would reduce violent reoffending (e.g., Harris & Rice, 1997; Steadman et al., 2000). The availability of empirically based risk assessment tools essentially redefines the task of risk assessment. Deviations from empirically validated actuarial assessments result in worse outcomes in the long run (Grove & Meehl, 1996). Given a limited number of secure forensic beds available within any system, detention of low risk offenders inevitably requires the release of higher risk offenders. Using published VRAG norms (Quinsey, Harris, et al., 1998) to calculate the likely recidivism rate of patients released in this study, we would expect 48% to recidivate violently within 10 years of eventual opportunity. Had release decisions been based entirely upon the VRAG, we would expect only 24% to recidivate violently.

There appears, therefore, to be grounds for moving the forensic clinician's role in risk assessment away from offering judgments of risk, and focusing more on the completion of actuarial assessments of violence. Clinical expertise is required, for example, in scoring the measures of psychopathy, personality disorder, and schizophrenia included in the VRAG. Measures (but not unaided judgments) of specific current symptoms and anti-social behavior can also add to the ability of actuarial assessments to predict reoffending in the proximate future (Quinsey et al., 1997), although evidence that such measures can improve upon actuarial tools assessing long-term risk of violence is still to come. In research with the HCR-20 (an aid to structured clinical assessment consisting of 20 historical, clinical, and risk management items), the Clinical scale, with variables including major mental illness and treatment response, has so far shown poorer performance than the Historical scale in predicting long-term violence (e.g., Douglas, Ogloff, Nicholls, & Grant, 1999; Webster, Douglas, Eaves, & Hart, 1997).

In summary, this study indicated that the availability of an empirically validated actuarial risk assessment report did not substantially influence clinical opinions or tribunal decisions to release forensic patients from maximum security. There was some evidence that tribunals tended to make decisions more consistent with actuarial risk of violent recidivism when acting independently of clinical opinion. It is apparent, however, that simply creating actuarial instruments and making the results available to decision makers does not alter long-established patterns of forensic decision making. Such decisions appear to maintain a traditional clinical focus on the assessment and treatment of symptomatic, disordered, or disruptive behavior. Focusing on conducting valid assessments for use in actuarial instruments rather than making unaided judgments of risk may be warranted for clinicians. We suggest that increased reliance on empirically valid risk assessment would increase public safety and fairness to forensic patients.

NOTES

1. Spearman's rank order correlations of tribunal decision to detain *vs.* transfer yielded statistics of only slightly lower magnitude and equal significance level to the Pearson correlations reported as significant here, and of equivalent magnitude but sometimes different direction from those reported as not significant.
2. To examine the predictive validity of the VRAG in this sample, we obtained follow-up data from a database current to March 1999 (Rice et al., 1999). Thirty-four patients (18.2%) had the opportunity to reoffend; that is, had lived in a minimum security facility or in the community. Nine (26.5%) were charged with a new offense. VRAG scores were not available for all patients. Recidivism was more strongly associated with VRAG score, $r(21) = .42$, than with either senior clinician testimony, $r(28) = .14$, or team recommendation, $r(25) = .16$. The difference in VRAG score between the recidivists and nonrecidivists was equivalent to a large effect size, (7.88 vs. -1.62), $t(19) = -2.02$, $p = .06$, two-tailed Cohen's $d = .91$.

REFERENCES

Adams, S. J., Pitre, N. L., & Cieszkowski, R. (1997). Who applies to regional review boards and what are the outcomes? *Canadian Journal of Psychiatry, 42,* 70–76.

Agnew, R. (1984). Appearance and delinquency. *Criminology: An Interdisciplinary Journal, 22,* 421–440.

Barbaree, H. E., & Seto, M. C. (1998, April). *Empirical evaluation of the WSBC Multifactorial Assessment of Sex Offender Risk for Reoffense.* 2nd Annual Research Day, Forensic Psychiatry Program, Department of Psychiatry, University of Toronto.

Bélanger, N., & Earls, C. (1996). Sex offender recidivism prediction. *Forum on Correctional Research, 8,* 22–24.

Bjørkly, S. (1995). Prediction of aggression in psychiatric patients: A review of prospective prediction studies. *Clinical Psychology Review, 15,* 475–502.

Dawes, R. M. (1994). *House of cards.* New York: The Free Press.

Dawes, R. M., Faust, D., & Meehl, P. E. (1989). Clinical versus actuarial judgment. *Science, 243,* 1668–1674.

Douglas, K. S., Ogloff, J. R., Nicholls, T. L., & Grant, I. (1999). Assessing risk for violence among psychiatric patients: The HCR-20 Violence Risk Assessment Scheme and the Psychopathy Checklist: Screening version. *Journal of Consulting and Clinical Psychology, 67,* 917–930.

Eagly, A. H., Ashmore, R. D., Makhijani, M. G., & Longo, L. C. (1991). What is beautiful is good, but . . .: A meta-analytic review of research on the physical attractiveness stereotype. *Psychological Bulletin, 110,* 109–128.

Esses, V. M., & Webster, C. D. (1988). Physical attractiveness, dangerousness, and the Canadian criminal code. *Journal of Applied Social Psychology, 18,* 1017–1031.

Fuller, J., & Cowan, J. (1999). Risk assessment in a multi-disciplinary forensic setting: Clinical judgement revisited. *The Journal of Forensic Psychiatry, 10,* 276–289.

Gardner, W., Lidz, C. W., Mulvey, E. P., & Shaw, E. C. (1996). Clinical versus actuarial predictions of violence in patients with mental illnesses. *Journal of Consulting and Clinical Psychology, 64,* 602–609.

Grann, M., Belfrage, H., & Tengström A. (2000). Actuarial assessment of risk for violence: Predictive validity of the VRAG and the historical part of the HCR-20. *Criminal Justice and Behavior, 27,* 97–114.

Green, B., & Baglioni, A. (1997). Judging the suitability for release of patients from a maximum security hospital by hospital and community staff. *International Journal of Law and Psychiatry, 20,* 323–335.

Grove, W. M., & Meehl, P. E. (1996). Comparative efficiency of formal (mechanical algorithmic) and informal (subjective impressionistic) prediction procedures: The clinical/statistical controversy. *Psychology, Public Policy and Law, 2,* 293–323.

Hanson, R. K. (1998). What do we know about sex offender risk assessment? *Psychology, Public Policy, and Law, 4,* 50–72.

Hanson, R. K., & Harris, A. (2000). Where should we intervene? Dynamic predictors of sex offense recidivism. *Criminal Justice and Behavior, 27,* 6–35.

Hanson, R. K., & Thornton, D. (2000). Improving risk assessments for sex offenders: A comparison of three actuarial scales. *Law and Human Behavior, 24,* 119–136.

Hare, R. (1991). *Psychopathy Checklist.* Toronto: Multi-Health Systems.

Harris, G. T., Hilton, N. Z., & Rice, M. E. (1993). Patients admitted to psychiatric hospital: Presenting problems and resolution at discharge. *Canadian Journal of Behavioural Science, 25,* 267–285.

Harris, G. T., & Rice, M. E. (1990). An empirical approach to classification and treatment planning for psychiatric inpatients. *Journal of Clinical Psychology, 46,* 3–15.

Harris, G. T., & Rice, M. E. (1997). Risk appraisal and management of violent behavior. *Psychiatric Services, 48,* 1168–1197.

Harris, G. T., Rice, M. E., & Quinsey, V. L. (1993). Violent recidivism of mentally disordered offenders: The development of a statistical prediction instrument. *Criminal Justice and Behavior, 20,* 315–335.

Heilbrun, K., O'Neill, M. L., Strohman, L. K., Bowman, Q., & Philipson, J. (2000). Expert approaches to communicating violence risk. *Law and Human Behavior, 24,* 137–148.

Herman, C. P., Zanna, M. P., & Higgins, E. T. (Eds.). (1986). *Physical appearance, stigma, and social behavior: The Ontario symposium, Vol. 3.* Hillsdale, NJ: Erlbaum.

Jackson, M. A. (1989). The clinical assessment and prediction of violent behavior: Toward a scientific analysis. *Criminal Justice and Behavior, 16,* 114–131.

Janus, E. S., & Meehl, P. E. (1997). Assessing the legal standard for predictions of dangerousness in sex offender commitment proceedings. *Psychology, Public Policy, and Law, 3,* 33–64.

Konečni, V., & Ebbesen, E. G. (1984). The mythology of legal decision making. *International Journal of Law and Psychiatry, 7,* 5–18.

Konečni, V. J., Mulcahy, E. M., & Ebbesen, E. B. (1980). Prison or mental hospital: Factors affecting the processing of persons suspected of being "mentally disordered sex offenders." In P. D. Lipsitt, & B. D. Sales (Eds.), *New directions in psychological research* (pp. 87–124). New York: Van Nostrand Reinhold.

Kropp, P. R., & Hart, S. D. (2000). The Spousal Assault Risk Assessment (SARA) Guide: Reliability and validity in adult male offenders. *Law and Human Behavior, 24,* 101–118.

Lidz, C. W., Mulvey, E. P., Apperson, L. J., Evanczuk, K., & Shea, S. (1992). Sources of disagreement among clinicians' assessments of dangerousness in a psychiatric emergency room. *International Journal of Law and Psychiatry, 15,* 237–250.

Litwack, T. R. (1993). On the ethics of dangerousness assessments. *Law and Human Behavior, 17,* 479–482.

MacCoun, R. J. (1990). The emergence of extralegal bias during jury deliberation. *Criminal Justice and Behavior, 17,* 303–314.

McNiel, D. E., & Binder, R. L. (1994). The relationship between acute psychiatric symptoms, diagnosis, and short-term risk of violence. *Hospital and Community Psychiatry, 45,* 133–137.

McNiel, D. E., Sandberg, D. A., & Binder, R. L. (1998). The relationship between confidence and accuracy in clinical assessment of psychiatric patients' potential for violence. *Law and Human Behavior, 22,* 655–669.

Monahan, J. (1996). Violence prediction: The past twenty and the next twenty years. *Criminal Justice and Behavior, 23,* 107–120.

Monahan, J., Steadman, H. J., Silver, E., Appelbaum, P. S., Robbins, P. C., Mulvey, E. P., Roth, L. H., Grisso, T., & Banks, S. (2001). *Rethinking risk assessment: The MacArthur study of mental disorder and violence,* Oxford: Oxford University Press.

Mossman, D. (1994). Assessing predictions of violence: Being accurate about accuracy. *Journal of Consulting and Clinical Psychology, 62,* 783–792.

Mullen, J. M., & Reinehr, R. C. (1982). Predicting dangerousness of maximum security forensic mental patients. *The Journal of Psychiatry and Law, 12,* 223–231.

Mulvey, E. P., & Lidz, C. W. (1998). Clinical prediction of violence as a conditional judgment. *Social Psychiatry and Psychaitric Epidemiology, 33,* S107–S113.

Peay, J. (1981). Mental health review tribunals. *Law and Human Behavior, 5,* 161–186.

Polvi, N. (1999). *The prediction of violence in pretrial forensic patients: The relative efficacy of statistical versus clinical predictions of dangerousness.* Unpublished doctoral dissertation, Simon Fraser University, Department of Psychology.

Price, R. (1997). On the risks of risk prediction. *Journal of Forensic Psychiatry, 8,* 1–4.

Quinsey, V. L. (1979). Assessments of the dangerousness of mental patients held in maximum security. *International Journal of Law and Psychiatry, 2,* 389–406.

Quinsey, V. L. (1999). Report of the Committee of Inquiry into the Personality Disorder Unit, Ashworth Special Hospital, Vol. 1. *The Journal of Forensic Psychiatry, 10,* 635–648.

Quinsey, V. L., & Ambtman, R. (1978). Psychiatric assessment of the dangerousness of mentally ill offenders. *Crime and Justice, 6,* 249–257.

Quinsey, V. L., & Ambtman, R. (1979). Variables affecting psychiatrists' and teachers' assessments of the dangerousness of mentally ill offenders. *Journal of Consulting and Clinical Psychology, 47,* 353–362.

Quinsey, V. L., Coleman, G., Jones, B., & Altrows, I. (1997). Proximal antecedents of eloping and reoffending among mentally disordered offenders. *Journal of Interpersonal Violence, 12,* 794–813.

Quinsey, V. L., & Cyr, M. (1986). Perceived dangerousness and treatability of offenders: The effects of internal versus external attributions of crime causality. *Journal of Interpersonal Violence, 1,* 458–471.

Quinsey, V. L., Cyr, M., & Lavallee, Y. J. (1988). Treatment opportunities in a maximum security psychiatric hospital: A problem survey. *International Journal of Law and Psychiatry, 11,* 174–190.

428

Quinsey, V. L., Harris, G. T., Rice, M. E., & Cormier, C. (1998). *Violent offenders: Appraising and managing risk*. Washington, DC: American Psychological Association.

Quinsey, V. L., Khanna, A., & Malcolm, P. C. (1998). A retrospective evaluation of the regional treatment centre sex offender treatment program. *Journal of Interpersonal Violence, 13*, 621–644.

Quinsey, V. L., & Maguire, A. (1986). Maximum security psychiatric patients: Actuarial and clinical prediction of dangerousness. *Journal of Interpersonal Violence, 1*, 143–171.

Rice, M. E., & Harris, G. T. (1988). An empirical approach to the classification and treatment of maximum security psychiatric patients. *Behavioral Sciences and the Law, 6*, 497–514.

Rice, M. E., & Harris, G. T. (1995). Violent recidivism: Assessing predictive validity. *Journal of Consulting and Clinical Psychology, 63*, 737–748.

Rice, M. E., & Harris, G. T. (1997). Cross validation and extension of the Violence Risk Appraisal Guide for child molesters and rapists. *Law and Human Behavior, 21*, 231–241.

Rice, M. E., Harris, G. T., Cormier, C., Lang, C., Coleman, G., & Smith Krans, T. (1999). *Forensic psychiatric patients in Ontario* (Research Department Report). Penetanguishene, Ontario: Mental Health Centre.

Rogers, R., & Webster, C. D. (1989). Assessing treatability in mentally disordered offenders. *Law and Human Behavior, 13*, 19–29.

Seto, M. C., & Barbaree, H. E. (1999). Psychopathy, treatment behavior, and sex offender recidivism. *Journal of Interpersonal Violence, 14*, 1235–1248.

Steadman, H. J., Silver, E., Monahan, J., Appelbaum, P. S., Clark Robbins, P., Mulvey, E. P., Grisso, T., Roth, L. H., & Banks, S. (2000). A classification tree approach to the development of actuarial violence risk assessment tools. *Law and Human Behavior, 24*, 83–100.

Taylor, P. J., Goldberg, E., Leese, M., Butwell, M., & Reed, A. (1999). Limits to the value of mental health review tribunals for offender patients: Suggestions for reform. *British Journal of Psychiatry, 174*, 164–169.

Thornhill, R., & Gangestad, S. W. (1993). Human facial beauty: Averageness, symmetry, and parasite resistance. *Human Nature, 4*, 237–269.

Webster, C. D., Douglas, K. S., Eaves, D., & Hart, S. D. (1997). Assessing risk of violence to others. In C. D. Webster, & M. A. Jackson (Eds.), *Impulsivity: Theory, assessment, and treatment* (pp. 251–277). New York: Guilford Press.

Webster, C. D., Sepejak, D. S., Menzies, R. J., Slomen, D. J., Jensen, F. A. S., & Butler, B. T. (1984). The reliability and validity of dangerous behavior predictions. *Bulletin of the American Academy of Psychiatry and the Law, 12*, 41–50.

Werner, P. D., Rose, T. L., & Yesavage, J. A. (1990). Aspects of consensus in clinical predictions of imminent violence. *Journal of Clinical Psychology, 46*, 534–538.

VI

Treatments,
Security and
Program Planning

Section VI

Introduction

Just as there has been a long-standing controversy about actuarial versus clinical prediction of violence (see Section IV), so too there has been a similar debate about the effectiveness of treatment in correctional, mental health and addiction services. Extreme positions, such as those offered by Quinsey et al. (2006) regarding the actuarial point of view and Martinson's (1974) "nothing works" position, deserve credit for holding practitioners and researchers accountable for their decisions and practices, even when the arguments in favour of such positions are overstated and polemical (Webster, 1990). (While it seems obvious that having a properly established actuarial estimate of risk can be helpful when making decisions, clinical considerations can also be helpful.)

While therapy can be effective, its success is not always easy to demonstrate. The study by **Elizabeth Walsh**, **Catherine Gilvarry**, **Chiara Samele**, **Kate Harvey**, **Catherine Manley**, **Peter Tyrer** and colleagues (Chapter 24) is included here precisely because, despite its large scale and attention to design details, it failed to produce an overall positive effect for intensive versus standard treatment. In this project, about 350 patients from four community mental health centres were randomly assigned to either an intensive or a standard case management protocol and were followed for two years. All patients had psychosis as well as a history of violence.

The perhaps surprising finding was that those in the intensive group (in which there was one supervisor for every 10 to 15 individuals) were no less violent than were those managed in the standard group (in which there was one supervisor to every 30 to 35 people). Baseline levels of violence, at 22 per cent, were high enough to permit proper testing of the hypotheses. (This study was not trying to find out whether or not treatment "works"; rather, the goal was to learn about the possible amplifying effects of adding staff to the regimen.)

This is not the only study that has yielded a counterintuitive finding. Monahan et al. (2001) found that increasing the size of a person's social network failed to decrease violence risk. Future research will likely cast new light on *how* mental health services can be optimally delivered rather than on the *amount* of services provided. In the study by Walsh et al., it could be hypothesized that increasing the intensity of the treatment may have had the effect of obscuring therapeutic subfactors that might have had value in treatment had they been isolated and made focal.

Randall T. Salekin and **Richard Rogers**'s article (Chapter 25) provides an excellent overview of best practices for treating patients found not guilty by reason of insanity (or not criminally responsible by reason of mental disorder). These authors combine data across 23 studies (more than 3,000 patients). About one in five of these people had a primary diagnosis of personality disorder. The largest group, about one-third, consisted of patients diagnosed with psychosis. Salekin and Rogers's paper shows that it is important to find out how ill people were at the time of the index offence and how serious the incident was—a view that other authors in this section, such as Kennedy, would agree with. Only with this information is it possible to create the best possible decisions in balancing on one hand security considerations (which themselves have implications for treatment) and on the other treatment planning and delivery. Although much knowledge about treating people with severe psychiatric symptoms is directly transferable from civil mental health and addiction services, motivation for treatment in the forensic mental health system is imposed and supervised by courts and tribunals.

Salekin and Rogers review the effectiveness of a range of psychopharmacologic treatments. They point to medications shown to specifically reduce violence, and they note that these positive effects can sometimes be enhanced with psychotherapy. Similar statements are made about the effect of different kinds of medications on mood disorders. Salekin and Rogers suggest that it is unfortunate that patients with serious mental illness *and* substance use problems are treated for these conditions separately rather than concurrently. They note that life skills and social skills deficits, as well as employment problems, can frequently be remedied.

The authors stress the necessity of monitoring specific behaviours and moods over defined periods of time, and they suggest that much can be learned by noting the discrepancies between self-reported and staff-noted observations. A particular problem in forensic settings is caused by the generally high levels of security and control within institutions. The authors comment that "Treatment needs of NGRI [not guilty by reason of insanity] patients, although important, are addressed only after security concerns" (page 464). They suggest that, because the usual patient-therapist relationship alters when the patient is defined as forensic, a formal written contract should be established before beginning treatment. Salekin and Rogers also visit the idea, taken up by Lewis and Appleby (in Section III) and Murphy (in Section V), that therapists may find it hard to overcome the strongly negative emotional reactions they have to some patients.

Based on their painstaking review, the authors offer numerous scientifically supported ideas to suggest how treatments for NGRI patients can be individualized and optimized.

Marnie E. Rice, **Grant T. Harris** and **Catherine A. Cormier**'s study (Chapter 26) is an important cautionary tale about the presumed beneficial effects of treatment. They examined "what actually happened" in a treatment program at the maximum secure division of Mental Health Centre Penetanguishene in Ontario. For several years they followed individuals who had received milieu therapy and other treatments in vogue in the 1960s, to determine the overall effectiveness of this venture. Generally, their sample consisted of two types of patients: those with various kinds of psychoses and those meeting Hare's criteria for psychopathy.[1] What they discovered was that the people with major mental illnesses recidivated at much lower rates than those classified as psychopathic. Indeed, the treatments *elevated* subsequent violence risk in people with psychopathy. However, it would be unwise to conclude that people with high psychopathy scores necessarily cannot benefit from treatment (Salekin echoes this point in his chapter in this section). The results point to the fact that different kinds of treatment are needed for different kinds of patients and prisoners, and some treatments are bound to have iatrogenic effects.

Salekin's review (Chapter 27) of 42 studies for treating psychopathy suggests that therapeutic pessimism is unwarranted, and that treatment for people with psychopathy should not be given less priority than treatment for people with other types of mental health problems. This is despite the fact that there remains a paucity of evidence about what treatments work best for this population. Salekin argues that further research into the condition's etiology may reveal treatable aspects that have so far eluded clinicians and researchers.

Sheilagh Hodgins and **Rudiger Müller-Isberner** (Chapter 28) offer recent information about the *dimensions* of the treatment challenge. Their project involved closely following 232 men with schizophrenic disorders from both forensic and civil settings. The study was unusual in that it drew on sites in four countries—Canada, Finland, Germany and Sweden. The idea was to determine the extent to which crimes could have been prevented, at least in theory. The authors conclude that, given the high rates of crime committed by the general psychiatric patients with schizophrenia spectrum conditions, it makes little sense not to provide them with the same levels of assessment, treatment and community support services as those that tend to be found in forensic mental health systems. Assessors should invariably carry out a simple but effective screening to assess patients for a history of criminality and violence, given the implications for future difficulties when these factors are present.

Hodgins and Müller-Isberner also note that civil patients are routinely discharged back to the very neighbourhoods they originally came from, where social and subcultural influences and limited health resources often continue to be a problem. Finally, the authors make it clear that interventions, when they are given at all, are frequently offered too late. Much more effort needs to be applied to the early treatment of children and adolescents with schizophrenia and related disorders. They note that men with antisocial personality disorder (a population who are often diagnosed early on with conduct disorder) tend to develop schizophrenia at a higher rate than men in the general population—a finding that is still unexplained. This implies that there may be a subgroup of patients within the schizophrenia spectrum deserving of special resources and interventions.

Salekin and Rogers, in their article in this section, correctly note that emphasizing security and control can sometimes impede the therapy. **Harry Kennedy** (Chapter 29) recognizes this fact but offers a piece that shows how security issues, properly defined, can be turned to advantage in treatment. He discusses three key aspects of security, defined earlier by Kinsley (1998). According to this scheme, *environmental security* deals with the physical plant and the staff associated with it. Architectural considerations are vital both to ensure security and to maximize comfort, especially for long-stay patients. *Procedural security* concerns policies and practices (e.g., in managing violent incidents and in using seclusion). *Relational security* stresses factors such as staff-to-patient ratios and recognizes how violence can be contained through adept interpersonal skills (i.e., the ability to defuse escalating risks and gain patients' trust). Kennedy argues that therapeutic rapport remains extremely important, even in units where patient turnover is high. Skill is needed to handle short stays effectively. Specialist management arrangements, which Kennedy also emphasizes the importance of, involve such considerations as ensuring that processes conform to legal and policy requirements, that inter-agency relationships are defined and are periodically reviewed, and that lines of reporting are clear.

The heart of Kennedy's article has to do with mapping services; in other words, how to administer interrelated responsibilities. He refers to Scott's piece (in Section I) to remind readers that violence risk is the probability or immediacy of risk and its seriousness. Much of overall treatment effectiveness concerns the stratification of risk, in that it is easier to develop remedial programs if the participants pose similar levels of risk of, for example, violence or escape. Kennedy argues that people should not be detained at a level of security higher than is clearly required and that this level should be reviewed frequently. Kennedy also insists that there be a treatment plan that can be evaluated. He provides a useful outline listing "signs of diminished need for security" (Table 7). He also points out that violence risk tends to rise at transition points and that it helps if clinicians agree with the key therapeutic recommendations when they assume responsibility for treating and supervising new patients. Kennedy emphasizes that senior clinicians, as well as paying close attention to patient-therapist considerations at the individual level, must take a keen interest in systemic, classificatory and organizational issues if the overall program is to succeed (i.e., minimizing detention and other restrictions without elevating violence risk).

The chapter by **Michael Collins** and **Steffan Davies** (Chapter 30) expands on and formalizes some of the ideas expressed by Kennedy. Recognizing that finding the optimal level of security for patients has vital implications for therapy, these authors have devised a Security Needs Assessment Profile (SNAP) that builds on the different levels of security function sketched by Kennedy. Yet their 22-item scale is quite specific about how security requirements should be assessed. The scale covers a host of items pertaining to physical security (e.g., perimeter, internal security, entry points), procedural security (e.g., intensity of the nursing effort, searches, access to potential weapons, leaves, children visitors) and relational skills (e.g., managing violence and aggression, police liaison). This innovative risk management scheme, though obviously at an early stage of development, addresses many issues of day-to-day concern to senior clinicians, correctional professionals and clinical criminologists.

Many readers will be familiar with the lead author of our final article (by **Marianne Farkas, Cheryl Gagne, William Anthony** and **Judi Chamberlin**; Chapter 31), as well as with the work of another of its authors, William Anthony, who, for years, has strongly opposed the view that "nothing works" when treating people with a history of mental illness. Anthony has long believed that much can be done to help people with mental disorders (a designation that includes people with personality disorders) and substance use problems. Of late, there has been a tendency for a generally optimistic, strength-oriented, evidence-based approach to fly under the banner of "recovery." Much of this is extremely well discussed by Spaulding et al. (2003).

The Farkas et al. chapter begins with a discussion of what the authors mean by a "program" (i.e., the administration, staffing and procedures) for delivering any treatment or rehabilitation service. A recovery-oriented program has to clearly lay out what it intends to accomplish and the policies and procedures it expects to use in accomplishing its objectives. There is an assumption that effort has to be expended to secure patients' involvement and that, properly supported, most patients inherently have the abilities required to make life more satisfying and productive. The piece by Farkas and colleagues urges organizations to pay close attention to how they are functioning and to ensure that they are acting in the patients' best interests.

NOTES

1. The Supreme Court of Canada's interpretation of what conditions were subsumed under the rubric of a mental disorder or "disease of the mind," together with the then-prevailing optimism concerning patients' potential for treatment, resulted in numerous people whose primary psychiatric disturbance was best classified as severe personality pathology (psychopathy) entering the Review Board system.

REFERENCES

Kinsley, J., Kaye, C. and Franey, A. (1998). Security and therapy. In C. Kaye & A. Franey, *Managing High Security Psychiatric Care*. London: Jessica Kingsley Publishers.

Martinson, R. (1974). What works? Questions and answers about prison reform. *Public Interest, 35*, 22–54.

Monahan, J., Steadman, H.J., Silver, E., Appelbaum, P.S., Clark Robins, P., Mulvey, E.P. et al. (2001). *Rethinking Risk Assessment: The MacArthur Study of Mental Disorder and Violence*. Oxford, U.K.: Oxford University Press.

Quinsey, V.L., Harris, G.T., Rice, M.E. & Cormier, C. (2006). *Violent Offenders: Appraising and Managing Risk* (2nd ed.). Washington, DC: American Psychological Association.

Spaulding, W.D., Sullivan, M.E. & Poland, J.S. (2003). *Treatment and Rehabilitation of Severe Mental Illness*. New York: Guilford.

Webster, C.D. (1990). Role of polemic in psychology. *Canadian Journal of Criminology, 32*, 191–196.

24

Reducing Violence in Severe Mental Illness: Randomized Controlled Trial of Intensive Case Management Compared with Standard Care

ELIZABETH WALSH, CATHERINE GILVARRY, CHIARA SAMELE, KATE HARVEY, CATHERINE MANLEY, PETER TYRER, FRANCIS CREED, ROBIN MURRAY AND THOMAS FAHY FOR THE UK700 GROUP

ABSTRACT

OBJECTIVES: *To establish whether intensive case management reduces violence in patients with psychosis in comparison with standard case management.*

DESIGN: *Randomised controlled trial with two year follow up.*

SETTING: *Four inner city community mental health services.*

PARTICIPANTS: *708 patients with established psychotic illness allocated at random to intervention (353) or control (355) group.*

INTERVENTION: *Intensive case management (caseload 10–15 per case manager) for two years compared with standard case management (30–35 per case manager).*

MAIN OUTCOME MEASURE: *Physical assault over two years measured by interviews with patients and case managers and examination of case notes.*

RESULTS: *No significant reduction in violence was found in the intensive case management group compared with the control group (22.7% v 21.9%, P = 0.86).*

CONCLUSIONS: *Intensive case management does not reduce the prevalence of violence in psychotic patients in comparison with standard care.*

Reprinted with permission. BMJ, 323, 1–5. © 2001 BMJ Publishing Group.

INTRODUCTION

Serious acts of violence committed by people with mental illness are statistically rare events.[1] Efforts of community services to prevent violence by the small subgroup at risk may be limited by the lack of effectiveness of standard treatment interventions, inadequate attention to clinical factors associated with violence—for example, drug misuse and poor engagement and treatment adherence by patients—and the difficulty of altering risk associated with impoverished and dangerous living environments.[2, 3] Fragmentation between services compounds the difficulties.

The care programme approach was introduced, partly to address this fragmentation, after several killings by people with severe mental illness were much reported in the media.[4] The key elements are assessment of need and risk, development of a care plan, nomination of a responsible key worker, and regular review. Case management incorporates these principles, with the key worker providing direct care and also organising the delivery of a range of other services tailored to each patient's individual needs. Intensive case management emphasises small caseloads (10–15 patients per case manager), with increased intensity of contact.

Surprisingly, no study has specifically examined the effect on violence of increasing the intensity of treatment in the community. As part of the largest randomised controlled trial of intensive case management in patients with psychosis conducted to date, we assessed whether intensive case management reduced the prevalence of violence in comparison with standard case management.

METHODS

Study Population

The participants in the trial were recruited as part of the UK700 randomised controlled trial of the efficacy of intensive case management in patients with psychosis. The methods have been reported in detail elsewhere.[5] Recruitment took place between February 1994 and April 1996 in four inner city mental health services—three in London (St George's Hospital, St Mary's Hospital, King's College Hospital) and one in Manchester (Manchester Royal Infirmary)—and occurred either at the point when patients were discharged from hospital or while they were receiving care in the community. Inclusion criteria were age between 18 and 65, a diagnosis of psychosis according to research diagnostic criteria,[6] and at least two inpatient admissions for psychotic illness, with one in the previous two years. Patients with a primary diagnosis of substance misuse or organic brain damage were excluded. The trial was approved by the four local ethics committees.

Intervention

Intensive case management was compared with standard care for two years. The study was designed so that only one key variable (size of caseload) differed between the experimental and control groups. Intensive case managers had caseloads of 10–15 patients, whereas standard case managers had 30 or more patients. Case managers were mostly community psychiatric nurses but could also be psychologists, occupational therapists, mental health support workers, or social workers. The level of training and skill was similar in the intensive and standard groups.[5]

We monitored activity of case managers throughout the trial and recorded five types of event: face to face contact with patient, contact by telephone (> 15 minutes), contact with carer (> 15 minutes), coordination (contact with other professional agencies) (> 15 minutes), and attempted (failed) face to face contact. For all face to face contacts, the primary focus of the event was categorised into 11 types, identified by a modified Delphi process and including housing, finance, medication, and criminal justice system. Staff were trained in and issued with guidelines on the use of event records and met frequently with the event record coordinator. The completeness of event records was verified by audits of case notes.[7]

Assignment

After giving written informed consent and being interviewed, patients were individually randomised to intensive case management or standard care. The randomisation list was drawn up using random numbers generated by computer. Randomisation was conducted by telephone or fax through an independent statistical centre and was stratified by centre, ethnic origin, and source of recruitment (at point of discharge or in the community). Outpatients were transferred to their case manager within four weeks, and inpatients were assigned when discharge was imminent.

Outcomes and Follow Up

Participants were interviewed by independent researchers at baseline and two years after randomisation. Researchers were senior trainee psychiatrists or psychology graduates who were totally independent of clinical care but, for safety purposes, were not always masked to treatment allocation. Researchers were asked to contact case managers before visiting patients at home. The primary outcome measure for the UK700 trial was number of days in hospital, and the results have been reported elsewhere.[5] For the current study the outcome of interest was physical assault in the two years of the trial.

Three data sources were combined to produce a binary outcome measure for each patient. A positive score on any of these sources indicated a positive score for assault. The frequency or seriousness of assault was not recorded. Firstly, as part of the World Health Organization's life chart process,[8] patients were asked whether they had physically assaulted anyone in the two year period. Where an interview with a participant was not possible, an attempt was made to complete the record with information from a carer. Secondly, case managers were interviewed in person or by telephone and asked about any physical assault committed by their patients. Thirdly, case notes at all sites were individually inspected for evidence of physical assault.

Possible sociodemographic (n = 12) and clinical (n = 13) risk factors for violence, chosen a priori on the basis of previous research, were estimated at baseline interview by using a battery of instruments.[8–11] Criminal records, including convictions for violence, were obtained from the Home Office for all participants. As the date of conviction rather than the date of offence is recorded in the index of offenders, it was not possible to include violent convictions during the follow up period in the main outcome measure.

Power Calculation and Statistical Analysis

The trial with 350 patients randomised to each group would be able to detect a 20% reduction in total violence in the intensive case management group as statistically significant at the 5% level with a high probability (power > 80%). We estimated the proportion of participants who committed assault during the trial and compared treatment groups by using the χ^2 test. Analyses were conducted with Stata 5 (Stata Corporation, College Station, TX). We used logistic regression to perform univariate and multivariate analyses to identify predictors of assault during the two years of the trial.

RESULTS

Recruitment

Eighty per cent of patients approached agreed to participate (Figure 1). In all, 708 patients were recruited, 353 (49.8%) in the intervention group and 355 (50.2%) in the control group. Comparisons between those who entered and those who did not revealed no significant differences in terms of demographic and clinical characteristics, apart from length of illness. Patients who entered the trial had been ill for longer (median duration 120 months v 96 months; U = 51899.0; P = 0.04). Details of the sociodemographic and clinical features of the participants in the UK700 trial have been described in detail elsewhere.[5]

Intervention

Patients in the intensive case management group received more than twice as much care as control patients, with a mean of 4.41 events per 30 days compared with 1.94 in the standard arm. The mean duration of face to face contacts was 40.6 (SD 0.3) minutes in the intensive management group and 37.4 (24.8) minutes in the standard group. Patients managed intensively had significantly more of each type of event apart from

FIGURE 1
Flowchart of Trial

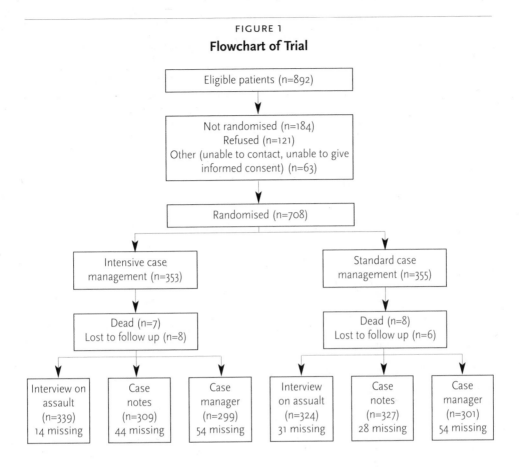

failed contacts and had significantly more contacts in nine of the 11 focus areas. Specifically, they received significantly more contacts related to the criminal justice system, engagement, finance, and medication—all variables that might influence the prevalence of violent behaviour.

Prevalence of Violence

Information on assault was available for all patients from at least one data source. During the two years of the trial 158 (22%) participants physically assaulted another person. Violent behaviour was reported by 104 (66%) of the 158 patients. Combining data from case notes and interviews with patients resulted in 143 (91%) of the 158 patients being reported as having been violent. The addition of interviews with case manager to these measures led to a further 15 (9%) patients being included. Only 16 (10%) patients were reported as violent by all three data sources. Eighty (23%) of the intervention group and 78 (22%) of the control group committed assault, representing no significant difference ($\chi^2 = 0.048$, P = 0.86). The relative risk for committing assault in the intensive group compared with the standard group was 1.03 (95% confidence interval 0.72 to 1.46). Identified risk factors for violence included previous violence,

TABLE 1

Sociodemographic and Clinical Predictors of Violent Behaviour

FACTOR	RISK RATIO (95% CI) ADJUSTED FOR ALL OTHER VARIABLES IN TABLE
AGE	
19–39 years	1.53 (1.12 to 2.02)*
40–64 years	1
SPECIAL EDUCATION	
No	1
Yes	1.61 (1.08 to 2.20)*
VICTIMISED IN PAST YEAR	
No	1
Yes	1.50 (1.08 to 2.02)*
DRUG USE/MISUSE	
None	1
One or more	1.49 (1.09 to 1.95)**
ASSAULT (PAST 2 YEARS)	
No	1
Yes	2.04 (1.54 to 2.56)***
HISTORY OF CONVICTION FOR VIOLENCE	
No	1
Yes	1.44 (1.02 to 2.61)*
RANDOMISATION	
Standard case management	1
Intensive case management	1.08 (0.78 to 1.44)

*P<0.05, **P<0.01, ***P<0.001.

younger age, drug misuse, victimisation, and learning difficulties (Table 1). After adjustment for these factors, the difference in prevalence of violence between the groups remained non-significant.

DISCUSSION

In the largest randomised trial to date comparing intensive case management with standard care in psychosis, no significant reduction in violence was found. Risk factors for violence included previous violence, drug misuse, younger age, and victimisation, confirming the results of previous studies in psychotic patients.[12, 13] Violence was also associated with a history of learning difficulties, a factor previously identified in non-psychotic populations.[14]

Strengths and Weaknesses of the Study

Different methods for measuring violence can produce very different prevalences. The recent use of multiple combined measures, as in this study, has highlighted the limitations of most previous studies, which relied on a single source. One study that specifically compared the yield of violence when different sources were used revealed a dramatically different picture of violence by patients depending on the source of information used.[15] Our results support the observation that self report methods consistently produce a higher frequency of violence than use of other records.[16] In a small proportion of cases the WHO life chart was completed from sources other than the patient, so the 94% response rate is a slight overestimate.

The optimal prevalence estimate would have been detected with 100% follow up on all data sources. Although we did not achieve this, we did obtain information on all participants from at least one source. One possible source of bias in this study is that intensive case managers may have detected more violent acts and that standard case managers may have under-reported violence. This could conceal an actual reduction in violence in the intensive group. This is unlikely to be the case as the interviews with case managers added only 15 participants who had not been identified by self report or review of case notes. These cases were evenly distributed between the groups. Additionally, we included only actual assaults, and not threats, in our definition so it is likely that most of these more serious incidents will have been detected irrespective of treatment allocation.

Possible bias arising from interviewers not always being blind to treatment group will have been minimised by the use of multiple data sources. The use of validated questionnaires and continual data monitoring at each centre and centrally will have maximised the robustness of the data. Participants were recruited from inner city locations, and results may not be generalisable to other settings. The multicentre design with over 700 patients should, however, increase the external validity.

Prevalence of Violent Behaviour

The finding that 22% of patients committed assault over the two year period is of concern but concurs with previous work. Studies indicate that between 10% and 40% of patients commit assault before admission to hospital, and the MacArthur risk assessment study found that 27.5% of discharged psychiatric patients committed at least one violent act within a year of discharge.[17, 18] Our study includes violence by both inpatients and outpatients.

Although intensively case managed patients received more face to face contacts with their case managers and more attention dedicated to medication, engagement, daily living skills, housing, and the criminal justice system, we found no evidence that intensive case management reduced the prevalence of violent behaviour over two years. This finding is not challenged by any of the published trials in this field. There have been at least seven randomised controlled trials examining the efficacy of assertive community treatment—the form of intensive case management favoured in the United States—that have included time in jail or legal contacts as an outcome measure.[19–25] None has examined violence specifically, and only two of the seven reported reductions in time in jail.[21, 22] Differences in the organisation of services, in

---

What is Already Known on This Topic

- Psychosis and violence are known to be associated
- Community psychiatric interventions aimed at reducing the risk of violence have not been evaluated

What This Study Adds

- Increasing the intensity of contact between patients and case managers does not reduce the prevalence of violent behaviour in patients with psychosis
- Younger age, learning difficulties, and a history of violence, drug misuse, and victimisation predict violent behaviour in psychotic patients

---

particular the absence of coordinated care in American standard practice, limit the generalisability of these findings to the British setting.

A randomised trial of the management of care by social services conducted in homeless people with severe mental illness in Oxford found a significant reduction in deviant behaviour in the care management group at 14 months' follow up in comparison with care as usual.[26] Although this result was encouraging, the study did not examine violent behaviour specifically, the intensity of the intervention was decided by the individual's care manager, and the level of care received by the control group was unclear. We must therefore conclude that intensive case management, or indeed assertive community treatment, has shown no efficacy in reducing violent behaviour in severely mentally ill patients.

Implications of the Study

It remains unclear why intensive community treatment has such a negligible effect on illegal behaviours. In those studies examining time in jail as a secondary outcome the base rate of time spent in jail may have been too low to detect a change in some samples. Alternatively, assertive community treatment and intensive case management have been designed as vehicles for providing clinical services and reducing reliance on inpatient facilities, and these interventions may need considerable modification to address the different needs of patients who are prone to engage in violent or illegal behaviour. Specific interventions to improve compliance with or uptake of treatment for substance misuse are probably important. More controlled research on this question is needed.

Despite the lack of empirical studies on the effect of increasing the intensity of treatment in the community on violence in general psychiatric or forensic populations, research in the United States is now focusing on the effect of combining community treatment with legally enforceable interventions to reduce violence. A recent study, with some important limitations in its methods, found that outpatient commitment (enforced community treatment) for longer than six months combined with regular services resulted in a significant reduction in community violence in severely mentally ill patients at risk of violence. Neither outpatient commitment nor regular services alone was effective.[27] Similar legislation for compulsory community treatment in England and Wales has recently been proposed in a government white paper.[28] Future research may have the challenging task of evaluating the effectiveness of combining specific clinical interventions within or without a protective legal framework.

REFERENCES

1. Monahan J. Mental disorder and violent behaviour: perceptions and evidence. *Am Psychol* 1992; 47:511–21.
2. Swartz MS, Swanson JW, Hiday VA, Borum R,Wagner HR, Burns BJ. Violence and severe mental illness. The effects of substance abuse and non-adherence to medication. *Am J Psychiatry* 1998; 155:226–31.
3. Silver E, Mulvey EP, Monahan J. Assessing violence risk among discharged psychiatric patients: toward an ecological approach. *Law Hum Behav* 1999;23:237–55.
4. Department of Health. *The care programme approach for people with a mental illness referred to the specialist psychiatric services.* London: Department of Health, 1990.
5. UK700 Group. Intensive versus standard case management for severe psychotic illness: a randomised trial. *Lancet* 1999;353:2185–9.
6. Spitzer R, Endicott J, Robins E. Research diagnostic criteria: rationale and reliability. *Arch Gen Psychiatry* 1978;35:773–82.
7. Burns T, Fiander M, Kent A, Ukoumunne OC, Byford S, Fahy T, et al. Effects of case-load size on the process of care of patients with severe psychotic illness. *Br J Psychiatry* 2000;177:427–33.
8. World Health Organization. *The life chart.* Geneva:WHO, 1992.
9. Asberg M, Montgomery SA, Perris C. The CPRS-development and applications of a psychiatric rating scale. *Acta Psychiatr Scand* 1978;271(suppl):5–27.
10. Andreason NC. *Modified scale for the assessment of negative symptoms.* Iowa City: University of Iowa, 1984.
11. Phelan M, Slade M, Thornicroft G, Dunn G, Holloway F, Wykes T, et al. The Camberwell assessment of need: the validity and reliability of an instrument to assess the needs of people with severe mental illness. *Br J Psychiatry* 1995;167:589–95.
12. Buchanan A. The investigation of acting on delusions as a tool for risk assessment in the mentally disordered. *Br J Psychiatry* 1997;170(suppl 32):12–6.
13. Swanson JW, Borum R, Swartz M, Hiday V. Violent behaviour preceding hospitalisation among persons with severe mental illness. *Law Hum Behav* 1999;23:185–204.
14. Hodgins S. Mental disorder, intellectual deficiency, and crime. Evidence from a birth cohort. *Arch Gen Psychiatry* 1992;49:476–83.
15. Mulvey EP, Shaw E, Lidz CW. Why use multiple sources in research on patient violence in the community? *Crim Behav Mental Health* 1994;4:253–8.
16. Elliott D, Huizinga D, Morse B. Self-reported violent offending: a descriptive analysis of juvenile violent offenders and their offending careers. *J Interpersonal Viol* 1986;1:472–513.
17. Steadman H, Mulvey EP, Monahan J, Robbins PC, Applebaum PS, Grisso T, et al. Violence by people discharged from acute psychiatric inpatient facilities and by others in the same neighborhoods. *Arch Gen Psychiatry* 1998;55:1–9.
18. Monahan J. Clinical and actuarial predictions of violence. In: Faigman D, Kaye D, Saks M, Sanders J, eds. *Modern scientific evidence: the law and science of expert testimony.* Vol 1. St Paul, MN: West Publishing Company, 1997:300–18.

19. Chandler D, Meisel J, McGowen M, Mintz J, Madison K. Client outcomes in two model capitated integrated service agencies. *Psychiatr Serv* 1996;47:175–80.
20. Bond GR, Miller LD, Krumwied RD, Ward RS. Assertive case management in three CMHCs: a controlled study. *Hosp Community Psychiatry* 1988;39:411–8.
21. Bond GR, Witheridge TF, Dincin J,Wasmer D,Webb J, De Graaf-Kaser R. Assertive community treatment for frequent users of psychiatric hospitals in a large city: a controlled study. *Am J Community Psychol* 1990;18:865–91.
22. Lehman AF, Dixon LB, Kernan E, DeForge B. A randomised trial of assertive community treatment for homeless persons with severe mental illness. *Arch Gen Psychiatry* 1997;54:1038–43.
23. Solomon P, Draine J. The efficacy of a consumer case management team: 2-year outcomes of a randomised trial. *J Mental Health Admin* 1995;22:126–34.
24. Stein LI, Test MA. Alternative tomental hospital treatment: 1. Conceptual model, treatment program, and clinical evaluation. *Arch Gen Psychiatry* 1980;37:392–7.
25. Test MA. Training in community living. In: Liberman RP, ed. *Handbook of psychiatric rehabilitation.* New York: Macmillan, 1992.
26. Marshall M, Lockwood A, Gath D. Social services case-management for long term mental disorders: a randomised controlled trial. *Lancet* 1995;345:409–12.
27. Swanson JW, Swartz MS, Borum R, Hiday VA, Wagner HR, Burns BJ. Involuntary out-patient commitment and reduction of violent behaviour in persons with severe mental illness. *Br J Psychiatry* 2000;176:324–31.
28. Secretary of State for Health. *Reforming the Mental Health Act.* London: Stationery Office, 2000.

25

Treating Patients Found Not Guilty by Reason of Insanity

RANDALL T. SALEKIN AND RICHARD ROGERS

Patients found not guilty by reason of insanity (NGRI patients) cause apprehension and concern for mental health professionals regarding their effective inpatient treatment, release, and aftercare in the community. Effective treatment and management of NGRI patients is especially challenging, because the verdict presents dual and possibly conflicting mandates to clinicians: beneficial treatment without undue constraints versus community safety. Favoring one mandate at the expense of the other generates serious problems, such as lack of a therapeutic progress or undue risk to the community. Developing a model that integrates both of these concepts is critical for successfully treating and managing these patients (Zonana & Norko, 1996). Overshadowing the treatment of NGRI patients are two related debates: (a) the appropriateness of the not guilty by reason of insanity defense itself, and (b) the standard to be used for NGRI verdicts.

The treatment of NGRI patients can only be understood in the context of the insanity defense itself and the remarkable ambivalence that it engenders in both public and professional arenas. Much of the public fear and foreboding is related to misperceptions of the insanity defense (Perlin, 1996; Silver, Cirincione, & Steadman, 1994). Perlin (1996) outlined common myths regarding the insanity defense: It (a) is overused;

(b) is limited to murder cases; (c) presents no risk to the defendant pleading insanity; (d) results in a quick release from custody; (e) is a ploy by criminal defendants "faking" insanity; (f) results in a financially driven "battle of the experts"; and (g) is inappropriately used by attorneys to obtain unwarranted acquittals. The public image of a wealthy person evading justice is likely to have a chilling effect on their tolerance of his or her postacquittal treatment and eventual release.

Empirical evidence has shown that these claims are less than accurate. In reality, the insanity defense is used in less than 1% of cases (Callahan, Steadman, McGreevy, & Clark, 1991; Steadman, Monahan, Harstone, Kantorowski-Davis, & Robbins, 1982), is frequently unsuccessful, and generally results in lengthy stays in restrictive maximum security facilities for longer periods than defendants convicted on similar crimes (Silver, 1995; Steadman, 1980, 1985). The insanity plea carries considerable risk because a failed defense is tantamount to a conviction. Moreover, if the defense fails, prison terms are significantly longer than comparable cases in which the defense is not raised (Perlin, 1996). The defense is most frequently pled in cases involving minor property crimes and is much less frequently used in crimes involving a victim's death (Steadman, 1985). In direct contrast to public perceptions, most cases do not involve a battle of the experts. Generally, both state and defense experts agree about both the severity of the defendant's mental illness and his or her criminal responsibility (Ogloff, Schweighofer, Turnbull, & Whittemore, 1992; Zonana, Bartel, Wells, Buchanan, & Getz, 1990; Zonana & Norko, 1996). According to Perlin (1996), feigned insanity is rarely attempted and often unsuccessful. Data from Rogers (1986) compiled across multiple sites found a prevalence of definite malingering to be rare (4.5%).

Debates regarding insanity standards have overshadowed treatment programs for NGRI patients. With respect to insanity standards, available data (Rogers, Seman, & Clark, 1986; Wettstein, Mulvey, & Rogers, 1991) suggest that specific standards are likely to have little effect on clinical determinations of criminal responsibility. For example, Ogloff (1991) found that mock jurors do not appreciate the legal nuances found in specific insanity standards. Instead, jurors focused on general issues when making decisions, such as the defendant's history of mental illness, expert testimony on the NGRI patient's disorder, and whether or not the defendant intended to harm. Whatever the standard used, once a person is adjudicated NGRI, most people believe that they are entitled to receive treatment for their disorders (Hans, 1986).

Yet we lack research on the treatment of these persons. This may be partially attributable to the fact that the indefinite commitment of NGRI patients is more punishment than treatment (Szasz, 1963). As German and Singer (1976) concluded, "No group of patients has been more deprived of treatment, discriminated against, or mistreated than persons acquitted of crimes on the grounds of insanity" (p. 1074). In this regard, Quinsey (1988) also concluded that the treatment of mentally disordered offenders receives very little attention in the literature both by itself and in comparison to other forensic issues (e.g., the prediction of dangerousness).

Despite this, treatment of NGRI patients remains a crucial responsibility for mental health professionals and society as a whole. Judge David Bazelon described the issue well when he stated. "Our collective conscience does not allow punishment where it cannot impose blame" (American Bar Association Criminal Justice Mental Health Systems, 1989, p. 324). Although we recognize the imperfections with the insanity defense and the concerns regarding its misuse, the very nature of this verdict would suggest that treatment of NGRI patients is both necessary and proper. In essence, we contend that NGRI patients require treatment that will allow them to return to live in the community without restrictions but, at the same time, without undue risk to the public.

The purpose of this chapter is to present specific information regarding the treatment needs of NGRI patients and to suggest modalities for providing that treatment. We also furnish information regarding follow-up of NGRI patients and what issues should be considered before NGRI patients are released to the community. A natural starting point for the chapter is a description of NGRI patients' characteristics with special attention to their treatment needs. We begin with demographic and psychiatric characteristics of NGRI patients.

DEMOGRAPHIC AND CLINICAL CHARACTERISTICS OF NGRI PATIENTS

A necessary precondition to treatment planning for NGRI patients is the examination of background and psychiatric data as a basis for clinical intervention. Research now exists on the demographic and clinical characteristics of NGRI patients across 16 states and two Canadian provinces. The goal of this review is to provide a clear picture of the NGRI patients' treatment needs to formulate a more reasoned and informed approach to effective treatment. First, we summarize the extensive research of Callahan, Steadman, McGreevy, and Robbins (1991). Second, we augment Callahan et al.'s research with our own literature review.

Callahan Study

Callahan and her colleagues (1991) compiled data on nearly one million felony indictments, spanning 49 counties and eight states. In addition to providing descriptive data on insanity pleas (9.3 per 1000) and resulting acquittals (2.6 per 1000), they supplied important data on 2565 NGRI patients. The great majority were male (86.5%), with an average age of 32.1 years. They were balanced between Black (42.6%) and White (50.4%) ethnic backgrounds. Most NGRI patients had been previously arrested (70.2%) and had psychiatric histories that included hospitalization (82.0%). As expected, primary diagnoses were made up of schizophrenic disorders (67.9%), other psychotic or mood disorders (16.0%), mental retardation (4.8%), and other mental disorders (4.5%). In addition, small numbers had a primary diagnosis of personality disorder (3.5%) or substance abuse (2.7%).

TABLE 1

Background and Diagnostic Characteristics of NGRI Patients

AUTHORS	N	BACKGROUND DATA				DIAGNOSTIC DATA								% VIOLENT CRIME
		AGE	% MALE	% HOSP	PSYCHOT	SCZ	ORGAN	MOOD	MR	PD	APD	SA HX	
Bogenberger et al. (1987)	107	29	94	22	64	51	3	13	6	7	—	—	52
Cooke & Sikorski (1974)	167	37	87	44	68	—	—	—	—	25	—	—	91
Criss & Racine (1980)	223	38	85	66	74	66	1	2	1	22	6	81	81
Gacono et al. (1995)	18	34	100	—	72	39	17	23	0	100	55	38	83
Greenland (1979)	103	31	78	53	47	—	—	—	7	—	—	—	95
Heilbrun, Griffin-Heilbrun, & Griffin (1988)	41	39	0	78	—	34	20	20	0	10	10	76	94
Hodgins, Hebert, & Baraldi (1986)	29	38	0	100	79	57	4	—	4	—	—	—	100
Linhorst & Dirks-Linhorst[a] (1997)	797	33	88	—	78	—	—	—	—	44	23	49	52
Morrow & Petersen (1966)	44	34	100	34	45	—	14	—	14	—	—	—	47
Norwood, Nicholson, Enyart, & Hickey (1991)	61	34	92	96	74	59	2	10	—	—	2	13	75
Pasewark, Jeffrey & Bieber (1987)[b]	36	32	100	100	64	64	3	7	3	8	0	3	54
Petrila (1982)	67	31	—	79	68	—	8	2	8	5	0	—	60
Phillips & Pasewark (1980)	25	28	92	61	40	36	—	—	—	48	—	—	20
Rice & Harris (1990)	53	33	—	75	66	—	—	—	—	13	—	—	100
Rogers & Bloom (1982)[b]	440	31	91	85	67	61	6	6	5	—	3	5	55

Seig, Ball, & Menninger (1995)	149	33	75	—	67	—	—	20	—	—	4	40	74
Shah, Greenberg, & Convit (1994)	62	41	84	—	90	—	3	2	0	0	0	68	95
Silver, Cohen, & Spodiak (1989)	127	31	100	59	71	71	6	3	8	8	—	—	69
Steadman (1980)	278	34	86	38	68	—	—	—	—	3	13	—	90
Steadman et al. (1983)	110	33	97	40	—	—	—	—	—	—	—	—	76
Wettstein & Mulvey (1988)	137	34	82	67	65	57	2	11	2	4	—	—	77
Zonana, Bartel, Wells, Buchanan, & Getz (1990)	62	32	50	75	68	49	11	12	—	16	—	61	85
Average[c]	3136	33.6	79.1	65.1	66.8	53.7	7.1	10.1	4.5	20.9	10.6	48.4	73.9

Note: All numbers represent percentages of NGRI patients. All categories are primary diagnoses. SA Hx = the total percentage of patients with substance abuse histories. N = the number of NGRI patients; % Hosp = prior psychiatric hospitalizations; Psychot = any type of psychotic disorder; Scz = schizophrenia; Organ = organic disorder; Mood = all mood disorders; MR = Mental retardation; PD = All Personality Disorders; API = Antisocial Personality Disorder; violent crime = violent index crime.

[a] These diagnoses were grouped as "major mental illness" with psychotic disorders being prominent.

[b] Formal diagnosis of substance abuse rather than a history.

[c] Average = averages for each of the columns with the exception of N which is the total number of NGRI patients.

Literature Review

In Table 1, we present data from 23 studies on a total of 3136 NGRI patients. Similar results were found across these studies to that of the Callahan et al. (1991) study. The majority of the NGRI patients were male (79.1%), with an average age of 33.6 years. The acquittees were composed of 39.1% Black and 51.6% White ethnic backgrounds. Approximately half of the NGRI patients had been previously arrested (51.2%). Most had psychiatric histories that included hospitalization (66.2%). As expected, primary diagnoses were made up predominantly of psychotic disorders (66.8%). Slightly more than half of the NGRI patients (53.5%) had a schizophrenic disorder. Present to a lesser extent were other psychotic or mood disorders (17.3%) and mental retardation (4.5%). Surprisingly, a substantial minority had a primary diagnosis of personality disorder (19.8%), one half of which carried the diagnosis of antisocial personality disorder (APD). Although not a primary diagnosis, approximately two thirds of the NGRI patients had substance abuse problems. Seventy-four percent of the index crimes committed by the NGRI patients were violent in nature.

Psychotic disorders, with one exception, were the predominant diagnostic category. In a small sample of 25 cases, Phillips and Pasewark (1980) found that 48% had personality disorders, and only 36% had schizophrenia. It is likely that this sample does not adequately represent NGRI acquittees in Connecticut. In fact, Zonana et al. (1990) has shown that major mental illness is more prevalent than personality disorders among NGRI patients in Connecticut.

Nonetheless, personality disorders are the second most frequent diagnosis, making up approximately 19.8% of the acquittees. Nearly 10% of the NGRI patients meet the criteria for a diagnosis of APD. The results of this study would indicate that the view that holds that the NGRI defense is the last refuge of sociopathic individuals who manipulate mental health and criminal justice systems to escape confinement in a penitentiary may only hold true for very few of the defendants.

Important gender differences were noted with regard to NGRI patients' diagnostic picture. Specifically, differences were found in the diagnostic frequency of disorders and in the potential for future dangerousness, which may suggest different treatment needs for female versus male NGRI patients. With regard to Axis I diagnoses, females were more likely than males to be diagnosed with mood disorders, although still constituting only a minority of NGRI patients. These data suggest a need for women's treatment programs emphasizing mood disorders. Few women were diagnosed ASPD. This is consistent with the literature, which shows a lower prevalence of this disorder and psychopathy in women (Salekin, Rogers, &, Sewell, 1997). Moreover, Axis II disorders in general were rarely diagnosed in females. When personality disorders were diagnosed, they tended to be borderline personality disorders. These gender differences suggest a need for treatment approaches for women designed to increase self-management of intense, labile emotion, interpersonal conflict, and identity confusion (Linehan, 1993). The less extensive criminal history and lower potential for repetitive violence suggest that treatment for many female NGRI patients may safely take place in relatively low-security settings.

One inescapable conclusion from these data is that most persons acquitted by reason of insanity were seriously mentally ill at the time of their entry into forensic mental health systems. As for locus of treatment issues, it is significant to note that in a substantial minority of the cases, relatively trivial offenses were overshadowed by severe disorders. More specifically, about one fourth of acquittees (26%) have minor or nonviolent offenses, but severe mental disorders; in such cases, security issues may pose less risk and treatment needs may assume greater importance.

Typically, NGRI treatment programs tend to be generic and not focused on the demographic and clinical profiles of NGRI patients. Rather, their presumed dangerousness appears to override all other considerations, except possibly the need to exact some retribution despite a "not guilty" determination (Hans, 1986; Quinsey, 1988). Thus the primary societal concern for NGRI patients is for a secure environment, regardless of such an environment's ability to foster appropriate treatment interventions. We contend that if a greater emphasis were given to treatment, issues of dangerousness prediction would require less attention.

TREATMENT OF NGRI PATIENTS

Current treatment of NGRI patients has favored a top-down approach in which general programs are devised and NGRI patients are served solely within the realm of the program's offerings. In contrast, a bottom-up perspective details the treatment needs of NGRI patients and then attempts to tailor interventions to these needs. In this section, we explore patient needs from a bottom-up perspective in an effort to tailor treatment to specific clinical needs. The basic goals of treatment are fourfold: (a) diagnose and treat the mental disorder, (b) reduce the risk of dangerousness, (c) prepare the NGRI patient for the community, and (d) monitor his or her adjustment in the community.

The research data currently available on NGRI patients offer a starting point for such treatment programs. The majority of NGRI patients warrant a diagnosis of schizophrenia, frequently complicated with substance abuse and personality disorders. Certainly, with one half to two thirds of most NGRI cohorts diagnosed with schizophrenia and a similar percentage of the acquittees diagnosed with substance abuse problems, these two areas seem like important targets for treatment. Moreover, ASPD and the related syndrome of psychopathy (Salekin, Rogers, & Sewell, 1996) are likely to complicate the management of NGRI patients.

NGRI patients are often characterized by severe symptomatology and less-than-optimum treatment response. Because of their frequent Axis I-Axis II disorders, state-of-the-art treatment is needed to alleviate acute symptomatology, maintain stability of patients' functioning, and prepare NGRI patients for community living. Once in the community, NGRI patients should continue to be monitored for symptomatology and general adjustment.

Though treatment strategies and techniques used with NGRI patients are often identical to those used with nonforensic patients, the context and settings in which health services are delivered are frequently unique. Treating NGRI patients has an explicit goal of minimizing future criminal activity. Treating NGRI patients also differs from nonforensic populations in that motivation for treatment is externally imposed and monitored. Therapeutic progress is often less important than compliance with treatment, and lack of treatment compliance often results in immediate sanctions. We first begin our review with specific treatment approaches to symptomatology common among NGRI patients. We then discuss five treatment-related issues that are frequently emphasized in preparing clinicians for NGRI treatment services.

TREATING NGRI PATIENTS WITH PSYCHOTIC SYMPTOMATOLOGY

The majority of NGRI patients are found nonresponsible on the basis of delusions and hallucinations. More specifically, Rogers (1986) found among defendants assessed as insane that delusions played a major role in 82.3% and hallucinations in 35.2% of the cases. Our own review also shows a high prevalence of psychotic symptomatology. Therefore, effective treatment of psychosis is equally important to both the clinical status of the patient and public safety. Because the majority of NGRI patients were strongly influenced by psychotic symptoms in committing often violent crimes, the compelling logic is that these same psychotic symptoms must be competently managed and treated to preclude further violent acts. From a preventative perspective, careful monitoring of psychotic symptoms for signs of possible decompensation is a crucial element of treatment.

Psychopharmacologic treatment has been shown to be very effective at ameliorating active psychotic symptomatology (Jacobsen, 1986; Kane & Freeman, 1994; Richelson, 1996). Neuroleptics, in general (e.g., Thorazine, Prolixin, Haloperidol, Mellaril, and Trilafon), have been most commonly used in treating psychotic disorders (Bezchlibnyk-Butler & Jeffries, 1996; Breslin, 1992; Pickar et al., 1992). New-generation medications shown to be highly effective with psychotic disorders include Clozapine, Risperidone, Olanzapine, Sertindole, and Quetiapine (Richelson, 1996). These new-generation medications have been shown to also have an impact on aggressive and violent behavior in psychotic patients. For example, Dalal, Larkin, Leese, and Taylor (1999) examined the effectiveness of Clozapine in reducing psychotic symptoms, reducing serious violent behavior, and facilitating discharge of 50 patients with schizophrenia in a forensic hospital facility. For patients who continued Clozapine treatment for a minimum of 12 months, the majority showed symptom reduction, and this symptom reduction was associated with a reduction in violence and a higher rate of discharge. Volavka and Citrome (1999) and Citrome and Volavka (2000) have also found that atypical antipsychotic medications (Clozapine, Risperidone, and Quetiapine) reduce psychotic symptoms and aggression in schizophrenic patients.

Psychotherapy has also been an effective means of treating psychotic symptoms independently or more commonly in combination with psychopharmacologic treatment (e.g., Breier & Strauss, 1983; Lowe & Chadwick, 1990; Paul & Lentz, 1977). For instance, Breier and Strauss (1983) have demonstrated that self-control methods in psychotic disorders can be an effective form of treatment. According to Breier and Strauss, the self-regulation process consists of three phases: (a) awareness of psychotic or prepsychotic behavior by self-monitoring, (b) recognition of certain behaviors as a signal of disorder by self-evaluation, and (c) employment of self-control methods. The most common methods of control are self-instruction and change in activity level. Meichenbaum (1977) has suggested that coping self-talk statements could be used to guide schizophrenic patients' attention. Detecting early signals that may herald the onset of psychotic symptoms and noting the sequences of events often followed by symptoms are particularly important. As noted by Rice, Harris, and Quinsey (1996), effective treatment of NGRI patients with combined pharmacological and psychotherapy treatments requires extensive planning and commitment of resources.

TREATING NGRI PATIENTS WITH MOOD DISORDERS

Treating depression in NGRI patients deserves special attention. Although only a minority of the NGRI patients have mood disorders as a primary diagnosis, substantial numbers have moderate to severe symptoms at the time of the offense (28.8% depressive and 15.9% manic symptoms; Rogers, 1986). Still other NGRI patients acquire depressive symptoms in the course of their postacquittal hospitalization (Hambridge, 1990). Much of this depression is related to the realization of (a) the crimes that they have committed and (b) their indefinite and lengthy hospitalizations. In fact, improvement in psychotic symptoms actually may increase depression in NGRI patients. That is, as psychotic symptoms abate, many NGRI patients begin to experience guilt and subsequent depression for the act(s) that led to their hospitalization.

A new class of 5-HT antidepressants have, at least preliminarily, shown considerable success with depressed patients. Such drugs include Mirtazipine, Nefazodone, and Venlafaxine. These drugs are less likely than tricylic drugs to have adverse effects and are less lethal if overdosed (Frazer, 1994; Nelson, 1997). Although these new drugs are promising, pharmacological treatment of more recalcitrant forms of depression often requires either cyclic antidepressants or monoamine oxidase inhibitors. Finally, electro-convulsive therapy can be useful for cases of major depression that have not responded adequately to drug treatment (Fink, 1987; Nelson, 1997).

For bipolar disorders, the treatment with the most empirical support is lithium carbonate and more recently Valproate or Carbamazepine. According to Gerner and Stanton (1992), the overall noncompliance and nonresponse rate to lithium in bipolar disorder is relatively high. However, Valproic acid is increasingly receiving support as an effective medication for bipolar disorders and is less likely to produce adverse effects in patients (Gerner & Stanton, 1992). Moreover, Valproate appears to be indicated in rapid cycling bipolar disorders more so than lithium carbonate. Long-term treatment is critical for NGRI patients with mood disorders given the substantial relapse rates (Rice et al., 1996).

We contend that psychotherapeutic approaches for treating depressed NGRI patients should include cognitive-behavioral therapy (CBT). CBT has proven successful across diverse clinical settings (Beck, Rush, Shaw, & Emery, 1979; Elkin et al., 1989; Meichenbaum, 1977; Persons, 1989; Scott, Williams, & Beck, 1995). More recently, CBT has been found to be effective with bipolar disorders (Satterfield, 1999; Zaretsky, Segal, & Gemar, 1999). Treatments using cognitive-behavioral approaches should focus on self-control and problem solving skills for NGRI patients. In addition, CBT should be used to correct negative or distorted self-schemas and beliefs that depressed NGRI patients may have. Meichenbaum (1977) has suggested that self-talk can be a useful strategy to change depressive thought patterns, and this cognitive strategy may also help bipolar patients better regulate their emotions. Other concrete treatment components for bipolar disorder focus on prevention of mood cycles, early detection of cycle onset, and mood stabilization during cycles. Interpersonal therapy might also be used, and although effective for depression there is less empirical research supporting its effectiveness for bipolar disorder (Weissman, 1994).

TREATMENT OF SUBSTANCE ABUSE AMONG NGRI PATIENTS

Clinical data on NGRI patients indicate that substance abuse is often a secondary diagnosis and an important treatment issue. In many psychotic patients, substance abuse may precipitate decompensation or impede further progress. Although rarely the central diagnostic issue for defendants found NGRI (Rogers, 1986), addressing substance abuse problems plays a critical role in their effective treatment. In cases of adjudicated NGRI patients, nearly one half warrant a secondary diagnosis of a substance abuse disorder. Moreover, the acquisition of use of illegal substances constitutes an additional offense. For NGRI patients in particular, rearrests typically constitute a treatment failure.

Miller (1982) recommended the use of alcohol-sensitizing drugs and behavioral treatment with high-risk patients. The positive effects may be limited, however, to persons with alcohol disorders whose problem drinking is confined to a few risk situations. Moreover, Moncrieff and Drummond (1997) argued that there is little evidence thus far that pharmacological treatment for alcohol problems is effective. These results were based on 16 studies that examined the effect of such drug treatments as Acomprosate, Natrexone, Bromocriptine, selective serotonin re-uptake inhibitors, and Buspirone. Ross and Lightfoot (1985) reviewed the literature on the treatment of alcohol-abusing offenders and found that aversion therapy, behavioral training in self-control, relaxation, communication, assertion, social skills, and family therapy were effective forms of treatment. Dimeff and Marlatt (1995) have shown that relapse prevention training is an effective way to prevent the drinking cycle. There is no reason to believe that relapse prevention would not work with other forms of drug abuse. General cognitive-behavioral strategies that have NGRI patients focus on the antecedents to their drug use and acquisition of self-control and problem-solving skills would be beneficial. Stacy (1997) has shown that cognitions often lead to increased drug use and that relapse prevention can provide a useful means of treating substance abusers. Unfortunately, many studies have not considered dually diagnosed offenders as is typically found with NGRI samples. NGRI patients with substance abuse problems would benefit maximally from treatment programs that addressed their substance abuse problems and other Axis I disorders concurrently.

TREATING ANXIETY DISORDERS IN NGRI PATIENTS

Rogers (1986) found severe or pervasive anxiety in 28.9% of defendants evaluated clinically as insane. It is important to note that the presence of psychotic symptoms does not preclude anxiety. Little is known of whether this anxiety serves to inhibit psychotically based behavior or, conversely, facilitate such behavior. Rogers and Wettstein (1985) found low levels of anxiety among most NGRI patients, but higher levels among treatment failures.

Although only evidenced in a minority of the NGRI patients, anxiety can be a distressing problem for these individuals. In the case of NGRI patients, some may be diagnosed with posttraumatic stress disorder given that they often are traumatized by the events that lead to their hospitalization (e.g., Hambridge, 1990).

Behavior therapy for anxiety disorders and panic disorders has been shown to be efficacious (Barlow, 1988; Chambless & Goldstein, 1980; Foa & Tillmanns, 1980; Fyer, Mannuzza, & Endicott, 1987; Koback, Greist, Jefferson, Katzelnick, & Henk, 1998; Nietzel & Bernstein, 1981; Silverman et al., 1999; Turner, 1984; Wolpe, 1990). According to Suinn (1990) and Wolpe (1990), anxiety management training that includes both induced anxiety and relaxation is recommended for those who have generalized anxiety that is manifested primarily by affective symptoms. Suinn (1990) and Wolpe (1990) contend that stress inoculation and systematic desensitization should be considered for persons whose symptoms are primarily in the cognitive domain. Others (e.g., Foa, Wilson, Foa, & Barlow, 1991) have suggested thought-stopping as a way in which patients can deal with intrusive anxiety-evoking thoughts and obsessions, by preventing such thoughts from entering his or her mind. Still others (e.g., Borkovec & Mathews, 1988; Ost, 1987) prescribe more generalized treatment, such as intensive relaxation training, in the hope that learning to relax when beginning to feel tense will keep anxiety from spiraling out of control. With this treatment, patients are taught to relax away tensions, responding to incipient anxiety with relaxation rather than alarm. This strategy has been found to be very effective in alleviating anxiety symptoms (Borkovec & Roemer, 1994; Borkovec & Whisman, 1996).

TREATING NGRI PATIENTS WHO LACK LIFE SKILLS

Life skills deficits are an important and pervasive problem for NGRI patients. Given the low educational attainment of NGRI patients, programs designed to increase their knowledge and general skills is likely to prove useful in allowing acquittees to be more adaptive in their communities (Rice et al., 1996). One method that can improve educational attainment is a contingency management approach to literacy and mathematical skills (Ayllon & Milan, 1979). Such programs are likely to have positive effects with regard to attaining employment once released. In addition, token economy programs that emphasize vocational and educational training in prison settings have been shown to reduce postrelease recidivism (Milan, 1987). With the high rate of unemployment among NGRI patients, developing job skills appears to be necessary before community release. Researchers (e.g., Furman, Geller, Simon, & Kelly, 1979; Kelly, Laughlin, Clairborne, & Patterson, 1979; Shady & Kue, 1977; Twentyman, Jensen, & Kloss, 1978) have shown that such programs have been highly successful in helping individuals obtain employment.

Another important component to the successful integration of patients into the community is appropriate follow-up to ensure that these individuals are able to maintain their employment in the community. Peckman and Muller (1999) followed-up seven schizophrenic patients living in a community to address the problems they face when entering the work force, which included (a) interpersonal, (b) episodic and unpredictable symptoms, (c) treatment interventions, and (d) inappropriate values. The patients provided the following useful coping strategies to successfully cope with work-related problems: (a) openness with employer, (b) taking on tasks step by step, and (c) positive self-talk. These schizophrenic patients offered many creative and practical solutions: (a) support (either by hotline or on-going workshops), (b) education for employers and the community, (c) personal training (problem-solving, money management, social skills), and (d) environmental stability. NGRI patients are likely to require assistance in the areas pinpointed by these patients with schizophrenia.

TEACHING SOCIAL SKILLS TO NGRI PATIENTS

The treatment of choice for socially inadequate behavior is social skills training. In brief, social skills training involves a variety of techniques that are used to change a person's social behavior in particular social situations (Rice et al., 1996). Use of behavioral components such as role playing, modeling, feedback, and coaching would likely prove useful for NGRI patients who require social skills training. Meta-analytic studies (Benton & Schroeder, 1990; Corrigan, 1991) have shown that social skills training can improve postrelease social functioning of schizophrenic and other seriously mentally ill patients with long-term effects. Strong support is marshaled for the conclusion that social skills training is beneficial for both low-functioning schizophrenic patients and higher functioning patients with other diagnoses (Benton & Schroeder, 1990; Corrigan, 1991; Mueser, Levine, Bellack, Douglas, & Brady, 1990; Rice, Harris, Quinsey, & Cyr, 1990). As Rice et al. (1996) highlighted, precautions should be taken to ensure that the unit policies do not admonish or punish the NGRI patients for socially appropriate assertive behaviors acquired in social skills training programs.

MANAGING ANGER, AGGRESSION, AND VIOLENCE
WITH NGRI PATIENTS

NGRI patients who display aggression pose a serious management problem. Anger, by itself, is a potential risk factor for violence among mentally disordered individuals (Novaco, 1994). Deffenbacher (1999) outlined cognitive-behavioral interventions for anger reduction. These strategies include enhancing one's self-awareness through using record-keeping, role plays, and behavioral experiments in which the individual attends to experiential and behavioral elements of their behavior. NGRI patients may experience increased efficacy in lowering anger as they become able to initiate coping strategies when they are aware of themselves and the triggers of their anger.

Other strategies proposed by Deffenbacher include the avoidance of anger-provoking events, distancing one's self emotionally from provocative cues (until one is able to deal more rationally with a problem), and taking time-outs. In addition, relaxation interventions that focus on emotional and physiological arousal may be helpful in training NGRI patients to lower arousal and increase a sense of calmness and control, thereby increasing their overall coping capacity.

Stress-inoculation training has been shown to be a particularly effective method of controlling anger (e.g., Novaco, 1977, 1997; Robins & Novaco, 1999). Novaco's stress-inoculation training program involves teaching patients to monitor anger, to observe its relationship to antecedent cognitions and environmental events, and to control experiences of anger when they arise, including the use of self-instructional techniques (Meichenbaum, 1975, 1977). Outcome studies found this approach to be effective with diverse groups suffering anger problems (Feindler, Marriott, & Iwata, 1984; Nomellini & Katz, 1983; Schlichter & Horan, 1981). Other studies have shown that the reduction of institutional aggression is an obtainable goal with the use of behavioral therapy (Etscheidt, 1991; Rice, Harris, Varney, & Quinsey, 1989; Wong, Slama, & Liberman, 1987; Wong, Woosley, Innocent, & Liberman, 1988).

Rice et al. (1989) outlined several classes of interventions to reduce assaultiveness. These interventions include (a) psychopharmacologic treatment, (b) seclusion and mechanical restraint, (c) behavioral treatment, and (d) staff training. As the authors acknowledge, psychopharmacological treatment and mechanical restraints are unlikely to be successful without other treatments. Within a behavioral paradigm, they recommended that specific consequences be set up for problem behaviors and inpatient reinforcement be arranged for prosocial behaviors that are incompatible with assaultiveness. In addition, they recommended staff training in verbal calming and defusing skills be combined with fair and reasonable management policies. Furthermore, Harris and Rice (1994) have suggested that effective prosocial models enhance the likelihood of improvement among forensic patients.

Problems of assaultiveness, property destruction, possession of weapons, and suicidal threats are extremely important to placement decisions of NGRI patients (Rice et al., 1996). Even the rare occurrence of these behaviors is likely to mean that the patient will not be considered for community discharge. Thus the successful reduction of physical aggression is inevitably a high priority for the patient as well as for proper and safe management of treatment facilities.

NGRI patients diagnosed as ASPD or as psychopathic can pose serious management and risk problems for other patients and staff. Gacono, Meloy, Sheppard, Speth, and Roske (1995) provided data on NGRI patients classified as both psychopathic and malingerers ($n = 18$). They found that this group of NGRI patients, when compared to other NGRI patients, posed numerous problems to staff, including problems with management, sexual intimacy with staff, verbal and physical assaultiveness, illicit drugs, and escape potential.

Rice et al. (1996) suggested the following interventions for APD forensic patients: (a) problem-solving combined with social skills training, (b) moral reasoning, (c) academic programs that emphasize democratic teaching methods with instructors as good role models, (d) contingency management procedures to reduce conflict at work and attitudes toward work, and (e) deliberately contrived opportunities for interactions with prosocial models. For both (c) and (e), they suggested that models be selected because of their interpersonal skills and be trained in how to respond to antisocial comments and rationalizations for law violation.

MONITORING NGRI PATIENTS' PROGRESS IN TREATMENT

Planned monitoring of NGRI patients' treatment progress is crucial to their evaluation and subsequent treatment modifications. Rogers, Harris, and Wasyliw (1983) were the first to assess systematically NGRI patients' progress in treatment. These authors assessed 32 NGRI outpatients in court-mandated treatment for patterns of psychopathology at the Isaac Ray Center. Using the SCL-90 (Derogatis, 1977) and the SADS-C (Spitzer & Endicott, 1978), they compared self-report and interview-based methods and found that the self-report method (SCL-90) elicited greater symptom severity on initial evaluations. In general, they found that NGRI patients manifested mild to moderate severity of psychopathology, with a substantial endorsement of depressive and aggressive symptoms. Given the low frequency of psychotic symptoms and mild-to-moderate impairment, Rogers et al. concluded that the NGRI patients were placed appropriately in outpatient treatment. However, as Rogers et al. observed, the sample was somewhat constrained because five NGRI patients were rehospitalized before data collection was completed, and therefore these patients were dropped from the analyses.

The treatment program at the Isaac Ray Center was comprised of an eclectic, problem-oriented treatment model that incorporates psychopharmacological and psychotherapeutic approaches. The authors assessed the observed psychopathology of the NGRI patient at two specified intervals ($M = 6.6$ months) in their mandatory treatment. They found a moderate degree of similarity between the observed symptoms and the patient's self-report and that most patients remained stable in their psychological impairment. However, three patients demonstrated a marked improvement, two others manifested substantial decompensation in their psychological functioning as rated by the global assessment scale of the SADS-C. Also, marked discrepancies between self-report and interviews were noted for certain symptoms (e.g., depressed feelings, obsessions and compulsions, the experience and expression of anger, agitation, and the severity of delusions). Given the potential relationship between these symptoms and dangerous behavior, such inconsistencies constitute a special concern for treating high-risk NGRI patients.

An obvious conclusion from this study is that multiple sources of data over specific periods of time is extremely useful in the monitoring of NGRI patients. In particular, discrepancies between observed versus self-reported symptoms is relevant to risk assessment among NGRI patients. These data could be further augmented through collateral interviews with family members and significant others within the NGRI patients' immediate environment.

ISSUES SPECIFICALLY RELATED TO NGRI PATIENTS

In the section that follows we discuss five treatment-related issues to prepare clinicians for NGRI treatment services. With this special population, psychologists should be aware of the difficult aspects of treatment that might affect their own perspective of what constitutes treatment and how outcome should be measured. Furthermore mental health professionals will need to consider what factors might affect their patient's perspective of treatment, client-therapist relationship, and outcome.

Security versus Treatment

A good starting point for addressing treatment issues specifically related to NGRI patients is to highlight the security versus treatment concern. Both inpatient and outpatient insanity treatment programs must balance security and compliance issues with individual treatment needs. Forensic inpatient facilities must emphasize security, which is characterized as minimizing escape risk and recidivism while ensuring the safety of patients and staff against the possibility of violent behaviors. The escape of even one NGRI patient is unacceptable to most forensic facilities, even if no violence occurs. This zero-tolerance perspective is reinforced by negative media, further limitations on other NGRI patients, and threats to continued funding for the treatment program and the facility. As a result, the institutionalized NGRI patient may experience restricted movement, tight control over emotional expression, and highly controlled patient-to-patient interactions. In addition, many safety policies may be imposed as real or symbolic protections.

Outpatient NGRI patients are monitored carefully regarding treatment compliance and possible decompensation. Missed appointments typically fall within the security concerns and are often interpreted as a need for protective or punitive actions. In this regard, court or review-board sanctions may be imposed because of a failure to keep outpatient appointments.

Treatment needs of NGRI patients, although important, are addressed only after security concerns. Clinicians have a professional responsibility to protect both the NGRI patient and others. An NGRI patient rearrested for a violent offense is likely to impede any progress in treatment and result in lengthy institutionalization. Although role conflicts arise, the forensic clinician can avert some potential conflicts by outlining the parameters of the relationship and by clearly explaining how treating NGRI patients differs from more typical therapist-client relationships. In defining the NGRI therapeutic relationship, we advocate a written contract of mutual responsibilities *before* beginning treatment.

Psychological Health versus Stabilization

Traditionally, forensic treatment goals have emphasized attaining therapeutic change and psychological growth within the individual patient (Cavanaugh, Wasyliw, & Rogers, 1985; Garfield & Bergin, 1994; Zonana & Norko, 1996). Creating an optimal therapeutic environment, allowing the development of genuineness, accurate empathy, and positive regard between the clinician and the patient is essential to the treatment process (Cavanaugh et al., 1985; Garfield & Bergin, 1994). In many cases, the overriding goal is improved functioning with a concomitant reduction of distress.

The treatment of chronically mentally disordered persons has given rise to clinical management as a goal in itself (Cavanaugh et al., 1985; Zonana & Norko, 1996). Interventions with both institutionalized and ambulatory NGRI patients often fall in the category of stabilization rather than continued progress. Clinical management typically takes center stage because of the following factors: (a) limited resources for more active treatment, (b) a lack of intrinsic motivation for change by some NGRI patients, (c) repeated failures of treatment to produce any further improvements, and (d) administrative-legal constraints on treatment. Especially on an outpatient basis, one primary goal of NGRI treatment is stabilization, although we believe that attempts to go beyond this level of treatment are necessary.

Motivation versus Apathy: Resistance to Treatment

Psychological treatment classically involves an individual who desires change, is aware of internal conflicts, and voluntarily seeks treatment (Cavanaugh et al., 1985; Garfield & Bergin, 1994). Within the forensic system, treatment is imposed on involuntary NGRI patients, who frequently are unwilling participants in the treatment process. Whereas the motivation in traditional psychotherapy is generally internal (e.g., increase self-awareness or reduce stress), NGRI patients understandably are motivated by external issues, such as increased liberty and eventual discharge. The NGRI patient may actively seek treatment because of an awareness that released patients have "demonstrated" to the staff that they had benefited from treatment. Whether such motivation is simply a manipulation of staff is a matter of perspective. We would submit that all persons trapped in an adversarial setting are likely to find methods to extricate themselves. The task for forensic clinicians is to understand and empathize with the various motivations of NGRI patients. Although many mental health professionals may feel uncomfortable with patient perceptions of staff (e.g., jailor or probation officer), understanding their perspectives will facilitate rapport and possible treatment alliance.

Therapists' Negative Feelings and Treatment of the NGRI Patient

The therapist's negative feelings toward violent NGRI patients has received increasing attention (Cavanaugh et al., 1985; Zonana & Norko, 1996). Some index crimes (e.g., a mother's killing of her own children) may evoke strong negative feelings that negates a therapeutic relationship. Although not prevalent in NGRI populations, assaults on clinicians or the perceived risk of such assaults may also impede treatment. Violent patients may elicit severe reactions in the clinician that interfere with treatment. For example, a therapist may be unduly rigid in setting limits and overly cautious in writing reports on a potentially aggressive patient. Conversely, a therapist may not be aware of his or her attempts to appease a violent patient and avoid any confrontation or direct feedback. Thus a difficult aspect of treating NGRI patients is confronting the issues of the patient's dangerousness and the therapist's personal reactions to it (Cavanaugh et al., 1985; Zonana & Norko, 1996). Consulting with colleagues when treating violent patients is likely to be an effective strategy for dealing with this problem (Madden, Lion, & Penna, 1977).

The Agency Problem

Monahan (1980) described agency in terms of a clinician's primary responsibilities and perceived role. In the forensic arena, agency is likely to affect psycholegal opinions and influence the course of treatment (Rogers, 1987). Many clinicians perceive themselves as agents of the court or forensic facility. In these instances, the clinicians' primary responsibility is to further the goals and objectives articulated by these facilities within the framework of ethical practice. Other clinicians will perceive themselves as agents of the patients. Their goals will be to fulfill the patients' needs within the framework of existing legal procedures and ethical practice.

Rogers (1986) argued that agency is likely to have subtle but real influences on how NGRI patients are evaluated. We believe that staff at forensic facilities should discuss openly their position on agency. If possible, a consensus should be achieved and disseminated on how agency is addressed at each facility. We speculate that many professional dilemmas arise from a lack of clarity regarding this issue.

A concrete example of agency problems emerges from confidentiality. In most forensic settings, limits are placed on confidentiality, with reporting relationships preestablished with courts or review boards. The question of how much to divulge regarding a patient's status clearly reflects the issue of agency. Clinicians who perceive themselves as agents of the courts are likely to produce extensive documentation. Those who view themselves as agents of the NGRI patients are more likely to invoke a "need-to-know" position and provide only essential information.

DANGEROUSNESS AND DISCHARGE

One of the most serious public concerns with regard to the insanity defense has been the real and perceived risks posed by the return of NGRI patients to the community (Tellefsen, Cohen, Silver, & Dougherty, 1992). This concern has presented numerous problems for mental health professionals. "Solutions" have included both increased security and longer periods of institutionalization as sincere efforts for protecting society. However, outcome studies, such as Baxstrom (e.g., Steadman & Cocozza, 1974), suggest that this concentration on security is sometimes unwarranted. Patients involuntarily placed in maximum-security facilities posed little risk when released by court order to less secure facilities and the community (Steadman & Cocozza, 1974). Nevertheless, risk assessment will and should continue to be an important component of NGRI patients' readiness to return to the community.

Two new measures of risk assessment for forensic patients were recently developed. Rice (1997) outlined how violence research could be used to make better predictions with regard to the dangerousness of NGRI patients, thereby increasing public safety. Rice described the Violence Risk Assessment Guide (VRAG) that performed well at predicting violent criminal behavior among male NGRI patients who previously had committed a violent crime. Based on two cross validations, Rice concluded that the VRAG's performance was robust across different follow-up periods. She surmised that use of the VRAG would lead to fewer new victims and fewer new violent crimes. In addition, a second measure of dangerousness, the HCR-20, was developed for risk assessments with forensic patients. Although validation studies are ongoing, the preliminary results appear promising (Webster, Douglas, Eaves, & Hart, 1997).

Rice suggested that violent recidivism among mentally disordered offenders is related to the same variables as found among nonmentally disordered offenders. Rice and her colleagues have shown that psychopathy is associated with a moderate likelihood of future violence. In a meta-analysis conducted by Salekin et al. (1996) psychopathy was shown to be a moderate predictor of violent recidivism. Although psychopathy is rarely considered a mental disorder for purposes of insanity acquittal, some NGRI patients who have committed a violent offense warrant this classification (Rice et al., 1990). The empirical data strongly suggest that violent recidivism would be reduced, and public safety thereby enhanced, by release decisions based on risk of future violence. It is important to note that preliminary data suggests that psychopathy may be less predictive among female psychopaths than their male counterparts (Salekin, Rogers, Ustad, & Sewell, 1998).

Cohen, Spodak, Silver, and Williams (1988) examined the adjustment of NGRI patients who were released into the community. Based on both actuarial and clinical predictors, a model for forensic release decisions was derived from data on 127 NGRI patients, a matched control of 127 convicted felons, and a comparison group of 135 mentally disordered prison transfer patients. These authors measured two outcome indicators: (a) rearrests within five years after release and (b) overall functioning in the community during a two and one half year period after release.

The first discriminant analysis accurately predicted 75% of those rearrested using the following six variables: adjustment in hospital, clinical assessment of hospital staff, Global Assessed Scale score at release, functioning before their offense, heroin addiction, and birth order. A second discriminant function analysis identified seven variables that accurately predicted the overall functioning of 80.4% of the NGRI patients. Variables associated with successful outcome after release differed between the NGRI and prison groups. The two discriminant analyses illustrated that statistical models can combine actuarial, clinical, and criminological data to determine the likelihood of success after release for NGRI patients. Several variables evidenced utility in determining release readiness, including adjustment in the hospital, clinical assessment of patient involvement, Global Assessed Scale score at release, and functioning before their offense. The first three variables related to the patient's progress at the hospital. Other variables (i.e., marital status, severity of offense, working before hospitalization, birth order, and heroin addiction) also predicted outcome but were not related to patient stay.

Eisner (1989) developed a specialized measure to determine the readiness of NGRI patients to return to the community. The instrument is designed to assess the patient's disorder, behavior, and medication. In addition, it focuses on the NGRI patients' acknowledgement of mental disorder and of criminal behavior and acceptance of treatment. Although this measure appears to assess relevant components regarding readiness of NGRI patients to be released, it has not been formally tested. Therefore the measure is of little use at this point since there is no empirical foundation to base decisions on (Rogers & Salekin, 1998).

REFORMS IN THE LOCUS OF TREATMENT

Two of the major reforms that have been enacted attempt to make significant changes in the locus of treatment. The GBMI alternative would place more people in state prisons in which mental health services would be mandated. The Oregon approach using a Psychiatric Security Review Board (PSRB) tends to emphasize outpatient treatment after inpatient treatment.

In 1975, Michigan was the first state to enact a GBMI verdict, with its primary goal being to decrease the number of insanity acquittals (Steadman, 1985). Michigan legislators hoped to use the new verdict to prevent the early release of dangerous NGRI patients by offering Michigan juries a substitute for the insanity verdict (Smith & Hall, 1982). Following the GBMI determination, a sentence is imposed and the defendant is committed to prison, where he or she is to be provided treatment by either corrections or mental health professionals when psychiatrically indicated. In practice, this statute changes the locus of control for treatment from the mental hospital to the prison. In fact, the new verdict has failed in its intended purpose (Smith & Hall, 1982; Steadman, 1985): The volume of NGRI cases has remained comparable to pre-GBMI levels. In effect, what has been created is simply another class of offenders for whom mental health treatment is mandated. The GBMI group tends to resemble the inmates more than NGRI patients, especially with more sex-related offenses, which are rarely found in NGRI populations (Smith & Hall, 1982).

Perlin (1996) argued that GBMI statutes do little to ensure effective treatment for offenders with mental disabilities. The director of the state correctional or mental health facility is mandated to provide a GBMI inmate with such treatment as he or she "determines necessary"; however, the GBMI inmate is not ensured treatment "beyond that available to other offenders" (Slobogin, 1985, p. 513). One comprehensive study of the GBMI verdict in Georgia revealed that only 3 of the 150 GBMI defendants were being treated in hospitals (Steadman et al., 1993, p. 195).

The Oregon program developed an independent review board that would balance the treatment needs of NGRI patients with community protection. The major innovation in this approach was to remove decisions of release away from both the criminal courts and the treating staff for the release and monitoring of NGRI patients. Oregon's reform attempted to shift the locus of treatment to the community.

Rogers and Bloom (1982) suggested that the program may have effected a change in locus of treatment with many benefits and few costs. For one cohort of NGRI patients studied, the mean length of hospitalization before conditional release under the review board's jurisdiction was 363 days. This number is substantially less than the 670 days for NGRI patients in New York (Steadman, 1985). However, the New York patients tended to have more serious offenses, and in both Oregon and New York states, length of hospitalization was related to seriousness of criminal offense.

CONCLUSIONS

Despite its importance, treating NGRI patients has been a relatively unresearched and undeveloped facet of forensic psychology. Necessary security constraints often impede the optimal treatment of NGRI patients. Although treatment of NGRI patients has tended to be generic, we have advocated greater attention to individualized needs and specific treatment interventions. Empirical reviews of NGRI patient data confirm commonly held diagnostic perceptions. Most NGRI patients have severe mental disorders with psychosis featured prominently. Alcohol and drug abuse are very common as secondary diagnoses that substantially complicate treatment. It is surprising to note that small but appreciable numbers were found insane without an Axis I disorder, at least at the time of their postacquittal admission to forensic facilities.

Treatment programs must target the specific symptoms and needs of individual NGRI patients. Of special concern is identifying symptoms and associated features that signal possible decompensation or recidivism. In this context, four basic goals were proposed: (a) diagnose and treat the mental disorder, (b) reduce the risk of dangerousness, (c) prepare the NGRI patients for discharge, and (d) monitor their adjustments in the community.

Two recurring themes in this chapter must be considered in NGRI patient treatment: individualization and balancing. As previously noted, individualization reflects on the basic need to augment actuarial data with specific characteristics of particular NGRI patients that predict both treatment success as well as failure. Balancing reflects the equilibristic efforts presented by conflicting forces from the criminal justice and mental health systems, public concerns, and patient needs.

REFERENCES

American Bar Association Criminal Justice and Mental Health Division. (1989). *American Bar Association Criminal Justice and Mental Health Standards.* Washington, DC: Author.

Ayllon, T., & Milan, M. A. (1979). *Correctional rehabilitation and management: A psychological approach.* Chichester, England: Wiley.

Barlow, D. H. (1988). *Anxiety and its disorders: The nature and treatment of anxiety and panic.* New York: Guilford Press.

Beck, A. T., Rush, A. J., Shaw, B. F., & Emery, G. (1979). *Cognitive therapy of depression.* New York: Guilford Press.

Benton, M. K., & Schroeder, H. E. (1990). Social skills training with schizophrenics: A meta-analytic evaluation. *Journal of Consulting and Clinical Psychology, 58,* 741–747.

Bezchlibnyk-Butler, K. Z., & Jeffries, J. J. (1996). *Clinical handbook of psychotropic drugs.* Toronto: Hogrefe & Huber.

Bogenberger, R. P., Pasewark, R. A., Gudeman, H., & Beiber, S. L. (1987). Follow-up of insanity acquittees in Hawaii. *International Journal of Law and Psychiatry, 10,* 283–295.

Borkovec, T. D., & Mathews, A. (1988). Treatment of nonphobic anxiety disorders: A comparison of nondirective, cognitive, and coping desensitization therapy. *Journal of Consulting and Clinical Psychology, 56,* 877–884.

Borkovec, T. D., & Roemer, L. (1994). Generalized anxiety disorder. In M. Hersen & R. T. Ammerman (Eds.), *Handbook of prescriptive treatments for adults* (pp. 261–281). New York: Plenum Press.

Borkovec, T. D., & Whisman, M. A. (1996). Psychosocial treatment for generalized anxiety disorder. In M. Marissakalian & R. E. Prien (Eds.), *Long-term treatment of anxiety disorders* (pp. 171–199). Washington, DC: American Psychiatric Association.

Breier, A., & Strauss, J. S. (1983). Self control in psychotic disorders. *Archives of General Psychiatry, 40,* 1141–1145.

Breslin, N. A. (1992). Treatment of schizophrenia: Current practice and future promise. *Hospital and Community Psychiatry, 43,* 877–885.

Callahan, L. A., Steadman, H. J., McGreevy, M. A., & Robbins, P. C. (1991). The volume and characteristics of insanity defense pleas: An eight-state study. *Bulletin of the American Academy of Psychiatry and Law; 19,* 331–338.

Cavanaugh, J. L., Wasyliw, O. E., & Rogers, R. (1985). Treatment of mentally disordered offenders. In J. O. Cavenar (Ed.), *Psychiatry* (pp. 1–27). Philadelphia: J.B. Lippincott.

Chambless, D., & Goldstein, A. (1980). The treatment of agoraphobia. In A. Goldstein & E. B. Foa (Eds.), *Handbook of behavioral interventions: A clinical guide* (pp. 332–415). New York: Wiley.

Citrome, L., & Volavka, J. (2000). Management of violence in schizophrenia. *Psychiatric Annals, 30,* 41–52.

Cohen, M. I., Spodak, M. K., Silver, S. B., & Williams, K. (1988). Predicting outcome of NGRI patients released to the community. *Behavioral Sciences and the Law, 6,* 515–530.

Cooke, G., & Sikorski, C. R. (1974). Factors affecting length of hospitalization in persons adjudicated not guilty by reason of insanity. *Bulletin of the American Academy of Psychiatry and Law, 8,* 251–261.

Corrigan, P. W. (1991). Social skills training in adult psychiatric populations: A meta-analysis. *Journal of Behavior Therapy and Experimental Psychiatry, 22,* 203–210.

Criss, M. L., & Racine, D. R. (1980). Impact of change in legal standard for those adjudicated not guilty by reason of insanity 1975–1979. *Bulletin of the American Academy of Psychiatry and Law, 8,* 261–271.

Dalal, B., Larkin, E., Leese, M., & Taylor, P. J. (1999). Clozapine treatment of long-standing schizophrenia and serious violence: A two-year follow-up study of the first 50 patients treated with Clozapine in Rampton high security hospital. *Criminal Behaviour and Mental Health, 9,* 168–178.

Deffenbacher, J. L. (1999). Cognitive-behavioral conceptualization and treatment of anger. *Journal of Clinical Psychology, 55,* 295–309.

Derogatis, L. R. (1977). *The SCL-90, R Version manual: Scoring administration and procedures for the SCL-90.* Baltimore: Johns Hopkins University Press.

Dimeff, L. A., & Marlatt, G. A. (1995). Relapse prevention. In R. K. Hester & W. R. Miller (Eds.), *Handbook of alcoholism treatment approaches: Effective alternatives* (pp. 176–194). Toronto: Allyn & Bacon.

Eisner, H. R. (1989). Returning the not guilty by reason of insanity to the community: A new scale to determine readiness. *Bulletin of the American Academy* of *Psychiatry and Law, 17,* 401–403.

Elkin, I., Shea, M. T., Watkins, J. T., Imber, S. D., Sotsky, S. M., Collins, J. F., Glass, D. R., Pilkonis, P. A., Leber, W. R., Docherty, J. P., Fiester, S. J., & Parloff, M. B. (1989). NIMH treatment of depression collaborative research program: 1. General effectiveness of treatments. *Archives of General Psychiatry, 46,* 971–983.

Etscheidt, S. (1991). Reducing aggressive behavior and improving self-control: A cognitive-behavioral training program for behaviorally disordered adolescents. *Behavioral Disorders, 16,* 107–115.

Feindler, E. L., Marriott, S. A., & Iwata, M. (1984). Group anger control training for high school delinquents. *Cognitive Therapy and Research, 8,* 299–399.

Fink, M. (1987). Convulsive therapy in affective disorders: A decade of understanding and acceptance. In H. Y Metzler (Ed.), *Psychopharmacology: The third generation of progress* (pp. 1071–1076). New York: Plenum Press.

Foa, E. B., & Tillmanns, A. (1980). The treatment of obsessive-compulsive neurosis. In A. Goldstein & E. B. Foa (Eds.), *Handbook of behavioral interventions: A clinical guide* (pp. 416–500). New York: Wiley.

Foa, E. B., Wilson, R., Foa, E. B., & Barlow, D. H. (1991). *Stop obsessing! How to overcome your obsessions and compulsions.* New York: Bantam Books.

Frazer, A. (1994). Antidepressant drugs. *Depression, 2,* 1–19.

Furman, W., Geller, M., Simon, S. J., & Kelly, J. A. (1979). The use of a behavioral rehearsal procedure for teaching job interviewing skills to psychiatric patients. *Behavior Therapy, 10,* 157–167.

Fyer, A. J., Mannuzza, S., & Endicott, J. (1987). Differential diagnosis and assessment of anxiety: Recent developments. In H. Y Meltzer (Ed.), *Psychopharmacology: The third generation of progress* (pp. 1177–1191). New York: Raven.

Gacono, G. B., Meloy, J. R., Sheppard, K., Speth, E., & Roske, A. (1995). A clinical investigation of malingering and psychopathy in hospitalized NGRI patients. *Bulletin of the American Academy of Psychiatry and Law, 23,* 387–397.

Garfield, S. L., & Bergin, A. E. (1994). *Handbook of psychotherapy and behavior change* (3rd ed.). New York: John Wiley.

German, J. R., & Singer, A. C. (1976). Punishing the not guilty: Hospitalization of persons acquitted by reason of insanity. *Rutgers Law Review, 29,* 1011–1083.

Gerner, R. H., & Stanton, A. (1992). Algorithm for patient management of acute manic states: Lithium, Valproate, or Carbamazepine? *Journal of Clinical Psychopharmacology, 12,* 57–63.

Greenland, C. (1979). Crime and the insanity defense, an international comparison: Ontario and New York state. *Bulletin of the American Academy of Psychiatry and Law, 7,* 125–137.

Hambridge, J. A. (1990). The grief process in those admitted to regional secure units following homicide. *Journal of Forensic Sciences, 35,* 1149–1154.

Hans, V. P. (1986). An analysis of public attitudes toward the insanity defense. *Criminology, 4,* 393–415.

Harris, G. T., & Rice, M. E. (1994). The violent patient. In R. T. Ammerman & M. Hersen (Eds.), *Handbook of prescriptive treatments for adults* (pp. 463–486). New York: Plenum Press.

Heilbrun, K., Griffin-Heilbrun, P. G., & Griffin, N. (1988). Comparing females acquitted by reason of insanity, convicted, and civilly committed in Florida: 1977:1984. *Law and Human Behavior, 12,* 295–311.

Hodgins, S., Hebert, J., & Baraldi, R. (1986). Women declared insane: A follow-up study. *International Journal of Law and Psychiatry, 8,* 203–216.

Jacobson, E. (1986). The early history of psychotherapeutic drugs. *Psychopharmacology, 89,* 138–144.

Kane, J. M., & Freeman, H. L. (1994). Towards more effective antipsychotic treatment. *British Journal of Psychiatry, 165,* 22–31.

Kelly, J. A., Laughlin, C., Clairborne, M., & Patterson, J. (1979). A group procedure for teaching job interviewing skills to formerly hospitalized psychiatric patients. *Behavior Therapy, 10,* 299–310.

Kobak, K. A., Greist, J. H., Jefferson, J. W., Katzelnick, D. J., & Henk, H. J. (1998). Behavioral versus pharmacological treatments of obsessive compulsive disorder: A meta-analysis. *Psychopharmacology, 136,* 205–216.

Linehan, M. M. (1993). *Cognitive-behavioral treatment of borderline personality disorder.* New York: Guilford Press.

Linhorst, D. M., & Dirks-Linhorst, P. A. (1997). The impact of insanity acquittees on Missouri's public mental health system. *Law and Human Behavior, 21,* 327–338.

Lowe, C. F., & Chadwick, P. D. (1990). Verbal control of delusions. *Behavior Therapy, 21,* 461–479.

Madden, D. J., Lion, J. R., & Penna, M. W. (1977). Assaults on psychiatrists by patients. *American Journal of Psychiatry, 133,* 422–429.

Meichenbaum, D. (1975). Self-instructional methods. In F. Kanfer & A. Goldstein (Eds.), *Helping people change.* New York: Pergamon Press.

Meichenbaum, D. (1977). *Cognitive-behavioral modification: An integrative approach.* New York: Plenum Press.

Milan, M. A., (1987). Token economy programs in closed institutions. In E. K. Morris & C. J. Braukmann (Eds.), *Behavioral approaches to crime and delinquency: A handbook of application, research, and concepts* (pp. 195–222). New York: Plenum Press.

Miller, W. R. (1982). Treating problem drinkers: What works? *The Behavior Therapist, 5,* 15–18.

Monahan, J. (1980). *Who is the client? The ethics of psychological intervention in the criminal justice system.* Washington, DC: American Psychological Association.

Moncrieff, J., & Drummond, D. C. (1997). New pharmacologic treatments for alcohol abusers. *Addiction, 92,* 939–947.

Morrow, W. R., & Petersen, D. B. (1966). Follow-up on discharged offenders—"Not Guilty by Reason of Insanity" and "Criminal Sexual Psychopaths." *Journal of Criminal Law, Criminology & Police Science, 57,* 31–34.

Mueser, K. T., Levine, S., Bellak, A. S., Douglas, M. S., & Brady, E. U. (1990). Social skills training for acute psychiatric inpatients. *Hospital and Community Psychiatry, 41,* 1249–1250.

Nelson, J. C. (1997, February). *Recently marketed antidepressants.* Paper presented at the ASCP President's Day weekend meeting, Barbados.

Nietzel, M. T., & Bernstein, D. A. (1981). Assessment of anxiety and fear. In M. Hersen & A. S. Bellack (Eds.), *Behavioral assessment: A practical handbook* (2nd ed., pp. 135–147). New York: Pergamon Press.

Nomellini, S., & Katz, R. C. (1983). Effects of anger control training on abusive patients. *Cognitive Research and Therapy, 7,* 57–67.

Norwood, S., Nicholson, R. A., Enyart, C., & Hickey, M. L. (1991). Characteristics and outcomes of NGRI patients in Oklahoma. *Behavioral Sciences and the Law, 9,* 487–500.

Novaco, R. W. (1977). Stress inoculation: A cognitive therapy for anger and its application to a case of depression. *Journal of Consulting and Clinical Psychology, 45,* 600–608.

Novaco, R. W. (1994). Anger as a risk factor for violence among the mentally disordered. In J. Monahan & H. J. Steadman (Eds.), *Violence and mental disorder* (pp. 21–60). Chicago: University of Chicago Press.

Novaco, R. W. (1997). Remediating anger and aggression with violent offenders. *Legal and Criminological Psychology, 2,* 77–88.

Ogloff, J. R. P. (1991). A comparison of insanity defense standards on juror decision making. *Law and Human Behavior, 15,* 509–521.

Ogloff, J. R. P., Schweighofer, A., Turnbull, S. D., & Whittemore, K. (1992). In J. R. P. Ogloff (Ed.), *Law and psychology: The broadening of the discipline* (pp. 171–207). Durham, NC: Carolina Academic Press.

Ost, L-G. (1987). Applied relaxation: Description of a coping technique and review of controlled studies. *Behavioral Research and Therapy, 25,* 397–409.

Pasewark, R. A., Jeffrey, R., & Bieber, S. (1987). Differentiating successful and unsuccessful insanity pleas defendants in Colorado. *Journal of Psychiatry and Law, 15,* 55–71.

Paul, G. L., & Lentz, R. J. (1977). *Psychosocial treatment of chronic mental patients: Milieu versus social learning programs.* Cambridge, MA: Harvard University Press.

Peckham, J., & Muller, J. (1999). Employment and schizophrenia: Recommendations to improve employability for individuals with schizophrenia. *Psychiatric Rehabilitation Journal, 22,* 399–402.

Perlin, M. L. (1996). The insanity defense: Deconstructing the myths and reconstructing the jurisprudence. In B. D. Sales & D. W Shuman (Eds.), *Law, mental health, and mental disorder.* Pacific Grove, CA: Brooks/Cole.

Persons, J. B. (1989). *Cognitive therapy in practice: A case formulation approach.* New York: W. W. Norton.

Petrila, J. (1982). The insanity defense and other mental health dispositions in Missouri. *International Journal of Law and Psychiatry, 5,* 81–101.

Phillips, B. L., & Pasewark, R. A. (1980). Insanity plea in Connecticut. *Bulletin of the American Academy of Psychiatry and Law, 8,* 325–344.

Pickar, D., Owen, R. R., Litman, R. E., Konicki, E., Gutierrez, R., & Rapaport, M. H. (1992). Clinical and biological response to clozapine in patients with schizophrenia. *Archives of General Psychiatry, 49,* 345–353.

Quinsey, V. L. (1988). Assessments of the treatability of forensic patients. *Behavioral Sciences and the Law, 6,* 443–452.

Rice, M. E. (1997). Violent offender research and implications for the criminal justice system. *American Psychologist, 52,* 414–423.

Rice, M. E., & Harris, G. T. (1990). The predictors of insanity acquittal. *International Journal of Law and Psychiatry, 13,* 217–224.

Rice, M. E., Harris, G. T. & Quinsey, V. L. (1996). Treatment of forensic patients. In B. D. Sales & S. A. Shah (Eds.), *Mental health and law: Research, policy and services* (pp. 141–189). Durham, NC: Carolina Academic Press.

Rice, M. E., Harris, G. T., Quinsey, V. L., & Cyr, M. (1990). Planning treatment programs in secure psychiatric facilities. In D. Weisstub (Ed.), *Law and mental health: International perspectives* (pp. 162–230). New York: Pergamon Press.

Rice, M. E., Harris, G. T., Varney, G. W., & Quinsey, V. L. (1989). *Violence in institutions: Understanding, prevention, and control.* Toronto: Hans Huber.

Richelson, E. (1996). Preclinical pharmacology of neuroleptics: Focus on new generation compounds. *Journal of Clinical Psychiatry, 57,* 4–11.

Robins, S., & Novaco, R. W. (1999). Systems conceptualization and treatment of anger. *Journal of Clinical Psychology, 55,* 325–337.

Rogers, J. L., & Bloom, J. D. (1982). Characteristics of persons committed to Oregon's Psychiatric Security Review. *Bulletin of the American Academy of Psychiatry and the Law, 10,* 15–164.

Rogers, R. (1986). *Conducting insanity evaluations.* New York: Van Nostrand Reinhold.

Rogers, R. (1987). Ethical dilemmas in forensic evaluations. *Behavioral Sciences and the Law, 5,* 149–160.

Rogers, R., Harris, M., & Wasyliw, O. E. (1983). Observed and self-reported psychopathology in NGRI acquittees in court-mandated outpatient treatment. *International Journal of Offender Therapy and Comparative Criminology, 27,* 143–149.

Rogers, R., & Salekin, R. T. (1998). Beguiled by Bayes: A reanalysis of Mossman and Hart's estimates of malingering. *Behavioral Sciences and the Law, 16,* 147–153.

Rogers, R., Seman, W., & Clark, C. C. (1986). Assessment of criminal responsibility: Initial validation of the R-CRAS with the M'Naghten and GBMI standards. *International Journal of Law and Psychiatry, 9,* 67–75.

Rogers, R., & Wettstein, R. M. (1985). Relapse in NGRI outpatients: An empirical study. *Journal of Offender Therapy, 29,* 227–236.

Ross, R. R., & Lightfoot, L. O. (1985). *Treatment of the alcohol-abusing offender.* Springfield, IL: Thomas.

Salekin, R. T., Rogers, R., & Sewell, K. W. (1996). A review and meta-analysis of the Psychopathy Checklist and Psychopathy Checklist—Revised: Predictive validity. *Clinical Psychology: Science and Practice, 3,* 203–315.

Salekin, R. T., Rogers, R., & Sewell, K. W. (1997). Construct validity of psychopathy in a female offender sample: A multitrait-multimethod evaluation. *Journal of Abnormal Psychology, 106,* 576–585.

Salekin, R. T., Rogers, R., Ustad, K. L., & Sewell, K. W. (1998). Psychopathy and recidivism: Generalizing across genders. *Law and Human Behavior, 22,* 109–128.

Satterfield, J. M. (1999). Adjunctive cognitive-behavioral therapy for rapid-cycling bipolar disorder: An empirical case study. *Psychiatry: Interpersonal and Biological Processes, 62,* 357–369.

Schlichter, K. J., & Horan, J. J. (1981). Effects of stress inoculation on the anger and aggression management of institutionalized juvenile delinquents. *Cognitive Therapy and Research, 5,* 359–369.

Scott, J., Williams, J. M. G., & Beck, A. T. (1995). *Cognitive therapy in clinical practice: An illustrative casebook.* New York: Routledge.

Seig, A., Ball, E., & Menninger, J. A. (1995). A comparison of female versus male insanity acquittees in Colorado. *Bulletin of the American Academy of Psychiatry and Law, 23,* 523–532.

Shady, G. A., & Kue, S. G. (1977). Preparing the hardcore disadvantaged for employment: Social skills orientation course—An evaluation. *Canadian Journal of Criminology and Corrections, 19,* 303–309.

Shah. P. J., Greenberg, W. M., & Convit. A. (1994). Hospitalized insanity acquittees' level of functioning. *Bulletin of the American Academy of Psychiatry and Law, 22,* 85–93.

Silver, E. (1995). Punishment or treatment: Comparing the lengths of confinement of successful and unsuccessful insanity defendants. *Law and Human Behavior, 19,* 375–388.

Silver, E., Cirincione, C., & Steadman, H. J. (1994). Demythologizing inaccurate perceptions of the insanity defense. *Law and Human Behavior, 18,* 63–70.

Silver, S. B., Cohen, M. I., & Spodiak, M. K. (1989). Follow-up after release of insanity acquittees, mentally disordered offenders, and convicted felons. *Bulletin of the American Academy of Psychiatry and Law, 17,* 387–400.

Silverman, W. K., Kurtines, W. M., Ginsburg, G. S., Weems, C. F., Rabian, B., & Serafini, L. T. (1999). *Journal of Consulting and Clinical Psychology, 67,* 675–687.

Slobogin, C. (1985). A rational approach to responsibility. *Michigan Law Review, 83,* 513–620.

Smith, G., & Hall, J. (1982). Evaluating Michigan's guilty but mentally ill verdict: An empirical study. *University of Michigan Journal of Law Reform, 16,* 77–114.

Spitzer, R. L., & Endicott, J. (1978). *Schedule of Affective Disorders and Schizophrenia-Change Version (SADS-C).* New York: Biometrics Research.

Stacy, A. W. (1997). Memory activation and expectancy as prospective predictors of alcohol and marijuana use. *Journal of Abnormal Psychology, 106,* 61–73.

Steadman, H. J. (1980). Insanity acquittals in New York state, 1965–1978. *American Journal of Psychiatry, 137,* 321–326.

Steadman, H. J. (1985). Insanity defense research and treatment of NGRI patients. *Behavioral Sciences and the Law, 3,* 37–48.

Steadman, H. J., & Cocozza, J. J. (1974). *Careers of the criminally insane.* Lexington, MA: Lexington Books.

Steadman, H. J., Keitner, L., Braff, J., & Arvanites, T. M. (1983). Factors associated with a successful insanity plea. *American Journal of Psychiatry, 140,* 401–405.

Steadman, H. J., McGreevy, M. A., Morrissey, J. P., Callahan, L. A., Robbins, P. C., & Cirincione, C. (1993). *Before and after Hinckley: Evaluating the insanity defense reform.* New York: Guilford Press.

Steadman, H. J., Monahan, J., Hartstone, E., Kantorowski-Davis, S., & Robbins, P. C. (1982). Mentally disordered offenders: A national survey of patients and facilities. *Law and Human Behavior, 6,* 31–38.

Steadman, H. J., Pasewark, R. A., Hawkins, M., Kiser, M., & Bieber, S. (1983). Hospitalization length of NGRI patients. *Journal of Clinical Psychology, 39,* 611–614.

Suinn, R. M. (1990). *Anxiety management training.* New York: Plenum Press.

Szasz, T. S. (1963). *Law, liberty, and psychiatry.* New York: MacMillan.

Tellefsen, C., Cohen, M. I., Silver, S. B., & Dougherty, C. (1992). Predicting success on conditional release for NGRI patients: Regionalized versus nonregionalized hospital patients. *Bulletin of the American Academy of Psychiatry and Law, 20,* 87–99.

Turner, S. M. (1984). *Behavioral theories and treatment of anxiety.* New York. Plenum Press.

Twentyman, C. T., Jensen, M., & Kloss, J. D. (1978). Social skills training for the complex offender: Employment seeking skills. *Journal of Clinical Psychology, 34,* 320–326.

Volavka, J., & Citrome, L. (1999). Atypical antipsychotics in the treatment of the persistently aggressive psychotic patient: Methodological concerns. *Schizophrenia Research, 35 Supplement,* 23–33.

Webster, C. D., Douglas, K., Eaves, D., & Hart, S. D. (1997). *The HCR-20 Scheme: The assessment of dangerousness and risk.* Burnaby, British Columbia, Canada: Simon Fraser University.

Weissman, M. M. (1994). Psychotherapy in the maintenance treatment of depression. *British Journal of Psychiatry, 165,* 42–50.

Wettstein, R. M., & Mulvey, E. (1988). Disposition of insanity acquittees in Illinois. *Bulletin of the American Academy of Psychiatry and the Law, 16,* 11–24.

Wettstein, R. M., Mulvey, E., & Rogers, R. (1991). Insanity defense standards: A prospective comparison. *American Journal of Psychiatry, 148,* 21–27.

Wolpe, J. (1990). *The practice of behavior therapy.* New York: Pergamon Press.

Wong, S. E., Slama, K. M., & Liberman, R. P. (1987). Behavioral analysis and therapy for aggressive psychiatric and developmentally disabled patients. In L. H. Roth (Ed.), *Clinical treatment of the violent person* (pp. 20–53). New York: Guilford Press.

Wong, S. E., Woosley, J. E., Innocent, A. J., & Liberman, R. P. (1988). Behavioral treatment of violent psychiatric patients. *Psychiatric Clinics of North America, 11,* 569–579.

Zaretsky, A. E., Segal, Z. V., & Gemar, M. (1999). Cognitive therapy for bipolar depression: A pilot study. *Canadian Journal of Psychiatry, 44,* 491–494.

Zonana, H., Bartel, R. L., Wells, J. A., Buchanan, J. A., & Getz, M. A. (1990). Part II: Sex differences in persons found not guilty by reason of insanity: Analysis of data from the Connecticut NGRI registry. *Bulletin of the American Academy of Psychiatry and Law, 18,* 129–142.

Zonana, H., & Norko, M. A. (1996). Mandated treatment. In W. Sledge and A. Tasman (Eds.), *Clinical challenges in psychiatry* (pp. 249–291). Washington, DC: American Psychiatric Press.

26

An Evaluation of a Maximum Security Therapeutic Community for Psychopaths and Other Mentally Disordered Offenders

MARNIE E. RICE, GRANT T. HARRIS, AND CATHERINE A. CORMIER

Psychopaths present serious problems for the criminal justice system because they are responsible for many serious crimes and appear to be very resistant to treatment. The present study was a retrospective evaluation of the efficacy of a maximum security therapeutic community program in reducing recidivism among mentally disordered offenders, some of whom were psychopaths. The study employed a matched group, quasiexperimental design. The results showed that, compared to no program (in most cases prison), treatment was associated with lower recidivism (especially violent recidivism) for nonpsychopaths and higher violent recidivism for psychopaths. The clinical and research utility of Hare's Psychopathy Checklist was strongly supported.

The therapeutic community evolved in psychiatric settings in England during the late 1940s, notably under the leadership of Maxwell Jones. Citizens of therapeutic communities care materially and emotionally for one another, follow the rules of the community, submit to the authority of the group, and suffer sanctions imposed by the group (Jones, 1955; 1968). Honesty, sincerity, and empathy for others are highly valued. Reports of the efficacy of therapeutic communities have been more testimonial than scientific (Fairweather, Saunders, Maynard, Cressler, & Black, 1969; Jones, 1968; 1976;

Reprinted with kind permission of Springer Science and Business Media. Law and Human Behavior, 16 (4), 399–412. © 1992 Plenum Publishing Corporation.

Maller, 1971). Unfortunately, the few controlled studies evaluating the ability of therapeutic communities to increase postdischarge socialization or work skills, or to prevent rehospitalization, showed modest effects, at best, compared to more traditional hospital programs (Paul & Lentz, 1977). Therapeutic communities continue to be recommended for addictions, for mentally disordered offenders, and for criminal offenders (DeLeon, 1985; Reid. 1989; Toch, 1980).

Those offenders diagnosed as psychopaths occupy many beds in correctional and forensic mental health facilities. Wong (1984) found that as many as 30% of Canadian federal prisoners could be categorized as psychopaths, depending upon institutional security level. The treatability of psychopaths has long concerned criminologists and mental health experts. Early reports indicated positive effects of psychotherapy (Corsini, 1958; Lipton, 1950; Rodgers, 1947; Rosow, 1955; Schmideberg, 1949; Showstack, 1956; Thorne, 1959), but others were pessimistic about the prognosis for psychopaths with or without treatment (Cleckley, 1982; Darling, 1945; McCann, 1948; Meloy, 1988). Most recent investigators, upon critically evaluating the evidence, argued that treatment for adult psychopaths is ineffective (Cleckley, 1982; Hare, 1970; McCord, 1982; Woody, McLellan, Rubersky, & O'Brien, 1985).

Acknowledging pessimistic evidence, Hare (1970) suggested that a therapeutic community that reshaped the social milieu might change some of the basic personality characteristics and interpersonal behavior of psychopaths. Although not substantiated by comparative outcome data, there have been several positive reports for therapeutic community programs for psychopaths (Barker & Mason, 1968; Copas, O'Brien, Roberts, & Whiteley, 1984; McCord, 1982; Whiteley, 1967).

One of the major problems in evaluating the effectiveness of various treatments upon the recidivism of psychopaths relates to the circularity in the definition of psychopathy (and the closely related term *antisocial personality disorder*) in that criminal behavior has been identified both as a defining property and as a result of the disorders (Gunn, 1977). It is axiomatic that future behavior is best predicted by past behavior, and thus it is not surprising that those diagnosed as psychopaths have been reported to have worse outcomes than other offenders with less serious criminal histories. Although their instrument contains some items obviously related to criminal history, the Psychopathy Checklist developed by Hare and his associates (Hare, 1980; Hare & McPherson, 1984; Schroeder, Schroeder, & Hare, 1983) primarily comprises items conceptually quite distinct from criminal behavior. There is little doubt that it is currently the best developed tool for the assessment of psychopathy among correctional populations (Hare, 1983; 1985; 1986; Schroeder et al., 1983; Widiger & Frances, 1987), and it correlates highly with such other clinical-behavioral measures as Cleckley's (1982) criteria for psychopathy and the *DSM-III* diagnosis of antisocial personality disorder (Hare, 1983; 1985).

Other Important Risk Factors

Among correctional populations in general, there have been many studies of the relationship between demographic and, more rarely, clinical variables and later recidivism and violent recidivism (for recent reviews see Monahan, 1981; Nuffield, 1982; Quinsey, 1984). The variables most consistently related to recidivism (whether violent or not) in previous studies of correctional or mentally disordered offender populations are age (Hodgins, 1983; Mandelzys, 1979; Molof, 1965; Nuffield, 1982; Pruesse & Quinsey, 1977; Quinsey & Maguire, 1986; Quinsey, Pruesse, & Fernley, 1975a; Steadman, 1973; Wormith & Goldstone, 1984), offense history (Black, 1982; Hodgins, 1983; Mandelzys, 1979; Wormith & Goldstone, 1984), and type of index offense (Hodgins, 1983; Nuffield, 1982; Quinsey, Pruesse, & Fernley, 1975b; Steadman, 1973; Tong & MacKay, 1959; Wormith & Goldstone, 1984; see also Simon 1971). Among mentally disordered offenders, a diagnosis of personality disorder has often been reported to be associated with recidivism (Black, 1982: Quinsey et al.; 1975a). Thus, any evaluation of treatment outcome for mentally disordered offenders must include methodological control for age, criminal history, offense, and diagnosis (especially psychopathy).

The Present Study

The present study evaluated an intensive therapeutic community for mentally disordered offenders that was thought to be especially suitable for psychopaths. The program operated for over a decade in a maximum security institution and drew worldwide attention for its novel approach to treatment (Barker, 1980; Barker & Buck, 1977; Barker & Mason, 1968; Barker, Mason, & Wilson, 1969; Barker & McLaughlin, 1977). In the present study, treated offenders were compared with untreated offenders matched with the treated subjects on those variables most consistently related to recidivism (age, criminal history, and index offense). The subjects of the study were a particularly serious group of offenders in that almost all had a history of violent criminality. Hare's Revised Psychopathy Checklist was used to identify psychopaths and nonpsychopaths in order to examine the interrelationships among treatment, psychopathy, and recidivism. In almost all cases, the comparison subjects were convicted of some offense(s) and served prison sentences. The outcome measures were criminal and violent recidivism and the average follow-up period exceeded 10 years.

METHOD

The Program

The therapeutic community program has been described at length elsewhere (Barker & Buck, 1977; Barker & Mason, 1968; Barker et al., 1969; Barker & McLaughlin, 1977; Maier, 1976; Quinsey, 1981). Briefly, the program was peer operated and involved intensive group therapy for up to 80 hours weekly. The goal was to create an environment where patients could develop empathy and responsibility for their peers. Patients participated in fixed and long-term daily sessions with one or two patients and sat on committees that monitored and structured all aspects of their lives. Patients who performed well in the program and who showed organizational talent were appointed to program leadership roles and led therapy groups and security and administrative committees. Patients participated in decisions about release and transfer.

There were other features of the program that may have been important. Patients had very little contact with professional staff. Very little effort was expended in organized recreational programs. Very few patients participated in academic upgrading or vocational training. Some patients worked in contract workshops, in the kitchen, or on cleaning gangs. However, such work was regarded as a temporary "rest" from therapy and such patients shared the wages they earned with the patients involved in intensive therapy. No programs were specifically aimed at altering procriminal attitudes and beliefs, teaching social skills or social problem solving, or training life skills. A small proportion of the patients were diagnosed as psychotic and were prescribed neuroleptic drugs, but efforts were made to keep doses as low as possible. One reason for including psychotic patients in the program was to give the psychopaths an opportunity to care for such individuals. Tight internal and external security was maintained by patients in cooperation with psychiatric attendants. Patients had very little opportunity for diversion; tight limits were imposed on viewing television, reading material, and even on social interaction among patients.

Entry to and participation in the therapeutic community was not voluntary and stated willingness to participate was not a selection criterion. For example, an individual found not guilty by reason of insanity or convicted of violent crime and then civilly committed could be assigned to the program even if he did not wish to be. Once in the program, patients who refused to engage in detailed discussion of their offenses, backgrounds, and feelings were sent to a subprogram where they discussed their motivation, attitudes, and participation until they complied with program requirements. Though patients could leave the therapeutic community by convincing staff or an independent review board that they had made clinical progress, they could not get out simply by misbehaving. Noncompliance and disruption were regarded as symptoms to be changed and this form of attrition was not permitted. There were several aspects of the program that might be seen to violate patients' rights by today's standards, but the program was very favorably reviewed on both ethical and clinical grounds at the time (Butler, Long, & Rowsell, 1977; Canada, 1977). Our evaluation of the program was entirely retrospective and we had no control over any aspect of the program.

Subjects

The treated subjects in this study were all 176 patients who spent at least 2 years in the therapeutic community program during the period of its most active operation (January, 1968, to February, 1978). Being at risk to reoffend was defined as being released to the street or being held in an open psychiatric institution. Three subjects failed after leaving the maximum security program but while still in another secure hospital, and thereby failed though technically not yet at risk to do so.

For most treated subjects, a matched comparison subject was selected from among the many forensic assessment cases (>100) admitted each year. Because the matching criteria were so strict, 30 treated subjects could not be matched. Preliminary analyses showed no differences between matched and unmatched patients. For the yoked pairs, the matching was performed according to several criteria: The treated and comparison subjects had to be (a) the same age within 1 year at the time of the index offense, (b) charged with the same index offense, (c) equivalent in criminal history for each of property and violent offenses according to a system developed by Akman and Normandeau (1967), and (d) charged with their index offenses no more than 2 years apart. In addition, comparison subjects could not have returned to the study institution for any treatment. Almost all (84%) comparison subjects spent some time in a correctional institution, $M = 50.7$ ($SD = 46.4$) months.

Procedure

A list of most of the study variables is shown in Table 1. All variables except those pertaining to outcome were coded from institutional files. These institutional files were exceptionally complete and included information from a variety of sources. These detailed files have been employed by other researchers in several studies (e.g., Quinsey & Maguire, 1983; 1986; Rice, Quinsey, & Houghton, 1990), but all variables were newly coded for this study. Outcome data were obtained from a variety of sources including the files of the Coroner's Office, the Lieutenant Governor's Review Board, the Royal Canadian Mounted Police (a national data base including INTERPOL reports), the National Parole Service of Canada, and provincial correctional and parole systems. In order to prevent inadvertent contamination of the historical variables by raters' knowledge of outcome, childhood history, adult adjustment, offense, and assessment variables were coded using only file information at the time the subject entered the program or was initially assessed, and outcome data were obtained only after all other variables had been coded. A randomly chosen 20 subjects were selected for an evaluation of the interrater reliability achieved.[1]

Subjects were classified as failures if they had incurred any new charge for a criminal offense, or had their parole revoked or were returned to the maximum security institution for behavior that could have, in the judgment of the research assistants, resulted in a criminal charge. Violent failure comprised any new charge against persons, or any parole revocation or return to the maximum security institution for violent behavior.

RESULTS

Interrater Reliability

Interrater agreement was assessed for all study variables by computing mean Pearson correlation coefficients for continuous variables and kappa statistics for categorical

TABLE 1

Characteristics of 176 Treated (*T*) and 146 Comparison (*C*) Samples of Criminals and Differences Between Groups

	T	C	TEST
CHILDHOOD HISTORY			
Highest grade	8.99 (2.24)	8.40 (2.24)	2.24
School maladjustment	2.22 (1.21)	2.29 (1.17)	—
School leaving age	14.7 (5.63)	14.9 (4.17)	—
Teen alcohol abuse	1.08 (1.06)	1.55 (1.01)	3.59
Socioeconomic status	313 (174)	308 (140)	—
Behavior problems	3.15 (2.77)	2.99 (2.50)	—
Childhood aggression	2.84 (1.94)	2.95 (1.79)	—
Ever suspended or expelled (%)	19	26	—
Arrested under 16 (%)	38	34	—
Separation from parents (%)	46	52	—
Parental criminality (%)	7	11	—
Parental psych history (%)	13	12	—
Parental alcoholism (%)	34	56	12.83*
ADULT HISTORY			
Longest job (months)	33.9 (119)	50.8 (149)	—
Times in corrections	1.45 (2.02)	1.34 (2.21)	—
Psychiatric admissions	1.25 (1.71)	.67 (1.27)	3.26
Aggression score	3.34 (1.99)	3.34 (1.91)	—
Psychopathy Checklist	19.23 (9.76)	18.93 (8.58)	—
Property charges	7.42 (16.2)	6.92 (12.6)	—
Violent charges	4.93 (11.6)	4.81 (9.82)	—
Level of Superversion Inventory	17.8 (8.46)	18.9 9.14)	—
Alcohol abuse score	1.51 (1.19)	1.83 (1.12)	2.30
Unemployed (%)	51	58	—
Previous violent offense (%)	27	30	—
Ever married (%)	27	41	6.74
Lived alone (%)	57	62	—
OFFENSE ASSESSMENT VARIABLES			
Age at offense	23.4 (6.53)	23.2 (6.25)	—
Number of victims	1.581 (1.60)	1.35 (1.06)	—
Victim injury	3.81 (2.34)	3.85 (2.35)	—
Offense seriousness	23.0 (30.2)	19.6 (17.8)	—
Elevated MMPI scales	3.56 (2.14)	3.51 (2.51)	—
Alcohol involved (%)	34	58	17.36*
Volunteered for treatment (%)	23	22	—
Expressed remorse (%)	21	26	—
Attitude supported crime (%)	40	43	—
Female victim (%)	53	60	—
Weapon used (%)	32	40	—
Sexual motive (%)	28	5	26.71*
MMPI elevated scale 4 (%)	32	31	—
Schizophrenia (%)	27	2	36.04*
Personality disordered (%)	49	60	3.99

Note: For continuous variables (those not followed by a % sign), the numbers under *T* and *C* are means with standard deviations in parentheses. For dichotomous variables (those followed by a % sign), numbers under T and C are percentages. Numbers under Test are statistically significant (α = .05) *t* (*df* > 100) scores (for continuous variables) or χ^2 values (for dichotomous variables). The actual number of observations for each test varied slightly because of missing observations. Asterisks indicate statistically significant (α = .001) differences after the application of a conservative Bonferroni correction.

variables. For both, the reliability criterion was .70 and individual variables not reaching this criterion were dropped from the study with the exception of Childhood Aggression ($r = .68$, $p < .01$). For all variables retained, mean correlation coefficient was .90 and mean kappa was .83. Because it formed the basis for several important analyses, we note that the mean interrater correlation for the Revised 20-item Psychopathy Checklist was .96.

Treated versus Untreated Subjects

Table 1 lists all study variables and indicates those on which the comparison of the two groups of matched subjects yielded statistically significant differences. The table also provides considerable detail on the demographic, clinical, social, and criminal history of the 292 matched subjects. Generally, the table indicates that these were a relatively serious group of offenders with lengthy criminal histories, emotional problems, and extensive social maladjustment. Probably the only important difference between the two groups was that the treated group comprised more psychotic (almost always schizophrenic) individuals. Further analyses explored the effect of this variable. There were a few other smaller differences between the groups; some might be hypothesized to represent higher risk for the treated subjects (e.g., sexual motive to index offense, less often married) while approximately the same number suggest the reverse (e.g., degree of alcohol abuse, educational achievement).

Treatment, Outcome, and Psychopathy

The mean duration of follow-up was 10.5 ($SD = 4.94$) years and there were no differences in mean follow-up time for treated versus untreated or for psychopathic versus nonpsychopathic subjects. Of the 176 subjects treated, 169 were at risk to fail for some time (or failed anyway) during the follow-up period ending in April, 1988; and of the 146 untreated yokes, 136 were at risk to fail. Considering any failure, 97 (57%) of the treated and 93 (68%) of the comparison subjects failed, $\chi^2 (1, N = 305) = 3.87$, $p < .05$. However, of those 140 treated and yoked subjects at risk to fail, 82 (59%) failed, $\chi^2 (1, N = 280) = 2.86$, $p < .10$. Considering violent failure there is even less evidence of an overall effect of treatment. The corresponding rates of violent failure were 39% and 46% for treated and untreated subjects respectively, and 40% for matched treated subjects.

Because the therapeutic community had been regarded as an especially promising treatment for psychopathy, treatment and outcome were compared for psychopaths and nonpsychopaths separately. Psychopathy Checklist scores were based solely on file information rather than on a combination of file and interview information. Wong (1984) reported that use of the customary cutoff of 30 when using file information alone underestimated the number of psychopaths, and that a cutoff of 25 would be more appropriate. He also showed that the correlation between the two ways (file only versus file plus interview) of scoring the Checklist was very high ($r = .93$). In view of Wong's findings, we adopted a cutoff of 25 out of 40. In an earlier paper, we examined whether our choice of cutoff affected the results obtained and found it did not (Harris, Rice, & Cormier, 1991).

For the 46 treated matched psychopaths (with opportunity to fail) and their comparison subjects, the rates of overall recidivism were 89% and 81%, respectively ($\chi^2 < 1$). The corresponding rates of violent recidivism were 78% and 55%, χ^2 (1, $N = 92$) = 5.49, $p < .05$. These results suggest that, especially for violent failure, the therapeutic community treatment was associated with poorer outcome for psychopaths. However, most treated psychopaths were matched to comparison subjects who did not themselves meet the criterion for psychopathy. Table 2 examines the effects of treatment on outcome for psychopaths and nonpsychopaths separately. All treated (not just those who had been yoked) and untreated subjects who had an opportunity to fail were included in this analysis. As can be seen in Table 2, there was, in the case of violent failure, an interaction of treatment with psychopathy upon recidivism such that treatment was associated with lower recidivism for nonpsychopaths but higher recidivism for psychopaths. A log-linear analysis yielded χ^2 (1, $N = 285$) = 9.92, $p < .002$ for the interaction.

TABLE 2
Recidivism Rates of Treated and Untreated Psychopaths and Nonpsychopaths

	TREATED	UNTREATED	χ^2 (1)
PSYCHOPATHS			
Any failure	87 (53)	90 (29)	< 1
Violent failure	77 (52)	55 (29)	4.12*
NONPSYCHOPATHS			
Any failure	44 (116)	58 (90)	3.87*
Violent failure	22 (114)	39 (90)	6.97*

Note: For each cell, rates are expressed as percentages and total n appears in parentheses.
* $p < .05$.

In order to evaluate the importance of this interaction, a multiple discriminant analysis was performed in which the predictor variables were psychopath (or not), treated (or not), and the interaction of these two; and the dependent variable was violent failure or not. The analysis showed that treatment made no significant contribution to the discriminant function but the other two variables (psychopath or not, and the interaction of psychopathy and treatment) yielded a statistically significant solution, regression $R = .346$, $F(2,289) = 19.59$, $p < .0001$. Setting the selection ratio equal to the base rate produced a 64% correct classification rate, and a relative improvement over chance (Loeber & Stouthamer-Loeber, 1986) of 27%, $p < .001$, using two variables alone to predict violent outcome.

Although the two study groups were very closely matched overall, the subgroup of treated psychopaths may have exhibited higher pretreatment risk of recidivism than the untreated psychopaths and such a confounding could have been responsible for the surprising results shown in Table 2. Thus, the two groups of psychopaths were compared on all study variables shown in Table 1. Though both groups had equivalent mean Psychopathy Checklist scores (29.4 vs. 30.0), untreated psychopaths had significantly worse teenage and adult alcohol abuse scores, were more often married, were less likely to be sex offenders, and had worse Level of Supervision Inventory scores (all p's < .05). Of the variables yielding nonsignificant differences between groups, the majority showed a trend in favor of higher risk for the untreated psychopaths. Thus, the differences between the two subgroups clearly do not support any contention that the treated psychopaths exhibited *higher* pretreatment risk of recidivism.

Because retrospectively coded *DSM-III* diagnosis was one of the few variables on which the treated and untreated groups differed at the outset, this relationship was examined further. The rates of violent failure among matched treated and untreated psychotic (schizophrenia or affective disorder) subjects were 15% and 25%, respectively; whereas among nonpsychopathic nonpsychotics, the comparable rates were 26% and 40%. Although neither comparison was statistically significant, they indicated that the main results in Table 2 are not due to differences in the diagnoses of the nonpsychopathic groups.

Psychopaths in the Therapeutic Community

The final analyses concerned the variables specific to the treatment program. These were variables that pertained at least in a general way to the patient's adjustment to the institution, his success in the program, and the degree to which he was trusted by the program's clinical staff. The results are summarized in Table 3. The interesting comparisons involved the ways in which psychopaths and nonpsychopaths differed. Psychopaths showed much poorer adjustment, assessed in terms of problem behaviors, both in their first year and in their last year. However, when variables that reflect the degree of trust by clinical staff are considered, psychopaths and nonpsychopaths showed no differences. Interestingly, the first set of variables, reflecting patient's behavior rather than staff trust, were consistently related to outcome.

DISCUSSION

Overall, the results showed no effect of the therapeutic community in reducing recidivism. However, the most important finding of this study was the differential effect of the program. Psychopaths who participated in the therapeutic community exhibited higher rates of violent recidivism than did the psychopaths who did not. The opposite result was obtained for nonpsychopaths, and it should be noted that the nonpsychopath groups comprised both psychotic and nonpsychotic individuals. Although there were more psychotics among the treated subjects, and although psychotic subjects showed lower rates of failure overall, those differences alone cannot explain the interaction of treatment and psychopathy. The interaction is especially surprising because the program was explicitly designed to effect positive changes in the psychopathic

TABLE 3

Differences Between Treated Psychopaths and Treated Nonpsychopaths

VARIABLE	NONPSYCHOPATHS	PSYCHOPATHS	TEST
Months in treatment	70.5 (45.8)	62.0 (38.4)	—
*Confinements first year[a]	1.18 (1.71)	1.82 (2.26)	2.03
Negative entries first year[b]	8.53 (7.72)	11.29 (8.48)	2.07
*Confinements last year[a]	.34 (.95)	.72 (1.66)	1.89
*Negative entries last year[b]	3.65 (4.41)	6.79 (8.75)	3.10
*Disciplinary subprogram[c]	1.19 (1.77)	2.57 (2.84)	3.62
Months to positive rec.[d]	32.9 (43.5)	45.9 (44.9)	—
Number of positive rec's.[d]	.68 (1.1)	.67 (.59)	—
Months as a program leader	4.89 (11.3)	4.84 (5.92)	—
Months on work ward	18.3 (24.6)	13.2 (15.9)	—
*Nonfailure misbehaviors (%)	25	46	5.19

Note: For continuous variables (those not followed by a % sign), the numbers under Psychopaths and Nonpsychopaths are means with standard deviations in parentheses. For dichotomous variables (those followed by a % sign), numbers under Psychopaths and Nonpsychopaths are percentages. Numbers under Test are statistically significant ($\alpha = .05$) t (df > 100) scores (for continuous variables) or χ^2 values (for dichotomous variables). The actual number of observations for each test varied slightly due to missing observations. Asterisks indicate variables that yielded a significant relationship with failure and/or violent failure.

[a] Total number of times subject was placed in seclusion for violent or disruptive behavior.

[b] Total number of notations in subject's clinical record that he had engaged in any disruptive or countertherapeutic behavior.

[c] Times referred to the disciplinary subprogram.

[d] Recommendations by hospital staff (to the Review Board) that the patient be released.

personality based on a solid theoretical background provided by the existing literature, and it provided extensive opportunities for patients to gain insight into their own behavior and to learn to be caring and empathic.

The present results give strong support to the importance of the concept of psychopathy and to the Psychopathy Checklist as a way to measure psychopathy. The Psychopathy Checklist score was strongly related to recidivism (more strongly than *DSM-III* diagnosis), but most importantly, it was a powerful predictor of response to treatment. Subjects who scored high (>25) on the PCL-R showed a negative effect of treatment while those who scored lower benefitted from the therapeutic community program. To our knowledge, this is the most powerful predictor of response to treatment yet reported in the area of criminal behavior and recidivism. The present results also lend support to the method employed in arriving at a PCL score using very complete case files. We hypothesize that interviews may actually increase measurement error with especially glib, manipulative psychopaths.

Given the pervasive pessimism about whether psychopaths can change in any significant way, the finding that participation changed the rate of violent recidivism (albeit for the worse) is remarkable. The finding belies conventional wisdom about the immutability of psychopathy and shows that an inappropriate institutional environment can actually increase criminal behavior. The results strongly suggest that the kind of therapeutic community described in this article is the wrong program for serious psychopathic offenders. It must be noted, however, that these psychopaths were an especially serious group of offenders; almost all (85%) had a history of violent crimes. This, in part, may be the reason that, in this study, violent recidivism was a more informative outcome variable than was general recidivism. It is unclear whether such a program would have the same results with a group of less violent, less criminal psychopaths. The present results are consistent with those of another study on the effect of therapeutic community treatment upon the recidivism of psychopaths (Craft, Stephenson, & Granger, 1964). Although the two studies used very different operational definitions of psychopathy, the combined results suggest that a therapeutic community is not the treatment of choice for psychopaths, particularly those with extensive criminal histories.

It is important to note too that our results show a positive effect (compared to prison) of the therapeutic community program in reducing recidivism for nonpsychopaths. These results lend support to those clinicians who employ therapeutic community treatment and suggest that, compared to prison, a therapeutic community is a clinically sound institutional environment for psychotic and nonpsychotic offenders as long as they are not psychopaths. Because, overall, psychopaths make up the minority of persons in institutions, the present results are good news for clinicians in such settings as long as treatment candidates can be properly selected.

Why did the therapeutic community in the present study have different effects on psychopaths and nonpsychopaths? The ways in which psychopaths and nonpsychopaths performed in the program lead to some speculation. Hare (1986) discussed the results of a lie detection study that suggested that psychopaths are especially interested in social cues in order to learn how to "read" people. Compared to prison, where it has been reported that offenders learn surprisingly little (Zamble & Porporino. 1988), we hypothesize that both psychopaths and nonpsychopaths in the therapeutic community learned how to perceive the feelings of others, take the perspective of others, use emotional language, act in a socially skilled manner, and delay gratification. However, such experiences represent a double-edged sword. To persons with generally prosocial, anticriminal values (nonpsychopaths) such new abilities would be associated with successful marital, family, social, and vocational adjustment. However, to psychopaths with antisocial, procriminal values, such new abilities could facilitate the manipulation and exploitation of others and could be associated with novel ways to commit violent crime.

We speculate, then, that patients learned a great deal from the intensive program but that the psychopaths put their new skills to quite unintended uses. What could the clinical staff have done to prevent this? An obvious suggestion comes from the finding that psychopaths were much more likely to be coded as having antisocial values compared to nonpsychopaths and that this was also related to violent outcome (Harris et al., 1991). According to modern behavioral formulations of differential association theory (Andrews, 1980), criminals behave as they do because they associate with other criminals and are thus exposed to criminal rather than anticriminal models. It has been suggested (Elliot, Huizinga, & Ageton, 1985) that therapeutic community programs fail because they place offenders in highly intensive interaction with one another and thereby foster rather than inhibit criminal identification and subsequent recidivism. Although there are no outcome data with adult psychopaths, one could predict on the basis of differential association theory that programs that involve highly structured interaction with prosocial models who demonstrate anticriminal attitudes and ways of thinking would be a more promising treatment approach (e.g., Andrews, Kiessling, Robinson, & Mickus, 1986; Wormith, 1984).

NOTE

1. Details on the coding of all study variables can be found in Harris, Rice, and Cormier (1991) or by writing to the authors.

REFERENCES

Akman, D. D., & Normandeau, A. (1967). The measurement of crime and delinquency in Canada: A replication study. *British Journal of Criminology, 7*, 129–149.

Andrews, D. A. (1980). Some experimental investigations of the principles of differential association through deliberate manipulations of the structure of service systems. *American Sociological Review, 45*, 448–462.

Andrews, D. A. (1982). *The level of supervision inventory (LSI).* Toronto: Ministry of Correctional Services (Ontario).

Andrews, D. A., Kiessling, J. J., Robinson, D., & Mickus, S. (1986). The risk principle of case classification: An outcome evaluation with young adult probationers. *Consulting Journal of Criminology, 28*, 377–384.

Barker, E. T. (1980). The Penetanguishene program: A personal review. In H. Toch (Ed.), *Therapeutic communities in corrections* (pp. 73–81). New York: Praeger.

Barker, E. T., & Buck, M. H. (1977). L.S.D. in a coercive milieu therapy program. *Canadian Psychiatric Association Journal, 22*, 311–314.

Barker, E. T., & Mason, M. H. (1968). The insane criminal as therapist. *Canadian Journal of Corrections, 10*, 553–561.

Barker, E. T., Mason, M. H., & Wilson, J. (1969). Defence-disrupting therapy. *Canadian Psychiatric Association Journal, 14*, 355–359.

Barker, E. T., & McClaughlin, A. J. (1977). The total encounter capsule. *Canadian Psychiatric Association Journal, 22*, 355–360.

Black, D. A. (1982). A 5-year followup study of male patients discharged from Broadmoor hospital. In J. Gunn and D. P. Farrington (Eds.), *Abnormal offenders, delinquency and the criminal justice system* (pp. 307–323). New York: Wiley.

Blishen, B. R., & McRoberts, H. A. (1976). A revised socioeconomic index for occupations in Canada. *Canadian Review of Sociology and Anthropology, 13*, 71–79.

Bonta, J., & Motiuk, L. L. (1985). Utilization of an interview-based classification instrument: A study of correctional halfway houses. *Criminal Justice and Behavior, 12*, 333–352.

Bonta, J., & Motiuk, L. L. (1987). The diversion of incarcerated offenders to correctional halfway houses. *Journal of Research in Crime and Delinquency, 24*, 302–323.

Buss, A. (1966). *Psychopathology.* New York: Wiley.

Butler, B., Long, J., & Rowsell, P. (1977). *Evaluative Study of the Social Therapy Unit.* Unpublished report to the Ombudsman of Ontario.

Canada. (1977). *Proceedings of the Subcommittee on the Penetentiary System in Canada. Standing Committee on Justice and Legal Affairs. House of Commons, Second Session of the Thirtieth Parliament.* March 8, 1977.

Cleckley, H. (1982). *The mask of sanity* (4th ed.). St. Louis: Mosby.

Copas, J. B., O'Brien, M., Roberts, J., & Whiteley, J. S. (1984). Treatment outcome in personality disorder: The effect of social psychological and behavioural variables. *Personality and Individual Differences, 5*, 565–573.

Corsini, R. (1958). Psychodrama with a psychopath. *Group Psychotherapy, 11*, 33–39.

Craft, M., Stephenson, G., & Granger, C. (1964). A controlled trial of authoritarian and self-governing regimes with adolescent psychopaths. *American Journal of Orthopsychiatry*, 543–554.

Darling, H. F. (1945). Definition of psychopathic personality. *Journal of Nervous and Mental Disease*, *101*, 121–126.

DeLeon, G. (1985). The therapeutic community: Status and evolution. *The International Journal of the Addictions*, *20*, 823–844.

Elliot, D. S., Huizinga, D., & Ageton, S. (1985). *Explaining delinquency and drug use.* Beverly Hills: Sage.

Fairweather, G. W., Sanders, D. H., Maynard, H., Cressler, D. L., & Bleck, D. S. (1969). *Community life for the mentally ill.* Chicago: Aldine.

Gunn, J. (1977). Criminal behaviour and mental disorder. *British Journal of Psychiatry*, *130*, 317–329.

Hare, R. D. (1970). *Psychopathy: Theory and research.* New York: Wiley.

Hare, R. D. (1980). A research scale for the assessment of psychopathy in criminal populations. *Personality and Individual Differences*, *1*, 111–117.

Hare, R. D. (1983). Diagnosis of antisocial personality disorder in two prison populations. *American Journal of Psychiatry*, *7*, 887–889.

Hare, R. D. (1985). Comparison of procedures for the assessment of psychopathy. *Journal of Consulting and Clinical Psychology*, *53*, 7–16.

Hare, R. D. (1986). Twenty years of experience with the Cleckley psychopath. In W. H. Reid, D. Dorr, J. J. Walker, & J. W. Bonner (Eds.), *Unmasking the psychopath* (pp. 3–27). New York: Norton.

Hare, R. D., & Jutai, J. W. (1983). Criminal history of the male psychopath: Some preliminary data. In K. T. VanDusen & S. A. Mednick (Eds.), *Prospective studies of crime and delinquency* (pp. 225–236). Boston: Kluwer-Nijhoff.

Hare, R. D., & McPherson, L. M. (1984). Violent and aggressive behavior by criminal psychopaths. *International Journal of Law and Psychiatry*, *7*, 35–50.

Harris, G. T., Rice, M. E., & Cormier, C. A. (1991). Psychopathy and violent recidivism. *Law and Human Behavior*, *15*, 625–637.

Hodgins, S. (1983). A followup study of persons found incompetent to stand trial and/or not guilty by reason of insanity in Quebec. *International Journal of Law and Psychiatry*, *6*, 399–411.

Jones, M. (1956). The concept of a therapeutic community. *American Journal of Psychiatry*, 647–650.

Jones, M. (1968). *Social psychiatry in practice.* Harmondsworth: Penguin.

Jones, M. (1976). *Maturation of the therapeutic community.* New York: Human Sciences Press.

Lipton, H. (1950). The psychopath. *Journal of Criminal Law, Criminology, and Police Science*, *6*, 399–411.

Loeber, R., & Stouthamer-Loeber, M. (1986). Prediction. In H. C. Quay (Ed.), *Handbook of juvenile delinquency* (pp. 225–282). New York: Wiley.

Maier, G. J. (1976). Therapy in prisons. In J. R. Lion and D. J. Madden (Eds.), *Rage, hate, assault and other forms of violence* (pp. 113–133). New York: Spectrum.

Maller, J. O. (1971). *The therapeutic community with chronic mental patients.* Basel: S. Karger AG.

Mandelzys, N. (1979). Correlates of offense severity and recidivism probability in a Canadian sample. *Journal of Clinical Psychology*, *35*, 897–907.

McCann, W. H. (1948). The psychopath and the psychoneurotic in relation to crime and delinquency. *Journal of Clinical and Experimental Psychopathology*, *9*, 551.

McCord, W. M. (1982). *The psychopath and milieu-therapy.* New York: Academic Press.

Meloy, J. R. (1988). *The psychopathic mind: Origins, dynamics and treatment.* Northvale, NY: Aronson.

Molof, M. J. (1965). *Prediction of future assaultive behavior among youthful offenders.* California Department of Youth Authority Research, Report 41.

Monahan, J. (1981). *Predicting violent behavior: An assessment of clinical techniques.* Beverly Hills: Sage.

Nuffield, J. (1982). *Parole decision-making in Canada.* Ottawa: Ministry of Supply and Services.

Paul, G. L., & Lentz, R. J. (1977). *Psychosocial treatment of chronic mental patients.* Cambridge: Harvard University Press.

Pruesse, M., & Quinsey, V. L. (1977). The dangerousness of patients released from maximum security: A replication. *Journal of Psychiatry and Law*, *5*, 293–299.

Quinsey, V. L. (1981). The long term management of the mentally disordered offender. In S. J. Hucker, C. D. Webster, & M. Ben-Aron (Eds.), *Mental disorder and criminal responsibility* (pp. 137–155). Toronto: Butterworths.

Quinsey, V. L. (1984). Politique institutionelle de liberation, identification des individus dangereux: une revue de la literature (Institutional release policy and the identification of dangerous men: a review of the literature). *Criminologie*, *17*, 53–78.

Quinsey, V. L., & Maguire, A. (1983). Offenders remanded for a psychiatric examination: Perceived treatability and disposition. *International Journal of Law and Psychiatry, 6*, 193–205.

Quinsey, V. L., & Maguire, A. (1986). Maximum security psychiatric patients: Actuarial and clinical prediction of dangerousness. *Journal of Interpersonal Violence, 1*, 143–171.

Quinsey, V. L., Pruesse, M., & Fernley, R. (1975a). Oak Ridge patients: Prerelease characteristics and postrelease adjustment. *Journal of Psychiatry and Law, 3*, 63–77.

Quinsey, V. L., Pruesse, M., & Fernley, R. (1975b). A followup of patients found not guilty by reason of insanity or unfit for trial. *Canadian Psychiatric Association Journal, 20*, 461–467.

Reid, W. H. (1989). *The treatment of psychiatric disorders.* New York: Brunner/Mazel.

Rice, M. E., Quinsey, V. L., & Houghton, R. (1990). Predicting treatment outcome and recidivism among patients in a maximum security token economy. *Behavioral Sciences and the Law, 8*, 313–326.

Rodgers, T. (1947). Hypnotherapy and character neuroses. *Journal of Clinical Psychopathology, 8*, 519–524.

Rosow, H. M. (1955). Some observations on group therapy with prison inmates. *Archives of Criminal Psychodynamics, 1*, 866–897.

Schmideberg, M. (1949). The analytic treatment of major criminals: Therapeutic results and technical problems. *International Journal of Psychoanalysis, 30*, 197.

Schroeder, M. L., Schroeder, K. G., & Hare, R. D. (1983). Generalizability of a checklist for assessment of psychopathy. *Journal of Consulting and Clinical Psychology, 51*, 511–516.

Showstack, N. (1956). Treatment of prisoners at the California Medical Facility. *American Journal of Psychiatry, 112*, 821–824.

Simon, F. (1971). *Prediction methods in criminology.* London: HMSO.

Steadman, H. J. (1973). Follow-up on Baxtrom patients returned to hospitals for the criminally insane. *American Journal of Psychiatry, 130*, 317–319.

Thorne, F. C. (1959). The etiology of sociopathic reactions. *American Journal of Psychotherapy, 13*, 310–330.

Toch, H. (Ed.). (1980). *Therapeutic communities in corrections.* New York: Praeger,

Tong, J. E., & MacKay, G. W. (1959). A statistical followup of mental defectives of dangerous or violent propensities. *British Journal of Delinquency, 9*, 276–284.

Whiteley, J. S. (1967). Concepts of psychopathy and its treatment. *Medico-legal Journal, 35*, 154–163.

Widiger, T. A., & Frances, A. (1987). Interviews and inventories for the measurement of personality disorders. *Clinical Psychology Review, 7*, 49–75.

Wong, S. (1984). *The criminal and institutional behaviours of psychopaths.* Ottawa: Ministry of the Solicitor General.

Woody, G. E., McLellan, A. T., Rubersky, L., & O'Brien, C. P. (1985). Sociopathy and psychotherapy outcome. *Archives of General Psychiatry, 42*, 1081–1086.

Wormith, J. S. (1984). Attitude and behavior change of a correctional clientele: A 3-year followup. *Criminology, 22*, 595–618.

Wormith, J. S., & Goldstone, C. S. (1984). The clinical and statistical prediction of recidivism. *Criminal Justice and Behavior, 11*, 3–34.

Zamble, E., & Porporino, F. (1988). *Coping behavior and adaptation in prison inmates.* New York: Springer-Verlag.

27

Psychopathy and Therapeutic Pessimism: Clinical Lore: or Clinical Reality?

RANDALL T. SALEKIN

ABSTRACT: *It is a widely held belief that psychopathic individuals are extremely difficult to treat, if not immune to treatment. This therapeutic pessimism is pervasive and undermines motivation to search for effective modes of intervention for psychopathic individuals. A review of 42 treatment studies on psychopathy revealed that there is little scientific basis for the belief that psychopathy is an untreatable disorder. Three significant problems with regard to the research on the psychopathy–treatment relation cast doubt on strident conclusions that deem the disorder untreatable. First, there is considerable disagreement as to the defining characteristics of psychopathy. Second, the etiology of psychopathy is not well understood. Third, there are relatively few empirical investigations of the psychopathy–treatment relationship and even fewer efforts that follow up psychopathic individuals after treatment. Psychologists are encouraged to investigate the psychopathy–treatment relation from multiple perspectives as well as to conduct long-term follow-up studies to establish a modern view of the psychopathy–treatment relation.*

KEYWORDS: *Psychopathy; Treatment; Meta-analysis*

Reprinted from Clinical Psychology Review, 22, *79–112.* © 2001, *with permission from Elsevier.*

1. PERSPECTIVE ON PSYCHOPATHY AND TREATMENT: A NEED FOR FURTHER INTEGRATION OF SCIENCE AND PRACTICE?

Clinical lore has led clinicians and researchers to believe that psychopathy is, essentially, an untreatable syndrome. This view is echoed by prominent theorists' claims that the disorder is difficult, if not impossible, to treat (e.g., Cleckley, 1941; Hare, 1991; McCord & McCord, 1964; Suedfeld & Landon, 1978). In his more recent writings on psychopathy, Cleckley (1981, p. 275) stated that he was "profoundly impressed by two difficulties that stood in the way of dealing effectively with the psychopath. One of these was his apparent immunity, or relative immunity, from control by the law. The other was his lack of response to psychiatric treatment of any kind." There is no doubt that psychopathy brings a considerable amount of therapeutic frustration, confusion, and pessimism to researchers and clinicians alike (e.g., Greenwald, 1967; Losel, 1998; Ogloff, Wong, & Greenwood, 1990; Rice, 1997). This frustration, however, may have blurred psychologists' perception of important clinical realities and stalled enthusiasm for research pursuits that would have produced and enhanced interventions for this complex clinical problem.

Social policy considerations make the search for effective treatments for psychopathic individuals even more pressing. For instance, continued problems with adult and juvenile offending indicate that untreated offenders will continue to create serious problems for society in both the short and long run. These problems are likely to include violent crimes given that violence, in part, stems from individuals who lack important human characteristics such as empathy and remorse (Hare & Hart, 1993). In fact, recent research efforts have shown that there is a relationship between psychopathy and both general and violent crimes (e.g., Salekin, Rogers, & Sewell, 1996), further emphasizing the need for preventative measures and treatment programs for those most at risk of committing future violent acts.

The purpose of the present article is to identify and characterize the current status of research that exists on psychopathy and treatment, to prompt and guide investigations in this area of investigation, and to encourage future research into the etiology of psychopathy. In order to address these purposes, I (a) briefly discuss problems that exist with classification of psychopathy specifically dealing with terminology and heterogeneity that make work in this area particularly difficult, (b) examine the developmental and etiological theories of psychopathy as they relate to treatment, and (c) present empirical evidence on the treatability of psychopathy in the form of a meta-analysis.

2. CLASSIFICATION OF PSYCHOPATHY

Abundant theoretical and empirical attention has been directed toward understanding the psychopathic personality since Phillippe Pinel first introduced the concept approximately 200 years ago. Most contemporary conceptualizations are linked, at least in part, to the work of Cleckley (1941) and his book *The Mask of Sanity*. Cleckley provided extensive clinical descriptions of the characteristics of psychopathy, which have now received widespread acceptance as typifying the concept of psychopathy.

Although Cleckley's definition of psychopathy was included in the DSM-II, subsequent revisions consisted largely of behavioral-based descriptions such as antisocial personality disorder (APD), conduct disorder (CD), and oppositional defiant disorder (ODD). Changes from primarily personality-based conceptualizations of the disorder to primarily behaviorally based ones were predicated on the notion that behavioral characteristics (e.g., truancy) were more reliably assessed than were personality traits (e.g., empathy) (Cloninger, 1978; Robins, 1978). Over the last two decades, however, researchers and clinicians have stressed that behavioral classifications alone are too narrow (Lilienfeld, 1994) and have emphasized the importance of a personality component to the assessment of psychopathy. As such, many researchers and clinicians have continued to make a distinction between psychopathy and DSM-IV classifications of ODD and CD in children and APD in adults (Frick, 1998; Hare & Hart, 1993).

An important development since Cleckley has been the Psychopathy Checklist (PCL; Hare, 1991). Hare's work on psychopathy with adult offenders has shown that two factors emerge: F_1 indicates the "selfish, callous, and remorseless use of others" and F_2 the "chronically unstable, antisocial, and socially deviant lifestyle." Forth, Kosson, and Hare (1994) have extended this construct to adolescents and Frick and Hare (in press) have extended the construct even further to include children with F_1 representing impulsive/conduct problems and F_2 representing callous/unemotional (CU) traits.

Wide-range utilization of psychopathy as a critical clinical construct for adults as well as the development of adolescent and childhood measures of psychopathy (Forth et al., 1994; Frick & Hare, in press) underscore the importance of reevaluating the clinical belief that psychopathy is an untreatable disorder. There are at least three issues related to classification and its implication for treatment that require highlighting here. First, while psychopathy has received increasing attention from both clinicians and scientists over the last two decades, it is important to note that the definitions of the disorder have drifted from earlier conceptualizations provided by Cleckley and theorists before him (Rogers, 1995). To address this important point more thoroughly, Rogers (1995) has shown that when examining the 16 Cleckley criteria only 7 (approximately half) are similar to the items on Hare's more contemporary classification system for psychopathy. Moreover, only one-third of the PCL-R items represent Cleckley criteria of psychopathy. In other words, although intended to assess the Cleckley psychopath, this more recent conceptualization of psychopathy may not capture important Cleckley criteria, some of which could have a direct impact on the degree to which psychopathy is treatable. For instance, the presence of anxiety at the initiation of therapy has been noted as a positive prognostic sign with adult patients (see Garfield, 1994). Thus, "absence of nervousness," a hallmark of earlier psychopathy definitions may fuel hypotheses that psychopathy is difficult to treat. However, psychopathy definitions not incorporating this item may identify individuals who are more amenable to treatment given that they are capable of experiencing some anxiety prior to, and at the initiation of, psychotherapy.

Second, current measures of psychopathy are polythetic in nature with numerous possible variations. Assessment, therefore, rests on the assumption that the criteria should be accorded equal weight and that any combination of the criteria that exceeds a predetermined cutoff score is sufficient to warrant the diagnosis of psychopathy and presumably a conclusion that the individual is unamenable to treatment. However, it may be that different constellations of psychopathy directly impact amenability to treatment. Frick (1998) has foreshadowed this point by suggesting that children with CU traits may be more difficult to treat than children displaying conduct problems alone although this supposition needs to be empirically investigated.

Third, deviations from traditional theory-based diagnosis (e.g., Cleckley, 1941) to contemporary conceptualizations (e.g., Hare, 1991) may have direct consequences with regard to psychologists' expectations as to the treatability of psychopathy. For example, if psychologists operate from a traditional psychoanalytic orientation, then viewing psychopathy as a treatable disorder may fall outside the set of assumptions that guide that particular paradigm. However, with more contemporary conceptualizations (e.g., Frick, 1998; Newman, 1998) psychologists are less bound by traditional theory and may view the disorder as amenable to intervention.

In summary, given that the concept of psychopathy rests upon the assumption that certain individuals have in common a particular set of behaviors and personality traits, the evolution of the disorder as well as the polythetic nature of many recent assessment measures complicate the thesis that psychopathy is an untreatable disorder. In addition, psychologists' paradigmatic perspective may affect their expectations of the likelihood of successful treatment, which in turn, may affect the degree to which clients see themselves as capable of change.

3. DEVELOPMENTAL AND ETIOLOGICAL THEORIES OF PSYCHOPATHY

Remarkably, theory has often been absent when considering treatment programs for psychological disorders (Kazdin, 1999). In order to shed light on why psychopathy is thought to be recalcitrant to efforts at rehabilitation, etiological literature of psychopathy is briefly reviewed. Developmental and etiological theories of psychopathy will likely provide psychologists with important information as to the treatability of psychopathic individuals.[1]

In this article, 12 developmental theories of psychopathy are briefly reviewed: (a) psychodynamic (Aichorn, 1966; Cleckley, 1941; Draughon, 1977; Redl & Wineman, 1951, 1952), (b) learning and cognitive theories (Eron, 1997; Templeman & Wollersheim, 1979), (c) role-playing (Gough, 1948), (d) sensation-seeking (Quay, 1965), (e) extraversion (Eysenck, 1975, 1981), (f) attachment-based (Bowlby, 1969), (g) Hare's neurological models (Hare, 1970, 1998), (h) response modulation (Newman, 1998), (i) low-fear model (Lykken, 1995), (j) somatic marker (Damasio, 1994), (k) CU temperament (Frick, 1998), and (l) psychopathy constraint (Lynam, 1996, 1997) (see Table 1). The purpose of this section is not to present a detailed review of each of the developmental/etiological theories, but rather to present a brief review of the theory and to (a) evaluate whether the theory is comprehensive (e.g., does the theory account for all the symptoms of psychopathy?), (b) examine whether these theories elucidate treatment difficulties that psychologists experience with psychopathic individuals, and (c) if possible, provide suggestions for where psychologists might best focus their treatment efforts.

3.1. Psychodynamic Theory of Psychopathy

Psychodynamic theories generally state that psychopathy is a function of poor ego and superego development (e.g., Aichorn, 1966; Draughon, 1977). According to Freud (1961), the superego, originally part of the ego, breaks off into a separate structure when the Oedipus or Electra complex is resolved. The functions of the superego include self-observation, conscience, and maintenance of the ideal. When the ego does not meet the demands of the superego, guilt is experienced by the individual. The crux of this theory is that psychopathic behavior is the result of childhood problems stemming from adverse child–parent interactions that stunt proper development of the superego. The underdevelopment of the superego is reflected in the child's lack of conscience and an inability to experience guilt (Greenacre, 1945; Johnson & Szurek, 1954).

The notion that psychopathy is untreatable may originate from psychoanalytic theory (Draughon, 1977), which suggests that personality is laid down in the first 5 to 6 years of life with relatively few changes made thereafter. However, more recent theories contend that personality is more malleable than previously believed. For instance, Draughon (1977) has found that an expanded view of the ego and superego allows for their development over a longer period of time and has also suggested that the ego can perform many functions of the superego including regulating emotion, delaying gratification, and reality testing.

Kohut (1982) argued for a movement away from the traditional psychoanalytic personality constructs of id, ego, and superego when conceptualizing psychopathology. Instead of focusing on Freud's structural model of the mind, he contended that dysfunction could be conceptualized as stemming from developmental disruptions in the self-structure. The self-structure is thought to consist of the self and internal representations of significant others. Building on Kohut's reformulations of psychoanalytic theory, Noshpitz (1984) argued that aggression stems from a child's need to protect an overly expansive self-system from harm. One hypothesized pathological variant, the "ruthless–psychopath," is characterized by a need to exploit and intimidate others and to use aggression and violence in an attempt to maintain an inflated sense of self, an illusion of control, and the perception of invulnerability.

The symptoms of psychopathy are accounted for in this theory by poor superego development (e.g., criminal activity, disregard for others) and defense mechanisms (e.g., grandiosity, superficial charm). With regard to treatment, whether utilizing an expanded view of the ego and superego (Draughon, 1977) or Kohut's reformulations of psychoanalytic theory, contemporary theories indicate that psychopathy is a treatable

TABLE 1

Developmental Pathways to Psychopathy

THEORIST	DEVELOPMENTAL PATHWAYS TO PSYCHOPATHY
Damasio (1994)	deficiency in somatic markers → inability to form or utilize affective associations → psychopathy
Draughon (1977)	poor ego development → infantile emotional level → egocentricity → poor empathy impulsivity, poor tolerance, poor planning, low self-esteem → psychopathy
Eysenck (1975)	cortical underarousal (high extraversion, neuroticism, and psychoticism) → impairment in ability to condition to environmental stimuli, especially in learning appropriate fear reactions to punishment → poorly conditioned moral and social responses, poorly developed conscience → a poorly socialized, neurotic, extravert → psychopathy
Frick (1998)	unique temperamental style → low behavioral inhibition → CU traits → conduct problems
Gough (1958)	deficiency in role-playing ability → poor anticipation comprehension of the role of others → lack of empathy, lack of remorse → psychopathy
Hare (1970)	brain lesions → loss of inhibitory mechanisms → diminished capacity to inhibit and a tendency for perseveratory responses → psychopathy

THEORIST	DEVELOPMENTAL PATHWAYS TO PSYCHOPATHY
Hare (1998)	subtle neurological problems → increased activation in occipital lobe → other neurological difficulties → psychopathy
Lykken (1995)	low fearfulness → child insufficiently motivated to avoid punishment → difficult to socialize using typical parenting → psychopathy
Lynam (1997)	deficient "psychopathy constraint" → difficulty incorporating feedback from the environment and using information to modulate responses while pursuing rewards → show signs of HIA complex: exhibit more exploratory behaviors and motor restlessness, does not respond to admonitions, and responds impulsively to rewards → mild conduct problems, oppositional defiant symptoms. Unable to control temper, arguing, lying, and blaming others for own actions → increases in structure (school) result in an appearance of heightened HIA and conduct problems including aggression and disregard for others → psychopathy
Newman (1998)	information-processing deficiency → failure to accommodate meaning of contextual cues → failure of self-regulation → psychopathy
Quay (1965)	hyperactive nervous system → stimulation-seeking child → behavior aversive to parents/others → parental retreat, inconsistency, rejection, and hostile detachment → fewer effective socializing experiences → psychopathy
	hyperactive nervous system → poor anticipatory responses to pain → early excessive punishment → increased resistance to effects of treatment → reduced level of stimulus input → psychopathy
Ullman and Krasner (1969)	reinforced at the wrong time for wrong things → psychopathy

495

disorder. Strengthening ego or superego functions or improving object relations might be the target of intervention depending upon the psychoanalytic theory utilized. More traditional theories would espouse having the interventions occur within the first 5 years of life. One problem with traditional psychoanalytic theory, if inaccurate, is that it may result in withholding treatment from those beyond the age of 5 or 6 years who might benefit from intervention. An additional concern is that it may inappropriately place blame on the parents of psychopathic youth.

3.2. Learning and Cognitive Theories of Psychopathy

Learning theories of psychopathy purport that the syndrome develops through modeling and conditioning (Bandura, 1973; Eron, 1997; Patterson, Dishion, & Chamberlain, 1993). Eron (1997), as well as Ullman and Krasner (1969), theorized that psychopaths are those who are reinforced at the wrong time and thus have developed a selective inattention to various social stimuli. In this sense, the lack of emotion in the psychopath is traceable to an early history of desensitization to emotional stimuli. More recently, researchers have introduced learning models based on current thinking in cognitive psychology (e.g., Berkowitz, 1990; Dodge, 1980; Guerra & Slaby, 1990). For example, Dodge (1980) emphasizes the importance of attributional biases. Antisocial children are viewed as having defective cognitive processes for the interpretation of others' behavior and the selection of their own behavior from a previously learned repertoire. Huesmann (1988), on the other hand, views the child as a processor of information who develops programs or scripts to guide their (social) behavior. The antisocial child is one who has developed many aggressive and antisocial scripts and few prosocial ones.

While learning theories are relatively comprehensive, it has not been easy to identify a reinforcement schedule that would consistently result in psychopathy. That is, children under similar conditioning environments often develop along very different pathways. Moreover, the various learning theories have differed in terms of exactly what is learned. Specifically, whether certain behaviors, cue–behavior connections, response biases, beliefs, or scripts are learned. In all cases, however, learning is hypothesized to occur both as a result of one's own behaviors and as a result of viewing others behave. With this perspective, researchers (e.g., Lochman, 1990; Rotenberg, 1975; Templeman & Wollersheim, 1979) have viewed behavioral aspects of psychopathy as treatable. Techniques such as counterconditioning, cognitive restructuring, and modeling may affect change.

3.3. Deficiency in Role-Playing Theory of Psychopathy

Gough (1948) formulated a sociological theory of psychopathy that described psychopaths as suffering from a deficiency in role-playing ability. As a result, psychopathic individuals are not able to adequately anticipate the reaction or comprehend the role of others. Because of this lack of understanding for others, the symptoms of psychopathy were purported to result. However, research investigating the role-playing abilities of psychopaths has been equivocal (e.g., Doren, 1987; Smith, 1978; Widom, 1976).

Even if psychopathic individuals are assumed to be deficient in role-playing abilities, Gough's (1948) theory lacks comprehensiveness and clarity. One problem with the theory is that it does not delineate underlying factors that would lead to defective role-playing in psychopaths. Another problem is that commonly listed psychopathic personality features, such as guiltlessness, superficial charm, manipulation, and sensation seeking, are difficult to explicate using Gough's theory. In fact, references in the literature (e.g., Cleckley, 1941) to the psychopath's manipulation, adeptness at telling others what they want to hear, and ability to make a positive impression suggest that psychopathic individuals may have a considerable talent at role-taking as opposed to a serious deficit (Doren, 1987). Any link between psychopathy and resistance to treatment is not apparent from this theory. Psychologists developing treatment programs from this etiological perspective may want to enhance these individuals' ability to take on different roles through in-session role-playing and the use of behavioral rehearsal. However, some psychologists may be concerned about the potential risk of increased manipulation by improving this skill with psychopaths.

3.4. Sensation-Seeking Theory of Psychopathy

Quay (1965) described the psychopathic disorder as a manifestation of excessive sensation-seeking behavior. Quay's theory consists of two facets: (a) psychopaths are characterized by an abnormality in their physiological reaction to sensory input, which requires a higher degree of sensory stimulation in order to obtain satisfaction and (b) because of psychopaths higher optimal level of stimulation, an extremely high degree of motivation is required in order to compensate for their underarousal.

Quay (1977) expanded on this theory to include environmental factors in the development of adult psychopathy. This formulation again stated that the psychopath began life with a hyperactive nervous system that resulted in one of two developmental pathways. The first developmental pathway suggests that children's sensation-seeking behavior becomes aversive to parents resulting in parent–child interactions that are hostile, inconsistent, and rejecting. These negative reactions, in turn, result in an increase in their deviancy, which then leads to more inconsistency and hostility on the part of the parent. According to Quay, an endless cycle of poor interpersonal patterns results in the eventual distancing of parents from their children and this decreases the likelihood that the child will experience any form of positive socialization.

The second developmental pathway suggests that psychopathic children are less able to anticipate physical pain due to an underactive nervous system. Thus, punishment by parents must be at a high level to produce avoidance. However, because of habituation, the child's ability to resist the effects of punishment tends to increase. At the same time, parents withdraw from the child who seems beyond their control. The net result is an undersocialized, sensation-seeking child developing along a pathway to adult psychopathy.

Using Quay's formulation alone, it is unclear why psychopaths would (a) be guilt-less, (b) be unable to form meaningful relationships, (c) lack morality, (d) lack insight, and (e) possess superficial charm. In short, Quay's theory focuses on sensation-seeking at the exclusion of other aspects of psychopathy. With regard to treatment, Quay did not view psychopathy as untreatable. In fact, Quay offered two types of treatment for psychopaths based on his theoretical notions. The first suggestion was to utilize psychopharmacology to "increase basal reactivity" or decrease their "rapidity of adaptation to stimuli." The second was to use strong, unconditioned stimuli to condition avoidance reactions in psychopaths, and use strong, unconditioned stimuli coupled with reinforcement to condition appropriate approach reactions from persons exhibiting the psychopathic disorder. Parent training may also benefit children with psychopathy because parents would be able to deal more effectively with this unique temperamental style.

3.5. Extraversion Theory of Psychopathy

Eysenck (1977) based his theory of psychopathy on his three-dimensional model of personality that included: (a) extraversion, (b) neuroticism, and (c) psychoticism. Eysenck's definition of psychoticism differed from more traditional views of psychosis in that he placed psychopathy on a continuum between normality and psychosis. In this theory, the neuroticism factor was viewed as one that dealt with the strength of emotional reactions. Extraversion was hypothesized to be related to the low baseline arousal state of an individual. Eysenck believed that psychopaths had an underaroused state because of an impairment in their ability to condition to environmental stimuli. According to Eysenck, this impairment is especially relevant to the learning of appropriate fear reactions to environmentally punishing contingencies.

More recently, Eysenck (1981) revised his theory of psychopathy. According to his new model, genetic factors contribute to individual differences in physiological processes (e.g., ascending reticular activating system). These differences in physiological processes drive fundamental psychological processes (e.g., motivation, learning) that result in stable differences in personality (e.g., extraversion–introversion), which ultimately influence a person's social behavior and risk for APD. Within Eysenck's model, the relation between personality and antisocial behavior is mediated by psychosocial processes such as perception, cognition, motivation, and emotion. These processes, in turn, influence learning and social adjustment. Thus, according to this theory, antisocial behavior must be understood in light of a myriad of person by situation interactions that shape an individual's response to the environment.

Similar to the aforementioned theories, Eysenck's theory does not clearly articulate why psychopaths would (a) be manipulative, (b) be guiltless, (c) lack morality, and (d) possess superficial charm. With regard to treatability, Eysenck's theory suggests that treatment might be hampered by learning and motivational deficits. The extent to which these problems would hamper treatment beyond other psychological disorders (e.g., motivational problems in depressed patients and learning deficits in patients with attention deficit–hyperactivity disorder (ADHD)) is unclear. Because this model of psychopathy is interactional with individuals having a predisposition that is effected by the environment, early intervention from the learning paradigm (e.g., counter-conditioning, modeling) may be most effective. In addition, parent training would likely augment treatment.

3.6. Attachment-Based Theory of Psychopathy

Several areas of research suggest that psychopathy may be related to neglect or a particular type of insecure attachment. One of the most compelling sources of evidence comes from the vast research on family histories of youth with psychopathy (e.g., McCord & McCord, 1964). Two bodies of research are relevant in this regard. First, numerous studies have consistently shown that family adversity, most notably low socioeconomic standing, single parenthood, parental psychopathology, and exposure to family violence and aggression is related to the development of psychopathy or the related disorder of CD in youth (Megargee & Golden, 1973; Morretti, Holland, & Peterson, 1994; Schuster, 1976). Second, studies (e.g., Patterson & Yoerger, 1993) have shown a robust relationship between punitive and inconsistent parenting practices and the development of psycho-pathy and related disorders. Family adversity and punitive and inadequate parenting practices commonly occur together (Rutter, Tizard, & Whitmore, 1970; Webster-Stratton, 1990), giving an overall impression that psychopathy may develop in the context of an impoverished and typically abusive primary socialization experience. As such, these individuals lack the attachment experiences that (a) lead to the development of mental representation that guide behavior and affect over time, (b) function to integrate experience, and (c) increase the likelihood of continuity over the life span.

The attachment-based theory of psychopathy is relatively comprehensive but clearer connections between the poor attachment and why psychopaths tend to be manipulative and possess superficial charm, need to be delineated. With regard to treatability, clearly, if this etiological theory is accurate, then treatment of psychopathic individuals may be possible. Treatment efforts that involve extensive training with parents and children and have an emphasis on reconnecting youth with the community may very well be beneficial to children displaying psychopathic traits.

3.7. Hare's Neurological Theory of Psychopathy

Hare (1970) delineated a perspective on psychopathy, which he termed response per-severation. In this early theory, psychopaths are viewed as having lesions in the limbic system of the brain which affect their ability to inhibit or disrupt ongoing behavior. One hypothesized effect of these lesions was a learning deficiency which made it dif-ficult to inhibit an action that was known to lead to punishment. Hare employed this theory to explain why psychopaths seem unable to learn from punishment and appear to be controlled by their immediate needs. Later, however, Hart, Forth, and Hare (1990) concluded that there exists no demonstrable evidence to support the notion that psychopaths have brain damage. Gale (1973) stated that EEG research, which purportedly demonstrated brain abnormalities in psychopaths, has been ambiguous and, if anything, leans against rather than in favor of the contention that psychopaths have brain lesions.

More recently, Hare (1998) suggested that there may be a more subtle neurological basis for psychopathy. In a neurological imaging study of psychopathic individuals with substance abuse disorders, psychopaths exhibited less anterior activation during processing of the neutral and emotional tasks than did nonpsychopaths (Intrator, Hare, Stritzke, Brichstwein, et al., 1997). Moreover, activation was less widespread in psychopaths than nonpsychopaths. For psychopaths, the greatest activation was in the occipital cortex. However, these findings are tempered by the fact that psychopaths differed less from other patient groups than controls suggesting that at least part of the pattern of activation of psychopaths was related to substance abuse.

Hare's early theory of psychopathy fails to account for some of the hallmarks of this syndrome such as superficial charm and manipulation. Given the lack of clarity with regard to psychopathy, brain organization, and neurochemistry it is difficult to critically evaluate Hare's more recent theory for two reasons: (a) it is exploratory and (b) it is incomplete. However, one criticism of Hare's theory is that it may be too reductionistic and fail to explain the intricacies of psychopathy. From a treatment perspective, it is important to note that with the advances in pharmacotherapy, irregularities in neurotransmission can be altered. Moreover, although tentative, Vaughan (1997) has suggested that there may be some evidence for the notion that neurochemistry and brain organization can be altered via psychotherapy. In this regard, both pharmacotherapy and psychotherapy may be worthy of further investigation with this syndrome.

3.8. Response Modulation Model of Psychopathy

Newman and his colleagues have conducted a series of rigorous laboratory studies that indicate that psychopathic individuals may have a form of disinhibitory psychopathology that includes difficulty in passive avoidance learning (Newman & Kosson, 1986; Newman, Patterson, Howland, & Nichols, 1990; Newman, Widom, & Nathan, 1985), inhibition of well-established dominant responses (Howland, Kosson, Patterson, & New-man, 1993), and poor response modulation (Newman, Patterson, & Kosson, 1987). According to Newman (1998), children at risk for psychopathy suffer from an information-processing deficit that interferes with effective self-regulation. Parental and societal failure to appreciate the existence of this problem and our consequent reactions to the child's behavior compound the risk of psychopathy. Newman's work has been fueled by earlier work on disinhibition conducted by Fowles (1980) and Gray (1987).

The response modulation hypothesis of psychopathy, although intriguing, does not readily account for some practitioners' and researchers' beliefs about psychopaths' ability to plot, manipulate, take on different roles, and display superficial charm to meet their needs. In this way, the theory is not yet comprehensive. If Newman's theory is accurate, then treatment may be hampered by psychopathic individuals' information-processing deficit. It is important to note, however, that Newman has not suggested that a diagnosis of psychopathy would equate to the disorder being unamenable to treatment. In fact, he has suggested that informing psychopaths of their deficit may be the first step toward change. While Newman's theory would indicate that there would be challenges to the treatment of psychopathy it does not lead to the conclusion that psychopathy is treatment refractory.

3.9. Low-Fear Model of Psychopathy

Lykken (1995) posits that the psychopath has an attenuated experience of anxiety and fear. Because of this below average endowment of innate fearfulness, psychopaths are more difficult to socialize using typical parenting methods that rely on a child being motivated to avoid punishment. Lykken's (1957) classic investigation of psychopathy and anxiety used a measure of passive avoidance learning to evaluate the low fearfulness hypothesis. He found that, in general, psychopaths were less fearful of receiving a shock than were nonpsychopaths.

Lykken's theory of psychopathy is relatively comprehensive but clearer connections among low fearfulness and manipulation and superficial charm require delineation. Overall, Lykken's theory is compelling given that most symptoms of psychopathy (Cleckley, 1941; Hare, 1991) can be accounted for with this hypothesis. While Lykken has suggested that there is a genotype for psychopathy, he also sees the development of psychopathy as being highly dependent upon socialization and parenting. Thus, according to Lykken, if parental competence is high, the development of psychopathy is avoidable. Extrapolating from this conclusion, psychotherapy might very well help augment and facilitate parental attempts to socialize children.

3.10. Somatic Marker Model of Psychopathy

A recent theoretical perspective for psychopathy is Damasio's (1994) somatic marker hypothesis. The concept of somatic markers refers to affect-related associations that come to be related with particular stimuli and responses. According to Damasio, somatic markers are created in our brains during the process of socialization and education by connecting specific classes of stimuli with specific classes of somatic state. Once formed, somatic markers facilitate decision-making and behavioral regulation by calling to mind the positively or negatively valenced outcomes that have been associated with particular situations or followed particular responses. Referring to their role in avoidance learning, Damasio stated that a somatic marker functions as an "automated alarm signal" that warns individuals of danger. According to Damasio, whereas normal individuals have a nonconscious process formulating future events or outcomes for a given situation, psychopaths are unable to use punishment or reward to contribute to the automated marking for prediction of future outcomes. Thus, psychopaths have a generalized deficit in the formation and/or utilization of affective associations.

While Damasio's (1994) formulation offers some interesting new theoretical insights into the etiology of psychopathy, it does not adequately account for why psychopaths would (a) con others, (b) be grandiose, and (c) possess superficial charm. Also, this etiological perspective does not explain the belief that psychopathy is an untreatable disorder. For instance other disorders, such as major depression and schizophrenia could also be explained by this theory but are not considered unamenable to treatment. Efforts at enhancing psychopathic individuals' associations between specific classes of stimuli with specific classes of somatic state would be the first step in treating psychopathy from Damasio's etiological perspective.

3.11. Callous/Unemotional Temperament in Children

Frick (1998) has proposed that psychopathy (a) is more etiologically homogeneous than CD and (b) has one causal pathway to conduct problems. CU traits (e.g., absence of empathy, a lack of guilt) are considered to develop as a function of a unique temperamental style and low behavioral inhibition that make a child more difficult to socialize (Frick & Jackson, 1993; Kochanska, 1993). Once they develop, CU traits make a child more likely to act against parental and societal norms and to violate the rights of others. Frick's theory is intriguing and helps to integrate diverse findings from previous research on the etiology of psychopathy. Importantly, the theory addresses directionality suggesting that parents may be reacting to children who are problematic and difficult to satisfy based on a genetic predisposition. Although Frick has suggested that CU traits may be more resistant to treatment than conduct problems, his theory also suggests that there is an important interaction between parents and children that can facilitate prosocial behavior. Frick's theory is relatively comprehensive and suggests that parental training and child psychotherapy in combination may be warranted to prevent the development of psychopathy.

3.12. Psychopathy Constraint Model

According to Lynam (1996), "fledgling psychopaths" are found to have a combination of hyperactivity–impulsivity–attention (HIA) and conduct problems from an early age. He has suggested that youth show similar deficits on similar laboratory, psychophysiological, and performance measures to that of adults. For example, Lynam suggests that poor passive avoidance seen in adult psychopaths (Lykken, 1995) is common in children with HIA. In addition, Lynam has drawn similarities between cortical underarousal, frontal lobe deficits, and response modulation in adult psychopaths to that of children with HIA.

Lynam (1996) suggests that psychopathic individuals begin life with a deficiency in constraint (he calls this psychopathic constraint), which hampers their ability to incorporate feedback from the environment and to use this information to modulate responses while pursuing rewards. Because of this lack in "psychopathic constraint," they show signs of HIA. As these individuals age and become more mobile and verbal, and as goal-directed behavior is frequently frustrated by parents, the deficit in constraint leads to mild CD or ODD symptoms. Lynam suggests that this deficit in psychopathic constraint leads to an inability to pause and empathize with others or to feel remorse and guilt and that ultimately these deficits result in psychopathy.

Lynam's theory of psychopathy is compelling but has similar shortcomings to theories previously mentioned when it comes to accounting for the symptomology of psychopathy. Symptom such as superficial charm and manipulation would suggest that psychopathic individuals might be extremely effective at emotion regulation as opposed to having symptoms of hyperactivity and inattention. If, however, this theory for psychopathy is accurate, then approaches designed to treat ADHD in children may be indicated as a first step in the treatment of psychopathic youth. Then, behavioral and parent training may have a beneficial effect on CD or ODD symptoms.

4. GENERAL COMMENTS ON THE ETIOLOGY OF PSYCHOPATHY

As with many psychological disorders, the etiology of psychopathy is not well known. Developmental and etiological theories of psychopathy provide some information as to why psychopathy may be viewed as untreatable (e.g., deficit in their ability to condition); they do not, however, provide strong support for clinical lore that contends psychopaths are unamenable to treatment. In fact, recent compelling theories by Frick (1998), Lykken (1995), Lynam (1997), and Newman (1998) suggest that the better we understand the etiology of psychopathy, the higher the likelihood of developing effective treatments become.

Nine of the twelve theories reviewed in the foregoing suggest that there is a predisposition for psychopathy whether it be a unique temperamental style (Frick, 1998), a deficiency in somatic markers (Damasio, 1994), low fearfulness (Lykken, 1995), a deficiency in psychopathy constraint (Lynam, 1997), or some other deficit. The three remaining theories (psychodynamic, cognitive–behavioral, and attachment based) suggest that psychopathy develops in children through a specific set of environmental conditions (e.g., poor attachment due to maltreatment). It is possible that psychopathy develops in different ways for different individuals with some individuals having a predisposition, others developing the condition through harsh environments, and still others through the interaction between temperament and environment. In fact, Lykken (1995) has suggested that this is the case and that the prevalence of "sociopathy" is increasing among the group that develops this condition primarily from the environment.

An important point from the aforementioned research is that a style in temperament (or a deficit in learning) does not necessitate that the disorder is untreatable. In fact, of the theorists who suggest there may be a temperamental style to psychopathy, none have purported that the disorder is untreatable (Frick, 1998; Lykken, 1995, Lynam, 1997; Newman, 1998). The theories proposed in the foregoing suggest that even individuals with a particular temperamental style interact with parents, peers, and society in ways that can either foster detachment and aggression or attachment and prosocial behavior in such youth. It may be that considerably more treatment effort is needed for those individuals highest at risk.

To this point in the article, two problems (classification and etiology of psychopathy) have been reviewed, which suggest that the clinical belief that psychopathy is untreatable or extremely difficult to treat is either complicated or not well supported by the available evidence. The next logical step is to examine the treatment studies of psychopathy to determine whether or not interventions attempted in the past have been successful. In the following section, I present research that specifically examines the treatability of psychopathy.

5. REVIEW OF STUDIES INVESTIGATING THE PSYCHOPATHY–TREATMENT RELATION

Previous researchers have rendered conclusions about the treatability of psychopathy based on clinical lore or their readings of the literature (e.g., Gacono, Nieberding, Owen, Rubel & Bodholt, 2001; Losel, 1998; Suedfeld & Landon, 1978). Unfortunately, this type of summary does not provide an overall comparison between theoretical orientations/techniques nor does it report quantitatively the magnitude of the outcome. The present investigation provides an integration of existing research on the relation between psychopathy and treatment. To this end, meta-analysis was employed to estimate the magnitude of the relationship between treatment and outcome. Also examined were the various theoretical orientations and their approach to the treatment of psychopathy and their reported outcome. An important aspect of the study was to evaluate whether treatment studies were aligned with developmental theories of psychopathy. This meta-analytic review of the effectiveness of intervention methods for psychopathy is unique in that no previous review has summarized quantitatively such a comprehensive database for the psychopathy–treatment relation.

5.1. Compilation of Psychopathy and Treatment Studies

A computerized search was performed to locate all studies that examined the psychopathy–treatment relationship. Articles that examined treatment outcome of psychopathy were of interest. The search was limited to psychopathy and not related disorders (e.g., APD, CD, ODD). Search procedures included use of the PsychLIT database, an examination of previous reviews of the literature, and the reference sections of individual studies and chapters. The last year of specialized journals that might address the issue of psychopathy and treatment that were too recent to be included in computer databases were also reviewed (i.e., *American Journal of Psychotherapy, American Psychologist, Clinical Psychology: Science and Practice, Clinical Psychology Review, International Journal of Offender Therapy, Journal of Clinical Psychology, Journal of the American Academy of Psychiatry and the Law, Journal of Consulting and Clinical Psychology, Journal of Forensic Psychiatry, Law and Human Behavior, Psychological Bulletin, Psychotherapy: Theory, Research, and Practice*). These search procedures yielded 42 published investigations with 44 samples and 43 effect sizes on treatment outcome.

5.2. Calculation of Effect Sizes

Meta-analytic studies employ different, although closely related, quantitative procedures. Because few studies have been conducted on psychopathy and treatment, the current study did not restrict the review to designs utilizing only control groups nor did it exclude case studies. One limitation of the current study was that not all studies utilized control groups. According to Hunter (1990), this limitation in individual studies can be circumvented in a meta-analysis because the control group for one intervention study can serve as a control group for other intervention studies that do not have control groups. Control groups are used to estimate the success rate without any treatment. Thus, the "treatment" is the same across all studies (i.e., no treatment), and findings for studies that include control groups can be generalized to studies that do not. The control group figure used should represent the average across all studies with control groups. Meta-analysts (e.g., Hunter, 1990; Hunter & Schmidt, 1990) state that a meta-analysis of the results from all available control groups provides a better benchmark to evaluate any intervention than does the control group from any one particular study because the idiosyncracies of the individual control groups are averaged out. Therefore, in the current meta-analysis, eight control group samples were meta-analyzed together to obtain a more robust and reliable estimate of the average reduction in psychopathic traits/behavior without any intervention. The resulting mean was then compared to the mean success rates for different interventions for psychopathy, thereby allowing estimates of "net" success rates.

In the present study, proportions of treatment success were cumulated. Available from each study were the sample sizes (n_i) used and the proportion who improved from psychotherapy (P_i). The mean success rate ($\bar{p}$) was computed as $\sum n_i P_i / \sum n_i$ and the observed variance is given as $\sum n_i (P_i - \bar{p})^2 / \sum n_i$. Thus, for each intervention method, the sample size-weighted mean and the sample size-weighted variance of success rates were obtained. The formula for sampling error variance of proportions was obtained from standard statistical textbooks as $P_i Q_i / n_i$, where $Q_i = 1 - P_i$. A sample-weighted mean of the sampling error variance of proportions to be cumulated was then obtained as $(\sum n_i P_i Q_i / \sum n_i) / \sum n_i = \sum P_i Q_i / \sum n_i$. This sample-weighted mean sampling error variance was then subtracted from the observed variance, yielding an estimate of the true variance plus variance due to other artifacts, such as unreliability (Hunter & Schmidt, 1990), that could not be corrected for. Lacking any information about other artifacts, it can be assumed that the true variance estimate is an upper bound value on the real variability of the effectiveness of an intervention method. Also calculated were effect sizes based on the formula from Rosenthal (1991) for proportions: $d' = P_{tx} - P_c$ where P_{tx} is the proportion of patients who benefited from psychotherapy and P_c is the proportion of patients who benefited without any formal treatment.

5.3. "File-Drawer" Analysis

Rosenthal's (1991) prescription for estimate of the number of unreported nonsignificant studies needed to reduce the current meta-analytic results to a significance of $P=.05$ or higher was utilized. This estimate is referred to as the "file-drawer" statistic, as these results languish unreported in various academic file-drawers. The following formula was used: $X=K(KZ_p{}^2-2.706)/2.706$ where K is the number of studies included in the analysis, Z_p is the mean of standard normal deviates of P for the studies analyzed, and X is the number of unpublished null studies needed to reduce the overall significance to $P=.05$ or less. The algebraic derivation of this formula results in the use of 2.706, the square of 1.645, the Z for $P=.05$.

6. RESULTS

A total of 42 studies on the treatment of psychopathy were compiled and yielded information about outcome for those who were treated for a psychopathic condition. The results from individual studies are presented in Table 2. The overall proportion of successful intervention for all treatment studies was .62 ($P<.01$). This number remained virtually the same when case studies were dropped from the analysis (.60). File-drawer analyses for the overall sample determined that 160 studies (almost four times the amount of studies reported in this review) with null results would be required to reduce the significance level of this finding to $P=.05$.

Most studies presented in this meta-analysis approached the treatment of psychopathy from a psychoanalytic orientation. Many of the studies (52%) conceptualized psychopathy from a Clecklian perspective and only four studies (9%) utilized the more contemporary conceptualization put forth by Hare (1991). Four other studies (9%) used Craft's conceptualization and two studies (4%) utilized Partridge's conceptualization. For 11 studies (26%), the conceptualization of psychopathy was not specified or was the only study that utilized a particular conceptualization (e.g., So scale of the California Personality Inventory; Gough, 1997). Although some studies did not specify the conceptualization utilized, most studies had hallmark psychopathic traits of psychopathy as described by Cleckley (1941). The average age of psychopathic individuals being treated was 22.38 and most were males (91%).

As can been seen in Table 2, a variety of treatment methods have been employed for psychopathic individuals ranging from electroconvulsive therapy (ECT; Cleckley & Beard, 1942) to psychodrama (Corsini, 1958) to traditional psychoanalysis (Schmideberg, 1978). Interestingly, when group psychotherapy was combined with individual psychotherapy the proportion of patients that improved was relatively high (81%). Also, the inclusion of family members in treatment programs appeared to increase the proportion of patients who improved (75%). Intensive individual psychotherapy (on average four sessions per week for 1 year or longer) had a highly successful treatment rate (91%). The success rates in column 10 of Table 2 provide a basis for comparing across the individual studies. Studies for which proportions could not be obtained were also included in Table 2 and provide descriptive information about the effectiveness of a given approach to the treatment of psychopathy.

6.1. Average Success Rates

In addition to providing information across individual studies, the mean success rates in column 4 of Table 3 provide a basis for comparison across the intervention methods. Values ranged from .22 for ECT to 1.00 for rational therapy, psychodrama, and personal construct therapy. ECT had no therapeutic effect on psychopathic individuals; the average success rate was approximately equal to that of the control sample (.20). Although rational therapy, psychodrama, and personal construct therapy were found to be effective modes of treatment for psychopathy, any optimism is tempered by the fact that these findings were based on single case studies.

A surprising finding was that psychoanalytic therapy appeared to be effective in the treatment of psychopathy. The average success rate was 59% based on 17 studies and 88 psychopathic individuals. These studies (e.g., Beacher, 1962; Berman, 1964; Chwast, 1961; Henderson, 1972; Humphreys, 1940; Noshpitz, 1984; Schmideberg, 1947, 1978; Szurek, 1942; Thorne, 1959; Vaillant, 1975) found that following psychoanalytic psychotherapy psychopathic individuals ranging widely in age (8 to 55 years) and across genders improved. This finding was surprising given that many early psychoanalytic therapists believed that personality remained relatively stable after the first 5–6 years of life. This finding indicates that insight-oriented therapies may decrease psychopathic traits and that psychopathic individuals gained some awareness of their general approach to life through this therapeutic approach.

Cognitive–behavioral therapies had a success rate of 62% suggesting that this approach might be slightly more effective than psychoanalytic therapies although the difference between the two perspectives is minuscule (3%). The average success rate for cognitive–behavioral therapies was a robust finding given that it was based on 5 studies and 246 psychopathic individuals. Cognitive–behavioral therapies may have been effective because they often addressed patients' thoughts about themselves, others, and society. Thus, they tended to directly treat some psychopathic traits. Eclectic therapies that often included a combination of both cognitive–behavioral techniques and insight-oriented approaches were also highly effective. The average success rate based on this method of psychotherapy was 86% suggesting that augmenting cognitive–behavioral therapies with insight therapies and other psychotherapeutic techniques may be optimal for the treatment of psychopathic individuals.

Therapeutic communities were the least effective methods for treating psychopathy with an average success rate of 25%. This success rate was based on 8 studies and 372 psychopathic individuals. Again, this rate of success was only slightly greater than that of the control group (20%). This finding is not particularly surprising. Although therapeutic communities have often been utilized for the treatment of psychopathic individuals the programs are not designed to target psychopathic symptomatology.

TABLE 2

Effects of Treatment for Psychopathic Personalities for 42 Studies

AUTHOR	ORIENTATION	PSYCHOPATHY CONCEPTUALIZATION	n	AGE	GENDER	FREQUENCY/ DURATION	PARENT/ GROUP	OUTCOME	P	d'
Beacher (1962)	psychoanalytic	Cleckley	1	29.0	m	2/18 mo	G	less hostile, more social, improved internalized value system, less grandiose, improved communication skills	1.00	.80
Berman (1964)	psychoanalytic	Cleckley	1	18.0	m	3/26 mo	P^m	warmer to family members, more productive (started working), court reports that patient's behavior has been good and was released from probation, improved relationships, long-term follow-up found patient to be in graduate school	1.00	.80
Borriello (1979)	psychoanalytic	Cleckley	4	a	m	—	G°	gained insight, less manipulative, internalized new value system, decreased acting out behaviors, improved perspective taking	1.00	.80
Butterworth (1951)	psychoanalytic	Cleckley	1	28.0	m	5/12 mo	N	improved ability to provide economic support for self (started work), improved planning abilities	1.00	.80
Chrzanowski (1965)	psychoanalytic	Cleckley	2	—	m	—	F	one terminated prematurely with having made no progress, a second case reported to be making progress	.50	.30
Chwast (1961)	psychoanalytic	Cleckley	10	20.5	8m/2f	1/6 mo	N	five dropped prematurely, five improved social relations	.50	.30

AUTHOR	ORIENTATION	PSYCHOPATHY CONCEPTUALIZATION	n	AGE	GENDER	FREQUENCY/ DURATION	PARENT/ GROUP	OUTCOME	p	d'
Cleckley & Beard (1942)	ECT	Cleckley	6	–	–	3/0.5 mo	N	three patients no change, three limited data	.00	–.20
Copas, O'Brien, Roberts, and Whiteley (1984)	therapeutic community	Cleckley	37	26.5	m/f	7/ > 0.5 mo	G	reduction in subsequent criminal convictions and psychiatric hospitalizations	.60	.40
Copas and Whiteley (1976)	therapeutic community	Cleckley	87	a	m	—	G°	did not reoffend	.47	.27
Corsini (1958)	psychodrama	Cleckley	1	15.0	m	?/8 mo	G	less destructive, respectful of others, significant drop in reprimands, adopted social norms, school work improved, respectful	1.00	.80
Craft (1968)	cognitive–behavioral	Craft	94	19.2	m	3/11.1 mo	G	success in treatment was based on offense rates	.63	.43
	cognitive–behavioral	Craft	92	18.3	m	2/9.1 mo	G	success in treatment was based on offense rates	.43	.23
Craft Stephenson, and Granger (1964)	cognitive–behavioral	Craft	23	19.0	m	7/12 mo	G	clinical improvement, improved work records	.83	.63
	therapeutic community	Craft	21	19.0	m	3/12 mo	G	clinical improvement, improved work records	.67	.47
Darling (1945)	ECT	Cleckley	3	20.7	m	—	N	drop in violent behavior, less hostility, increased stability	.66	.46
Ellis (1961)	rational therapy	Cleckley	1	25.0	m	1/12 mo	N	stopped antisocial behavior	1.00	.80

AUTHOR	ORIENTATION	PSYCHOPATHY CONCEPTUALIZATION	n	AGE	GENDER	FREQUENCY/ DURATION	PARENT/ GROUP	OUTCOME	P	d'
Glaus (1968)	cognitive–behavioral	Cleckley	3	a	m	–/>12 mo	—	increased stability	1.00	.80
Heaver (1943)	psychoanalytic	Cheney	40	28.7	m	7/3.85 mo	G	conformed with society's expectations	.40	.20
Henderson (1972)	psychoanalytic	DSM-II/Cleckley	3	—	m	1/–	G	not reported	–	–
Humphreys (1940)	psychoanalytic	Hendersen	3	30.7	m		N	no improvement	.00	–.20
Ingram, Gerard, Quay, and Levinson (1970)	action-oriented	Quay	20	y	m	7/6 mo	G	decrease in institutional aggressive behavior	.75	.55
								overall improved adjustment in community	1.00	.80
Kiger (1967)	therapeutic community	Cleckley	100	—	m/f	5/3 mo	G	better able to handle feelings about authority, less impulsive, more giving, increased self-respect, responsible, less need to control, less blaming	–	–
Korey (1944)	pharmacotherapy, Benzedrine sulfate	Cleckley	6	16.0	m	20 mg qd/1 mo	N	increased work effort/efficacy, accelerated school performance, increased sociability, decreased number of misconducts, more temperate	.57	.37
Kristiansson (1995)	pharmacotherapy (lithium or SSRI) and cognitive behavioral	Hare-PCL-R	4	41.5	m		N	improved socially and behaviorally	1.00	.80
Maas (1966)	personal construct	Gough	46	25.0	f	2/3.3 mo	G	significant decrease in sociopathy scores	.63	.43

AUTHOR	ORIENTATION	PSYCHOPATHY CONCEPTUALIZATION	n	AGE	GENDER	FREQUENCY/ DURATION	PARENT/ GROUP	OUTCOME	p	d'
Miles (1969)	therapeutic community	Cleckley	40	21.7	m	7/12 mo	G	improvement in ability to communicate and solve problems, improved empathy more social	.65	.45
Noshpitz (1984)	psychoanalytic	Cleckley	5	14.0	2m/3f	3/6–16 mo	G	patients were able to experience guilt and anxiety, decrease in aggressive behavior	1.00	.80
Ogloff et al. (1990)	therapeutic community	Hare-PCL-R	21	26.9	m	5/3.3 mo	N	"slight" improvement in treatment and "slight" no motivation for treatment	.16	–.04
Partridge (1928)	not specified	Partridge	6	29.7	3m/3f	—	—	more productive, more cooperative	.17	–.03
Persons (1965)	eclectic	Applezweig	12	22.0	m	2/2.5 mo	N	lower sociopathy scores on two measures, significant decrease in disciplinary reports issued by correctional officers	.92	.72
Reiss, Grubin, and Meux (1996)	eclectic	Legal Hare-PCL-R	40	19.2	m	5/4.6 years	G	improvement in social activity/relations did not offend, PCL-R scores were not related to offending	.89 .80	.69 .69
Rice, Harris, and Cormier (1992)	therapeutic community	Hare-PCL-R	46	23.4	m	7/≥24 mo	G°	did not recidivate violently, treatment group had a 78% violent recidivism rate while the control group had only a 55% violent recidivism rate indicating a reverse effect	.22	.02
Sandhu (1970)	therapeutic community	Cleckley	18	a	m	7/9 mo	G°	improved attitude to work, improved conduct in prison	.72	.52

AUTHOR	ORIENTATION	PSYCHOPATHY CONCEPTUALIZATION	n	AGE	GENDER	FREQUENCY/ DURATION	PARENT/ GROUP	OUTCOME	P	d'
Savitt (1940)	psychoanalytic	Cheney	2	15.0	m	7/0.75 mo	p^{mf}	moderate improvement	1.00	.80
Schmideberg (1947)	psychoanalytic	not specified	2	—	m	—	N	unclear	—	—
Schmideberg (1978)	psychoanalytic	Cleckley	1	16.5	m	5/10 mo	N	ncrease in ability to experience guilt, started work, began to develop career plans, increase in social relations with meaningful relationships	1.00	.80
Skolnick and Zuckerman (1979)	therapeutic community	MMPI-Pd	59	—	m	5/7 mo	G	change in Pd scores, decrease in sensation-seeking	.00	-.20
Sturup (1948)	psychotherapy, castration (for sex offenders)	not specified	300	—	m	—	—	normal life in the community	.55	.35
Szurek (1942)	psychoanalytic	Partridge	1	8.0	m	7/6 mo	P^m	increase in concern for others, progressive increase in attention span, interest in school work, decrease in destructive behavior, hyperactivity, and erratic behaviors, more consistent concern about the rights of others	1.00	.80
Thorne (1959)	psychoanalytic	Thorne/Cleckley	7	—	m	-/1–10 years	N	less sociopathic/more honest	1.00	.80
Vaillant (1975)	psychoanalytic	Cleckley	4	27.5	2m/2f	1/12 mo	P	less sociopathic	1.00	.80

AUTHOR	ORIENTATION	PSYCHOPATHY CONCEPTUALIZATION	n	AGE	GENDER	FREQUENCY/ DURATION	PARENT/ GROUP	OUTCOME	P	d'
Whitaker and Burdy (1969)	psychoanalytic	not specified	1	–	f	1/6 mo	P	no improvement	.00	–.20
Whiteley (1970)	therapeutic community	Whiteley	122	25.0	m	7/4 mo	G	high drop-out rate (87%), did not offend	.65	.45
Woody, McLellen, Rubersky, and O'Brien (1985)	cognitive–behavioral/ supportive–expressive	RDC	30	a	m	25 sessions	N	improvement in employment, less drug and alcohol use, drop in legal problems	.80	.60
	psychodynamic	Cleckley	1308	22.3	m	4/12.3 mo	G	less sociopathic	.62	.48

RDC = Research Diagnostic Criteria for APD; m = male; mo = months; Parent/group = either the parent or the psychopathic individual was receiving treatment in a group signified by P = parent received psychotherapy along with the youth; G = patient also participated in group psychotherapy; G° = group therapy only usually in the form of a therapeutic community; N = neither the parents were treated nor did the youth participate in group psychotherapy. ES = effect size that is signified by the proportion of patients who benefited from psychotherapy. – = not reported. Where age was not provided we used "y" for children and adolescents and "a" for adults.

Therapeutic community programs tended to have little psychologist–patient contact. This factor may have had a direct impact on the effectiveness of these programs. In fact, this issue was raised by Warren (1994) to explain the variance across therapeutic community treatment outcome studies.

A treatment program specifically designed by Ingram et al. (1970) to address psychopathic symptomatology in youth demonstrated a high success rate (88%). Unlike therapeutic communities, the Ingram et al. treatment program was designed specifically for psychopathic youth and they selected staff based on their training and ability to deal with psychopathic youth. The program was based on the sensation-seeking model and as such kept youth interested in treatment. These two factors may, in part, account for the success of this treatment program.

Two very small-scaled studies utilized pharmacotherapy to target psychopathic traits and behaviors. The average success rate for these studies was 70%. However, it should be noted that one study (Kristiansson, 1995) combined cognitive–behavioral therapy with pharmacotherapy (either the use of lithium or an SSRI). This study had an average success rate of 100% but this was found for a small sample of only four psychopathic individuals. The second study (Korey, 1944), consisted of six adolescents who received Benzedrine sulfate. The average success rate for this group was 57%. Because of the very small sample sizes utilized in these two studies and the use of cognitive–behavioral therapy in one study, the effectiveness of pharmacotherapy for the treatment of psychopathy requires further study.

Several other approaches were reviewed but many consist of only a single study and sometimes these involved only a single psychopathic individual. While these studies are important to include in a review such as this, the conclusions that can be drawn from them are minimal. At best, they may be utilized to spur further research in that area. These studies (e.g., rational emotive therapy; Ellis, 1961) are depicted in Tables 2 and 3.

The success rate of the control group indicates the percentage of psychopathic individuals who had a decrease in psychopathic traits/behaviors without any intervention. The present analysis included eight control groups, with a total sample of 287, indicated that 19.8% of psychopathic individuals showed improvement over time without any intervention. To determine the net effectiveness of the intervention methods in Tables 2 and 3, 20 percentage points must be subtracted from each success rate. Adjustments produce larger percentage reductions for some interventions than others. For example, the for the cognitive–behavioral interventions, the adjustment is .62–.20=.42, a 32% reduction, whereas for therapeutic communities, the adjustment is .23–.20=.03, an 87% reduction. Thus, the control group adjustment changes the ratios of success rates. For example, the net effectiveness of cognitive–behavioral interventions is 14 times greater than that of therapeutic communities. But for unadjusted success rates, cognitive–behavioral therapies would be found to be only 2.7 times greater than that of therapeutic communities. Therefore, in comparing relative success rates, the control group adjustment is very important. Moreover, as can be seen for therapeutic communities, such an adjustment has important implications for the absolute value of the intervention; the

TABLE 3

Meta-analysis Results for Psychopathy Intervention Studies

TYPE OF PSYCHOTHERAPY	NUMBER OF STUDIES	TOTAL SAMPLE	MEAN p (SUCCESS RATE)	OBSERVED VARIANCE	SAMPLING ERROR VARIANCE	PERCENT VARIANCE ACCOUNTED FOR	CORRECTED S.D.[a]	80% CREDIBILITY INTERVAL[b]
1. Psychoanalytic	17	88	0.59	.0879	.0089	10.1	.17	.34–.84
2. Cognitive–behavioral	5	246	0.62	.0238	.0026	10.9	.03	.58–.66
3. Therapeutic communities	8	371	0.25	.1768	.0035	1.9	.06	.17–.33
4. Actional procedures	1	20	0.88	–	.0053	–	–	–
5. Eclectic	2	62	0.86	.0024	.0036	100.0	.01	.85–.87
6. Pharmacotherapy (2)[c]	2	10	0.70	.0461	.0245	53.1	.10	.55–.85
7. ECT	2	9	0.22	.1789	.0242	13.5	.17	–.03–.47
8. Personal construct	1	46	1.00	–	–	–	–	–
9. Rational therapy	1	1	1.00	–	–	–	–	–
10. Psychodrama	1	1	1.00	–	–	–	–	–
11. Not specified	1	6	0.17	–	.0235	–	–	–
12. Control	8	287	0.20	.0428	.0038	8.8	.04	.18–.29

– = unable to calculate because statistics are based on a single or few cases.

[a] Standard deviation of success rates after the effects of sampling error have been eliminated.

[b] The 80th credibility interval values indicate the range of proportions after the extreme 10% of values on either side of the mean have been eliminated from the distribution.

[c] Meta-analysis results when studies in those categories are combined.

net effectiveness of therapeutic communities is nearly zero. Table 2 provides d' effect sizes for all treatment studies that calculates the aforementioned adjustments.

6.2. Tests of Possible Moderator Effects

In order to test for the presence of moderator effects, the classification of psychopathy (e.g., Cleckley, Hare-PCL-R), patient age, and treatment duration were examined to determine if they had an impact on treatment outcome results. Table 4 summarizes the effect size estimates for all analyses reported below. Cautious interpretation of moderator effects are warranted given that the number of samples is small. Future research will be needed to conclusively clarify these differences.

TABLE 4

Examination of Potential Moderators of Effect

MODERATOR	PROPORTION	NUMBER OF SAMPLES
CLASSIFICATION		
Cleckley	$.88_a$	19
Hare-PCL-R	$.57_b$	4
Craft	$.64_b$	4
Partridge	$.59_b$	2
Other	$.56_b$	11
AGE OF PSYCHOPATH		
Youth	$.96_a$	8
Adult	$.63_b$	33
DURATION OF PSYCHOTHERAPY		
< 6 months	$\frac{3}{4}^1$	1°
≥ 6 months		23
> 12 months	$.91_b$	12

Proportions with different subscripts differ significantly from each other within categories. These differences are based on small sample sizes and replication will be necessary in the future.

6.2.1. CLASSIFICATION OF PSYCHOPATHY

All samples were grouped according to classification type: Cleckley ($n=22$), Hare-PCL-R ($n=4$), Craft ($n=4$), Partridge ($n=2$), and other ($n=11$). Treatment outcome studies showed that psychotherapy was more effective with psychopaths defined by Cleckley criteria (.88) than those individuals meeting Hare-PCL-R (.57), Craft (.64), or Partridge (.59) criteria. Craft psychopaths also benefited from treatment to a greater degree than any of the other conceptualizations with the exception of Cleckley (1941). Differences in the types of treatment provided for the differing conceptualizations limit these findings and suggest that further research is needed in this area. Interestingly, no matter which way psychopathy was defined all classifications showed some benefit from treatment.

6.2.2. Age of Psychopathic Individual

Studies were also coded for subject age: youth (n=8), and adults (n=22). The results revealed that a greater proportion of psychopathic youth benefited from psychotherapy than did adults. The proportion of youth (.96) that benefited from treatment was substantially higher than the proportion of adults (.63) that benefited from treatment. Yet, treatment appeared to be effective for both.

6.2.3. Duration of Psychotherapy

Studies were classified based on the duration of psychotherapy: short term (<6 months) and long term (≥6 months). If treatment lasted less than 6 months, then psychopathic individuals were less likely to benefit from treatment than if they participated in treatment that lasted longer than 6 months. If the treatment lasted for a year or longer, 91% of the psychopathic individuals were found to have benefited from treatment (on average these individuals met four times a week with a mental health professional).

7. GENERAL DISCUSSION

In many clinical circles, psychopaths are seen as untreatable although there is little scientific support for this belief. In the current review, cognitive–behavioral, psychodynamic, and eclectic intervention methods for psychopathy were shown to be effective. Moreover, psychopathic individuals were shown to have improved following rational therapy, personal construct psychotherapy, and other more specific psychotherapy programs. The most notable benefits included a reduction in psychopathic traits and characteristics (e.g., a decrease in lying, an increase in remorse and empathy, improved relations with others) and a reduction in recidivism. These findings indicate that contrary to clinical lore, the syndrome of psychopathy does not appear to be completely recalcitrant to treatment. Because of the high cost these individuals pose to society and themselves, the findings from the present review are encouraging and have important implications for future development and implementation of treatment programs for psychopathy.

The most successful interventions (e.g., cognitive–behavioral and psychoanalytic) tended to be intensive including an average of four sessions of individual psychotherapy per week for at least 1 year. Individual psychotherapy when augmented with group psychotherapy, at least preliminarily appears to be beneficial. In addition, treatment programs that incorporate family members appears to be beneficial. These results indicate, at least preliminarily, that for complex problems such as psychopathy, more elaborate and intensive intervention programs involving individual psychotherapy, treatment of family members, and input from groups (other patients/inmates) are beneficial and may enhance their overall effectiveness. Thus, based on the current review, the scope, intensity, and duration of treatment for psychopathy may have been key in the overall adjustment of these individuals.

Not unexpectedly, the review revealed that intervention programs with little professional psychological input and little-to-no one-to-one patient–psychologist contact resulted in poor treatment outcomes. This was most notable with therapeutic communities where mental health professionals had little or no contact with patients and essentially allowed inmates to "treat" other inmates often with very different symptom patterns. In the case of therapeutic communities, 25% of the patients benefited from treatment. Of the ones that did not benefit, significant costs to the community resulted in terms of violent recidivism (see Rice et al., 1992). These results suggest that when mental health professionals are not directly involved in treatment programs for serious forms of psychopathology then, clinically, patients exhibit little or no change and "interventions" possibly allow psychopathic conditions to worsen (Rice et al., 1992).

Several specific psychotherapy techniques were found to decrease psychopathic traits/characteristics. Specifically, four techniques/approaches that appeared to reduce psychopathic traits and characteristics included rational therapy, action-oriented therapies, interventions that involved fixed-role therapy, and psychodrama. The action-oriented program that involved intensive treatment of psychopathic youth was highly successful (75% of the sample decreased institutional infractions and the entire group (100%) made positive adjustments to the community). Maas (1966) found that fixed-role psychotherapy and role-playing in general with a group of psychopathic women was beneficial and significantly reduced psychopathic traits. Ellis (1961) found that one individual improved after the use of rational therapy. Finally, Corsini (1958) found that a youth improved after the use of psychodrama.

There is little question that from a purely scientific perspective that many of the studies reviewed in this review and meta-analysis, including some of the experimentally designed studies, could have been improved in terms of their internal, external, construct, and statistical conclusion validity. However, dismissing this early research as well as clinical opinions and treatment experience with psychopathic individuals written in case study form when reviewing a first generation of research on psychopathy would, in my opinion, be neglectful. In fact, Strupp (1996) has stressed the importance of looking at previous literature on treatment outcome and using it to inform current treatment outcome studies. Though the studies in the current review may be less than optimal in scientific rigor, their inclusion is considered to be both necessary and important given our current state of knowledge on psychopathy.

Although the current article's primary purpose was to clarify our current state of knowledge on the psychopathy–treatment relation, an equally important goal of this article was to spur a second generation of research on this important topic area. In order to address the problems experienced with the first generation of research it is necessary to underscore the limitations in past research that psychologists should attempt to rectify in the future. This process involves first asking what problems exist and where we as psychologists should go with regard to treatment outcome studies for psychopathy. Both the current problems and suggested future directions are highlighted in the next several paragraphs.

Three problem areas are clear from the present review. First, classification is a critical issue with regard to treatment. Further clarity regarding the features of the disorder are necessary with regard to the treatment amenability query. This clarity can, in part, be gained by specifying the conceptualization of psychopathy utilized in treatment outcome studies as well as the specific constellation of symptomatology that the psychopathic individual(s) have. Relatedly, use of polythetic models of psychopathy will likely mean that researchers will have to investigate the relative effect of various constellations of psychopathic traits on treatment amenability.

Related to this problem and possibly more problematic to the conclusions about the treatability of psychopathy in this article is that there are few studies that examine the psychopathy–treatment relation from the contemporary conceptualization of the disorder. A finding of the current meta-analysis was that the Cleckley psychopath was the most frequently investigated conception of the syndrome in treatment outcome studies. Yet, many researchers and clinicians utilize Hare's conceptualization of psychopathy. Given that his definition differs from Cleckley, treatment outcome studies that employ this definition are necessary, particularly if psychologists are to make statements about treatment amenability based on the PCL-R.

Second, etiological theories of psychopathy require refinement. If effective treatment programs are to be developed for psychopathy then it will be necessary for psychologists to determine the specific causes of the disorder. Furthermore, there was only a low-to-moderate degree of correspondence between treatment programs and current etiological/developmental theories. More specifically, while psychodynamic, cognitive–behavioral, and sensation-seeking theories tended to be incorporated into the treatment programs investigated in this review, several developmental theories have not been formally tested. Specifically, no studies had treatment programs that focused on deficits in learning, few studies emphasized the need for improving role-playing abilities of psychopaths, and there have been few programs developed from attachment-based theories. Expectedly, more recent theories of psychopathy (Frick, 1998; Hare, 1998; Lykken, 1995; Lynam, 1997; Newman, 1998) have not yet been implemented in treatment studies. In the future, such theories may furnish psychologists with the necessary therapeutic guidelines for treatment programs. Rudderless treatment investigations are likely to be less successful.

Third, to better understand the psychopathy–treatment relationship, several issues should be addressed in future treatment studies. Treatment programs should be developed with specific aims and experimental research is needed to systematically determine the effects of different treatment modalities with psychopathic individuals in well-controlled experimental designs. For example, researchers should utilize psychopathy instruments pre- and posttreatment in order to examine changes in symptomatology. Such ratings should be made by masked raters. Third, external criteria such as recidivism and conduct problems should be systematically investigated. This type of information would inform psychologists as to whether there is evidence that psychological change implies reduced risk of reoffending. In addition, research needs to make some attempt to determine whether clients are "faking good" in treatment studies or whether the changes are genuine.

Finally, prevention of psychopathy requires study. Because many of the developmental theories suggest that there is a predisposition (temperamental style) to this syndrome, early intervention may be particularly important. Lykken has shed light on this issue by suggesting that with competent parenting and "skillful help" children can in fact be socialized, albeit this effort is considerable. Nevertheless, given the high cost of this disorder on society, early intervention seems worthy. Moreover, withholding treatment from youth thought to develop psychopathy because of beliefs that the disorder is refractory to treatment would be unethical.

It seems clear from the current review that the widely held clinical belief that psychopathy is an untreatable disorder is unwarranted and that conclusions either way for this first generation of research are premature. At best, what we can glean scientifically suggests that psychopathy may be treatable. Further research on the psychopathy–treatment relation will help to increase the accountability of the profession for the treatment of those individuals who are psychopathic. Collaborative efforts between clinicians and researchers will enhance the richness and complexity of the psychotherapeutic process with psychopathic individuals as it unfolds over time. Considering the present state of our knowledge, the current review suggests that therapeutic pessimism with regard to the psychopathy–treatment relation is not warranted and efforts to develop and advance treatment technology in this area should be initiated.

NOTES

1. Because there are numerous theories of psychopathy, it is beyond the scope of this paper to cover comprehensively all etiological theories. Psychologists investigating the etiology and/or treatment of psychopathy should also investigate the utility of other developmental theories of psychopathy not covered in this review (e.g., Millon, 1990; Patrick, 1994; Schmauk, 1970; Zuckerman, 1995).

REFERENCES

Aichorn, A. (1966). *Wayward youth*. New York: Viking Press.

Bandura, A. (1973). *Aggression: a social learning analysis*. Englewood Cliffs, NJ: Prentice-Hall.

*Beacher, A. I. (1962). Psychoanalytic treatment of a sociopath in a group situation. *American Journal of Psychotherapy*, *16*, 278–288.

Berkowitz, L. (1990). On the formation and regulation of anger and aggression: a neo-associationistic analysis. *American Psychologist*, *45*, 497–503.

*Berman, S. (1964). Techniques of treatment of a form of juvenile delinquency, the antisocial character disorder. *Journal of the American Academy of Child Psychiatry*, *3*, 24–52.

*Borriello, J. F. (1979). Group psychotherapy with acting-out patients: specific problems and techniques. *American Journal of Psychotherapy*, *33*, 521–530.

Bowlby, J. (1969). *Attachment and loss, vol. 1. Attachment* (2nd ed.). New York: Basic Books.

*Butterworth, A. T. (1951). Psychopathic personality in treatment. *New Orleans Medical Journal*, *104*, 197–200.

*Chrzanowski, G. (1965). The psychotherapeutic management of sociopathy. *American Journal of Psychotherapy*, *19*, 372–381.

*Chwast, J. (1961). Reversibility–irreversibility: problems in the treatment of offenders. *American Journal of Psychotherapy*, *15*, 221–232.

Cleckley, H. (1941). *The mask of sanity*. St. Louis, MO: Mosby.

Cleckley, H. (1981). *The mask of sanity* (4th ed.). St. Louis, MO: Mosby.

*Cleckley, H., & Beard, B. (1942). Electric shock therapy in personality disorders. *Journal of the Medical Association of Georgia, 31,* 303–308.

Cloninger, C. R. (1978). The antisocial personality. *Hospital Practice, 13,* 97–106.

*Copas, J. B., & Whiteley, J. S. (1976). Predicting success in the treatment of psychopaths. *British Journal of Psychiatry, 129,* 388–392.

*Copas, J. V., O'Brien, M., Roberts, J., & Whiteley, J. S. (1984). Treatment outcome in personality disorder: the effects of social, psychological and behavioral variables. *Personality and Individual Differences, 5,* 565–573.

*Corsini, R. J. (1958). Psychodrama with a psychopath. *Group Psychotherapy, 11,* 33–39.

*Craft, M. (1968). Psychopathic disorder: a second trial of treatment. *British Journal of Psychiatry, 114,* 812–820.

*Craft, M., Stephenson, G., & Granger, C. (1964). A controlled trial of authoritarian and self-governing regimes with adolescent psychopaths. *American Journal of Orthopsychiatry, 34,* 543–554.

Damasio, A. R. (1994). *Descartes' error: emotion, reason and the human brain.* New York: Putnam.

*Darling, H. F. (1945). Electric shock treatment in psychopathic personality. *Journal of Nervous and Mental Disease, 101,* 247–250.

Dodge, K. A. (1980). Social cognition and children's aggressive behavior. *Child Development, 53,* 620–635.

Doren, D. M. (1987). *Understanding and treating the psychopath.* New York: Wiley.

Draughon, M. (1977). Ego-building: an aspect of the treatment of psychopaths. *Psychological Reports, 40,* 615–626.

Ellis, A. (1961). The treatment of a psychopath with rational psychotherapy. *Journal of Psychology, 51,* 141–150.

Eron, L. D. (1997). The development of antisocial behavior from a learning perspective. In: D. M. Stoff, J. Breiling, & J. D. Maser (Eds.), *Handbook of antisocial behavior* (pp. 140–147). New York: Wiley.

Eysenck, H. J. (1975). Genetic factors in personality development. In: A. R. Kaplan (Ed.), *Human behavior genetics.* Springfield, IL: Thomas.

Eysenck, H. J. (1977). *Crime and personality* (3rd ed.). London: Routledge & Kegan Paul.

Eysenck, H. J. (1981). General features of the model. In: H. J. Eysenck (Ed.), *A model for personality* (pp. 1–37). New York: Springer-Verlag.

Forth, A. E., Kosson, D., & Hare, R. D. (1994). *Psychopathy Checklist — Youth Version.* Toronto, ON: Multi-Health Systems.

Fowles, D. C. (1980). The three arousal model: implications of Gray's two factor learning theory for heart rate, electrodermal activity, and psychopathy. *Psychophysiology, 17,* 87–104.

Freud, S. (1961). The ego and the id. In: J. Strachey (Ed.), *The standard edition of the complete psychological works of Sigmund Freud, vol. 19* (pp. 3–56). London: Hogarth.

Frick, P. J. (1998). Callous–unemotional traits and conduct problems: a two factor model of psychopathy in children. In: D. J. Cooke, A. E. Forth, & R. D. Hare (Eds.), *Psychopathy: theory, research, and implication for society* (pp. 161–188). Dordrecht, Netherlands: Kluwer Academic Publishing.

Frick, P. J., & Hare, R. D. (in press). *The psychopathy screening device.* Toronto, ON: Multi-Health Systems.

Frick, P. J., & Jackson, Y. K. (1993). Family functioning and childhood antisocial behavior: yet another reinterpretation. *Journal of Clinical Child Psychology, 22,* 410–419.

Gacono, C. B., Nieberding, R. J., Owen, A., Rubel, J., & Bodholt, K. (2001). Treating conduct disorder, antisocial, and psychopatic personalities. In J. B. Ashford, B. D. Sales, & W. H. Reid (Eds.), *Treating adult and juvenile offenders with special needs.* Washington, DC: American Psychological Association.

Gale, A. (1973). The physiology of individual differences: studies on extraversion and the EEG. In: P. Kline (Ed.), *New approaches to physiological measurement.* Chichester, England: Wiley.

Garfield, S. L. (1994). Research on client variables in psychotherapy. In: S. L. Garfield, & A. E. Bergin (Eds.), *Handbook of psychotherapy and behavior change* (3rd ed.) (pp. 190–228). New York: Wiley.

*Glaus, A. (1968). The handling of criminal psychopaths in Switzerland. *International Journal of Offender Therapy, 12,* 29–36.

Gough, H. G. (1948). A sociological theory of psychopathy. *American Journal of Sociology, 53,* 359–366.

Gough, H. G. (1958). *California Psychological Inventory.* Palo Alto, CA: Consulting Psychologists Press.

Gough, G. H. (1997). *California Psychological Inventory (revised)*. Palo Alto, CA: Consulting Psycho-logists Press.

Gray, J. A. (1987). *The psychology of fear and stress* (2nd ed.). Cambridge: Cambridge Univ. Press.

Greenacre, P. (1945). Conscience in the psychopath. *American Journal of Orthopsychiatry, 15*, 495–509.

Greenwald, H. (1967). Treatment of the psychopath. *Voices, 3*, 50–60.

Guerra, N. G., & Slaby, R. G. (1990). Evaluative factors in social problem solving by aggressive boys. *Journal of Abnormal Child Psychology, 17*, 277–289.

Hare, R. D. (1970). *Psychopathy: theory and research*. New York: Wiley.

Hare, R. D. (1991). *Manual for the revised Psychopathy Checklist*. Toronto, ON: Multi-Health Systems.

Hare, R. D. (1998). Psychopathy, affect, and behavior. In: D. J. Cooke, A. E. Forth, & R. D. Hare (Eds.), *Psychopathy: theory, research, and implications for society* (pp. 105–138). Dordrecht, Netherlands: Kluwer Academic Publishing.

Hare, R. D., & Hart, R. D. (1993). Psychopathy, mental disorder, and crime. In: S. Hodgins (Ed.), *Mental disorder and crime* (pp. 104–115). Newbury Park, CA: Sage.

Hart, S. D., Forth, A. E., & Hare, R. D. (1990). Performance of criminal psychopaths on selected neuropsychological tests. *Journal of Abnormal Psychology, 99*, 374–379.

Howland, E. W., Kosson, P. S., Patterson, C. M. & Newman, J. P. (1993). Altering a dominant response: performance of psychopaths and low socialization college students.

*Heaver, W. L. (1943). A study of forty male psychopathic personalities before, during and after hospitalization. *American Journal of Psychiatry, 100*, 342–346.

*Henderson, J. M. (1972). The doing character. *Adolescence, 7*, 309–326.

*Humphreys, E. J. (1940). Psychopathic personality among the mentally defective. *Psychiatric Quarterly, 14*, 231–247.

Hunter, J. E. (1990). *The control group and meta-analysis*. Unpublished manuscript, Department of Psychology, Michigan State University (May).

Hunter, J. E., & Schmidt, F. L. (1990). *Methods of meta-analysis: correcting error and bias in research findings*. Newbury Park, CA: Sage.

*Ingram, G. L., Gerard, R. E., Quay, H. C., & Levison, R. B. (1970). An experimental program for the psychopathic delinquent: looking in the "correctional wastebasket." *Journal of Research in Crime and Delinquency, 7*, 24–30.

Intrator, J., Hare, R. D., Stritzke, P., Brichstwein, K., Dorfman, D., Harper, T., Bernstein, D., Handelsman, L., Keilp, J., Rosen, J., & Machac, J. (1997). A brain imaging (SPECT) study of semantic and affective processing in psychopaths. *Biological Psychiatry, 42*, 96–103.

Johnson, A. M., & Szurek, S. A. (1954). Etiology of antisocial behavior in delinquents and psychopaths. *Journal of the American Medical Association, 154*, 814–817.

Kazdin, A. E. (1999). Current (lack of) status of theory in child and adolescent psychotherapy research. *Journal of Clinical Child Psychology, 28*, 533–543.

*Kiger, R. S. (1967). Treating the psychopathic patient in a therapeutic community. *Hospital and Community Psychiatry, 18*, 191–196.

Kochanska, G. (1993). Toward a synthesis of parental socialization and child temperament in early development of conscience. *Child Development, 64*, 325–347.

Kohut, H. (1982). Introspection, empathy, and the semi-circle of mental health. *International Journal of Psychoanalysis, 63*, 395–407.

*Korey, S. R. (1944). The effects of Benzedrine sulfate on the behavior of psychopathic and neurotic juvenile delinquents. *Psychiatric Quarterly, 18*, 127–137.

*Kristiansson, M. (1995). Incurable psychopaths? *Bulletin of the American Academy of Psychiatry and the Law, 23*, 555–562.

Lilienfeld, S. O. (1994). Conceptual problems in the assessment of psychopathy. *Clinical Psychology Review, 14*, 17–38.

Lochman, J. E. (1990). Modification of childhood aggression. In: A. M. Hersen, R. Ersler, & P. Miller (Eds.), *Progress in behavior modification* (p. 23). New York: Academic Press.

Losel, F. (1998). Treatment and management of psychopaths. In: D. J. Cooke, A. E. Forth, & R. D. Hare (Eds.), *Psychopathy: theory, research, and implications for society* (pp. 105–138). Dordrecht, Netherlands: Kluwer Academic Publishing.

Lykken, D. T. (1957). A study of anxiety in the sociopathic personality. *Journal of Abnormal and Social Psychology, 55*, 6–10.

Lykken, D. T. (1995). *The antisocial personalities*. Hillsdale, NJ: Erlbaum.

Lynam, D. R. (1996). The early identification of chronic offenders: who is the fledgling psychopath? *Psychological Bulletin, 120,* 209–234.

Lynam, D. R. (1997). Pursuing the psychopath: capturing the fledgling psychopath in a nomological net. *Journal of Abnormal Psychology, 106,* 425–438.

*Maas, J. (1966). The use of actional procedures in group psychotherapy with sociopathic women. *International Journal of Group Psychotherapy, 16,* 190–197.

McCord, W., & McCord, J. (1964). *The psychopath: an essay on the criminal mind.* New York: Van Nostrand-Reinhold.

Megargee, E. I., & Golden, R. E. (1973). Parental attitudes of psychopathic and subcultural delinquents. *Criminology, 35,* 427–439.

*Miles, A. E. (1969). The effects of therapeutic community on the interpersonal relationships of a group of psychopaths. *British Journal of Criminology, 9,* 22–38.

Millon, T. (1990). *Toward a new personology: an evolutionary model.* New York: Wiley.

Morretti, M. M., Holland, R., & Peterson, S. (1994). Long term outcome of an attachment-based program for conduct disorder. *Canadian Journal of Psychiatry, 39,* 360–370.

Newman, J. P. (1998). Psychopathic behavior: an information processing perspective. In: R. D. Hare, D. J. Cooke, & A. E. Forth (Eds.), *Psychopathy: theory, research, and implication for society* (pp. 81–104). Dordrecht, Netherlands: Kluwer Academic Publishing.

Newman, J. P., & Kosson, D. S. (1986). Passive avoidance learning in psychopathic and nonpsychopathic offenders. *Journal of Abnormal Psychology, 95,* 252–256.

Newman, J. P., Patterson, C. M., Howland, E. W., & Nichols, S. L. (1990). Passive avoidance in psychopaths: the effects of reward. *Personality and Individual Differences, 11,* 1101–1114.

Newman, J. P., Patterson, C. M., & Kosson, D. S. (1987). Response perseveration in psychopaths. *Journal of Abnormal Psychology, 96,* 145–148.

Newman, J. P., Widom, C. S., & Nathan, S. (1985). Passive–avoidance in syndromes of disinhibition: psychopathy and extraversion. *Journal of Personality and Social Psychology, 48,* 1316–1327.

*Noshpitz, J. D. (1984). Opening phase in the psychotherapy of adolescents with character disorders. *Bulletin of the Menninger Clinic, 21,* 153–164.

*Ogloff, J. R. P., Wong, S., & Greenwood, A. (1990). Treating criminal psychopaths in a therapeutic community program. *Behavioral Sciences and the Law, 8,* 181–190.

*Partridge, G. E. (1928). A study of 50 cases of psychopathic personality. *American Journal of Psychiatry, 7,* 953–973.

Patrick, C. J. (1994). Emotion and psychopathy: startling new insights. *Psychophysiology, 31,* 319–330.

Patterson, G. R., Dishion, T. J., & Chamberlain, P. (1993). Outcomes and methodological issues relating to the treatment of antisocial children. In: T. R. Giles (Ed.), *Effective psychotherapy: a handbook of comparative research* (pp. 43–88). New York: Plenum.

Patterson, G. R., & Yoerger, K. (1993). Developmental models for delinquent behavior. In: S. Hodgins (Ed.), *Mental disorder and crime* (pp. 140–172). London: Sage.

*Persons, R. W. (1965). Psychotherapy with sociopathic offenders: an empirical evaluation. *Journal of Clinical Psychology, 21,* 205–207.

Quay, H. C. (1965). Psychopathic personality as pathological sensation-seeking. *American Journal of Psychiatry, 122,* 180–183.

Quay, H. C. (1977). Psychopathic behavior: reflections on its nature, origins, and treatment. In: I. Uzgiris, & F. Weizmann (Eds.), *The structuring of experience.* New York: Plenum.

Redl, F., & Wineman, D. (1951). *Children who hate.* New York: Free Press.

Redl, F., & Wineman, D. (1952). *Controls from within: techniques for the treatment of the aggressive child.* New York: Free Press.

*Reiss, D., Grubin, D., & Meux, C. (1996). Young "psychopaths" in special hospital: treatment and outcome. *British Journal of Psychiatry, 168,* 99–104.

Rice, M. E. (1997). Violent offender research and implications for the criminal justice system. *American Psychologist, 52,* 414–432.

*Rice, M. E., Harris, G. T., & Cormier, C. A. (1992). An evaluation of a maximum security therapeutic community for psychopaths and other mentally disordered offenders. *Law and Human Behavior, 16,* 399–412.

Robins, L. N. (1978). Etiological implications in childhood histories relating to antisocial personality. In: R. D. Hare, & D. Schalling (Eds.), *Psychopathic behavior: approaches to research* (pp. 255–272).

Rogers, R. (1995). *Diagnostic and structured interviewing: a handbook for psychologists*. Odessa, FL: Psychological Assessment Resources.

Rosenthal, R. (1991). *Meta-analytic procedures for social research* (2nd ed.). Beverly Hills, CA: Sage.

Rotenberg, M. (1975). Psychopathy, insensitivity, and socialization. *Professional Psychology*, 6, 283–292.

Rutter, M., Tizard, J., & Whitmore, K. (1970). *Education, health, and behavior*. London: Longman.

Salekin, R. T., Rogers, R., & Sewell, K. W. (1996). A review and meta-analysis of the Psychopathy Checklist and Psychopathy Checklist — Revised. *Clinical Psychology: Science and Practice*, 3, 203–215.

*Sandhu, H. S. (1970). Therapy with violent psychopaths in an Indian prison community. *International Journal of Offender Therapy*, 14, 138–144.

*Savitt, R. A. (1940). An approach to the problem of psychopathic personality. *Psychiatric Quarterly*, 14, 255–263.

Schmauk, F. J. (1970). Punishment, arousal, and avoidance learning in sociopaths. *Journal of Abnormal Psychology*, 76, 325–335.

*Schmideberg, M. (1947). The treatment of psychopaths and borderline patients. *American Journal of Psychotherapy*, 1, 45–70.

*Schmideberg, M. (1978). The treatment of a juvenile "psychopath". *International Journal of Offender Therapy and Comparative Criminology*, 22, 21–28.

Schuster, R. (1976). Trust: its implication in the etiology and treatment of psychopathic youth. *International Journal of Offender Therapy*, 20, 128–133.

Skolnick, N. J., & Zuckerman, M. (1979). Personality change in drug abusers: a comparison of therapeutic community and prison groups. *Journal of Consulting and Clinical Psychology*, 47, 768–770.

Smith, R. J. (1978). *The psychopath in society*. New York: Academic Press.

Strupp, H. H. (1996). The tripartite model and the consumer reports study. *American Psychologist*, 51, 1017–1024.

*Sturup, G. K. (1948). The management and treatment of psychopaths in a special institution in Denmark. *Proceedings of the Royal Society of Medicine*, 41, 765–768.

Suedfeld, P., & Landon, P. B. (1978). Approaches to treatment. In: R. D. Hare, & D. Schalling (Eds.), *Psychopathic behavior: approaches to research* (pp. 347–378). New York: Wiley.

*Szurek, S. A. (1942). Notes on the genesis of psychopathic personality trends. *Psychiatry*, 5, 1–6.

Templeman, T. L., & Wollersheim, J. P. (1979). A cognitive–behavioral approach to the treatment of psychopathy. *Psychotherapy: Research and Practice*, 16, 132–139.

*Thorne, F. C. (1959). The etiology of sociopathic reactions. *American Journal of Psychotherapy*, 13, 319–330.

Ullman, L. P., & Krasner, L. (1969). *A psychological approach to abnormal behavior*. New York: Prentice-Hall.

*Vaillant, G. E. (1975). Sociopathy as a human process: a viewpoint. *Archives of General Psychiatry*, 32, 178–183.

Vaughan, S. C. (1997). *The talking cure: the science behind psychotherapy*. New York: G.P. Putnam and Sons.

Warren, F. (1994). What do we mean by a "therapeutic community" for offenders? Commentary on papers by Harris et al. and Cullen. *Therapeutic Communities: International Journal of Therapeutic and Supportive Organizations*, 15, 312–318.

Webster-Stratton, C. (1990). A potential disrupter of parent perceptions and family interactions. *Journal of Clinical Child Psychology*, 19, 302–312.

*Whitaker, C. A., & Burdy, J. (1969). Family psychotherapy of a psychopathic personality: must every member change? *Comprehensive Psychiatry*, 10, 361–364.

*Whiteley, J. S. (1970). The response of psychopaths to a therapeutic community. *British Journal of Psychiatry*, 116, 517–529.

Widom, C. S. (1976). Interpersonal conflict and cooperation in psychopaths. *Journal of Abnormal Psychology*, 85, 330–334.

*Woody, G. E., McLellan, A. T., Luborsky, L., & O'Brien, C. P. (1985). Sociopathy and psychotherapy outcome. *Archives of General Psychiatry*, 42, 1081–1086.

Zuckerman, M. (1995). Good and bad humors: biochemical bases of personality and its disorders. *Psychological Science*, 6, 325–332.

28

Preventing Crime by People with Schizophrenic Disorders: The Role of Psychiatric Services

S. HODGINS AND R. MÜLLER-ISBERNER

ABSTRACT

BACKGROUND: *Knowledge of when and how to implement treatments to prevent criminal offending among people with schizophrenia is urgently needed.*

AIMS: *To identify opportunities for interventions to prevent offending among men with schizophrenic disorders by tracking their histories of offending and admissions to hospital.*

METHOD: *We examined 232 men with schizophrenic disorders discharged from forensic and general psychiatric hospitals. Data were collected from participants, family members and official records.*

RESULTS: *More than three-quarters (77.8%) of the forensic patients had previously been admitted to general psychiatric services; 24.3% of the general psychiatric patients had a criminal record. Offences had been committed by 39.8% of the forensic patients and 10.8% of the general psychiatric patients before their first admission to general psychiatry, and after their first admission these 59 patients committed 195 non-violent and 59 violent offences. Subsequently, 49 of them committed serious violent offences that led to forensic hospital admission. The offenders were distinguished by a pervasive and stable pattern of antisocial behaviour evident from at least mid-adolescence.*

CONCLUSIONS: *General psychiatry requires resources in order to prevent criminal offending among a subgroup of patients with schizophrenic disorders.*

Reprinted with permission. British Journal of Psychiatry, 185, *245–250.* © *2004 Royal College of Psychiatrists.*

Investigations of birth and population cohorts have found that people who develop schizophrenia are at increased risk (compared with the general population) of non-violent offending, and are at even higher risk of violent offending (Arseneault et al, 2000; Brennan et al, 2000; Mullen et al, 2000) and of homicide (Erb et al, 2001). The proportion of people who have or who are developing schizophrenia who are convicted of crimes varies by country, and parallels but exceeds the proportions of criminals in the general population (Mullen et al, 2000; Hodgins & Janson, 2002). In order to incorporate interventions designed to reduce offending into mental health services, it is necessary to know when offending begins, when such individuals first contact psychiatric services, and the problems that they present at first contact.

METHOD

Our study compared patients being discharged from forensic psychiatric hospitals in four countries—Canada, Finland, Germany and Sweden—with patients with the same primary diagnosis, gender and age being discharged from general psychiatric services in the same geographic region as the forensic hospitals. Consistent with findings from the epidemiological investigations cited above, almost all of the patients from the forensic hospitals were men and almost all had a principal diagnosis of schizophrenia, schizoaffective disorder or schizophreniform disorder. Consequently, the present study included only those men with these three diagnoses. Three questions were addressed.

(a) Were men with schizophrenia who committed serious violent offences that led to treatment in forensic settings previously in general psychiatric care?

(b) What proportion of men with schizophrenia treated by general psychiatric services have a record of criminality?

(c) Were problems present at the time of admission to general psychiatric care that indicated the need for treatments and services designed to prevent criminality?

Study Procedure

Within each study site, each patient with a diagnosis of a major mental disorder about to be discharged from the forensic hospital was invited to participate in the study. If the patient formally consented to take part, a structured diagnostic interview was completed. If the diagnosis of a major mental disorder was confirmed, the participant was included in the study; the other interviews and assessments were completed and information was collected from patient records and family members. For each forensic patient recruited, a patient from a general psychiatric hospital in the same geographical region of the same gender and age (±5 years) and with the same principal diagnosis was identified and invited to participate. The same information was then collected from both sets of patients. Participants were asked for permission to contact their mother or an older sibling to collect family and childhood histories of them and their families. If the participant agreed, the relative was invited to participate.

Participants

The sample consisted of 158 consecutively discharged male patients with diagnoses of schizophrenia, schizophreniform and schizoaffective disorder who had received inpatient care from the forensic psychiatric hospital in one of the four sites. The study sites were selected because almost all—if not all—people with mental illness who are accused of crimes in these catchment areas are assessed prior to trial and sentenced to psychiatric treatment if the court is convinced that the person has committed the crime (Hodgins *et al*, 2004). Seventy-four men with the same primary diagnosis and age were recruited from general psychiatric hospitals in the same geographical regions as the forensic hospitals. In total 232 patients consented (Canada, *n*=90; Germany, *n*=63; Finland, *n*=57; Sweden, *n*=22), representing, 72.8% of the male forensic patients and 57.8% of the male general psychiatric patients who were invited to participate in the study. All participants gave written informed consent to be interviewed at study entry and on five occasions during the 24 months after discharge, authorised access to medical and criminal records, and named a family member to provide information about them.

Information Collected at Discharge

Information on socio-demographic characteristics, mental disorders, criminality and substance misuse among parents and siblings, and problems and academic performance during childhood and adolescence was collected from the patient, his family, and from his school, medical and social service files. Information about all previous psychiatric treatment was extracted from hospital files. Information on criminality was extracted from official criminal files; crimes included both those that led to convictions and those leading to judgments of non-responsibility due to mental illness or diminished responsibility. Violent crimes were defined as all offences causing physical harm, threats of violence or harassment, all types of sexual aggression, illegal possession of firearms or explosives, all types of forcible confinement, arson and robbery. All other crimes were defined as non-violent.

Primary, secondary and tertiary diagnoses, lifetime and current, were made using the Structured Clinical Interview for DSM–IV (SCID) for both Axis I and Axis II disorders (Spitzer *et al*, 1992). The SCID interview was administered by experienced psychiatrists trained to use this diagnostic interview protocol by those who developed the instrument.

Once all of the information had been collected from files, relatives and participants, the psychiatrist who had administered the SCID and assessed symptoms rated the case using the Psychopathy Checklist—Revised (PCL–R; Hare, 1991). Upon completion of training to use this instrument, psychiatrists were examined by rating English-language videotapes of interviews and case vignettes. The PCL–R includes 20 items, each rated 0, 1 or 2. Factor analyses have indicated that psychopathy is composed of two personality traits and an impulsive and irresponsible lifestyle (Cooke & Michie, 2001). The two personality traits are presumed to emerge early in life and to be stable over time (Blair, 2003). In our study only the score for Deficient Affective Experience was used, our hypothesis being that it is associated with repetitive violence. The Deficient Affective Experience score is the total score for four items: "lack of remorse or guilt," "shallow affect," "callous/lack of empathy" and "failure to accept responsibility for own actions."

RESULTS

History of Prior Treatment in General Psychiatry

Of the 158 patients recruited from the forensic psychiatric hospitals, 123 (77.8%) had been admitted to a general psychiatric service at least once before committing the offence that led to admission to forensic psychiatric care (Figure 1), with a mean of 5.6 admissions (s.d.=6.6). These 123 patients (GP–FP group) did not differ from the 35 patients with no prior admission to general psychiatric care with respect to age (GP–FP group: mean 40.0 years, s.d.=11.6; no prior admission group: mean=38.1 years, s.d.=10.01; $t(156)=-0.902$, $P=0.368$) and the proportion born outside the site country (10.6% v. 17.1%; $\chi^2(1)=1.113$, $P=0.291$).

FIGURE 1

Profile of Study Sample

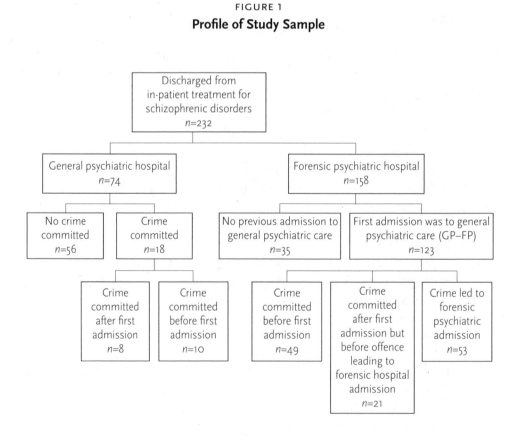

Criminal Records of General Psychiatric Patients

Of the 74 general psychiatric patients, 18 (24%) had a record of at least one criminal offence.

Offending Prior to First General Psychiatric Admission

Ten of the general psychiatric patients (13%) had committed at least one offence before their first admission to general psychiatric care and another 8 (11%) had committed their first offence after their first admission. Among the 123 GP–FP patients, 49 (39.8%) had committed their first offence before their first admission to a general psychiatric ward; 21 (17.1%) had committed their first offence after their first admission to general psychiatric care but before the crime that led to admission to a forensic hospital; and the remaining 53 (43.1%) committed their first criminal offence some time after their first admission to general psychiatry, and the commission of this offence led to admission to a forensic hospital.

Ten general psychiatric patients and 49 GP–FP patients had a record of criminal offending before their first admission to general psychiatric services. We examined their criminal activities during the period when they were in and out of general psychiatric care (for the GP–FP group, we excluded the offence that led to admission to the forensic hospital). After their first admission to general psychiatric care, these 59 patients had committed 195 non-violent and 59 violent offences. In the GP–FP group, 70 patients had committed at least one crime before the offence that led to their admission to a forensic psychiatric hospital. Before committing the crime that led to this admission, these 70 patients had committed 270 non-violent crimes and 75 violent crimes. In addition to the offences counted above, the GP–FP patients committed on average 2.5 violent and 2.7 non-violent offences and those treated only in forensic psychiatric care committed 2.7 violent and 8.1 non-violent offences that gained them admission to a forensic hospital. Twenty-seven of the GP–FP group (22%) and 9 (26%) of the forensic care only group were admitted to forensic hospital following the commission of murder or attempted murder.

Were Problems Present at First General Psychiatric Admission That Indicated Needs for Specific Anti-Crime Interventions?

Table 1 presents comparisons between the group of participants (general psychiatric and GP–FP patients) who had committed crimes before their first admission to general psychiatric services and those with no criminal record. Patients in the former group were, on average, 5 years older at study entry than those with no record of criminal offending, and were also older at first admission. Proportionately more of those who had committed one or more offences before their first admission to general psychiatric care compared with the non-offenders were characterised by behavioural problems during childhood and adolescence, substance misuse before age 18 years, a diagnosis of alcohol abuse or dependence at first admission, and antisocial personality disorder. These characteristics would have been present at the time of first admission. A logistic regression equation was calculated to predict crime v. no crime, including the general psychiatry and GP–FP patients who had committed a crime before first admission to general psychiatry and the non-offenders. The predictors included only characteristics that would have been present and measurable at the time of first admission and that distinguished crime/no crime groups in univariate analyses. Three categorical variables were entered as predictors: antisocial personality disorder, being institutionalized before age 18 years and a diagnosis of alcohol abuse or dependence at first admission. Age at study entry was used as a control variable. A diagnosis of antisocial personality disorder increased the risk of offending 6.05 times (95% CI 1.92–19.04), having been institutionalised before age 18 years increased it 2.89 times (95% CI 1.05–10.84) and a diagnosis of alcohol dependence at first admission, 4.06 times (95% CI 1.52–10.82). Of the 59 patients who had offended before their first admission, 14 (23.7%) were not characterised by any of the four predictors, 19 (32.2%) were characterised by one predictor, 23 (39.0%) by two predictors and 3 (5.1%) by three predictors. The model could not be improved upon to a statistically significant degree by the addition of any further variables and yielded an overall likelihood ratio of 35.38 ($P<0.001$).

Patients who had committed crimes before their first admission to general psychiatric care differed from those with no history of crime at study entry as to their score on the PCL–R for the trait of Deficient Affective Experience (Table 1). It is likely that this trait would have been present at the time of first admission. The data do not permit us to establish the dates when patients first met diagnostic criteria for drug misuse and/or dependence.

Were Problems Present during General Psychiatric In-Patient Treatment That Indicated Needs for Specific Anti-Crime Interventions?

A regression equation similar to that described above was calculated. Included in these analyses were the general psychiatric and GP–FP patients who had a record of criminality beginning after their first admission to general psychiatric care but (for the GP–FP group) before the crime that led to admission to a forensic hospital, and the general psychiatric patients who had committed no crime. The predictors included only characteristics that would have been present and measurable at the time of treatment in general psychiatry and that distinguished crime/no crime groups in univariate analyses at $P=0.25$ or less. Only two factors entered the model. The model could not be improved upon to a statistically significant degree by the addition of any further variables and yielded an overall likelihood ratio statistic of 17.41 ($P=0.001$). Behaviour problems in the community before age 18 years increased the risk of criminality 5.8 times (95% CI 1.79–18.99) and a diagnosis of alcohol abuse or dependence at first admission increased the risk 4.3 times (95% CI 1.27–14.53).

TABLE 1

Comparisons of Men with Schizophrenia Who Had or Had Not Committed a Criminal Offence before First Admission to General Psychiatric Services

	CRIME BEFORE FIRST ADMISSION ($n=59$)	NO CRIME ($n=56$)	
Age at data collection (years): mean (s.d.)	41.2 (11.79)	35.1 (10.62)	$t(1,113)=-2.935$ $P=0.004$
CHARACTERISTICS AT TIME OF FIRST ADMISSION			
Born outside site country, %	8.5	14.3	$\chi^2=0.968$ ($n=115$) $P=0.325$
Age at first hospitalisation (years): mean (s.d.)	27.2 (8.24)	24.0 (7.42)	$t(1,112)=-2.147$ $P=0.034$
Age at onset of prodrome (years): mean (s.d.)	21.4 (5.13)	20.0 (6.14)	$t(1,42)=-0.841$ $P=0.405$
Age at onset of schizophrenia (years): mean (s.d.)	24.7 (7.60)	22.90 (7.09)	$t(1,96)=-1.231$ $P=0.228$
Diagnosis of alcohol abuse/dependence, %	49.2	14.3	$\chi^2=16.005$ ($n=115$) $P<0.001$
PROBLEMS PRESENT BEFORE AGE 18 YEARS			
Behaviour problems at home, %	57.6	28.6	$\chi^2=9.870$ ($n=115$) $P=0.002$
Behaviour problems at school, %	54.2	33.9	$\chi^2=4.801$ ($n=115$) $P=0.030$
Behaviour problems in the community, %	49.2	16.1	$\chi^2=14.211$ ($n=115$) $P<0.001$
Substance misuse, %	60.3	39.3	$\chi^2=5.5054$ ($n=114$) $P=.025$
Institutionalised, %	39.7	17.9	$\chi^2=6.582$ ($n=114$) $P=0.010$
Poor parenting, %	28.8	12.7	$\chi^2=6.881$ ($n=114$) $P=0.032$
Diagnosis of conduct disorder, %	37.3	10.7	$\chi^2=11.015$ ($n=115$) $P=0.001$
CHARACTERISTICS AT STUDY ENTRY			
Antisocial personality disorder, %	39.0	8.9	$\chi^2=14.089$ ($n=115$) $P<0.001$
Drug abuse/ dependence, %	59.3	26.8	$\chi^2=12.376$ ($n=115$) $P<0.001$
Deficient Affective Experience score: mean (s.d.)	4.3 (2.04)	2.63 (2.08)	$t(1,112)=-4.376$ $P<0.001$

DISCUSSION

The study recruited men with schizophrenia, schizophreniform disorder or schizoaffective disorder at discharge from forensic and general psychiatric hospitals in four countries. Seventy-eight per cent of the forensic patients had been admitted to general psychiatric wards before committing the offence that led to their admission to a forensic hospital. Twenty-four per cent of the general psychiatric patients had a record of criminal activity. Although 14% of the general psychiatric patients had committed an offence before their first admission to general psychiatry, 40% of the forensic patients admitted to general psychiatry had done so. The number of offences committed by these men during the period when they were receiving care from general psychiatric services is notable. These findings compel us to develop policies and procedures to identify patients engaging in antisocial and criminal behaviours and to provide them with interventions to prevent such behaviours. The human and financial costs of waiting to intervene until they commit a serious, violent offence are too high to tolerate.

Patients who have committed an offence before their first admission to general psychiatric services can be easily identified, either by asking them about their history of crime in a sympathetic yet challenging manner or by consulting official criminal records. As past criminality is the best predictor of future criminality (Bonta *et al*, 1998), this information should signal a need for additional assessment, and for treatment, supervision and community placements designed to reduce antisocial behaviours. Failing to collect information on prior offending leads to the unacceptable situation described above, in which the complexity of the disorders presented by such individuals is not recognised and the necessary treatments and services are not provided.

Univariate comparisons indicated differences between patients offending before first admission to general psychiatric care and non-offending general psychiatric patients on problems present before age 18 years, alcohol abuse or dependence at first admission, antisocial personality disorder and Deficient Affective Experience score. A multivariate model of factors associated with criminal offending before first admission to general psychiatry services identified predictors that index antisocial behaviour (including substance misuse) that emerges in childhood and escalates in severity culminating in criminal offending. The diagnosis of antisocial personality disorder is given when an individual presents a "pervasive pattern of disregard for and violation of the rights of others occurring since age 15 years" (American Psychiatric Association, 1994) and behaviours present before age 15 years that meet criteria for a diagnosis of conduct disorder as indicated by "repetitive and persistent pattern of behaviour in which the rights of others or major age-appropriate societal norms or rules are violated" (American Psychiatric Association, 1994). Prospective, longitudinal investigations conducted in several different countries have observed that approximately 5% of males display antisocial behaviour from early childhood which escalates in severity with age, until criminal offending begins during adolescence (Moffitt, 1993). Such men commit most of the crimes that are committed (Kratzer & Hodgins, 1999). Even at young ages, the antisocial behaviour is accompanied by personality traits, callousness and insensitivity to others, novelty-seeking and cognitive deficits (Moffitt & Caspi, 2002). These men meet criteria for conduct disorder in childhood and/or adolescence and for antisocial personality disorder in adulthood. For reasons that are currently not understood, both antisocial personality disorder—and by definition conduct disorder—are much more prevalent among men who develop schizophrenia than among men in the general population (Robins *et al*, 1991; Kim-Cohen *et al*, 2003).

At first admission, once the acute symptoms of psychosis have been reduced, assessment of childhood, adolescent and adult patterns of antisocial behaviour, attitudes and the personality traits associated with these patterns of behaviour is indicated. In our study, such an assessment would have demonstrated that patients who had already offended before their first admission presented needs for specific treatments aimed at reducing antisocial behaviours and attitudes, and increasing pro-social skills. Cognitive–behavioural programmes targeting these attitudes and behaviours have been shown to be effective in offenders who are not mentally ill (McGuire, 1995), and are being adapted and tested with offenders with schizophrenia. These patients also require an intervention aimed at ending misuse of alcohol, adapted both to the presence of schizophrenia and to antisocial attitudes and behaviours. Furthermore, once discharged to the community, these patients require more intense supervision to ensure that they take their medications and comply with other forms of treatment. Also, they need to be housed in neighbourhoods where they can neither easily associate with other offenders, nor access drugs and weapons (Silver, 2000).

Most general psychiatric services do not—and could not, at present—provide the kinds of treatments described above. General psychiatric services in most places would not have sufficient staff who are trained to conduct the type of assessments and implement the cognitive–behavioural programmes described, nor to provide the intense supervision required once patients are discharged to the community. Naturalistic follow-up studies indicate that court-ordered community treatment (Heilbrun & Peters, 2000; Swanson *et al*, 2000) and legal powers to admit patients for short periods, involuntarily if necessary, contribute to reducing recidivism and prolonging safe community tenure (Hodgins *et al*, 1999). Such legal powers are useless, however, if in-patient beds are unavailable when needed. Further, general psychiatric services are often geographically based, so that patients are discharged to the neighbourhoods where they lived prior to admission, areas characterised by high rates of crime and drug use and low rates of employment.

The association of a stable pattern of antisocial behaviour with substance misuse is important. Children and adolescents who display conduct problems are exposed to alcohol and drugs earlier than others and an earlier onset of substance misuse is associated with persistence (Armstrong & Costello, 2002). Even among people who do not have schizophrenia, the presence of antisocial personality disorder is associated with failure to benefit from substance misuse treatment (King *et al*, 2001). Thus, intervening as early as possible with programmes specifically adapted to the needs of the patients is imperative. Furthermore, among children at genetic risk of schizophrenia, prospectively collected data indicate that high doses of cannabis in adolescence significantly increase

---

Clinical Implications

- Men experiencing their first episode of schizophrenia or schizoaffective disorder should be assessed for conduct disorder in childhood (prior to age 15 years) and for antisocial personality disorder and substance use disorders.
- Once psychotic symptoms are reduced, patients with a history of antisocial behaviour require cognitive-behavioural interventions aimed at changing antisocial behaviours and the associated attitudes and ways of thinking.
- These men require long-term care in communities that limit access to drugs and offenders and that support newly learned pro-social behaviours, attitudes and ways of thinking.

Limitations

- The forensic sample included only patients who had been discharged.
- Patients with schizophrenia and a childhood history of antisocial behaviour had a higher rate of refusal to participate than did patients with the same primary diagnosis but without a history of antisocial behaviour.
- Information on childhood and adolescence was obtained retrospectively.

---

the risk of developing schizophrenia (Arseneault *et al*, 2004). In addition, evidence suggests that men with schizophrenia sustain damage to specific neural structures from lower amounts of alcohol compared with men with no mental disorder (Mathalon *et al*, 2002). Again, intervening early to reduce substance misuse is indicated.

Using comorbid diagnoses of conduct disorder and antisocial personality disorder is helpful in characterising a subgroup of patients with schizophrenia. These disorders, currently defined, index a stable pattern of antisocial behaviour that emerges early in life and remains stable well into adulthood (Simonoff *et al*, 2004). Men with schizophrenia who have displayed a stable pattern of antisocial behaviour from childhood have been shown to be similar to men with this behaviour pattern who do not develop schizophrenia, with respect to age at first crime and types and frequencies of crimes (Hodgins & Côté, 1993). Although there is little research examining the differences between individuals with conduct disorder who do and who do not develop a schizophrenic disorder, such differences are likely to be important, both for the development of effective treatments for antisocial behaviour and schizophrenia, and for advancing our understanding of aetiological factors. The repeated finding that it is more common for men who develop schizophrenia (compared with those who do not) to display an early-onset, stable pattern of antisocial behaviour suggests that there is a link between the two. This link and its determinants are poorly understood. Most importantly, there is no evidence, to our knowledge, about the response to early intervention programmes designed to reduce conduct problems among children who are at risk of later schizophrenia. If such childhood interventions were effective, they could reduce substance misuse in adolescence and thereby, perhaps, reduce the risk of schizophrenia. If schizophrenia developed, pro-social skills learned in a childhood intervention programme, along with the absence of antisocial behaviour and substance misuse, could have a positive impact on compliance with medication and the course of schizophrenia.

REFERENCES

American Psychiatric Association (1994) *Diagnostic and Statistical Manual of Mental Disorders* (4th edn) (DSM-IV). Washington, DC: APA.

Armstrong, T. & Costello, E. J. (2002) Community studies on adolescent substance use, abuse, or dependence and psychiatric comorbidity. *Journal of Consulting and Clinical Psychology*, 70, 1224–1239.

Arseneault, L., Moffitt, T. E., Caspi, A., et al (2000) Mental disorders and violence in a total birth cohort. *Archives of General Psychiatry*, 5, 979–986.

Arseneault, L., Cannon, M., Witton, J., et al (2004) Causal association between cannabis and psychosis: examination of the evidence. *British Journal of Psychiatry*, 184, 110–117.

Blair, R. J. R. (2003) Neurobiological basis of psychopathy. *British Journal of Psychiatry*, 182, 5–7.

Bonta, J., Law, M. & Hanson, K. (1998) The prediction of criminal and violent recidivism among mentally disordered offenders: a meta-analysis. *Psychological Bulletin*, 123, 123–142.

Brennan, A., Mednick, S. A. & Hodgins, S. (2000) Major mental disorders and criminal violence in a Danish birth cohort. *Archives of General Psychiatry*, 57, 494–500.

Cooke, D. J. & Michie, C. (2001) Refining the construct of psychopathy: towards a hierarchical model. *Psychological Assessment*, 13, 171–188.

Erb, M., Hodgins, S., Freese, R., et al (2001) Homicide and schizophrenia: maybe treatment does have a preventive effect. *Criminal Behaviour and Mental Health*, 11, 6–26.

Hare, R. D. (1991) *The Hare Psychopathy Checklist Revised*. Toronto: Multi-Health Systems.

Heilbrun, K. & Peters, L. (2000) The efficacy and effectiveness of community treatment programmes in preventing crime and violence among those with severe mental illness in the community. In *Violence Among the Mentally Ill: Effective Treatments and Management Strategies* (ed. S. Hodgins), pp. 341–357. Dordrecht: Kluwer.

Hodgins, S. & Côté, G. (1993) The criminality of mentally disordered offenders. *Criminal Justice and Behavior*, 28, 115–129.

Hodgins, S. & Janson, C.-G. (2002) *Criminality and Violence Among the Mentally Disordered: The Stockholm Metropolitan Project*. Cambridge: Cambridge University Press.

Hodgins, S., Lapalme, M. & Toupin, J. (1999) Criminal activities and substance use of patients with major affective disorders and schizophrenia: a two-year follow up. *Journal of Affective Disorders*, 55, 187–202.

Hodgins, S., Tengstrom, A., Ostermann, R., et al (2004) An international comparison of community treatment programs for mentally ill persons who have committed criminal offences. *Criminal Justice and Behavior*, in press.

Kim-Cohen, J., Caspi, A., Moffitt, T. E., et al (2003) Prior juvenile diagnoses in adults with mental disorder. *Archives of General Psychiatry*, 60, 709–714.

King, V. L., Kidorf, M. S., Stoller, K. B., et al (2001) Influence of antisocial personality subtypes on drug abuse treatment response. *Journal of Nervous and Mental Disease*, 189, 593–601.

Kratzer, L. & Hodgins, S. (1999) A typology of offenders: a test of Moffitt's theory among males and females from childhood to age 30. *Criminal Behaviour and Mental Health*, 9, 57–73.

Mathalon, D.H., Pfefferbaum, A., Lim, K.O., et al (2002) Compounded brain volume deficits in schizophrenia-alcoholism comorbidity. *Archives of General Psychiatry*, 60, 245–252.

McGuire, J. (1995) *What Works: Reducing Reoffending—Guidelines from Research and Practice*. Chichester: John Wiley & Sons.

Moffitt, T. E. (1993) Adolescent-limited and life-course persistent antisocial behavior: a developmental taxonomy. *Psychological Review*, 100, 674–701.

Moffitt, T. E. & Caspi, A. (2002) Childhood predictors differentiate life-course persistent and adolescence-limited antisocial pathways among males and females. *Development and Psychopathology*, 13, 355–375.

Mullen, P. E., Burgess, P., Wallace, C., *et al* (2000) Community care and criminal offending in schizophrenia. *Lancet*, 355, 614–617.

Robins, L.N., Tipp, J. & Przybeck, T. (1991) Antisocial personality. In *Psychiatric Disorders in America: The Epidemiologic Catchment Area Study* (eds L.N. Robins & D. Reiger), pp. 258–290. New York: Macmillan/Free Press.

Silver, E. (2000) Race, neighbourhood disadvantage, and violence among persons with mental disorders: the importance of contextual measurement. *Law and Human Behavior*, 24, 449–456.

Simonoff, E., Elander, J., Holmshaw, J., *et al* (2004) Predictors of antisocial personality: continuities from childhood to adult life. *British Journal of Psychiatry*, 184, 118–127.

Spitzer, R. L., Williams, J. B.W., Gibbon, M., *et al* (1992) The structured clinical interview for DSM-III-R (SCID) I: History, rationale, and description. *Archives of General Psychiatry, 49,* 624–629.

Swanson, J.W., Swartz, M. S., Wagner, H. R., *et al* (2000) Involuntary out-patient commitment and reduction of violent behaviour in persons with severe mental illness. *British Journal of Psychiatry*, 176, 324–331.

29

Therapeutic Uses of Security: Mapping Forensic Mental Health Services by Stratifying Risk

H. G. KENNEDY

The syllabus for higher training in forensic psychiatry requires knowledge of the therapeutic uses of security, although there are no references to this in standard texts. Similarly, the process of mapping a mental health service is an essential first step in planning, audit and needs assessment. All mental health services, not just forensic services, are organised to stratify patients according to the risk they present so that they can be cared for in an environment that is safe but imposes the minimum necessary restrictions and intrusions. Forensic mental health services differ from other mental health services mainly by including subsystems which are at higher levels of security than those necessary in local services. Although they have a general orientation towards risk awareness and risk management, they remain integral parts of the mental health services for the populations they serve.

A history of the evolution of secure psychiatric services in the UK is given in the Butler report (Home Office & Department of Health and Social Services, 1975). An international perspective can be found in Bluglass & Bowden (1990). Definitions of secure services often rely on descriptions of services currently available, so that a given level of security is defined, by default, as that which falls between adjacent levels. Attempts are being made to define and validate the characteristics of groups of patients that may require elements of security as part of their care (Cohen & Eastman, 2000), but this is difficult to achieve without relying on current practice for validation in a circular

Reprinted with permission. Advances in Psychiatric Treatment, 8, *433–443.* © *2002 Royal College of Psychiatrists.*

way. Secure settings are found in general and forensic mental health services and in the independent sector. There is a wide variation between services, e.g. in the level of physical security in medium secure units. Published needs assessments all illustrate a considerable degree of inappropriate placement within the overall system, partly reflecting delays in transfer and partly due to the varied pattern of provision across the country.

PRINCIPLES

The Butler (Home Office & Department of Health and Social Services, 1975) and Reed (1992) reports set out principles which are widely acknowledged as the basis for secure psychiatric services. More recently, the King's Fund report, *London's Mental Health* (Johnson *et al*, 1997), contains much to guide the mapping of mental health services in urban settings. A current approach to mapping any mental health service would emphasise the importance of a whole-system approach, with cooperation between agencies ensuring that service boundaries do not operate as barriers to the movement of individuals across levels of security, according to their needs.

Continuity of responsibility is as important as continuity of care and it ensures the safe transition of individuals between levels of security. Services can best be organised so that multi-disciplinary teams have responsibilities across adjacent levels of security, within a given facility or across services.

Facilities should provide individuals with an environment that is least restrictive, safest, homely and local. Decreasing reliance on distant providers should therefore be a priority for service development. The sharing of information between agencies should take account of both public safety and confidentiality, and should occur to the extent that those with responsibility for treatment need to know.

DEFINITIONS

Any mental health service, be it a special hospital or a community mental health team (CMHT), an old age service or a child psychiatry service, can be described according to its environmental, relational and procedural security characteristics (Box 1).

Environmental Security

Measures for environmental or physical security are often installed, at high capital cost, to help manage public confidence. Table 1 summarises the constructional and hardware characteristics of high, medium and low secure units. A useful guide to best practice in the design and construction of medium secure units is given in a publication by the National Health Service Estates Agency (1999). The Royal College of Psychiatrists (1998) has published a set of recommendations regarding the quality and design of new acute adult mental health in-patient units. These emphasise the importance of ensuring that there is a high standard of maintenance and decoration as a tangible sign of

---

BOX 1
Definitions of Security (After Kinsley, 1998)

ENVIRONMENTAL SECURITY
Design and maintenance of estate and fittings
The staff necessary to operate them

RELATIONAL SECURITY
Quantitative: the staff-to-patient ratio and amount of time spent in face-to-face contact
Qualitative: the balance between intrusiveness and openness; trust between patients and professionals

PROCEDURAL SECURITY
Policies and practices for controlling risk:
- At the patient level: systems and routines for the control and checking of patients' movements and communication generally
- At the systems level: arrangements for professional governance, risk management, crisis and contingency planning, formalized reviews and transfer of responsibilities

SPECIALIST MANAGEMENT ARRANGEMENTS
Lines of responsibility:
- Management resources, lines of reporting and responsibility
- Weekly monitoring and benchmarking of admission, transfer and discharge criteria
- Processes for ensuring compliance with legal and policy requirements
- Maintenance of inter-agency relationships and boundaries

---

respect for the patients detained within. There are theoretical grounds for believing that swift action on repairs and maintenance prevents a general increase in vandalism (Wilson & Kelling, 1982). Guides to standards for the physical environment were set out by the Special Hospitals Service Authority (Hinton, 1998). These have been revised with reference only to high-security units (Tilt, 2001).

It is notable that, in general, long-term units require larger grounds within the secure perimeter and perhaps 30% more floor space per patient.

Relational Security

Relational security is nearer to quality of care and is closely linked to resources or recurring (revenue) cost.

Medium-term units typically have high staffing ratios and intensive treatment programmes for all patients (Table 2). There is a tendency for the larger units to have

TABLE 1

Environmental Security

(The features of lower security levels are assumed also
to apply at higher security levels)

SECURITY FEATURE	FORENSIC COMMUNITY SERVICES	OPEN WARDS AND 24-HOUR NURSED CARE	LOW SECURE	MEDIUM SECURE	HIGH SECURE
Perimeter	N/A	N/A	Fenced garden area	Retardant, e.g. 3-m close-mesh fence	Escape-proof, e.g. 6-m wall
Buildings	N/A	Controlled access to building	Doors and windows locked	Escape-proof building	Controlled access to entire site
Observation systems	N/A	Some patient areas unobserved	Designed to allow staff observation and interaction at all times if necessary	CCTV in some areas	CCTV and floodlights in grounds
Alarm systems	Mobile phones	Wall-mounted in some areas	Staff personal alarms Wall-mounted in all areas	Increasing complexity, e.g. staff tracking via electronic keys	All previously listed

lower overall nurse-to-patient ratios, since their pre-discharge wards typically operate at lower levels of relational security. Larger units tend to have higher ratios of psychologists to patients, suggesting better organised specialist treatment programmes. There has been little research on these variations (Royal College of Psychiatrists, 1975). For long-stay units there are usually lower levels of relational security (lower staff-to-patient ratios), although some units compensate for this with higher levels of environmental and procedural security.

Relational security is not solely dependent on staff-to-patient ratios. James *et al* (1990) report more violent incidents on a locked psychiatric intensive-care ward when nursing shifts included higher proportions of agency or bank staff. This suggests that therapeutic rapport is important, even in high-turnover wards where patients are very disturbed. Table 3 shows features distinguishing different types of unit.

Procedural Security

Procedural security is increasingly the subject of governmental directive, mental health legislation and judicial review at national or European level. It includes policies and practices relating to patients which control access, communication, personal finances

TABLE 2

Relational Security (Quantitative): Mean Staff-to-Patient Ratios for Seven National Health Service Medium Secure Units in London

	MEAN	MINIMUM	MAXIMUM
Beds (7 medium secure units)	51.7	23	91
Staff per bed			
Nurses	1.85	1.65	2.3
Beds per staff member			
Occupational therapists	6.25	0.0	3.6
Psychologists	9.1	16.7	4.8
Social workers	11.1	25.0	5.9
Consultants	9.1	14.3	7.7
Specialist registrars	16.7	0.0	10.0
Senior house officers	16.7	25.0	10.0

Source: Dr Sian Rees.

TABLE 3

Relational Security Guidelines (Quantitative)

SECURITY FEATURE	FORENSIC COMMUNITY SERVICES	OPEN WARDS AND 24-HOUR NURSED CARE	LOW SECURE	MEDIUM SECURE	HIGH SECURE
Staff-to-patient ratios	Two key workers Higher ratios for high-risk patients	Variable according to risk Higher in acute units	Lower than in Table 2	As in Table 2 some reductions in long-term units	As in Table 2
Team reviews of risk and treatment plans	2- to 12-week intervals Higher for recent discharges	2- to 12-week intervals according to time since admission	1- to 4-weekly for acute units 12-weekly for long-term units	4-weekly up 18 months 6-weekly after 18 months	As for medium secure
Specialist treatment skills	Family work Social re-integration	Illness awareness Addictions work	Victim awareness Anger management	Specialist cognitive and psychodynamic	All previously listed
Inter-agency work	Local CMHT liaison Benefits agencies Primary care	Housing Social services Home Office/ Department of Justice	Courts Prisons Probation	Host Regional Health Authorities	National agencies and all previously listed
Recreational programmes	Community based	Sheltered workshops	Sports and diversion	Education Occupational rehabilitation	All previously listed

CMHT, community mental health team.

and possessions. Procedural security within a service or an institution also covers policies and practices in relation to quality and governance, including information management, legal obligations, audit, research and human resources. It is summarised in Table 4 by patient-focused policies and practices. Box 1 shows additional management issues.

Specific aspects of procedural security include the management of violent incidents and acute excited states, including de-escalation, breakaway techniques, control and restraint, seclusion and forced medication (Royal College of Psychiatrists, 1995). There has been little systematic study in this area although, from time to time, it receives intense media interest.

TABLE 4

Procedural Security Guidelines

	FORENSIC COMMUNITY SERVICES	OPEN WARDS AND 24-HOUR NURSED CARE	LOW SECURE	MEDIUM SECURE	HIGH SECURE
Visits	No restrictions	Some visitors excluded	Ex-patients often excluded Parcels, bags, etc. searched on entry	Visits only identified list Child visits specially controlled Visits observed	Visits by prior written arrangement Visitors require identification Pat-down searches
Communication	No restrictions	No restrictions	Parcels opened	Communication to specific individuals may be limited or prevented	Letters and telephone calls in and out monitored Legal communications not monitored
Searches	N/A	Searching for weapons and intoxicants in specific cases	Parcels and purchases searched on return from leave	Regular searches of room and property Regular searches of site	Pat-down searches when relevant
Access to money	No restrictions	No restrictions	Patient trades not allowed	Access to cash limited	All financial affairs monitored

Monahan (1993) has outlined a scheme for risk containment to reduce the incidence of violence and establish a standard for best practice. Risk containment includes risk assessment, risk management, documentation, policy and damage control. Powell (1998) describes both the broad and the specific problems dealt with as policy issues in institutions (e.g. the definition of seclusion) and also as management issues around changing institutional culture. Tilt (2000) has recently criticised the prevailing norms for procedural and physical security in high-security hospitals. The Tilt team recommended enhanced physical security to match category B prisons in the UK, including a greater emphasis on procedural security, with increased numbers of dedicated security staff, greater security training and more security audits. The extent to which this will permeate all secure hospital services remains to be seen.

MAPPING SYSTEMS

For mapping purposes, any mental health service can be described as a system made up of subsystems. Forensic services are, therefore, always a subsystem of the mental health service for a given region. Table 5 sets out a matrix which stratifies units (subsystems) according to security, length of stay and population served. This attempts to describe a whole system by including open and community units at local and regional levels. The interdependence of these services can be seen in the apparent inverse relationship between the availability of local low secure beds and demand for regional medium secure beds (O'Grady, 1990; Coid *et al*, 2001a). Every system, and every subsystem within it, can be mapped according to its structures, processes and outcomes (Box 2). This is also a useful approach when drafting operational policies.

Certain groups of patients may require additional specialised services organised at regional or supraregional level, e.g. services for women, adolescents or those with learning disabilities.

RISK STRATIFICATION MAPS

Scott (1977) described dangerousness as a dangerous concept and defined it as the product of probability (or immediacy) of risk and the gravity of the risk. Stratification of patients, by allocating them to appropriate levels of security according to their dangerousness, is essential for the safe and effective deployment of limited resources. The most important element of security is the staffing ratio, which is also the most expensive resource. Appropriate levels of staffing maintain a safe environment. This enables all other elements of treatment to proceed and is itself a key feature of any therapeutic milieu. Patients are acutely aware of the day-to-day safety of their environment. Dangerous patients can be managed economically *in extremis* by confining them to their rooms, but no therapeutic progress will then be achieved. Admission units typically have higher staffing levels than rehabilitation or long-term care units. Similarly, frequency of contact with community care services is usually greater in the months immediately after discharge than in later months.

Research has recently shown that fewer patients are admitted on civil sections to London's forensic services, and also that London has a higher proportion of restriction-order patients than do other regions of England (Coid *et al*, 2001b). At the same time, the numbers admitted to special hospitals are falling year on year (Jamieson *et al*, 2000). It appears that admission thresholds are drifting upwards in a responsive but unplanned manner, determined by availability of resources rather than any more objective criteria. By allowing the threshold for admission to secure services to become a flexible function

TABLE 5

Mapping Whole Systems: Security, Length Of Stay and Population Served

	COMMUNITY	OPEN HOSPITAL	LOW SECURE	MEDIUM SECURE	HIGH SECURE
Short-term, under 6 months	ICM, ACT; crisis house; police station, court and prison liaison and diversion teams	Generic/local mental health unit	Locked generic/local PICU, FICU	Regional medium secure unit	Medium secure unit admission wards, special hospital
Medium-term, 6 months to 3 years	ICM, ACT, CMHT, day hospital, hostel, forensic community teams (integrative model)	Rehabilitation wards	FICU, long-term low secure unit	Medium-term medium secure unit	Special hospital
Long-term	Core and cluster, day centre, sheltered workshop; forensic community teams (parallel)	24-hour nursed care, general or forensic	Long-term low secure unit	Long-term medium secure unit	Special hospital
Population served	Local or district, 30 000–50 000	District, 200 000–400 000	District or regional, 1.5–3.5 million	Regional, 1.5–3.5 million	Regional/national

ICM, intensive case management; ACT, assertive community treatment; CMHT, community mental health team; PICU, psychiatric intensive care unit; FICU, forensic intensive care unit.

of demand and available resources, an equitable service for all dangerous patients can be provided for a given region. However, thresholds can then become inconsistent between regions and they are disconnected from any guideline level of clinical risk or outcome measure.

Patients should be detained at no greater level of security than is necessary. This principle can be seen in the organisation of secure psychiatric services according to stratified risk. A secure environment must, within the limits of mental health legislation, restrict freedom of movement, access and communication, and it tends to intrude into areas that are normally kept private. Imposing a treatment plan on a patient who is incompetent to give or withhold consent can be justified ethically if, by so doing, the patient can receive services which restore him or her to mental health and, with it, to autonomy, responsibility and increased freedom (Eastman, 1997). The current level of detention should therefore be regularly reviewed under a clearly recorded risk assessment and clinical risk management plan (a treatment plan). This should be explicit about the treatments required and the markers for progress towards transfer to a lower level of security.

BOX 2

Mapping Models

STRUCTURES

Stratified according to the risk currently presented by the patient; length of stay; pathways through care; specialised or generic

PROCESSES

Ascertainment (e.g. screening services or referral routes); assessment; treatment; rehabilitation; continuing care (or transfer or discharge) (see also procedural security)

OUTCOMES

Hard outcomes:
- suicide and unnatural death
- homicide and violence to others
- (time to) full remission of symptoms
- period relapse-free, and continued contact with services when outside hospital

Soft outcomes:
- patient's and relatives' satisfaction
- public confidence
- economic (cost)-effectiveness measures

Risk Assessment in a Stratified System

From a clinical point of view, all decisions to admit, transfer to a lower level of security or discharge can be reduced to a single triage process in which the patient is matched to the appropriate level of available security. In the real world, risk assessment is never separate from risk management; there are only varieties of triage decisions. From a statistical point of view, having a high threshold for admission enables subsequent clinical risk assessment and risk management to be more accurate, with fewer false positives, both by increasing the average risk within the selected patient group and by reducing the amount of variation in the patient population.

Recorded crimes of violence are much more common than homicide, by a factor of at least 200 for the general population (Kennedy *et al*, 1999), and the real rate of violence in the community is even greater. Violence should, therefore, be easier to predict than homicide or suicide, with extra services being targeted at about 11% of patients with severe mental illness (Kennedy, 2001).

It is wrong to assume that all groups of psychiatric patients are actually at the average level of risk for such patients on a national basis. The prevailing rate of violence in the community by patients with schizophrenia is already modified by risk stratification in mental health services. Snowden *et al* (1999) points out that three-quarters of patients under a restriction order are in hospital at any one time. Even for populations of patients defined by local sectors, most of those at the highest risk will be in hospital owing to acute relapses. For inner-city populations where violent crime is more common (Kennedy *et al*, 1999), a higher proportion will be in secure forensic units (Glover *et al*, 1999). In community forensic populations, the average risk of grade 1 or grade 2 violence (Table 6) is higher than for patients in general psychiatric community services. For a test with a given sensitivity, the predictive value of the instrument improves as the prevalence of the disorder in the test population increases (Goldstein & Simpson, 1995). Stratification of risk, therefore, favours more accurate prediction of risk of serious harm in both forensic and general patient populations, by raising the average risk of serious harm in the forensic population while at the same time reducing the average risk of serious harm in the general psychiatric population.

Risk is also stratified in time. The risk of suicide is greatest in the year after discharge from hospital, and is of the order of 1 per 100 patient-years (Geddes *et al*, 1997). The risk of violence is also highest in the months immediately after discharge from hospital (Steadman *et al*, 1998). This natural stratification of risk should enable more accurate risk assessments to be made for the period immediately after leaving hospital because of the higher average risk during that period. More intensive contact with mental health services (relational and procedural security) might be expected to manage the risk within the bounds of what is possible or predictable. The importance of early review after discharge from hospital has been emphasised (Appleby, 1997; Royal College of Psychiatrists, 2000), as 40% of postdischarge suicides occur before the first follow-up appointment.

Just as it is wrong to assume that all patient populations are at the national average for a given risk, it is wrong to assume that the average risk in any patient group is made up from a wide range of risk. Within forensic services, the aim is to stratify patients so as to narrow the range of individual risk within each group. This allows the levels of therapeutic security to be matched to the current need, determining the pace of progress through treatment settings, from admission to rehabilitation to community placement. Forensic patients are selected for discharge (see Table 7) when they are stable, predictable and willing to tolerate a degree of intrusion and control by clinicians in the community. Those in the community should also be stratified according to risk. This stratification across treated groups tends to increase variation and improves the reliability of predictive measures (Shrout, 1995). For all psychiatric facilities, length of stay may be a function of the match between need and resources and this can appear to influence risk management. For example, a disproportionate number of suicides within 3 months of hospital discharge were found to have had final admissions lasting 7 days or less (Appleby, 1997). Geddes *et al* (1997) have drawn attention to the apparent link between a rise in early post-discharge suicides and the fall in the number of hospital beds.

An important caveat regarding risk prediction concerns the assumption that all local populations from which patients are drawn are at the same average risk as the

TABLE 6

Violence at Presentation as a Guide to Security Needed at the Time of Admission
(NB: This should never be taken in isolation from the other factors listed in Table 8)

GRAVENESS OF VIOLENCE	BEHAVIOUR
High (grade 1)	Homicide
	Stabbing penetrates body cavity
	Fractures skull
	Strangulation
	Serial penetrative sexual assaults
	Kidnap, torture, poisoning
Medium (grade 2)	Use of weapons to injure
	Arson
	Causes concussion or fractures long bones
	Sexual assaults
	Stalking with threats to kill
Low (grade 3)	Repetitive assaults causing bruising
	Self-harm or attempted suicide that cannot be prevented by two-to-one nursing in open conditions

total population. This is not true. In inner-city boroughs, the population risk of homicide, suicide or recorded crimes of violence increases exponentially with population density or deprivation (Kennedy *et al*, 1999). This variable background of environmental risk probably makes the risk of adverse outcomes such as violence, homicide or suicide worse for a given patient and probably limits the clinician's capacity to make anything more than short-term predictions when the environmental risk is high.

This long-standing structural risk management at the systems level may have been lost in modern sectorised CMHTs and small generic in-patient units. If general psychiatrists manage mixed populations of patients, most of whom are at a 1 in 10 000 per year risk of committing homicide, as Szmukler (2000) suggests, they may be unaware that a few of their patients are at a much higher risk. Even with little regard for risk management, most psychiatrists responsible for catchment populations of 30 000 to 50 000 would seldom experience adverse outcomes and they may be unaware of the risks they run in some cases. It follows that the mixing of all patients from a catchment area in small-sector generic services is bad risk management at the systems level. The commissioning of services at local or primary care level is similarly flawed. If plans are made for a population that is too small, the need to stratify some patients to specialised care for the higher, less common levels of risk will rarely arise and will never be anticipated. This can make risk assessment less accurate and risk management too diffused. These forms of functional risk-blindness are likely to be particularly hazardous in high-risk inner-city boroughs. A greater emphasis is needed on systems defences to harness human variability and to avert or mitigate the effects of errors and adverse outcomes (Reason, 2000).

TABLE 7

Signs of Diminished Need for Security

MOVE	HIGH TO MEDIUM SECURE	MEDIUM TO LOW SECURE	TO COMMUNITY OR OPEN PLACEMENTS
Stability	Two years' stability Relapses may be abrupt, over days	One year's stability Relapses may be abrupt, over days	Relapses occur over weeks and are predictable
Insight	Accepts legal obligations to take treatment as a minimum	Accepts treatment and legal obligations Is encouraged to do so by closest friends or family	Realistic appraisal of risk of relapse Practical approach to relapse prevention Family and friends, if involved, are aware and supportive
Rapport	Tolerates daily intrusions and constrictions of hospital life Participates in treatment and occupational programmes	Capable of openness and trust with members of multi-disciplinary team Capable of limited exploration of current mental state as related to risk	Open and trusting with all members of multi-disciplinary team Capable of communicating matters relevant to risk Tolerates intrusion and restricted autonomy of treatment plan Not excessively dependent on others
Leave	None necessary Visits prior to trial leave as usual	Can use escorted leave in hospital grounds most of the time and escorted community leave sometimes	Capable of using unescorted leave in the community for over 6 months

PATIENT CHARACTERISTICS

All patients in secure psychiatric services are likely to share certain characteristics. There is an inherent problem of circularity in seeking to define the patient characteristics appropriate for a type of secure unit or define the level of security by describing those currently in such units, when to operate according to a strictly theoretical model creates a system that can never be tested by experiment. Audit cycles for whole clinical services to a defined population (whole systems) offer the possibility of the evolution of pragmatic criteria over time.

Gunn & Robertson (1976) published a system for profiling patients according to their criminal history. Shaw *et al* (1994) published a description of the clinical characteristics of patients in high-security situations and related these to placement needs. Many similar studies have followed. Coid & Kahtan (2000) have published a 4-point scale for describing patients according to severity of offence and levels of security on admission. The scale takes into account the patient's status within the criminal justice system, specifically for England and Wales. Cohen and Eastman (2000) offer

TABLE 8

Dangerousness as a guide to security needed on admission

(Specialist forensic need is not necessarily correlated with dangerousness)

ADMISSION GUIDELINES	FORENSIC COMMUNITY SERVICES	OPEN WARDS AND 24-HOUR NURSED CARE	LOW SECURE	MEDIUM SECURE	HIGH SECURE
Violence (grades refer to Table 6)	No recent violence	Self-harm Lesser degrees of violence	Grade 3 Public order/ nuisance offending	Grade 2	Grade 1
Immediacy	Does not need daily monitoring	Confides in staff	Acute illness or crisis likely to resolve in 3–6 months	Relapses abrupt Unpredictable	Unpredictable Inaccessible to staff
Specialist forensic need	Self-medicates Previous admissions to medium or high secure units Reintegrating with local services	Cannot cooperate with voluntary treatment Compliant when formally detained	Recall or crisis of former medium-/high-security patient Current mental state associated with violence	Arson Jealousy Resentful stalking Exceeds low secure capacity	Sadistic Paraphilias associated with violence Exceeds medium security
Absconding	Will not break off contact	If absconded, would not present an immediate danger	Impulsive absconding	Pre-sentence serious charge Other obvious motivation to abscond	Can coordinate outside help Past absconding from medium or high security
Public confidence issues	No local victim sensitivities No high-risk relationships	No local notoriety	Short-term family sensitivities	Predictable potential victims Local notoriety	National notoriety

theoretical headings under which working admission criteria can be developed for research purposes.

Tables 6 and 8 summarise relevant guidelines for admission. They are derived from the panel rating process for 122 patients detained in high and medium secure units described by Pierzchniak *et al* (1999). It is not proposed here that Grade 1 violence alone automatically equates to need for high security, since other factors are also relevant. As outlined above, there is likely to be considerable variation between institutions and catchment areas which has more to do with local morbidity and resource allocation than any theoretical construct.

Guidelines for moving a patient to lower levels of security and eventually to community care are much more difficult to operationalise. It cannot be presumed that all patients will automatically progress within defined periods of time. Nor does the time spent at a given level of security without gross disturbance automatically indicate that the patient could be safely managed in a less secure place. Reasonable clinical criteria include evidence that dispositional, situational and mental illness factors relevant to the risk of violent behaviour are understood and are reduced by treatment, and that changes indicating risk could be monitored and managed at a lower level of security. This requires evidence that the patient is capable of engaging honestly in a positive therapeutic rapport with clinicians over sustained periods, that they tolerate intrusive clinicians and are open with them, that they accept some loss of autonomy in relation to treatment and the care plan generally, and that the patient's friends and family can be fully engaged with the clinical team in future monitoring and treatment. Local and victim issues must also be taken into account and they can result in longer detention at higher levels of security than might strictly be necessary to manage risk. Table 7 summarises these considerations, again based on the panel ratings and discussions described in Pierzchniak *et al* (1999).

Continuity of Responsibility

Moving a patient to a new placement or new clinical team is, in itself, likely to increase risk. Recommendations for taking such therapeutic risks are more credible if they are made by the clinicians who will take responsibility for the risk. Clinicians are sensitive to this and the decision to move the patient is more likely to be implemented quickly and successfully if the recommendation is made under these conditions. Failure to observe this ethical continuity often gives rise to conflict and undermines therapeutic relationships (e.g. R *v*. Mental Health Review Tribunal and Others ex parte Hall, 1999).

It is better to stagger the change in placement and clinicians. For this to happen, clinical teams should have responsibility for places at more than one level of security. The new team of clinicians can then establish rapport and trust with the patient before a further move is made down the ladder of security.

COMMUNITY FORENSIC SERVICES

The processes required by a comprehensive forensic mental health service include ascertainment and continuing care, which are the pathways into and out of secure forensic mental health services (Box 2).

Ascertainment Services

Forensic mental health services typically provide psychiatric sessions to remand and dispersal prisons. The very large numbers of young men passing through the reception at remand prisons present a unique opportunity for health interventions in a high-risk group. Mental health needs are only a part of the problem, but the principal task should be to find those at increased risk of suicide and take appropriate action to reduce this risk (Birmingham *et al*, 1996), to identify those with severe mental illness and divert them to hospital and to provide rehabilitation services for those with addictions. These tasks are likely to overlap extensively. Since the greatest rise in suicides is among young men in inner cities and the very large remand population is predominantly drawn from these areas, it is likely that the remand prison reception centre is a common point of contact for many eventual suicides who will make no other contact with mental health services.

The growth of psychiatric diversion teams in magistrates' courts has been described in detail by James (1999). These teams can be shown to greatly reduce the time taken to divert mentally disordered offenders to hospital, particularly when there is close liaison or overlap with the remand prison psychiatrists (Pierzchniak *et al*, 1997). It can be argued that the numbers of patients recently discharged from mental health services re-presenting via court diversion schemes, expressed as a rate per 1000 discharges from local mental health services, could be used as a measure of the success or failure of community mental health policies and services (Purchase *et al*, 1996).

The extension of liaison and diversion services into police stations, typically by providing specialist community psychiatric nurses, can be shown to further enhance diversion of mentally disordered offenders to psychiatric services while also offering advice on services to those with addictions. These services supplement the work of the forensic medical examiner in the police station. The initiation of Mental Health Act assessments in police stations rather than in hospital-designated places of safety remains a problem. This probably arises, in part, from a lack of resources to staff such hospital units safely, and perhaps also from neglect of patients stigmatised by their presentation through the criminal justice system.

Continuing Care

Gunn (1977) distinguished between integrated and parallel forensic follow-up services for those discharged from secure hospitals. More recently, Snowden *et al* (1999) have described a hybrid model, in which all those leaving medium or high secure beds are followed in the community by forensic community teams with low case-loads (high relational security) and an assertive community treatment approach. Once the patient has been settled and stable in a long-term community place for 6 to 12 months, a planned and phased transfer of care to the local mental health team is completed.

CONCLUSIONS

All mental health services maintain a safe and effective process of treatment and rehabilitation through the stratification of patients according to the risks they present. Awareness of the therapeutic importance of environmental, relational and procedural security is valuable in drafting safe treatment plans for patients and in the organization and management of all mental health services. Relational security is by far the most important element in the maintenance of therapeutic progress of patients. Psychiatrists should be aware of the management, funding and policy issues relevant to maintaining this most essential part of the mental health services that we provide.

The definitions of levels of security given here are simplified guidelines only, but have been of benefit in planning and organising a catchment area service and in choosing appropriate placements for patients when these had to be out of area. The definitions and categories are also of some assistance in organizing the operational policies for secure and other mental health units and broad services, particularly in relation to the resources required for risk management. The guidelines for transfer of patients from one level of security to another should also be taken to be flexible and for implementation only by experienced clinicians who can make an assessment of the individual patient. However, it is increasingly necessary to be able to communicate the form and content of such assessments as the basis of a clinical opinion when reporting to mental health tribunals, the Home Office and similar scrutinising authorities.

REFERENCES

Appleby, L. (1997) *National Confidential Inquiry into Suicide and Homicide by People with Mental illness: Progress Report 1997.* London: Department of Health.

Birmingham, L., Mason, D. & Grubin, D. (1996) Prevalence of mental disorder in remand prisoners: consecutive case study. *BMJ, 313,* 1521–1524.

Bluglass, R. & Bowden, P. (eds) (1990) *Principles and Practice of Forensic Psychiatry.* London: Churchill Livingston.

Cohen, A. & Eastman, N. (2000) *Assessing Forensic Mental Health Need: Policy, Theory and Research.* London: Gaskell.

Coid, J. & Kahtan, N. (2000) An instrument to measure the security needs of patients in medium security. *Journal of Forensic Psychiatry, 11,* 119–134.

——, ——, Cook, A., *et al* (2001a) Predicting admission rates to secure forensic psychiatry services. *Psychological Medicine, 31,* 531–539.

——, ——, Gault, S., et al (2001b) Medium secure forensic psychiatry services: comparison of seven English health regions. *British Journal of Psychiatry, 178,* 55–61.

Eastman, N. (1997) The Mental Health (Patients in the Community) Act 1995. A clinical analysis. *British Journal of Psychiatry, 170,* 492–496.

Geddes, J. R., Juszcak, E., O'Brien, F., et al (1997) Suicide in the 12 months after discharge from psychiatric inpatient care, Scotland 1968–92. *Journal of Epidemiology and Community Health, 51,* 430–434.

Glover, G. R., Leese, M. & McCrone, P. (1999) More severe mental illness is more concentrated in deprived areas. *British Journal of Psychiatry, 175,* 544–548.

Goldstein, J. M. & Simpson, J. C. (1995) Validity: definitions and applications to psychiatric research. In *Textbook in Psychiatric Epidemiology* (eds M. T. Tsuang, M. Tohen & G. E. P. Zahner), pp. 233–236. New York: Wiley-Liss.

Gunn, J. (1977) Management of the mentally abnormal offender: integrated or parallel. *Proceedings of the Royal Society of Medicine, 70,* 887–890.

—— & Robertson, G. (1976) Drawing a criminal profile. British Journal of Criminology, 16, 156–160.

Hinton, R. (1998) The physical environment. *In Managing High Security Psychiatric Care* (eds C. Kaye & A. Franey). London: Jessica Kingsley

Home Office & Department of Health and Social Services (1975) *Report of the Committee on Mentally Abnormal Offenders* (Butler Report). London: HMSO.

James, D. V. (1999) Court diversion at 10 years: can it work, does it work and has it a future? *Journal of Forensic Psychiatry, 10,* 507–524.

——, Finberg, N. A., Shah, A. K., et al (1990) An increase in violence on an acute psychiatric ward. A study of associated factors. *British Journal of Psychiatry, 156,* 846–852.

Jamieson, E., Butwell, M., Taylor, P., et al (2000) Trends in special (high-security) hospitals. 1: Referrals and admissions. *British Journal of Psychiatry, 176,* 253–259.

Johnson, S., Ramsey, R., Thornicroft, G., et al (1997) *London's Mental Health: The Report to the King's Fund London Commission.* London: King's Fund.

Kennedy, H. (2001) Risk assessment is inseparable from risk management. Comment on Szmuckler. *Psychiatric Bulletin, 25,* 208–211.

——, Iveson, R. C. & Hill, O. (1999) Violence, homicide and suicide: strong correlation and wide variation across districts. *British Journal of Psychiatry, 175,* 462–466.

Kinsley, J. (1998) Security and therapy. In *Managing High Security Psychiatric Care* (eds C. Kaye & A. Franey). London: Jessica Kingsley.

Monahan, J. (1993) Limiting therapist exposure to Tarasoff liability: guidelines for risk containment. *American Psychologist, 48,* 242–250.

National Health Service Estates (1999) *Design Guide: Medium Secure Psychiatric Units.* Leeds: NHS Estates.

O'Grady, J. (1990) The complementary role of regional and local secure provision for psychiatric patients. *Health Trends, 22,* 14–16.

Pierzchniak, P., Purchase, N. & Kennedy, H. G. (1997) Liaison between court, prison and psychiatric services. *Health Trends, 29,* 26–29.

——, Farnham, F., DeTaranto, N., *et al* (1999) Assessing the needs of patients in secure settings: a multidisciplinary approach. *Journal of Forensic Psychiatry, 23,* 343–354.

Powell, F. (1998) Freedom from restraint. In *Managing High Security Psychiatric Care* (eds C. Kaye & A. Franey). London: Jessica Kingsley.

Purchase, N. D., McCallum, A. K. & Kennedy, H. G. (1996) Evaluation of a psychiatric court liaison scheme in north London. *BMJ, 313,* 531–532.

Reason, J. (2000) Human error: models and management. *BMJ, 320,* 768–770.

Reed, J. (1992) *Review of Health and Social Services for Mentally Disordered Offenders and Others Requiring Similar Services: Final Summary Report* (Cm 2088). London: Stationery Office.

Royal College of Psychiatrists (1975) 'Norms' for medical staffing of a forensic psychiatry service within the National Health Service in England and Wales. *British Journal of Psychiatry News and Notes,* June, pp. 5–10.

—— (1995) *Strategies for the Management of Disturbed and Violent Patients in Psychiatric Units (Council Report CR41).* London: Royal College of Psychiatrists.

—— (1998) *'Not Just Bricks and Mortar': Report of the Royal College of Psychiatrists Working Group on the Size, Staffing, Structure, Siting and Security of New Acute Adult Psychiatric In-patient Units (Council Report CR62).* London: Royal College of Psychiatrists.

—— (2000) *Good Medical Practice in the Psychiatric Care of Potentially Violent Patients in the Community (Council Report, CR80).* London: Royal College of Psychiatrists.

Scott, P. D. (1977) Assessing dangerousness in criminals. *British Journal of Psychiatry, 131,* 127–142.

Shaw, J., McKenna, J., Snowden, P., et al (1994) Clinical features and placement needs of all North West Region patients currently in Special Hospital. *Journal of Forensic Psychiatry, 5,* 93–106.

Shrout, P. E. (1995) Reliability. In *Textbook in Psychiatric Epidemiology* (eds M. T. Tsuang, M. Tohen & G. E. P. Zahner), pp. 213–227. New York: Wiley-Liss.

Snowden, P., McKenna, J. & Jasper, A. (1999) Management of conditionally discharged patients and others who present similar risks in the community: integrated or parallel? *Journal of Forensic Psychiatry, 10,* 583–596.

Steadman, H. J., Mulvey, E., Monahan, J., et al (1998) Violence by people discharged from acute psychiatric inpatient facilities and by others in the same neighbourhoods. *Archives of General Psychiatry, 55,* 393–401.

Szmukler, G. (2000) Homicide inquiries: What sense do they make? *Psychiatric Bulletin, 24,* 6–10.

Tilt, R. (2000) *Report of the Review of Security at the High Security Hospitals.* London: Department of Health.

Wilson, J. Q. & Kelling, G. (1982) Broken windows. *Atlantic Monthly,* March, 29–38.

R v. Mental Health Review Tribunal and Others ex parte Hall [1999] 4 *AllER* 883.

30

The Security Needs
Assessment Profile:
A Multidimensional Approach to
Measuring Security Needs

MICHAEL COLLINS AND STEFFAN DAVIES

ABSTRACT: *Although levels of security in UK forensic psychiatric services are generally accepted as being divided into high, medium and low security there are few detailed descriptors beyond those of high security. The lack of clear definitions of security poses problems for researchers, clinicians and patients. Developments in forensic care increasingly demand that patients should receive care under conditions of security that are no greater than necessary to manage the risks they present. This is not a simple proposition; a number of complex areas have to be addressed by clinicians when defining a patient's individual needs for security. In an attempt to provide a more comprehensive description of patients' security needs the authors developed the Security Needs Assessment Profile (S.N.A.P). This instrument builds on the three traditional dimensions of security: physical, procedural and relational. Each dimension is sub-divided into a number of items, 22 overall. Each item was described on a four-point scale, each point being carefully defined to provide reference points for users. This article briefly outlines the background, instrument development, instrument structure, sample and results. Initial results indicate that the instrument can distinguish between patients who require different levels of security. An emerging component structure is also described. A preliminary version of the instrument is described for use in forensic settings.*

Reprinted with permission. International Journal of Forensic Mental Health, 4 *(1), 39–52.* © 2005 *International Association of Forensic Mental Health Services.*

Forensic psychiatric patients are treated under differing levels of security, yet definitions of security are often simplistic and do not reflect the complexity of differing needs associated with different risk behaviors. Secure services in the UK are traditionally categorized as high, medium and low yet there are no widely accepted definitions outside of high security making such distinctions, at times, difficult to quantify. Kennedy (2002) describes "a wide variation between services, e.g. in the level of physical security in medium secure units" (p. 433). This is changing in some areas; the security provided by the UK High Secure Hospitals has been standardized following a recent review of security (Tilt Report, 2000). There has been some critical debate regarding the focus of this report on physical and procedural security (e.g., Exworthy & Gunn, 2003). Low security environments may become more standardized by complying with recent guidelines for "National Minimum Standards for General Adult Services in Psychiatric Intensive Care Units (PICU) and Low Secure Environments" (Department of Health 2002). Our clinical experience suggests wide variation between services. One example is varying fence height across services that provide medium security despite the design guidance issued by NHS Estates (Department of Health, 1993). These guidelines included recommendations for perimeter fence height, structure, and a range of environmental features.

Other security elements (e.g., staffing levels) and procedural and relational measures may enable a service to provide "medium" security without over reliance on a perimeter fence of a particular height being the most important factor in the designation of security level. In some countries, the United States being one, fence height may have little to do with security designation; in the UK, it tends to reflect the degree of internal restriction faced by patients. The lack of any widely accepted definitions of security provision or ability to measure security in any fine-grained, reliable way is a barrier to the clinical desire to provide a more needs led service.

In the UK, there is a history of patients being detained under conditions of security greater than is necessary, in particular in high security. A number of studies have highlighted these problems (Bartlett, Cohen, Backhouse, Highet, & Eastman, 1996; Maden, Curle, Meux, Burrow, & Gunn, 1993; Murray, Rudge, Lack, & Dolan, 1994; Pierzchniak et al., 1999; Shaw et al., 1994; Taylor, Butwell, Dacey, & Kaye, 1991). A feature of such studies is varying estimates of the numbers of patients who are inappropriately detained. This may be due to differing methodologies, regional variations and changes in patient characteristics over time. Certainly recent years have seen reductions in patient numbers detained in high security as a response to such studies and government policy. Abbot (2002) describes how reductions in the number of patients in the high-security hospitals over the last 10 years is a result of "creaming off" whereby the least complex cases are discharged first. The implication is that the high security hospitals will be left with smaller numbers of more complex and higher risk patients. Sayal and Maden (2002) describe how previous estimates of levels of inappropriate detention may now be outdated, and question discrepancies between views of the team treating the patient within high security and the team who would care for them in a lower secure setting. Such discrepancies can exist for many reasons, and the authors hope that the use of the instrument described in this paper may help resolve such differences.

UK National policy has striven towards the detention of patients under conditions of security commensurate with the risk that they present. This was emphasized in the Reed Report (1994), the NHS National Service Framework (NSF) for Mental Health (Department of Health, 1999) and the Tilt Report (2000). More recently Part II of the White Paper Reforming the Mental Health Act 1983 (Department of Health and Home Office, 2000) states: "Where individuals are detained as a result of their mental disorder, they must be held in a therapeutic environment which is designed to address their needs effectively. This is not just a matter of new places, important though that is, but also properly trained staff, new approaches to assessment and treatment, and a rigorous program of research and evaluation" (paragraph 6.23). The Mental Health (Care and Treatment) (Scotland) Act (2003) goes further and gives patients a right to appeal to be transferred to conditions of lower security. There is evidence of an emerging rigorous research program, but we argue that more studies must focus on the fine-grained definition and measurement of security need in terms of new approaches to assessment.

Defining Security

In the UK, members of direct care staff usually provide and administer security, as well as manage individualized modes of treatment (although members of qualified nursing staff are usually responsible for more complex security decisions). The complexity of this task, particularly in regards to high security levels, is easily underestimated. Parker (1985) identified four factors of security: physical security, quality of nursing care, the control of patients, and patient motivation. The 1990s saw some of the first extended policy definitions of security from Kinsley (1992) who described how a combination of good basic physical security and related systems should provide the opportunity for a relatively relaxed regime within these boundaries. Furthermore, efficient security measures should improve treatment and provide a safe environment within which patients can progress. This reference to related systems can be considered as dynamic elements and these are described further under the headings of procedural and relational security that follow. Later literature expanded these concepts describing security and therapy as not mutually exclusive but complimentary factors (Kinsley, 1998). These developments should be considered in light of not only the growing body of evidence that there were a large number of patients detained in inappropriately high levels of security, but also in the context of an attempt to challenge the sometimes misplaced image of security being provided without reference to any therapeutic factors. Security is currently considered as having a theoretical separation into three domains:

Physical. The most obvious aspect of security is the physical elements. These can include: perimeter fences of particular height and style of construction, electronic intrusion alarms, locks (including electronic locking mechanisms), doors and CCTV cameras.

Procedural. This domain covers the variety of procedures that take place within the physical elements to maintain security integrity. Examples include the restriction of certain items within a unit, the searching of patients and the environment, frequency of patient observation, staff to patient ratio and supervision/restriction of visitors.

Relational. This domain is more complex, but in general refers to a detailed understanding of those receiving secure care and how to manage them. For example, a competent forensic nurse will have an extensive knowledge of a patient. This will include potential risk behaviors and a relationship with the patient that includes an open acknowledgement of the potential for dangerous behavior. This level of knowledge allows the practitioner to constantly assess behaviors, patterns of behavior and changes in mental state that have a direct relationship to any immediate or potentially dangerous behavior or similarity to offending patterns. This level of knowledge can enable care to be delivered in an environment where levels of restriction and supervision can be varied according to the needs of the patient while maintaining the protection of others.

The combination of these three domains is sometimes termed as therapeutic security, whereby therapeutic interventions take place within the domains and that these are tailored as far as is practical to the individual patient need. Therefore, while any separation may be regarded as artificial because good secure care will involve a combination of all three domains, it is useful to make theoretical distinctions to aid assessment.

The Measurement of Security Need

Traditional concepts of security either make the error of restricting themselves to descriptions of physical elements, such as perimeter fences, doors and locks, or use ill defined terms such as low, medium and high, making the assumption that these are descriptive enough in their own right. Over a decade ago the Reed Report (1994) called for "a patient focused definition of what high security connotes" (p. 21); a recommendation that is equally relevant to other levels of security.

The measurement or assessment of security need is complex. Maden et al. (1993) described the ill definition of the boundary between medium and maximum security and how the security needs of most patients had more of a relationship with nursing care and the internal hospital environment, as opposed to the perimeter fence. If we ask the question "what do we mean when we say a patient requires high security?" once we get past basic considerations like the height of the fence and other physical elements, other factors become far more difficult to quantify. These other factors are numerous; Taylor, Maden, and Jones (1996) outline some further aspects to be considered when assessing security need including physical and detailed staffing issues as well as perimeter and internal hospital security. They reasoned that distinctions between high security and purpose designed medium secure units were diminishing. While this may have been the case, a recent review of high secure services in the UK has created more standardization and heightened physical and procedural security measures (Tilt Report, 2000). The ability to measure subtle differences, particularly within procedural and relational security, offer greater possibility for discrimination between regimes in high and medium security. Security is, of course, only one aspect of a patient's needs within secure services (e.g., Exworthy, 2000); however, given the considerable expenditure devoted to patients in secure services and a desire to get levels of security right for patients in these services, attention to the measurement of security need is of paramount importance and developments have lagged behind other areas of needs and risk assessment.

There have been more recent endeavors to develop measures that address security needs. Coid and Kahtan (2000) developed an instrument to predict the security needs of patients in medium security. They describe the need for accurate definitions of security need and a lack of agreement on definitions and methods currently available to allocate patients to the correct levels of security. Their four point rating scale is designed for use within medium security and describes patient characteristics that are related to security need in terms of low, medium and high security. They concluded that "there is no single criterion that can determine the security needs of an individual patient" (p. 125).

Shaw, Davies, and Morley (2001) developed a measure of the security, dependency and treatment needs of patients (SDTP). The measurement of security needs concentrated upon risk of violence and absconding and utilized a visual analogue scale for Responsible Medical Officers to rate need. While such a scalar measurement method provides greater scope for differentiation amongst patients, the authors acknowledge that the scale has "no external reference points" (p. 626). One of the findings of this study was that differentiation of patients was more accurate using dependency needs than security needs.

In a review of recent academic literature Williams, Badger, Nursten, and Woodward (1999) described how "few of the studies define 'high' or 'medium' security, or differentiate between and observational security measures" (p. 307). Sayal and Maden (2002) outlined the need for the development of standardized scales to measure security needs and also called for further research into the interrelationships between risk, level of functioning, and environmental conditions and their relevance to the appropriate placement of patients. Beck-Sander and Kinsella (1998) describe the need for developing standardized criteria to measure patient suitability for admission, internal transfer and progress within the unit.

Measurement of security need is underdeveloped in relation to measures of dependency, risk, and more global needs assessment. This may be a conceptual issue and there is some inevitable overlap between certain areas of dependency and security. For example, nursing supervision is traditionally regarded as a measure of dependency and in many contexts this may be the case (e.g., assisting with personal care). However, if supervision is provided as part of a forensic risk management care package, then we must consider that within this context it is more accurately categorized as a security need. Within most UK forensic settings it is members of direct care staff that administer security. The staffing ratio in a unit is often regarded as a highly important security measure; however, the training and ability of the staff in terms of security are also important. There is a developing forensic nursing literature that describes the importance of relational security (e.g., Burrow, 1994; Collins, 1999; Woods, Collins & Kettles, 2002) as part of forensic psychiatric care.

Despite recent work on assessing security needs, there remains a need for an instrument that comprehensively describes the elements of security provided within forensic psychiatric services. Such an instrument needs to be multi-dimensional to capture the many different components of security provided in modern forensic services and needs to have clear definitions of its items to encourage greater consistency in patient assessment, definition of services and for research purposes.

Instrument Development

The *Security Needs Assessment Profile* (S.N.A.P.) attempts to measure security need across open, low, medium and high secure forensic mental health services. The end result of an assessment is a security needs profile that is able to match a patient to a service. The individual items were initially derived from the perspective of High Security, as patients are more likely to exhibit the most extensive range of security needs. We arrived at 22 criteria after extensive consultation with multidisciplinary colleagues which, importantly, included consultation with specialist security liaison nurses. (These are mental health nurses with specialist training in security attached to clinical teams to provide expert advice on security issues related to individual patient need and treatment). Each of the 22 criteria was categorized into physical, procedural or relational security. Following further consultation with colleagues in medium, low, and open forensic services, the criteria were carefully defined and an ordinal scale of zero to three developed. Zero represented the absence of security need and three represented the highest level. Broadly this corresponds to traditional definitions of open, low, medium and high security but is not intended to be prescriptive due to high levels of variance amongst some units that offer the same ostensible level of security. Each ordinal item was criterion referenced. Criterion referencing involves attaching a descriptor to each ordinal scalar item. This improves interrater reliability and has advantages over Likert-type scales which tend not to define scalar items in any great detail. This approach to measurement in forensic psychiatry has an established and successful pedigree (e.g., The Behavioural Status Index; Reed, Woods, & Robinson, 2000).

Such definition is important in the light of other study findings; for example, Burrow (1993) found differences between ratings of security need between psychiatrists and nurses. Similarly the differences between accepting and referring teams outlined by Sayal and Maden (2002) highlight the need for a more reliable, comprehensive, and structured method of security needs assessment. The draft instrument was again reviewed by multi-disciplinary colleagues and further refined. Initial guided piloting resulted in further amendments.

SECURITY NEEDS ASSESSMENT PROFILE CRITERIA

Domain 1. Physical Security Items

1. Perimeter. A perimeter of some type represents one of the primary physical security measures. Perimeter fences or walls vary in height and type. They may be of a single or double perimeter type and be constructed from climb proof mesh. Electronic detection systems, closed circuit television and security lighting also play an important role.

2. Internal. A good perimeter is not necessarily a deterrent to the most agile and determined absconder, nor does it provide internal structural protection for others. Internal building quality and general layout vary according to security level and need. Examples include the resilience of doors, ceilings, locking mechanisms and windows to prevent attack from individuals and the provision of alarms and internal closed circuit television.

3. Entry. Any security system needs to have a point (or points) of control over what comes in and out of the secure area. Generally the higher the risk containment required the higher would be the level of control needed. The highest levels of security will have a very limited number of entry or exit points with facilities to scrutinize both people and goods.

4. Facilities. When patients have to leave the secure perimeter, the level of risk is raised. For example, risk of the opportunity to abscond increases. If all routine recreational and treatment facilities are housed within the secure perimeter, risks and inconveniences to patients are minimized. Such a high level of provision is a particular feature of high secure services in the UK where most recreational and limited general medical facilities are provided within the secure perimeter, negating the need for patients to leave the perimeter for any routine or common reasons. It is likely, however, that special circumstances will remain in which it will be necessary for patients to leave the perimeter (court attendance for example, although in some hospitals in the United States, courtrooms are provided).

Domain 2. Procedural Security Items

5. Nursing Intensity. This is a collective term for the level and frequency of direct patient supervision. Such supervision is related to risk management, maintenance of security integrity and safety. The details of patient whereabouts and activity will be noted at specified time intervals. The ability of a service to respond with heightened observations/supervision/incident support without compromising the level of care offered to other patients is also a key aspect of this item.

6. Patient Characteristics. Careful consideration needs to be given to placing patients in particular environments. Areas for consideration include diagnoses, gender, and offence profile. An example would be ensuring that patients with a predatory nature are not mixed with those who are vulnerable.

7. Searching. It is necessary to search individuals for prohibited items. At higher levels of security, patients, their belongings and living areas are subject to routine and random searches, including when patients move to and from different areas within and outside the perimeter. The frequency of such searches will depend on the type and severity of the risk being managed. This includes "pat-down searches" of patients, room searches and also non-intrusive measures using metal detector portals and X – Ray machines.

8. Access to potential weapons and fire setting materials (including items that may be used to breach security). Weapons are often conceptualized in the form of knives and guns or other obvious items. While patients may need access to such daily items as knives and forks, these can be managed by regular checks. It is, however, easy to fashion a weapon or device to breach security from everyday items. For example, adhesive tape can make a very effective garrote or a coat hanger can become an effective device for scaling a fence. Differing levels of control and procedures limit access to such items and help ensure the safety of patients and staff.

9. Internal movement. At the highest level of security, internal movement of patients is subject to high levels of supervision, which may involve centralized control and permission being sought for all movements. There may need to be a general awareness of all patient locations at regular intervals; all movement must be carried out under varying degrees of supervision. However, even within high secure facilities, provision exists for the introduction of more relaxed regimes such as internal ground parole.

10. Leave. When patients leave the secure area they are subject to a varying degree of restriction. High security has the provision for special secure vehicles which are self contained, including toilet facilities and radio communications. Conversely, systems exist for increasing freedom and moving eventually towards unsupervised leave.

11. External Communications. It may be necessary to place restrictions upon or to monitor external communications. This may be for the protection of others (for example previous victims), the patient (e.g., manipulation by others), or to prevent collusion/ illicit activities (e.g., planned escapes). Methods of external communication vary widely, the most common being the postal and telecommunications systems.

12. Visitors. Visitors represent a vital and therapeutic part of hospitalization but can present a weak link within a security system. Visitors will be subject to varying levels of scrutiny and supervision (they may be at risk from patients, or present a risk to patients) as will any items that they bring in for the patient.

13. Visiting children. Children may be at risk when visiting a secure establishment. This may not only be from the individual being visited but also from other detained individuals, who could for example have a history of offences against children. In appropriate situations, such visits may have vital therapeutic value, but may need to be catered for in special visiting areas, under the supervision of staff trained in child protection.

14. Media exposure. Certain patients generate intense media interest. This needs to be monitored and in some instances managed. Some units have developed sophisticated techniques for handling media interest, including dedicated media relations staff and external PR consultants.

15. Access to illicit substances. A number of patients within forensic services often have some history of substance misuse. Access to illicit substances may lead to deterioration in mental state. Trading in illicit substances can lead to problems with discipline, bullying, extortion and repeated attempts to undermine security. Varying systems exist (over and above general searching) to detect such substances. For example, the use of random drug testing procedures.

16. Access to alcohol. This is similar to the category above, but is included as a separate item because supervised access may be permitted in lower security. Special awareness may also be required for illegal homemade alcohol.

17. Access to pornographic materials. Public availability of pornography has widened in recent years not only in published form, but also via video and other audiovisual mediums (the Internet is considered as a separate category). Certain offenders may obtain sexual stimulation from seemingly innocuous sources and this phenomenon should be considered as part of any risk management strategy. Generally, this is an issue of monitoring access and patients at any level of security may be able to have access to pornography that is legally obtainable. There may however be circumstances within certain treatment plans that restrict the possession of pornography.

18. Access to information technology. Information technology has created a whole new range of security issues. The availability of pornography or sensitive information on the Internet can create a range of security issues as can the possibility of collusion between individuals. Varying levels of restriction exist to control such risks, ranging from no access to limited access under supervision or the use of dedicated restriction software.

Domain 3. Relational Skills Items

19. Management of violence and aggression (MVA). These skills fall into two main areas. First and foremost are the skills of recognizing and dealing with situations before they escalate to physical aggression. Second are the physical skills from basic breakaway techniques to physical intervention. High level skills include the use of protective equipment and hostage negotiation skills. In all units where MVA skills are regularly used, training should be regularly updated and where possible regular supervision provided by staff who provide the specialist training.

20. Relational nursing skills. Close knowledge of individual patients and how offending behavior is mirrored within a secure environment is vital to treatment, progress, and risk management. For example, a patient's ability to conspire and manipulate can present enormous safety and security problems if unchecked, while the identification and management of such behaviors can be valuable contributors to treatment. Nursing knowledge and observation contribute to formal risk assessment, risk management and treatment planning and can identify risk behaviors before they reach crisis point.

21. Response to nursing interventions and treatment program. The response of patients to nursing interventions and all other treatment components is an important relational security consideration. Non-response and active avoidance of treatment or even attempts to subvert procedures usually have implications for heightened security measures. Specific skills are required to engage patients in treatment.

22. Security intelligence and police liaison. Patients in forensic care are often offenders. Although unusual, some patients have extensive networks of criminal contacts. Security considerations include attempts to escape, attempts to bring in weapons or other illicit items, and intimidation of staff and patients. Active security intelligence systems may prevent security breaches and contribute to risk assessment, management and treatment. Higher levels of security will generally have dedicated security liaison staff and systems for recording and building security intelligence. At higher levels of security, there may also be a greater need for police liaison and other elements of law enforcement.

An example of detailed ordinal descriptors is provided for item 19 in text box 1.

The decision on the different ordinal levels was taken on an examination of current forensic services, mainly within Trent region in the UK but drawing on experience of other services. While level 3 generally represents high security, the provision of security varies more widely in units classified as low or medium secure.

Should a subject demonstrate a high level of need on some of the criteria, then the only placement suitable would be a high security hospital. This indicates that within the instrument there will be some items that represent "drop dead" issues. For example, if a patient presented a high and immediate risk to others if at liberty and a risk of escape that necessitated a high level of perimeter security then the patient would be detained in high security, irrespective of scores on other items. This would not prevent

---

TEXT BOX 1

Example of Ordinal Descriptors for Item 19, When Considering the Needs of the Patient in Terms of Management of Violence and Aggression (MVA)

3: All direct care staff fully trained in MVA techniques. Some staff will have extended training in the use of protective equipment and hostage negotiation skills. There will be recourse to large numbers of trained staff backup in emergency situations for extended periods.

2: All direct care staff trained in basic breakaway techniques, at least 80% of staff with full basic MVA training. There will be limited recourse to staff backup in emergency situations for limited time periods.

1: All direct care staff trained in basic breakaway techniques, selected staff members with full basic MVA training.

0: All direct care staff are required to know basic non-physical intervention skills and breakaway techniques.

(N.B. MVA training includes recognition of warning signs, verbal de-escalation and avoiding physical confrontation etc.)

a more tailored care package within the perimeter. Other items are quite obviously cumulative in nature, so that a person with 10 points over a range of items is likely to need lower security than a person with 20 points. This is why the instrument is an aid to clinical decision-making, and while scoring properties are useful, practitioners should not lose sight of examining each criterion on its individual and cumulative merit. We intend to examine these issues in extended clinical studies.

The instrument was initially piloted and utilized at Rampton High Security Hospital in the UK (as part of a wider study assessing patient needs, approved by Rampton Hospital Ethics committee). It was also used for an audit of Trent Region patients' security and treatment needs and submitted in a report (Davies, Collins, Hogue, Barrs, & Eitel–Smith, 2001). Two of the primary aims were to compare the S.N.A.P. scores to clinician overall ratings of security need and make a preliminary examination of the instrument properties.

RESULTS

We obtained S.N.A.P. data on 147 subjects. These were male patients with a mental disorder (excluding those with learning disability) detained in secure services across the UK. Data were obtained from either the patient's psychiatrist (termed the Responsible Medical Officer [RMO]), or primary nurse. For 110 of the subjects we were able to obtain a rating from both the RMO and primary nurse. Table 1 outlines the levels of security from which the sample were drawn.

TABLE 1

Security Level Placement of Subjects at Time of Assessment

SECURITY LEVEL	NUMBER	PERCENT
Low	20	13.6
Medium	68	46.3
High	59	40.1
Total	147	100.0

While decision-making regarding placement needs to be informed individually by the 22 items, the authors envisaged that scoring patterns would provide useful information about the sample. The RMO/primary nurse were also asked to state what they thought would be the best placement for the patient e.g. long-term, severe mental illness service and level of security rated as: **0** – Open, **1** – Low Security, **2** – Medium Security, **3** – High Security. While none of the patients in the sample were in open settings it was still important to include an open setting as an option as patients may be appropriate for such settings. We have to point out an inherent weakness in our methodology at this point, in that asking both the RMO/primary nurse to provide both the S.N.A.P. and best placement rating is a potential methodological weakness.

"Blind" ratings, where the best placement rater did not know the S.N.A.P. ratings would have been preferable. This would have been possible through the use of external rating teams or trained observers. We did however feel that a comprehensive S.N.A.P. and best placement rating requires an in-depth knowledge of the patient's security needs that is difficult to achieve using external assessors. The best placement rating was felt to be a superior comparator for S.N.A.P. scores over the current placement as it removed any inherent bias of patients detained at an inappropriate level of security. Despite some inherent covariance the data gathered still provides useful preliminary data about the S.N.A.P.

Table 2 shows mean patient scores in the physical, procedural and relational domains of the instrument compared to the clinician best placement ratings. The table demonstrates that high best placement ratings are associated with greater domain scores. These have to be treated with some caution as the standard deviations (SD) are high, particularly for procedural security. The SD indicates to what extent individual scores are dispersed around the mean. This can be accounted for by the larger number of items within the procedural security domain and the fact that individual patient needs in this area will be variable, even when they have the same best placement rating. For example, two patients may both have medium needs for searching and access to weapons but very different needs for access to pornography and information technology. The final column shows the cumulative effect, but it is interesting to note that those patients with a best placement rating of high security have the lowest SD despite having the highest instrument score. For this part of the analysis we used the RMO S.N.A.P. score and best placement ratings in preference to the primary nurse ratings. The split

TABLE 2

Mean Security Scores Compared to Clinician Best Placement Rating

BEST PLACEMENT RATING		PHYSICAL SECURITY TOTAL	PROCEDURAL SECURITY TOTAL	SKILLS TOTAL	COMBINED PHYSICAL, PROCEDURAL AND SKILLS TOTAL
Open	Mean	2.57	9.04	3.50	15.11
	N	28	28	28	28
	SD	2.834	8.804	2.301	12.968
Low Security	Mean	5.22	15.51	5.46	26.19
	N	37	37	37	37
	SD	3.020	8.211	1.980	11.190
Medium Security	Mean	6.94	19.35	6.09	32.39
	N	54	54	54	54
	SD	2.543	7.870	2.268	11.273
High Security	Mean	10.39	30.71	8.64	49.75
	N	28	28	28	28
	SD	1.950	6.765	1.660	9.793

Maximum Possible Scores: Physical =12 Procedural = 42 Skills = 12 was 129 RMO ratings and 18 primary nurse ratings (we had 18 missing RMO ratings). This is because out of the two clinicians the RMO is the one ultimately responsible for recommendations in patient security placement.

We were interested to know if there was any statistically significant difference between the mean overall scores for the open, low, medium and high best placement groups. These were 15.11, 26.19, 32.39 and 49.75 respectively. A one-way analysis of variance (ANOVA) test revealed a significant difference, F (3, 143) = 46.37, $p < 0.01$. This result indicates a difference between the means but, as there are four groups (open, low, medium and high security best placement ratings), we conducted a Tukey honestly significant difference comparison to reveal where the statistically significant results occurred. We found that when comparing medium and low security they were not significantly different. The mean difference in overall score was 6.2, $p > .05$. All other possible comparisons showed significant differences (high/medium, 17.6, $p < .01$; high/low, 23.6, $p < .01$; high/open, 34.6, $p < .01$; medium/open, 17.3, $p < .01$; low/open, 11.1, $p < .01$).

This is further illustrated in Figure 1, a box and whisker plot, an alternative way of presenting the data. This is based on medians (the value that is halfway through the ordered data set above and below which there are an equal number of values). In figure 1 the bold horizontal line in each of the four shaded boxes indicates the median for each of the four best placement groups. The lower portion of the shaded boxes represents the 25th percentile and the upper portion the 75th percentile. The vertical

FIGURE 1

Box—Whisker Plot for Total Security Needs Score

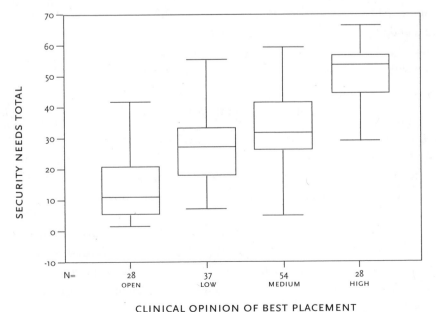

CLINICAL OPINION OF BEST PLACEMENT

lines or whiskers represent values out of this range (outliers). It is also noticeable that outliers contribute to score variation. We deliberately left outliers in the data set, as in this study they are not necessarily representative of "flawed data." This is an indication of the complexity of the subject area where a patient's need profile is lower or higher than the main groupings. We referred earlier to "drop dead" items and this again suggests that there will always be a need to consider the results of any instrument, in the light of supporting clinical judgment and public safety considerations.

The greatest overlap occurs between low and medium classifications. Overlap may exist because of common characteristics between security settings. The lack of overlap between the high and medium security profiles probably represents the very distinct specifications that exist in high secure provision.

The instrument scores provide useful information and general guidance, but as emphasized previously the individual patient profiles need to be examined in terms of a placement that best meets them. A high level of need does not automatically mean a patient requires high security and vice versa, but generally from this study this appears to be the case.

Interrater Reliability

During the study we obtained dual ratings by Responsible Medical Officer and Primary Nurse on 110 subjects, as we wanted to compare RMO and primary nurse ratings for the same patient, covariance is again a potential problem. Overall security needs scores show strong correlations (agreement) between raters. Conducting a Pearson test gives a correlation coefficient of .732, which is significant at $p < 0.01$ (two tailed). Conducting the same test separately on physical, procedural and relational totals all provide significant results at $p < 0.01$ (two tailed). However, there was also a trend for primary nurses to rate higher than RMOs. Other studies have found differences, for example, Burrow (1993) found the trend to be reversed. This reinforces the idea that needs ratings should be made by consensus between the care team and also points to the need for further development of a user manual for the S.N.A.P. and specific training.

Principal Components Analysis

The results obtained consist of a large number of variables. The 147 completed instruments resulted in 3234 individual scores (for this part of the analysis we used the 129 RMO and 18 primary nurse ratings detailed earlier). To try and make sense of the large number of possible correlations between variables an exploratory statistical technique called principal components analysis was used. This is a standard technique used in the development of instruments that allows an assessment of the degree to which individual items are measuring the same concept. While the instrument items belong to obvious theoretical subsets of the same dimension (i.e physical, procedural and relational security) we wanted to examine them further for any underlying statistical dimensions that may have further practical utility.

Such an analysis will produce a number of factors (items on the instrument that are grouped together). Not all these will be used and we accepted factors with eigenvalues greater than 1. An eigenvalue indicates the relative importance of the factor and a value over 1 suggests strong importance. Each instrument item receives a loading value for each factor. The highest loading value will then generally be accepted as the factor to which the item belongs. This is better demonstrated in table 3. This shows that 3 factors (described in the following paragraph) were returned with eigenvalues over 1 and shows where the highest loadings for each of the 22 S.N.A.P. items fell. Loadings are expressed as a percentage and the closer to the value of 1 the stronger they are.

This table also represents the data after we applied a procedure called varimax rotation. This procedure improves interpretation by strengthening the loading on to the predominant factor. As reliability in this kind of analysis is dependant on sample size there are various suggestions as to the number of subjects in relation to variables. Generally a lower limit of 5 subjects per variable is acceptable and this study works on just over 6 subjects per variable (S.N.A.P. items). The data were also screened prior to applying the procedure. The Kaiser–Meyer–Olkin (KMO) measure and Bartlett's test were applied. The first test looks at sampling adequacy and the second checks that there are significant relationships between variables. The result of this screening was

TABLE 3

S.N.A.P. Item Factor Loadings

		FACTOR		
		1	2	3
Item 5	Nursing Intensity	.809		
Item 21	Response to nursing interventions – Relational skills	.735		
Item 20	Relational nursing skills – Relational skills	.678		
Item 19	Management of violence and aggression – Relational skills	.675		
Item 2	Internal – Physical security	.671		
Item 9	Internal movement – Procedural Security	.664		
Item 4	Facilities – Physical Security	.658		
Item 1	Perimeter – Physical Security	.574		
Item 10	Leave – Procedural Security	.569		
Item 6	Patient Characteristics	.562		
Item 3	Entry – Physical Security	.538		
Item 8	Access to potential weapons and fire setting materials – Procedural security	.537		
Item 16	Access to alcohol – Procedural security		.799	
Item 17	Access to pornographic material – Procedural security		.743	
Item 15	Access to illicit substances – Procedural security		.714	
Item 18	Access to Information Technology – Procedural security		.697	
Item 12	Visitors – Procedural security		.650	
Item 11	External communications – Procedural security		.544	
Item 13	Visiting children – Procedural security		.536	
Item 7	Searching – Procedural security		.533	
Item 22	Security intelligence – Relational skills			.806
Item 14	Media exposure – Procedural Security			.718

that a principal component analysis would be appropriate. The loadings in the table are strong; Gaudagnoli and Velicier (1988) argue that if a factor has four or more loadings greater than 0.6 then it is reliable regardless of sample size. Clearly for the first two factors this is the case. However the final factor only has two items but these are strong loadings and, importantly, the items make clinical sense. With an analysis of this type the researchers examine the item groupings to see if they have a rational connection to one another. In this analysis we felt that this was the case and named the factors as follows:

Factor one: Internal management and protection of others. This contains items related to internal patient management (e.g., nursing intensity and components for the protection of others, which include management of violence and aggression).

Factor two: Management of external influence. This contains items strongly related to minimizing/controlling external influence that may be detrimental or dangerous (as opposed to internal control). For example, the monitoring of external communication and supervision and searching of visitors.

Factor three: Notoriety. This only contains two items (and cannot statistically be regarded as a factor) but these have a strong logical connection. A high level of media interest will often necessitate a higher need for security intelligence and police liaison. Conversely, a patient that creates a high level of organizational need for security intelligence and police liaison may often generate media interest.

Cronbach's alphas statistic was utilized to examine the internal consistency of the instrument. This statistic looks at correlation of the items within the factors. Generally a score of over 0.7 indicates reliability. For the first two factors the scores are very strong, 0.94 and 0.90 respectively. It is not appropriate to do such a calculation on the two items in factor 3. The internal consistency of the original items is also strong; using the same statistic, physical security produces a score of 0.92, procedural security 0.93 and relational skills 0.71.

Practical Utilization

The factors are undoubtedly of clinical relevance, but also require further validation. It is unlikely that our original items would group as factors because they are theoretical domains. Patient characteristics will mean that a combination of physical, procedural and relational items will correlate to produce the best management profile. A total score will be good basic guidance as to level of security need. However we would discourage any undue reliance on scores other than for the purposes of research and instrument development. It is of far more importance to consider the subject being assessed and the possible placement. Can the placement cater to the needs identified? This should be assessed practically by looking at each item in turn. Unit security provision varies considerably throughout the UK outside of high security, so it will be this that is an important consideration. Using the theoretical items the assessor will be able to say with some degree of certainty what level of physical, procedural and relational security will be needed. The factors currently provide additional useful information in terms of whether the greatest level of need is on factors 1, 2 or 3. Caution should also be noted in the size of the sample in that while respectable it is still relatively small.

Missing Data and Nonrelevant Items

The scoring system adopted by the S.N.A.P. allows missing data to be treated in two ways. It can be rated as an absence of need in which case there will be no contribution to the overall score. More realistically, clinicians will be cautious and rate higher levels of need if information is inadequate. For example, a patient may not have had the opportunity to go on leave at the time of rating; however, given the level of risk being managed a high rating would be necessary. Any items that are not relevant to a particular patient can be rated as zero meaning that the item will make no contribution to any overall score or need profile; for example, pornography often may not be rated.

Potential Uses for the S.N.A.P.

The primary purpose in developing the S.N.A.P. is to provide a comprehensive instrument to aid experienced forensic clinicians to assess patients' security needs across a range of security dimensions. The instrument can only be used by experienced clinicians and cannot replace clinical judgment. But we argue that it should guide clinical judgment, and will help to ensure that no relevant variable is ignored. It is hoped that by providing clear and comprehensive definitions of security items, greater agreement can be reached between clinicians and areas of disagreement addressed. The instrument may also aid the design of hospitals. The debate about whether a patient is "high" or "medium" will hopefully move on to one about individual patients' specific security needs and how best to meet these. We would envisage the S.N.A.P. as being particularly useful at points of transition, e.g., admission to psychiatric services from the criminal justice system or transfer between levels of security. Having a comprehensive description of a patient's security needs should also assist in drawing up a risk management plan. Such a plan can be dynamic and form a part of regular treatment and risk management reviews. Predominantly the S.N.A.P. is a risk management instrument. Security is provided to manage the risk of harm an individual my pose to others, yet it can often be applied generically, whereby all patients in a particular area are subject to the "worst case scenario" type of approach. While some elements of security cannot be readily adjusted (the perimeter fence for example) others can (level and intensity of searching for example). The provision of detailed descriptors of security can also be used to describe the security provided by an individual unit of service. This can be used to help inform placement decisions by matching patients to units. A further use may be found in providing a framework to assist units in auditing the security they provide. Finally, the provision of detailed and hopefully reliable descriptors of security should be an aid to further research, audit and clinical governance in forensic psychiatric services.

Planned Developments of SNAP

1. The development of a comprehensive user manual including security descriptors, clinical vignettes for each item and case studies.
2. A National survey of secure units in England to refine the 22 items in relation to actual provision. This study has been outlined by Collins, Davies, and Ashwell (2003) and is supported by a grant from the NHS National Programme on Forensic Mental Health R&D. The work referred to here pre-dates this grant; the views expressed are those of the authors and not necessarily those of the Programme or the Department of Health.
3. Extended clinical studies using the SNAP across low, medium and high secure units (the authors would be pleased to hear from any clinicians interested in utilizing SNAP in clinical practice).

CONCLUSION

The increasing size and complexity of forensic psychiatric services has lead to the need to develop a better understanding of the elements of security they provide. The development of the S.N.A.P. intends to aid this by providing comprehensive and clearly described definitions of the elements of security present in secure psychiatric services. Overall S.N.A.P. scores differentiate between clinicians' opinion of levels of security required and the instrument has encouraging psychometric properties. The S.N.A.P. hopefully has a number of clinical and research applications when used by experienced forensic clinicians. Further development work including a user manual, national survey of secure psychiatric services and evaluation of use in clinical practice is underway.

REFERENCES

Abbott, P. (2002). Reconfiguration of the high-security hospitals: some lessons from the mental hospital retraction and reprovision programme in the United Kingdom 1960-2000. *Journal of Forensic Psychiatry, 13*, 107-122.

Bartlett, A., Cohen, A., Backhouse, A., Highet, N., & Eastman, N. (1996). Security needs of South West Thames Special Hospital patients: 1992 and 1993. No way out? *Journal of Forensic Psychiatry, 7*, 256-270.

Beck-Sander, A., & Kinsella, C. (1998). Patient selection and management in medium and low security hospitals. *Psychiatric Care, 5*, 86-91.

Burrow, S. (1993). The treatment and security needs of special hospital patients: A nursing perspective. *Journal of Advanced Nursing, 18*, 1267-1278.

Burrow, S. (1994). Therapeutic security and the mentally disordered offender. *British Journal of Nursing, 3*, 314-15.

Coid, J., & Kahtan, N. (2000). An instrument to measure the security needs of patients in medium security. *Journal of Forensic Psychiatry, 11*, 119-134.

Collins, M. (1999). The practitioner new to the role of forensic psychiatric nurse. In D. Robinson & A. Kettles (Eds.), *Forensic nursing and the multidisciplinary care of the mentally disordered offender* (pp. 39-50). London: Jessica Kingsley.

Collins, M., Davies, S., & Ashwell, C. (2003). Meeting patients' needs in secure forensic psychiatric units. *Nursing Standard, 17*, 49, 33-34.

Davies, S., Collins, M., Hogue, T., Barrs, H., & Eitel–Smith, G. (2001). An audit of the treatment and security needs of Trent patients in secure care with particular reference to the development of long-term medium and low-secure services. In *An Audit Report Commissioned by Forensic Services Specialist Commissioning Team* (pp. 1-18). North Nottinghamshire Health Authority: United Kingdom.

Department of Health. (1993). *Design guide: Medium secure psychiatric units*. NHS Estates: London.

Department of Health. (1999). *The National Service framework for mental health*. London.

Department of Health and Home Office. (2000). *Reforming the Mental Health Act. Part II – High Risk Patients, Developing specialist services for those who are dangerous and severely personality disordered*. Cm 5016II. London: The Stationary Office.

Department of Health. (2002). *Mental health policy implementation guide: National minimum standards for general adult services in psychiatric intensive care units (PICU) and low secure environments*. London: Department of Health Publications.

Exworthy, T., & Gunn, J. (2003). Taking another tilt at high secure hospitals. *British Journal of Psychiatry, 182*, 469-471.

Exworthy, T. (2000). Secure psychiatric services. *Current Opinion in Psychiatry, 13*, 581-585.

Guadagnoli, E., & Velicier, W. (1988). Relation of sample size to the stability of component patterns. *Psychological Bulletin, 103*, 265-275.

Kennedy, H. (2002). Therapeutic uses of security: mapping forensic mental health services by stratifying risk. *Advances in Psychiatric Treatment 8*, 433-443.

Kinsley, J. (1992). *Security in the special hospitals a special task*. London. SHSA.

Kinsley, J. (1998). Security and therapy. In C. Kaye & A. Franey (Eds.), *Managing high security psychiatric care* (pp. 75-84). London: Jessica Kingsley.

Maden, A., Curle, C., Meux, C., Burrow, S., & Gunn, J. (1993). The treatment and security needs of patients in special hospitals. *Criminal Behaviour and Mental Health, 3*, 290-306.

Mental Health (Care and Treatment) (Scotland) Act (2003). Edinburgh: The Stationary Office. Part 17, Chapter 3.

Murray, K., Rudge, S., Lack, S., & Dolan, R. (1994). How many high security beds are needed? Implications from an audit of one region's special hospital patients. *Journal of Forensic Psychiatry, 5*, 487-99.

Parker, E. (1985). The development of secure provision. In L. Gostin (Ed.), *Secure provision* (pp. 15-65). London: Tavistock.

Pierzchniak, P., Farnham, F., De Taranto, N., Bull, D., Gill, H., Bester, P., McCallum, A., & Kennedy, H. (1999). Assessing the needs of patients in secure settings: A multi-disciplinary approach. *Journal of Forensic Psychiatry, 10*, 343-354.

Reed, J. (1994). *Report of the working group on high security and related psychiatric provision*. London: Department of Health.

Reed, V., Woods, P., & Robinson, D. (2000). *Behavioural Status Index (Best-index): A life skills assessment for selecting and monitoring therapy in mental health care*. United Kingdom: Psychometric Press.

Sayal, K., & Maden, A. (2002). The treatment and security needs of patients in special hospitals: Views of referring and accepting teams. *Criminal Behaviour and Mental Health, 12*, 244-53.

Shaw, J., McKenna, J., Snowden, P., Boyd, C., McMahon, D., & Kilshaw, J. (1994). Clinical features and placement needs of all North West Region patients currently in special hospital. *Journal of Forensic Psychiatry 5*, 93-106.

Shaw, J., Davies, J., & Morley, H. (2001). An assessment of the security, dependency and treatment needs of all patients in secure services in a UK health region. *The Journal of Forensic Psychiatry, 12*, 610-637.

Taylor, P. J., Butwell, M., Dacey, R., & Kaye, C. (1991). *Within maximum security hospitals: A survey of need*. London: Special Hospitals Service Authority.

Taylor, P., Maden, M., & Jones, D. (1996). Long-term medium-security hospital units: a service gap of the 1990's? *Criminal Behaviour and Mental Health, 6*, 213-229.

Tilt Report. (2000). *Report of the review of security at the high security hospitals*. London: NHS Executive.

Williams, P., Badger, D., Nursten, J., & Woodward, M. (1999) A review of recent academic literature on the characteristics of patients in British special hospitals. *Criminal Behaviour and Mental Health, 9*, 296-314.

Woods, P., Collins, M., & Kettles, A. (2002). Forensic nursing interventions and future directions for forensic mental health practice. In A. Kettles, P. Woods., & M. Collins (Eds.), *Therapeutic interventions for forensic mental health nurses* (pp. 240-245). London: Jessica Kingsley.

31

Implementing Recovery Oriented Evidence Based Programs: Identifying the Critical Dimensions

MARIANNE FARKAS, CHERYL GAGNE, WILLIAM ANTHONY
AND JUDI CHAMBERLIN

ABSTRACT: *In the decade of the 1990s many mental health programs and the systems that fund these programs have identified themselves as recovery-oriented. A program that is grounded in a vision of recovery is based on the notion that a majority of people can grow beyond the catastrophe of a severe mental illness and lead a meaningful life in their own community. First person accounts of recovery and empirical research have led to a developing consensus about the service delivery values underlying recovery. The emphasis on recovery-oriented programming has been concurrent with a focus in the field on evidence-based practices. We propose that evidence based practices be implemented in a manner that is recovery compatible. Program dimensions for evidence based practice, such as program mission, policies, procedures, record keeping and staffing should be consistent with recovery values in order for a program to be considered to be recovery-oriented. This article describes the critical dimensions of such value based practice, regardless of the service the recovery oriented mental health programs provide (e.g., treatment, case management, rehabilitation). The aim of this first attempt at conceptualizing recovery-oriented mental health programs is to both provide direction to those involved in program implementation of evidence based mental health practices, as well as providing a stimulus for further discussion in the field.*

KEYWORDS: *recovery oriented mental health program dimensions; evidence based practice; values based practice; program mission; policies; procedures; record keeping; staffing.*

Reprinted with kind permission of Springer Science and Business Media. Community Mental Health Journal, 41 *(2),* 141–158. © 2005 Springer Science and Business Media.

INTRODUCTION

One of the most pressing problems facing the mental health field today is our lack of knowledge about the interventions and services that will help people recover from severe mental illnesses. Program administrators and therefore service delivery over most of the last century, have been heavily influenced by the mistaken assumption that people with severe mental illnesses do not recover and, in contrast deteriorate over time (Bond et al., 2001). The President's New Freedom Commission on Mental Health (2003) concluded that the mental health system is "not oriented to the single most important goal of the people it serves—the hope of recovery" (p. 3). Programs have been designed to fend off relapse and deterioration and, more recently, to maintain people in the community (Anthony, Cohen, Farkas, & Gagne, 2002). As a result, much of the existing evidence based practice research was conceived without an understanding of the emergence of the recovery concept (Anthony, Rogers, & Farkas, 2003). Program development and planning implications of evidence based practice research are deficient in speaking to the possibilities of recovery. The President's New Freedom Commission on Mental Health (2003) begins its report with a vision statement: "We envision a future when everyone with a mental illness will recover... a future when everyone with a mental illness at any stage of life has access to effective treatment and supports— essentials for living, working, learning and participating fully in the community" (p. 1). This paper is an initial effort in bridging the gap between evidence-based practice and the vision of recovery.

International and U.S. longitudinal studies of recovery from major mental illnesses have over the past 30 years demonstrated recovery rates of between 49 and 68% (Harding, in press). Yet it is only within the last decade of the 20th century that program administrators and developers became conversant with the notion of recovery from severe mental illnesses. There is a growing body of literature examining the concept of recovery from mental illnesses, its definition, process, phases, tasks and outcomes (e.g. Anthony, 1993; Farkas, Gagne, & Anthony, 2001; Harding & Zahniser, 1994; Davidson & Strauss, 1992; Spaniol, Gagne, & Koehler, 1999; Spaniol, Wewiorski, Gagne, & Anthony, 2002). People with psychiatric disabilities have published their experiences of recovery (Deegan, 1990, 1993; Fisher & Ahern, 1999; Mead & Copeland, 2000; Ridgway, 2001; Spaniol et al., 1999; Sullivan, 1994; Unzicker, 1989; Weingarten, 1994), and with like minded professionals are advocating for system and agency strategies to facilitate recovery (e.g., Frese, Stanley, Kress, & Vogel-Scibilia, 2001; Jacobson & Greenley, 2001; Torgalsboen & Rund, 1998). Increasing number of states (Beale & Lambric, 1995; Jacobson & Curtis, 2000; State of Wisconsin Blue Ribbon Commission on Mental Health, 1997), as well as entire countries like New Zealand (Lapsley Waimarie Nikora, & Black, 2002) are aligning their vision and mission with a recovery philosophy.

Concurrent with these attempts to embed the vision of recovery in mental health programming has been the impetus for evidence-based practice within these programs. The term evidence based practices includes "promising practices" that are accumulating evidence to become designated as evidence based practices (Anthony et al., 2003). An initial group of evidence based practices have been identified (Bond et al., 2001; Sanderson, 2002; Torrey et al., 2001). Evidence based practice has been, in fact defined as "the integration of best researched evidence and clinical expertise with patient values" (Institute of Medicine, 2001). However, relatively little description is given to the value base for these practices (Drake et al., 2001). While the value base underlying evidence based practices can in theory reinforce recovery (Drake et al., 2001), no attempt has been made to explicate recovery values in evidence based practices, nor to detail how these recovery values might be translated into specific program dimensions. Based on commonly accepted values underlying the notion of recovery, this article proposes recovery-oriented program dimensions that are compatible with evidence-based practices, and that can strengthen evidence based practice implementation. Recovery-oriented program dimensions can guide the entire range of mental health services (e.g., case management, treatment, rehabilitation) including those already identified as evidence based.

THE ESSENTIAL INGREDIENTS OF A RECOVERY ORIENTED MENTAL HEALTH PROGRAM (ROMHP)

In order to identify the essential ingredients of a ROMHP it is important to define what is meant by a program. A program consists of the administration, staffing and procedures for the delivery of any service (e.g., treatment, rehabilitation) for which the program is responsible. A program may be organized to deliver more than one service. For example, an ACT program may provide case management, treatment, crisis intervention and rehabilitation services in a specific way detailed through its program structures and staffing. A self-help program may provide crisis intervention and advocacy. Any one of the preceding program examples could be a recovery-oriented program depending upon the extent to which its program structures and staffing incorporate the basic values of recovery. A ROMHP is characterized by program structures such as mission, policies, procedures, record keeping and quality assurance that are consistent with fundamental recovery values. Similarly, staffing concerns such as selection, training and supervision are guided by the fundamental values of recovery.

Based on the present state of our knowledge about what constitutes recovery, its process and its outcomes, it is possible to identify some key ingredients of a recovery oriented program, regardless of which evidence based practice is used. When evidence-based practices are developed, described and replicated (Torrey et al., 2001), possible important philosophical elements of a practice may be omitted because they are not empirically linked to the traditional outcomes reported. Yet some features of a program are important, not necessarily because there is evidence that they produce traditional outcomes such as increased community tenure or employment rates but because they are, from a values perspective, important to the overall approach and can significantly alter the consumer's personal experience of the program and their unique process of recovery (Anthony, 2001; Anthony et al., 2003). A ROMHP is made up of such value-based ingredients regardless of the specific mental health service that it delivers.

VALUES BASED PRACTICE:
THE FUNDAMENTAL VALUES OF A ROMHP

Values Based Practice (VBP) explicates the values or guiding principles that are the underlying beliefs held by the program. VBP designs and monitors programs based on explicated values. VBP guides the way in which staff are hired, trained and supervised. While there are many values that may be associated with recovery-oriented services, there are at least four key values that support the recovery process and that appear to be commonly reflected in the consumer and recovery literature. These values are: person orientation, person involvement, self-determination/choice and growth potential, initially described by Farkas, Anthony, and Cohen (1989) (see Table 1).

Person Orientation

Davidson & Strauss (1992) mention the importance of understanding the strengths and weaknesses of the individual. "Person orientation" implies that individuals are more than what they may demonstrate in the limited roles of "patient" or "client" or "service recipient." The majority are adults, who may also have roles as fathers, mothers, brothers, students, workers, and advocates. Individuals represent the full range of human interests, talents, intellect and personalities that are evident in the general population. First person narratives convey that people with psychiatric disabilities appreciate when mental health professionals express interest in them as a person and in roles other than as "patient" (McQuillan, 1994; Weingarten, 1994). They may feel damaged by professionals who refuse to connect in a more holistic way (Deegan, 1990).

Person Involvement

Research data in rehabilitation suggest that outcomes are better for people who have an opportunity for meaningful involvement in the planning and delivery of their services (e.g., Majumder, Walls, & Fullmer, 1998). Consumer involvement in designing and delivering services (e.g., program planning, implementation and evaluation) is seen as a critical component of a quality management system for a mental health service (Blackwell, Eilers, & Robinson 2000).

Self-Determination/Choice

Several mental health program models such as psychiatric rehabilitation (Farkas, Cohen, & Nemec, 1988), supported housing (Carling, 1995), psychosocial clubhouses (Beard, Propst, & Malamud, 1982) and some case management programs (Pyke, Lancaster, & Pritchard, 1997) articulate the values of choice and partnership. Davidson and Strauss (1992) note, based on their qualitative research, that coercion has the effect of diminishing, rather than strengthening the self. "Getting someone simply to 'comply' with treatment may in fact end up having an effect opposite to the one intended, for example, if it leaves the patient continuing to feel controlled from the outside, only now by her/his

TABLE 1

Key Recovery Values

PERSON ORIENTATION	The service focuses on the individual first and foremost as an individual with strengths, talents, interests as well as limitations, rather than focusing on the person as a "case," exhibiting indicators of disease.
PERSON INVOLVEMENT	The service focuses on people's right to full partnership in all aspects of their recovery, including partnership in designing, planning, implementing and evaluating the service that supports their recovery.
SELF-DETERMINATION/CHOICE	The service focuses on people's right to make individual decisions or choices about all aspects of their own recovery process, including areas such as the desired goals and outcomes, preferred services used to achieve the outcomes, preferred moments to engage or disengage in services.
GROWTH POTENTIAL	The service focuses on the inherent capacity of any individual to recover, regardless of whether, at the moment, he or she is overwhelmed by the disability, struggling, living with or living beyond the disability.

Adapted from Farkas, Anthony, and Cohen (1989).

doctor rather than by her/his hallucinations" (Davidson & Strauss, p. 138). Two studies that have examined vocational programs and client choice, report a positive relationship between choice and rehabilitation outcome (Becker, Drake, Farabaugh, & Bond, 1996; Bell & Lysaker, 1996).

Growth Potential

Hope for the future is an essential ingredient in all recovery-oriented services. A value on "growth potential" implies a commitment to maintaining hopefulness in both service participants and their practitioners. It includes evaluating progress towards growth, adjusting services to allow progress to be noticed or acknowledged, as well as altering services to improve progress.

VALUES DRIVEN DIMENSIONS: ORGANIZATION AND STAFFING

A ROMHP is made up of two dimensions: organization/administration and staffing. The organization/administration dimension includes the structural components of the program that provide an institutional framework for recovery efforts based on the key recovery values. The staffing dimension ensures that the people in the organization deliver the service in a manner consistent with the values of recovery. Table 2 provides a summary of the key recovery-oriented mental health program ingredients, along with examples of standards based on recovery values and standards that are not. The text that follows amplifies on the examples in Table 2.

TABLE 2

Examples of Values Based Recovery Standards by Program Dimensions

PROGRAM DIMENSIONS	EXAMPLE OF VALUE BASED RECOVERY STANDARD	EXAMPLE OF CURRENT NON-RECOVERY STANDARD
ORGANIZATION AND ADMINISTRATION		
Mission	To help people improve their functioning so that they can be successful and satisfied in the environment of their choice *(person orientation, self-determination/choice, growth potential)*.	To provide comprehensive treatment and rehabilitation service to clients that emphasizes continuity of care *(focus on service delivery not outcome; no self determination)*.
Policies	People will have the opportunities and assistance necessary to choose and plan for whatever services they want to promote their own recovery *(self-determination)*.	People must attend the day treatment center to be accepted as a resident in Green Valley apartments. *(no self-determination; no individualization that would reflect a person orientation)*.
Procedures	A detailed list of orientation steps provided in different individualized communication modalities to ensure that clients receive program information based on what they want to know and how they take in information. Orientation includes information about what the program offers, cannot offer, what it expects, how clients can give feedback *(person involvement)*.	A generic orientation packet is provided to each new client *(while this may be helpful for some, it is not a sufficiently comprehensive procedure to ensure that most clients will be engaged in understanding what they are entering; no person orientation)*.
Record keeping	Records are designed to include process and outcome measures related directly to the program's mission *(growth potential)*.	Records are designed to capture service utilization measures *(while important for administration, does not provide possibility to change program based on results of service provision; no growth potential)*.
Quality assurance	Monitoring program outcomes include measures selected by clients *(person involvement; self-determination)*.	Monitoring program outcomes only reflect measures dictated by state regulations *(programs can be in compliance but have little relevance to clients; no person involvement)*.
Physical setting	Program facilities are for everyone's use *(person orientation)*.	Bathrooms are limited to those for staff and those for clients *(sets a tone of "us the well, you the unwell"; no person orientation)*.
Network	Program links to services in both community and professional settings *(person orientation)*.	Program staff provide on-site recreation activities, on-site chaplain services, crafts and on-site educational opportunities *(creates a segregated mental health service universe; no growth orientation)*.

STAFFING

Selection	Staff are hired based on their knowledge, attitudes and skills in recovery *(consistent with the basic recovery values)*.	Staff are hired based on their credentials and years of service *(assumes staff are taught recovery knowledge, attitudes and skills in their credentialing process; no recovery values considered)*.
Training	Staff training includes interaction and interviews with individuals who are living beyond their disability/have recovered *(growth potential)*.	Staff training focuses exclusively on issues of relapse, non-compliance, dangerousness and risk assessment *(prepares staff to handle difficulties but not success; no growth potential; no person orientation)*.
Supervision	Promotions, rewards and supervisor reinforcement reflects staff's ability to demonstrate the knowledge, attitudes and skills necessary for recovery and recovery outcomes *(all recovery values)*.	Promotions, rewards and reinforcement reflects measures such as: years of service; yearly attendance; number of training events completed *(rewards presence not competence; no recovery values)*.

The Organization/Administration

The organization/administration dimension includes components such as the program mission, policies, procedures, record keeping systems, quality assurance mechanisms, the physical setting of the program itself, and the network of services either linked to or controlled by the program (Farkas et al., 1989).

Mission

A ROMHP is guided by a mission that reflects the key values at a minimum. A mission statement identifies intended outcome(s) in behavioral terms, rather than simply the provision of service to an identified target population (Farkas et al., 1988). Some recovery outcomes that have been identified in the literature include: gaining or regaining the role of worker, community member, tenant, or student; experiencing increased success and satisfaction in these roles; reducing or controlling symptoms; increasing a sense of empowerment; increasing feelings of well being; increasing measures of physical and/or spiritual health; and increasing a sense of self-esteem (Campbell & Schraiber, 1989; Mead & Copeland, 2000; Ralph, Lambric, & Steele, 1996; Spaniol et al., 2003; Young & Ensing, 1999).

Mission statements should not be simply bureaucratic statements, unrelated to the everyday provision of services. They should drive program development and service delivery. An effective recovery-oriented mission is known, discussed and understood by all clients and providers of the service. It should be posted in locations that are easily read by everyone entering or using the service *(person involvement)*.

Policies

A ROMHP has policy statements that, at a minimum, reflect the four recovery values. Policy statements should provide general value based principles for the delivery of the service's unique process of assessment or diagnosis, planning, and interventions. For example, a policy statement might read: "All Blue Hill's program staff will refer to individuals receiving services in 'person first' language." All policy statements are written in language that reflects respect for the individuals using the service *(person orientation)*. Reflecting self-determination, a policy statement may read: "People may choose the intensity of support services provided by the program." Policies reflecting growth potential might require the development of quality assurance mechanisms that allow, for example, program data on processes and outcomes to be evaluated with respect to the clients' recovery goals.

Policies can be written for any aspect of the program. For example, policies can provide principles for areas such as record keeping (e.g., "Records will be available to the person, at any time they request it"—*self-determination*); quality assurance (e.g., "Consumers will be recruited to be integral members of the program evaluation team, helping to design program evaluation questions as well as to interpret the results"—*person involvement*) or policies about the setting itself (e.g., "The architectural layout, building resources and decorations within the setting will be welcoming to clients, and visitors as well as staff"—*person orientation*).

Procedures

In order to ensure that policies are meaningful directives for programs, ROMHP develops procedures for each policy. Procedures are designed to detail the steps that staff should perform to deliver the engagement, diagnostic, planning, intervention and disengagement or termination components of a program. For example, a policy may state: "Participants will be actively involved in the service process." Some of the procedures used to put this policy into practice may detail how those entering the program will be oriented in order to begin engaging the individuals in the program *(person involvement)*. This may include how to select the preferred orientation format (written material, discussion or both), for example. Based on a policy of program choice, another set of procedures may detail how to organize activities within the program so that program participants have an opportunity to choose whether and when they want to engage in a specific activity *(self-determination)*.

Record Keeping

Record-keeping reflects the four basic values as well. For example, records are designed not only to facilitate staff's documentation efforts but also to facilitate program participant's ability to read them *(person involvement)*. This includes issues such as large enough spaces for writing to be legible and using everyday language as much as possible in the documentation system. Records should reflect both what a person's strengths, talents, and interests are as well as what a person has difficulty with *(person orientation;*

growth potential). In addition, procedures should be in place that gives clients either copies of their own records or the ability to review their records with a minimal amount of waiting *(self-determination)*. Records should be organized so that clients are, at a minimum, able to write comments about what is recorded *(person involvement)* or ideally, able to change what is recorded if necessary *(self-determination)*.

Quality Assurance

Accountability has become a programmatic aspect of ever increasing importance. ROMHP quality assurance mechanisms allow supervisors and administrators to monitor the quality with which services are delivered. These include the use of service plans that are action-oriented, behaviorally written, and developed by both staff and those using the services, so that progress can be easily monitored *(person involvement; growth potential)*. In addition, ROMH programs involve all participants (staff, supervisors, consumers) in developing, planning and implementing the quality assurance mechanisms *(person involvement)*. For example, a ROMH program may choose to organize an ongoing Quality Management Team with representation from of all groups to accomplish this. Outcomes that are monitored include those selected by consumers (e.g., goal attainment, satisfaction with services and process) *(person involvement, self-determination)*.

Physical Setting

The physical environment of a program provides significant cues to those entering the setting, as to the kind of service provided and its values. A ROMH program makes an effort to welcome individuals using the services as well as professional visitors. Bathrooms, coat racks and coffee service set out in reception areas are for everyone's use, rather than being categorized as those used by clients and those used by staff and visitors *(person orientation)*. A ROMH program asks individuals receiving their services for input regarding decorating the setting, architectural or building resources that are required, in order to provide a welcoming and supportive environment *(person involvement)*.

Network of service

A ROMHP designs its services to link with or engage all types of services whether they occur in a general community environment (e.g., YMCA, places of worship, adult education centers) or in a formal mental health setting. While a ROMHP can advocate for the adoption of recovery oriented values in services or environments to which it links, or services or environments from which it accepts referrals or applications, the program can only dictate actually policies for those services which are within its own control.

Staffing

People with psychiatric disabilities indicate that the most critical facilitator or barriers to their own recovery are how people interact with them (Kramer & Gagne, 1997). Program dimensions for staff include components describing how programs select, train and supervise staff who are facilitating their clients' recovery.

Selection

In order to ensure that a ROMHP is delivered in a way that is consonant with recovery values, it is critical that staff candidates come to the program with the basic knowledge, attitudes and skills needed to promote recovery. Basic knowledge includes knowing the current research with respect to recovery and recovery outcomes as well as, for example, research related to the role of prejudice and discrimination as obstacles to recovery. Basic attitudes include the extent to which the four key values are incorporated into a candidate's way of thinking about individuals with disabilities or psychiatric histories. For example, does the person believe in *involving* participants in all aspects of their service process? Can they give examples of how they think this might be done? Does the candidate demonstrate a belief in *growth potential* or hopefulness? Do they have the skills to act on their values? Basic skills include skills such as the skill of engaging an individual in a partnership, inspiring hopefulness, connecting with that individual in a personal way, as well as supporting and facilitating the individual's recovery journey. Consistent with ROMHP emphasis on *person orientation* and *self-determination*, ROMHP value staff who have personal experience with mental health issues. A ROMH program assigns priority to those candidates who have both the required demonstrated competencies and consumer/survivor or ex-patient experience to bring to their work.

The selection process includes both in-depth interviews with potential staff and specific methods of directly assessing incoming staff's knowledge, attitudes and skills related to the recovery values (e.g., audiotape samples of client–staff candidate helping interviews and arranging for a trial visit so that the candidate can spend some hours or a day in the program). In addition, in keeping with the value of person involvement, ROMHP selection process includes program participants in a meaningful way. For example, this can include helping to determine selection criteria for new staff, interviewing staff candidates, reviewing resumes or providing input into the selection decisions.

Training

In addition to providing staff with training on aspects of the particular kind of ROMHP involved (e.g., research on new medications, clinical techniques for a treatment program, on effective means for networking and advocating for new services for case management programs), ROMHP designs training programs reflecting recovery values to increase staff knowledge, positive attitudes and skills. Providing staff with the resources to access new information consistent with these values (e.g., certain journal subscriptions, conferences, seminars), opportunities to meet with and understand the experiences of those who are recovering, as well as designing more long term competency building training programs compatible with these values, all serve to increase staff's ability to deliver a ROMHP. Indirect methods of training, such as involving new staff in teams whose values are compatible with recovery can also prove effective. For example, increasing staff's expectation of improvement (*growth potential*) may be accomplished by involving new staff in team meetings where higher expectations for outcomes are the norm (Alexander et al., 1997).

Supervision

Organizational climate has proven to be an important predictor of positive service outcomes (Glisson & Hemmelgarn, 1998; Mayer & Schoorman, 1992). Organizational climate is comprised of attitudes shared by staff about their work. Supervision is an important factor in promoting a positive organizational climate. Supervision sessions include a focus on recovery principles and competencies to ensure that recovery values are indeed translated into action in the program. For example, supervisors reinforce staff discussions of participants' strengths and possibilities in team planning and review meetings (*growth potential*). Supervisors review ways in which staff facilitates participants in making well-informed decisions throughout the service process (*self-determination*), even when staff disagree with the decisions. The supervisory process itself should be consistent with the recovery values. In other words, the process should involve staff, should focus on strengths as well as limitations, should concentrate on setting meaningful professional goals for improvement with respect to the delivery of recovery services as well as training plans to achieve the goals.

CONCLUSION

Evidence based practice, while able to produce specific outcomes such as reduced symptomatology, decreased hospitalization, fewer relapses or improved employment, may vary on its compatibility with recovery values and ingredients. We do not know at this time whether or not a values based practice adds unique outcome variance, either through improving the intended outcomes of the evidence based practice or by impacting outcomes more closely related to recovery (e.g., self-esteem, empowerment, well being). A program's ability, however, to describe a particular evidence based practice in relation to these ingredients can benefit the field in several ways. Consumers and advocates will have another set of criteria to more specifically evaluate the types of services they will receive from a particular organization. Administrators and program developers can evaluate how many recovery-oriented program dimensions their setting actually contains and develop plans for those areas in which they are not as strong. Researchers can more accurately describe the ingredients of the programs they research so that generalization issues can be addressed more specifically. The conceptualization of program dimensions by recovery values reflects our present knowledge about what values are believed to promote recovery practices for participants of mental health programs. It is our intent that these proposed ingredients be used to further the dialogue about the concept of recovery and its implication for evidence based service delivery. Future work can serve to further refine these recovery oriented program dimensions so that they can serve as a guide to the development of more comprehensive recovery-oriented mental health programs and contribute to making the vision statement of the President's New Freedom Commission on Mental Health a reality.

REFERENCES

Alexander, J. A., Lichtenstein, R., Daunno, T. A., McCormick, R., Muramatsu, N., & Ullman, E. (1997). Determinants of mental health providers' expectations of patients' improvement. *Psychiatric Services, 48*(5), 671–677.

Anthony, W. A. (1993). Recovery from mental illness: The guiding vision of the mental health service system in the 1990s. *Psychosocial Rehabilitation Journal, 16*(4), 11–23.

Anthony, W. A. (2001). The need for recovery-compatible evidence based practices. *Mental Health Weekly,* November 5, p. 5

Anthony, W. A., Cohen, M. R., Farkas, M., & Gagne, C. (2002). *Psychiatric rehabilitation.* Boston, MA: Center for Psychiatric Rehabilitation.

Anthony, W. A., Rogers, E. S., & Farkas, M. (2003). Evidence based practice in mental health. *Community Mental Health Journal, 39,* 101–114.

Beale, V. & Lambric, T. (1995). *The recovery concept: Implementation in the mental health system* (Report by the Community Support Program Advisory Committee). Columbus, OH: Ohio Department of Mental Health.

Beard, J. H., Propst, R. N., & Malamud, T. J. (1982). The Fountain House model of psychiatric rehabilitation. *Psychosocial Rehabilitation Journal, 5*(1), 47–53.

Becker, D. R., Drake, R. E., Farabaugh, A., & Bond, G. R. (1996). Job preferences of clients with severe psychiatric disorders participating in supported employment programs. *Psychiatric Services, 47*(11), 1223–1226.

Bell, M. & Lysaker, P. (1996). Levels of expectation for work activity in schizophrenia: Clinical and rehabilitation outcomes. *Psychiatric Rehabilitation Journal, 19*(3), 71–76.

Blackwell, B., Eiders, K., & Robinson, D. (2000). The consumer's role in assessing quality. In G. Stricker & W. Troy (Eds.), *Handbook of quality management in behavioral health: Issues in the practice of psychology.*

Bond, G. R., Becker, D. R., Drake, R. E., Rapp, C. A., Meisler, N., Lehman, A. F., Bell, M. D., & Blyler, C. R. (2001). Implementing supported employment as an evidence-based practice. *Psychiatric Services, 52*(3), 313–322.

Campbell, J. & Schraiber, R. (1989). *In pursuit of wellness: The well-being project: Mental health clients speak for themselves.* Sacramento, CA: California Department of Mental Health.

Carling, P. J. (1995). *Return to community: Building support systems for people with psychiatric disabilities.* New York: The Guilford Press.

Davidson, L. & Strauss, J. S. (1992). Sense of self in recovery from severe mental illness. *British Journal of Medical Psychology, 65*(2), 131–145.

Deegan, P. E. (1990). Spirit breaking: When the helping professions hurt. *Humanistic Psychologist, 18*(3), 301–313.

Deegan, P. E. (1993). Recovering our sense of value after being labeled. *Journal of Psychosocial Nursing and Mental Health, 31*(4), 7–11.

Drake, R. E., Goldman, H. H., Leff, H. S., Lehman, A. F., Dixon, L., Mueser, K. T., & Torrey, W. C. (2001). Implementing evidence-based practices in routine mental health service settings. *Psychiatric Services, 52*(2), 179–182.

Farkas, M. D., Anthony, W. A., & Cohen, M. R. (1989). An overview of psychiatric rehabilitation: The approach and its programs. In M. D. Farkas & W. A. Anthony (Eds.), *Psychiatric programs: Putting theory into practice.* Baltimore, MD: Johns Hopkins University Press.

Farkas, M., Cohen, M., & Nemec, P. (1988) Psychiatric rehabilitation programs: Putting concepts into practice. *Community Mental Health Journal, 24*(1), 7–21.

Farkas, M., Gagne, C., & Anthony, W. A. (2001). Recovery and rehabilitation: A paradigm for the new millennium. *La rehabilitacio psicosocial integral a la comunitat i amb la communitat, 1*(7/8), 13–16.

Fisher, D. & Ahern, L. (1999, Spring). People can recover from mental illness. *National Empowerment Center Newsletter,* 8–9. Lawrence, MA.

Frese, F. J., Stanley, J., Kress, K., & Vogel-Scibilia, S. (2001). Integrating evidence-based practices and the recovery model. *Psychiatric Services, 52*(11), 1462–1468.

Glisson, C., & Hemmelgarn, A. (1998). The effects of organizational climate and interorganization coordination on the quality and outcomes of children's service systems. *Child Abuse and Neglect, 22*(5), 401–421.

Harding, C. M. (in press). Overcoming the persistent resistance of clinicians to ideas of recovery in serious mental illness. In P. Ridgway & P. Deegan (Eds.), *Deepening the mental health recovery paradigm: Defining implications for practice.* Lawrence, Kansas: University of Kansas Press.

Harding, C., & Zahniser, J. (1994). Empirical correction of seven myths about schizophrenia with implications for treatment. *Acta Psychiatrica Scandinavica Supplementum, 90*(Suppl 384), 140–146.

Institute of Medicine Committee on Quality of Health Care in America (2001). *Crossing the Quality Chasm: A new Health System for the 21st Century.* Washington, DC: National Academies Press.

Jacobson, N., & Curtis, L. (2000). Recovery as policy in mental health services: Strategies emerging from the states. *Psychiatric Rehabilitation Journal, 23*(4), 333–341.

Jacobson, N., & Greenley, D. (2001). A conceptual model and explication. *Psychiatric Services, 52*(4), 482–485.

Kramer, P. J., & Gagne, C. A. (1997). Barriers to recovery and empowerment for people with psychiatric disabilities. In L. Spaniol, C. Gagne, & M. Koehler (Eds.), *The psychological and social aspects of psychiatric disability.* Boston, MA: Center for Psychiatric Rehabilitation.

Lapsley, H., Waimarie Nikora, L., & Black, R. (2002). Kia Mauri Tau! Narratives of Recovery from Disabling Mental Health Problems. University of Waikato Mental Health Narratives Project.

Majumder, R. K., Walls, R. T., & Fullmer, S. L. (1998). Rehabilitation client involvement in employment decisions. *Rehabilitation Counseling Bulletin, 42*(2), 162–173.

Mayer, R., & Schoorman, I. (1992). Predicting participation and production outcomes through a two dimensional model of organizational commitment. *Academy of Management Journal, 35*, 671–684.

McQuillan, B. (1994). My life with schizophrenia. In L. Spaniol & M. Koehler (Eds.), *The experience of recovery.* Boston, MA: Center for Psychiatric Rehabilitation.

Mead, S., & Copeland M. E. (2000). What recovery means to us: Consumers' perspective. *Community Mental Health Journal, 36*(3), 315–328.

Pyke, J., Lancaster, J., & Pritchard, J. (1997). Training for partnership. *Psychiatric Rehabilitation Journal, 21*(1), 64–66.

Ralph, R. O., Lambric, T. M., & Steele, R. B. (1996). Recovery Issues in a consumer developed evaluation of the mental health system. Presentation at *6th Annual Mental Health Services Research and Evaluation Conference*, Arlington, VA, February, pp.1–13.

Ridgway, P. (2001). ReStorying psychiatric disability: Learning from first person recovery narratives. *Psychiatric Rehabilitation Journal, 24*(4), 335–343.

Sanderson, W. C. (2002). Comment on Hansen et al: Would the results be the same if patients were receiving an evidence-based treatment? *Clinical Psychology Science and Practice, 9*(3): 350– 352.

Spaniol, L., Gagne, C., & Koehler, M. (1999). Recovery from serious mental illness: What it is and how to support people in their recovery. In R. P. Marinelli & A. E. Dell Orto (Eds.), *The psychological and social impact of disability* (4th ed.). New York: Springer Publishing.

Spaniol, L., & Gagne, C., et al. (2003). The recovery framework in rehabilitation: Concepts and practices from the field of serious mental illness. Sourcebook of rehabilitation and mental health services. J. R. Finch and D. Moxley. New York, Plenum. pp. 37–50.

Spaniol, L., Wewiorsky, N., Gagne, C., & Anthony, W. A. (2002). The process of recovery from schizophrenia. *International Review of psychiatry, 14*, 327–336.

State of Wisconsin Blue Ribbon Commission on Mental Health (1997). [On-line], Available: http://www.dhfs.state.wi.us/MH_BCMH/bluerib.htm.

Sullivan, W. P. (1994). A long and winding road: The process of recovery from severe mental illness. *Innovations and Research, 3*(3), 19–27.

The President's New Freedom Commission on Mental Health (2003). Achieving the Promise: Transforming Mental Health Care in America. Final Report.

Torgalsboen, A. K., & B. R. Rund (1998). Full recovery from schizophrenia in the long term: A ten-year follow-up of eight former schizophrenic patients. *Psychiatry: Interpersonal and Biological Processes, 61*(1), 20–34.

Torrey, W. C., Drake, R. E., Dixon, L., Burns, B. J., Flynn, L., Rush, A. J., Clark, R. E., & Klatzker, D. (2001). *Implementing evidence-based practices for persons with severe mental illnesses. Psychiatric Services, 52*(1), 45–50.

Unzincker, R. (1989). On my own: A personal journey through madness and re-emergence. *Psychosocial Rehabilitation Journal, 13*(1), 71–77.

Weingarten, R. (1994). The ongoing process of recovery. *Psychiatry, 57*, 369–375.

Young, S. L., & Ensing, D. S. (1999). Exploring recovery from the perspective of people with psychiatric disabilities. *Psychiatric Rehabilitation Journal, 22*(3), 219–231.

Appendices

Appendix A

A Summary of Each Article and Book Chapter's Contribution to the Field

I THE HISTORICAL SHIFT FROM "DANGEROUSNESS" TO VIOLENCE RISK ASSESSMENT

1 Assessing dangerousness in criminals

SCOTT, 1977

- Stresses the importance of a thorough assessment.
- Suggests that information not be taken at face value.
- States that there are no direct indicators of dangerousness. Each factor may become important in the presence of others or be neutralized by others.
- Advocates an organized and systematic approach drawing on polydimensional domains of information.
- Hints at the relevance of what will become known as Factor 1 psychopathy features.

2 Dangerousness: Conceptual, prediction and public policy issues

SHAH, 1981

- Addresses the significance of situational factors.
- Creates first of its kind list of decision points that involve consideration of an individual's dangerousness.

- Argues that accuracy can be improved through various means, including relying on actuarial and statistical information.
- Challenges the myth that people with mental illness are an inherently dangerous group.
- Insists that experts (who testify in the courts) be knowledgeable about both the relevant legal issues and questions, and the scientific and professional literature in the field.

3 Improving the clinical practice of violence risk assessment: Technology, guidelines, and training

BORUM, 1996

- Calls for the creation of professional standards for violence risk assessment.
- Recommends that specialized training programs be developed for people who conduct violence risk assessments.

4 The Canadian contribution to violence risk assessment: History and implications for current psychiatric practice

BLOOM ET AL., 2005

- Reviews historical background of Canada's contribution to the field of violence risk assessment.
- Provides 10 broad risk assessment principles.
- Describes how progenitor tools spawned series of population and situation-specific structured professional judgment (SPJ) guides.

II THE EMERGENCE OF ACTUARIAL VIOLENCE PREDICTION

5 Understanding prediction instruments

MOSSMAN, 2004

- States that clinicians and researchers can easily underestimate the benefit of actuarial instruments and the help they can provide to evaluators. Yet it is possible to attach more significance to actuarial results than intended by the developers of such measures.
- Reviews the statistical basics of actuarial risk assessment in a straightforward easily understandable format, and describes the essential features and orientation of some of the commonly used schemes.
- Emphasizes that actuarial tools focus a clinician's attention on specific aspects, behaviour or other characteristics of the person being examined.
- Comments on the distinction between actuarial measures and clinical judgment by suggesting that the actuarial method is probably better for assessing violence risk. This is in part because clinicians do not ascribe appropriate value to the

kinds of information used in these schemes. As well, they tend not to place appropriate weight on aspects of the clinical information on which they base their decisions.

- Notes that actuarial tools have the advantage of being transparent and offer explicitly prescribed methods for combining data.
- Advises clinicians conducting a risk assessment to focus on "research-proven factors" that affect an individual's risk for violence.

6   The accuracy of predictions of violence to others

LIDZ, MULVEY & GARDNER, 1993

- Points out that the accuracy of risk prediction could be improved if clinicians were provided with accurate up-to-date information on rates of recidivism and violence in the reference group to which the individual being assessed belongs (e.g., sex offenders, domestic assaulters).
- Provides data to suggest that clinicians were particularly poor at predicting violence in women, in part owing to their tendency to underestimate the rate of violence in female patients, and in part due to their failing to recognize those cues that herald violence in that population.

7   Violent recidivism of mentally disordered offenders: The development of a statistical prediction instrument

HARRIS, RICE & QUINSEY, 1993

- Describes the research, based on more than 600 men, that inspired the development of the VRAG.
- Identifies the inherent difficulty of predicting events that occur infrequently (i.e., that have low base rates).
- Describes how the 12 (statistically weighted) factors of the VRAG correlate with violent recidivism. These factors include the Hare PCL-R list scores, elementary school maladjustment, separation from parents under age 16, age at index offence and failure on prior conditional release.
- Concludes that actuarial estimates of risk can anchor clinical judgment and that dynamic information can be used to adjust actuarially derived scores.

8   Forecasting recidivism in mentally ill offenders released from prison

GAGLIARDI ET AL., 2004

- Examines nine variables, five of which turn out to function protectively, to determine which one(s) have predictive power in certain populations.
- Uses readily available file information (gender, first-time sex offender, history of residential mental health treatment in prison) to reach a notable level of accuracy akin to published actuarial schemes.
- Points out that clinicians in the "clinical vs. actuarial debate" may be disadvantaged

due to the inaccessibility of potentially influential clinical information arising daily. Frequent and continual re-assessment of dynamic factors could increase the accuracy of all predictions and allow for effective interventions.
- Suggests that a few correctional records could be as accurate as more elaborate risk assessment schemes in predicting recidivism. This finding has significance for resource and budgetary allocations.

III CLINICAL PREDICTION AND ASSESSMENT

9 Risk assessment, prediction, and foreseeability

REID, 2003

- Reminds us that risk assessment is not a three-minute exercise.
- Takes an optimistic approach centred on what clinicians can do effectively around risk assessment vs. what they cannot do.
- Reviews the benefits and shortcomings of checklists and the problem of over-relying on any checklist or actuarial tool.

10 Personality disorder: The patients psychiatrists dislike

LEWIS & APPLEBY, 1988

- Questions whether personality disorder should be preserved in diagnostic nomenclature.
- Demonstrates that the designation "personality disorder" can result in prejudicial treatment.

11 Utility of decision support tools for assessing acute risk of violence

MCNIEL ET AL., 2003

- Strongly suggests that risk factors for violence in acute exacerbation of mental illness are not the same as those for assessing more chronic risk.

12 The prediction of violence in acute psychiatric units

WATTS ET AL., 2003

- Says that clinical factors are to be accorded the greatest weight in assessing risk for violence in patients who are seriously mentally ill.
- Finds that hostile-suspiciousness is the most potent factor predicting actual assaults.
- Observes that withdrawal-retardation is the best predictor of aggressive behaviour.
- Stresses that different risk factors may be predictive of different untoward behavioural outcomes in different people.

13   The uncritical acceptance of risk assessment in forensic practice

ROGERS, 2000

- Argues that risk assessments should be adjusted to account for the potentially moderating effects of protective factors.
- Suggests the importance of a balanced evaluation that keeps in perspective the contributions of risk and protective factors, and the interrelationship between these factors.
- Asserts that uncritical overreliance on static factors may result in a lopsided evaluation that deprives the subject of more liberty than is necessary and leads to undue consumption of resources.

14   The short-term assessment of risk and treatability (START): A prospective validation study in a forensic psychiatric sample

NICHOLLS ET AL., 2006

- Proposes an SPJ scheme for evaluating various risks in the short term.
- Emphasizes the necessity of assessing patients' strengths as well as vulnerabilities.
- States that some but not all patients and prisoners display "signature risk signs." These are idiosyncratic markers that can forecast violence in the individual case.

IV   THE ACTUARIAL VERSUS CLINICAL CONTROVERSY

15   Transcending the actuarial versus clinical polemic in assessing risk for violence

WEBSTER, HUCKER & BLOOM, 2002

- Portrays the divisive nature of the debate between the actuarial and clinical camps as being counterproductive. Information from both domains may be of varying importance depending on the specific decision to be made.
- Suggests that risk assessments must be consistent with the legal test or standard under which they are authorized.
- Provides five basic criteria for conducting and presenting a risk assessment to an adjudicatory board or tribunal.

16   Actuarial versus clinical assessments of dangerousness

LITWACK, 2001

- Argues that actuarial predictions are not superior to clinical predictions when it comes to assessments of dangerousness.
- Asserts that it is premature to substitute actuarial for clinical assessments of violence risk.
- Offers an authoritative overview of the actuarial versus clinical debate.

• Suggests that it may be unethical for experts to definitively claim (in the courtroom) that either assessment approach has more predictive power than the other.

17 Risk assessment and release decision-making: Toward resolving the great debate

DVOSKIN & HEILBRUN, 2001

• Asserts that forensic release decision making should distinguish between three aspects of risk:
  - Imminence, defined by the pattern of violence in a person's prior career, as well as their statements, plans, target availability and life circumstances
  - Severity, defined by prior violence to date, including the current charges and
  - Probability, defined best by actuarial models.
• Confirms that the safest way to free or derestrict an individual is by incrementally decreasing structure and increasing freedom. Increments must depend on the degree of concern about any of the three aspects referred to above. The threshold should be met successfully and next steps negotiated to justify giving the person greater freedom.
• Posits that whether the actuarial or clinical approach is to be preferred depends on whether the task at hand involves a long-term actuarial prediction or recommendations for interventions that might reduce risk following discharge from hospital.

18 Violent storms and violent people: How meteorology can inform risk communication in mental health law

MONAHAN & STEADMAN, 1996

• Draws on weather forecasting as an analogy for assessing risk for violence. Apart from longer term forecasts (the actuarial component, by analogy) that provide a general, albeit not infallible, sense of what lies ahead, assessing local conditions through knowledge of unique local circumstances (the clinical component, by analogy) allows for a more specific forecast.
• Explains how the purpose of a risk assessment, by analogy to any warning system, is to enable those responsible to take the appropriate steps to avert harm.
• Argues that understanding how best to communicate assessments of risk is as important to mental health laws as improving the validity of those assessments themselves.

V DECISION MAKING

19 Offenders remanded for a psychiatric examination: Perceived treatability and disposition

QUINSEY & MAGUIRE, 1983

• Elicits the views of a multidisciplinary team that assessed 200 consecutive remands to a maximum-security remand facility. Even after each evaluee was conferenced by the team, there was surprisingly little agreement (except regarding the administration of antipsychotic medication for patients with schizophrenia). There was little agreement about what psychological and other non-pharmacological interventions would be of benefit.

- Captures the view in the field at a time when there was much pessimism about treatment for offenders with personality disorders.

20 Risk assessment as collective clinical judgment

MURPHY, 2002

- Provides a number of often-not-considered insights to increase the accuracy of risk assessments and to diminish attendant risks of the process, including that:
  - collective judgment (by a multidisciplinary team) is less biased than the opinion of sole practitioners.
  - apart from potential physical dangers that risk assessors contend with (and look to avoid), clinicians must consider the risk of psychological harm or suffering associated with proximity to difficult patients.
  - assessing teams should be clear about the task at hand, as ambiguity arouses anxiety and other unpleasant affects.
  - anxiety engendered by working with difficult people in stressful forensic settings can lead to various maladaptive responses, including a countertherapeutic, militaristic environment, sadistic behaviour and dehumanizing conduct.
  - danger intensifies feelings—idealization or disaffection—about leaders. Leaders may be pushed to become more authoritarian or, at the other extreme, let chaos reign supreme.
  - the environment should be less authoritarian and more democratic so that patients can join and then internalize the values of the group.
  - patients require space in which to reflect.
- Risk assessment is best described as a human endeavour, and not in the language of scientific measurement.

21 The impact of confidence on the accuracy of structured professional and actuarial violence risk judgments in a sample of forensic psychiatric patients

DOUGLAS & OGLOFF, 2003

- Illustrates how ratings of risk (including the historical component) on the HCR-20 (and presumably any other schemes) become more accurate when the assessors have confidence in their ratings.

22 Building mental health professionals' decisional models into tests of predictive validity: The accuracy of contextualized predictions of violence

SKEEM, MULVEY & LIDZ, 2000

- Argues for a circumstancial approach to evaluating mental health professionals' risk assessments by considering the conditions that these professionals believe to be important in making patient violence likely.
- Examines whether it is possible to increase clinicians' accuracy levels through "contextualized" predictions of violence. Using drinking behaviour as a key factor, the authors demonstrate that clinicians show little ability to predict violence-related incidents.
- Concludes that knowing who drank and who didn't drink did not increase the predictive power of binary predictions of who would become violent.
- Reaches beyond disappointing results to show that the study supports the importance of addressing the precise circumstances (through environmental or victim factors, or interaction of more than one risk factor) in which violence will result. It is vitally important that research isolates theoretical and actuarial factors that bring about violence in a predisposed individual.

23 The influence of actuarial risk assessment in clinical judgments and tribunal decisions about mentally disordered offenders in maximum security

HILTON & SIMMONS, 2001

- Suggests that actuarial risk assessment scores exerted little influence on both clinical judgment and tribunal decisions concerning the release/derestriction of accused people with mental disorders at a maximum-security forensic facility.
- Reveals how senior clinicians who testified about the patient's risk tended to emphasize clinical progress more than demonstrated criminogenic and other factors better associated with actual risk.
- Notes (as have other authors) a bias in favour of attractive-appearing patients. They are more apt to be recommended for release than unattractive patients.

VI TREATMENTS, SECURITY AND PROGRAM PLANNING

24 Reducing violence in severe mental illness: Randomised controlled trial of intensive case management compared with standard care

WALSH ET AL., 2001

- Reports how intensive case management did not reduce violence in psychotic patients in comparison with standard case management.
- Supports the view that decisions concerning the quantity, intensity, and efficacy of treatment need to be evidence based, given the problem of resource allocation.

25   Treating patients found not guilty by reason of insanity

SALEKIN & ROGERS, 2001

- Addresses the implications of treatment being invariably imposed and motivation being external in NGRI/NCR accused patients.
- Advises treatment should be tailored to the patient's specific clinical needs.
- Finds the goals of treatment are fourfold:
  - Diagnose and treat mental disorder
  - Reduce the risk of dangerousness
  - Prepare the NGRI patient for return to the community
  - Monitor his or her adjustment in the community
- Posits that patients could benefit from concurrent treatment of their psychosis and (often secondarily diagnosed) substance use problems through pharmaco-therapy and psychotherapy, as well as life skills, social skills, vocational counselling and anger management, as applicable.

26   An evaluation of a maximum security therapeutic community for psychopaths and other mentally disordered offenders

RICE, HARRIS & CORMIER, 1992

- Discusses how treatment in a maximum-security therapeutic community program was effective in reducing recidivism in non-psychopathic patients.
- Discovers that psychopathic patients in the program (paradoxically) exhibited higher rates of recidivism.
- Draws the conclusion that the Hare psychopathy checklist scores strongly correlate with recidivism.
- Questions whether people with psychopathic tendencies may use programs (social environments) of this kind as a means of becoming more adept at crime.

27   Psychopathy and therapeutic pessimism: Clinical lore or clinical reality?

SALEKIN, 2001

- Reviews 42 treatment studies on psychopathy and concludes that there is an insufficient scientific basis for the belief that psychopathy is untreatable.
- Reveals that psychological interventions (such as psychoanalytically oriented therapy or cognitive-behavioural approaches) were surprisingly effective.
- Establishes how further research is needed to identify what aspects of psychopathy are amenable to treatment (and what effect that would have on recidivism).
- Suggests that research into the specific cause(s) of the disorder may have important implications for isolating as yet untested treatment approaches, depending on the cause(s) identified.
- Concludes that, pending the outcome of research, therapeutic pessimism of the kind that has enveloped the psychopathy-treatment relationship is unwarranted.

28 Preventing crime by people with schizophrenic disorders: The role of psychiatric services

HODGINS & MÜLLER-ISBERNER, 2004

- Demonstrates how patients admitted to psychiatric facilities for schizophrenia spectrum conditions should be screened for a history of conduct disorder/antisocial personality disorder. Patients with schizophrenia who have these characteristics and substance use problems commit crime and violence at increased rates. Once their psychosis subsides, they should receive cognitive behavioural interventions to reduce criminal attitudes and associated behaviours.
- Suggests that conduct disorder and substance misuse may be a risk factor for schizophrenia in some individuals.

29 Therapeutic uses of security: Mapping forensic mental health services by stratifying risk

KENNEDY, 2002

- States that security at any greater level than is necessary to contain risk is counter-therapeutic.
- Distinguishes in detail the different aspects of security—environmental, relational and procedural—and their relative contribution to patient management.
- Stresses that forensic planners, administrators and clinicians must understand and strive to create a forensic services system that stratifies each patient to the appropriate level of risk—for security, therapeutic and resource allocations reasons.
- Emphasizes that senior clinicians must take a keen interest in systemic, definitional and organizational issues to achieve the program's objective—contain risk, minimize detention and advance therapeutic goals.
- Concludes that moving a patient to a new placement or new clinical team is, in itself, likely to increase risk. Recommendations for taking such therapeutic risks are more credible if they are made by clinicians who will take responsibility for the risk.

30 The security needs assessment profile: A multidimensional approach to measuring security needs

COLLINS & DAVIES, 2005

- Develops the 22-item Security Needs Assessment Profile (SNAP) as a means of comprehensively describing a patient's security needs, and aids experienced forensic clinicians to assess patients' security needs across a range of security dimensions.

31 Implementing recovery oriented evidence based programs: Identifying the critical dimensions

FARKAS ET AL., 2005

- Challenges the long-held assumption that people with severe mental disorder cannot and do not recover, and on the contrary, deteriorate over time.
- Laments the fact that mental health policy and treatment programs are not oriented to recovery.
- Describes the ideal components of a recovery-oriented mental health program (ROMHP)—mission statements, policies, procedures, record keeping practices and quality assurance processes—consistent with fundamental recovery values.

Appendix B

Resources

Over the past quarter century, a great deal has been written on risk assessment and risk management. Some of this is scientific, some is professional, and some addresses administrative, policy and legal issues. Recent work is based in the areas of civil psychiatry, forensic mental health and corrections. This appendix draws attention to particularly vital books, monographs and manuals in this field.

KEY RESOURCES

Monahan, J. (1981). *Predicting Violent Behavior: An Assessment of Clinical Techniques.* **Beverly Hills, CA: Sage.**

Though published close to three decades ago, this short text by John Monahan remains surprisingly fresh in its outlook. It marks the transition from the older construct of "dangerousness" to the newer idea of "risk." Monahan distinguishes between the so-called actuarial (static) approach and the clinical (dynamic) point of view. When it comes to making predictions, at least over the long term, an actuarial approach tends to rely on static factors, which can usually be obtained from existing records. A clinical approach, on the other hand, is often more concerned with professional assessment practices than predicting future violence *per se:* the clinician has the opportunity to consider how, within the individual, numerous factors change and interact with one another. The assessment challenge is to isolate the number of factors currently in play and to estimate their roles in the future. In practice, it is often difficult to draw a clear distinction between statistically driven, static factors and individual-centred, dynamic considerations. Mental health professionals should consider both when conducting violence risk assessments.

At one point in the text, Monahan argues, on the basis of the then-extant evidence, that mental illness is a "non-correlate" of violence. We now know that the relationship between mental disorder and violence does exist, but that it tends to be small, except when substance use problems are involved. (See Monahan et al., 2001, page 605).

(See also an excellent book from the same period, *Violence and the Violent Individual*, edited by Hays, Roberts & Soloway [1981].)

Quinsey, V.L., Harris, G.T., Rice, M.E. & Cormier, C. (2006). *Violent Offenders: Appraising and Managing Risk* (2nd ed.) Washington, DC: American Psychological Association. (Originally published in 1998.)

Within the forensic mental health field, this book provides the best-known treatment of actuarial factors in the prediction of violence. It is required reading for all researchers and clinicians in the area of violence risk assessment. The text details a 12-item Violence Risk Appraisal Guide (VRAG). This scheme, which has attracted much attention in recent years, is based on a study of more than 600 men treated for at least two years in the maximum-security mental health facility in Penetanguishene, Ontario. Factors possibly predictive of subsequent violence were examined systematically in file reviews. These factors were then tested against actual outcome 10 years later, after the men had been released to the community. The VRAG was achieved by extracting and weighting the 12 most powerful predictor variables. The authors are able to show an orderly relationship between VRAG score (across nine equal-sized "bins") and subsequent violence.

Hare, R. (2003). *Hare Psychopathy Checklist—Revised: 2nd Edition.* Toronto: Multi-Health Systems. (Manual originally published in 1991.)

In the VRAG scheme, psychopathy—as measured by the Hare Psychopathy Checklist—Revised (PCL-R)—was the variable most predictive of future violence. Although Hare never originally conceived his psychopathy checklist as a violence prediction scheme, it is included in this appendix because of its predictive power. The notion of psychopathy, elaborated as early as 1941 by the American psychiatrist Hervey Cleckley, has been studied extensively by Hare and others over many years. Hare has articulated the construct of psychopathy and shown how it can be measured. His scheme relies on 20 items, all clearly defined in his manual.

The bulk of modern studies that have included Hare PCL-R scores as a violence predictor do indeed show an association between Hare PCL-R scores and subsequent violence, even though Hare PCL-R was never originally developed as a risk assessment device. The Hare approach to psychopathy is structured: that is, items are defined and "manualized," with a clear method for scoring each item. Hare and many others have been able to demonstrate that colleagues in various mental health, forensic and correctional disciplines can code the items reliably (i.e., one assessor achieves scores similar to those of another given interview access to the same patient and that patient's documents).

Those wishing a less technical, but nonetheless informative, account of psychopathy are referred to Hare's popular text *Without Conscience: The Disturbing World of the Psychopaths Among Us* (1998) and Bakiak and Hare's *Snakes in Suits: When Psychopaths Go to Work* (2006). Readers may also wish to consult the *Handbook of Psychopathy*, a recently edited book on the topic (Patrick, 2006).

Webster, C.D., Douglas K.S., Eaves, D. & Hart, S.D. (1997). *HCR-20: Assessing Risk for Violence (version 2).* Burnaby, BC: Mental Health Law and Policy Institute, Simon Fraser University. (Originally published in 1995.)

This structured, violence risk assessment guide is designed for mental health practitioners. Like the Hare PCL-R scheme, it contains 20 defined items all scored 0, 1 or 2. However, this scheme is different from others in that it divides variables into three distinct categories: past (historical), present (clinical) and future (risk management). The authors identify 10 historical items, five clinical items and five risk management items. The HCR-20 has been translated into several languages.

An annotated bibliography of the HCR-20, *HCR-20: Violence Risk Management Companion Guide* by Kevin Douglas and colleagues (2001), provides an up-to-date summary of research evidence and commentary in support of the HCR-20. For a more fully developed account of this and related "structured decision-enhancing" schemes, see *Impulsivity* (1997) by Webster and Jackson. Some readers will also be interested in Douglas et al.'s 2001 discussion of how the individual C and R items of the HCR-20 can prompt clinicians to think about how best to help patients create changes in their lives and how such changes can be measured.

Monahan, J., Steadman, H.J., Silver, E., Appelbaum, P.S., Robbins, P.C., Mulvey, E.P., Roth, L., Grisso, T. & Banks, S. (2001). *Rethinking Risk Assessment: The MacArthur Study of Mental Disorder and Violence.* Oxford: Oxford University Press.

This long-anticipated book summarizes the authors' painstaking research over several years on the "MacArthur project." Their large scale, multi-site study relied on a thorough assessment of about 1,000 civil patients released into the community. Consistent with other emerging results from contemporary research, the study showed that various aspects of previous violence and Hare PCL-R psychopathy link to subsequent violence. The findings also buttress the fact that violence at follow-up is elevated when someone has both a major mental illness and a substance use problem. By itself, major mental illness was not found to be a particularly strong variable in predicting violence, but increased markedly in predictive power when the person also had a substance use problem.

While, generally, the variable-by-variable results from the MacArthur study are consistent with findings from other modern investigations, Monahan and colleagues suggest that further research should focus not so much on isolating and further refining the definition of actuarial and dynamic variables but on finding out how these variables combine and interact in individual clinical cases. They argue that, while mental health professionals will have to continue—for now—to rely on clinical acumen, it may be possible, eventually, to develop computer software that will help clinicians make judgments on behalf of their patients. The text contains a wealth of new information and commentary.

Hodgins, S. & Janson, C.G. (2001). *Criminality and Violence Among the Mentally Disordered: The Stockholm Metropolitan Project.* Cambridge: Cambridge University Press.

The "Stockholm project" takes advantage of a very large data set, maintained over many years. Whereas the Monahan undertaking was largely psychiatric and psychological in emphasis, the Hodgins and Janson study is weighted more toward sociological and epidemiological interests—though by no means ignoring psychological and clinical variables. It reveals how variables isolated in early childhood continue to play an exceedingly important role throughout the life span. The authors also provide evidence supporting the idea that clinicians who work in the civil psychiatric area should thoroughly assess their patients for possible violence against others.

Loeber, R. & Farrington, D.P. (Eds.) (2001). *Child Delinquents: Development, Interventions and Service Needs.* Thousand Oaks, CA: Sage.

This edited text emphasizes how crucial it is to consider early childhood factors when assessing and managing risk in adolescence and adulthood.

Three practical guides—*Early Assessment Risk List for Boys: EARL-20B* by L. Augimeri et al., 2001; *Early Assessment Risk List for Girls: EARL-21G* by K. Levene et al., 2001, and the *Manual for the Structured Assessment of Violence Risk in Youth (SAVRY)* by Borum et al., 2002—draw on the material contained in this book. The first two guides are designed for assessing children under 12, while the third is intended for assessing adolescents. This third guide uses the same basic format as the two EARL manuals and the HCR-20.

Ashford, J.B., Sales, B.D. & Reid, W.H. (Eds.) (2001). *Treating Adult and Juvenile Offenders with Special Needs.* **Washington, D.C.: American Psychological Association.**

With emerging knowledge about risk assessment and management, Ashford, Sales and Reid have edited a useful and authoritative compendium on best practices in risk assessment and management. This is largely "population-based," in that editors have tried to capture how basic risk assessment and risk management principles can be applied to a variety of populations, such as offenders with intellectual disabilities, sex offenders and perpetrators of spousal assault.

Blumenthal, S. & Lavender, T. (2000). *Violence and Mental Disorder: A Critical Aid to the Assessment and Management of Risk.* **London: Jessica Kingsley.**

This short, easy-to-read text provides a historical overview on the topic, discusses the seemingly pointless debate about the relative merits of actuarial versus clinical variables, and comments lightly on such topics as psychopathy, variables arising in early childhood and risk management issues.

Webster, C.D. & Hucker, S.J. (2007). *Violence Risk Assessment and Management.* **(Originally published by St. Joseph's Healthcare, Hamilton, in 2003.)**

This book is similar to the Blumenthal and Lavender text, in that it is an introduction to the topic of violence risk assessment and management, though it's more up to date. It covers such topics as legal issues, theories, diagnoses, structured professional judgment, treatment, evidence and the communication of violence-related risks. It also includes a series of questions at the end, which readers can use to test their knowledge of the content. Short case vignettes are provided throughout. The book contains original contributions on perpetrators of spousal assault (Randy Kropp), sex offenders (Karl Hanson) and managing transitions during phases of recovery (Mary-Lou Martin).

ADDITIONAL RESOURCES

Augimeri, L., Koegl, C., Webster, C.D. & Levene, K. (2001). *The Early Assessment Risk List for Boys:* EARL-20B (Version 2). Toronto: Earlscourt Child and Family Centre.

Babiak, P. & Hare, R.D. (2006). *Snakes in Suits: When Psychopaths Go to Work.* New York: HarperCollins.

Borum, R., Bartel, P. & Forth, A. (2003). *Manual for the Structured Assessment of Violence Risk in Youth (SAVRY).* (Version 1.1). Tampa, FL: University of South Florida. (Original version, 2002.)

Cleckley, H. (1941). *The Mask of Sanity*. St. Louis, MO: Mosby.

Douglas, K.S., Webster, C.D., Eaves, D., Hart, S.D. & Ogloff, J.R.P. (Eds.). (2001). *HCR-20: Violence Risk Management Companion Guide*. Burnaby, B.C.: Mental Health Law and Policy Institute, Simon Fraser University and Tampa: The Louis de la Parte Florida: Mental Health Institute, University of South Florida.

Hare, R. (1985). A checklist for the assessment in criminal populations. In M.H. Ben-Aron, S.J. Hucker & C.D. Webster (Eds.), *Clinical Criminology: The Assessment and Treatment of Criminal Behaviour*. Toronto: M and M Graphics.

Hare, R. (1991). *Manual for the Hare Psychopathy Checklist—Revised*. Toronto: Multi-Health Systems.

Hare (1998). *Without Conscience: The Disturbing World of the Psychopaths Among Us*. New York: Guilford.

Hays, J.R., Roberts, T.K. & Soloway, K.S. (Eds.). (1981). *Violence and the Violent Individual*. New York: SP Medical and Scientific Books.

Hodgins, S. (Ed.). (2000). *Violence Among the Mentally Ill: Effective Treatment and Management Strategies*. Dordrecht, The Netherlands: Kluwer Academic.

Hodgins, S. & Müller-Isberner, R. (Eds.). (2000). *Violence, Crime and Mentally Disordered Offenders: Concepts and Methods for Effective Treatment and Prevention*. Chichester: Wiley.

Hollin, C.R. (Ed.). (2004). *The Essential Handbook of Offender Assessment and Treatment*. Chichester: Wiley.

Levene, K.S., Augimeri, L.K., Pepler, D.J., Walsh, M.M., Webster, C.D. & Koegl, C.J. (2001). *Early Assessment Risk List for Girls: EARL-21G* (Version 1, Consultation Edition). Toronto: Earlscourt Child and Family Centre.

Monahan, J. & Steadman, H.J. (Eds.) (1994). *Violence and Mental Disorder: Developments in Risk Assessment*. Chicago, IL: University of Chicago Press.

Pagani, L., & Pinard, G.-F. (Eds.). (2001). *Clinical Assessment of Dangerousness*. Cambridge: Cambridge University Press.

Patrick, C.J. (Ed.). (2006). *Handbook of Psychopathy*. New York: Guilford.

Webster, C.D., Ben-Aron, M.H. & Hucker, S.J. (1985). *Dangerousness: Probability and Prediction, Psychiatry and Public Policy*. New York: Cambridge University Press.

Webster, C.D. & Jackson, M.A. (1997). *Impulsivity: Theory, Assessment, and Treatment*. New York: Guilford.

Appendix C

Reference List of Reprinted Journal Articles and Book Chapters

I THE HISTORICAL SHIFT FROM "DANGEROUSNESS" TO VIOLENCE RISK ASSESSMENT

1. Scott, P.D. (1977). Assessing dangerousness in criminals. *British Journal of Psychiatry, 13* (1), 127–142.

2. Shah, S.A. (1981). Dangerousness: Conceptual, prediction and public policy issues. In J.R. Hays, T.K. Roberts & K.S. Solway (Eds.), *Violence and the Violent Individual* (pp. 151–178). New York: SP Medical and Scientific Books.

3. Borum, R. (1996). Improving the clinical practice of violence risk assessment: Technology, guidelines, and training. *American Psychologist, 51* (9), 945–956.

4. Bloom, H., Webster C., Hucker, S. & De Freitas, K. (2005). The Canadian contribution to violence risk assessment: History and implications for current psychiatric practice. *Canadian Journal of Psychiatry, 50* (1), 3–11.

II THE EMERGENCE OF ACTUARIAL VIOLENCE PREDICTION

5. Mossman, D. (2004). Understanding prediction instruments. In R.I. Simon & L.H. Gold (Eds.), *Textbook of Forensic Psychiatry* (pp. 501–523). Washington, DC: American Psychiatric Publishing.

6. Lidz, C.W., Mulvey, E.P. & Gardner, W. (1993). The accuracy of predictions of violence to others. *Journal of the American Medical Association, 269* (8), 1007–1011.

7. Harris, G.T., Rice, M.E. & Quinsey, V.L. (1993). Violent recidivism of mentally disordered offenders: The development of a statistical prediction instrument. *Criminal Justice and Behavior, 20*, 315–335.

8. Gagliardi, G.J., Lovell, D., Peterson, P.D. & Jemelka, R. (2004). Forecasting recidivism in mentally ill offenders released from prison. *Law and Human Behavior, 28* (2), 133–155.

III CLINICAL PREDICTION AND ASSESSMENT

9. Reid, W.H. (2003). Risk assessment, prediction, and foreseeability. *Journal of Psychiatric Practice, 9* (1), 82–86.

10. Lewis, G. & Appleby, L. (1988). Personality disorder: The patients psychiatrists dislike. *British Journal of Psychiatry, 153*, 44–49.

11. McNiel, D.E., Gregory, A.L., Lam, J.N., Binder, R.L. & Sullivan, G.R. (2003). Utility of Decision Support Tools for Assessing Acute Risk of Violence. *Journal of Consulting and Clinical Psychology, 71* (5), 945–953.

12. Watts, D., Leese, M., Thomas, S., Atakan, Z. & Wykes, T. (2003). The prediction of violence in acute psychiatric units. *International Journal of Forensic Mental Health, 2* (2), 173–180

13. Rogers, R. (2000). The uncritical acceptance of risk assessment in forensic practice. *Law and Human Behavior, 24* (5), 595–605.

14. Nicholls, T.L., Brink J., Desmarais, S.L., Webster, C.D. & Martin, M-L. (2006). The Short-Term Assessment of Risk and Treatability (START): A prospective validation study in a forensic psychiatric sample. *Assessment, 13*, 313–327.

IV THE ACTUARIAL VERSUS CLINICAL CONTROVERSY

15. Webster, C.D., Hucker, S.J. & Bloom, H. (2002). Transcending the actuarial versus clinical polemic in assessing risk for violence. *Criminal Justice and Behavior, 29*, 659–665.

16. Litwack, T.R. (2001). Actuarial versus clinical assessments of dangerousness. *Psychology, Public Policy and Law, 7* (2), 409–443.

17. Dvoskin, J.A. & Heilbrun, K. (2001). Risk assessment and release decision-making: Toward resolving the great debate. *The Journal of the American Academy of Psychiatry and the Law, 29*, 6–10.

18. Monahan, J. & Steadman, H.J. (1996). Violent storms and violent people: How meteorology can inform risk communication in mental health law. *American Psychologist, 51* (9), 931–938.

V DECISION MAKING

19. Quinsey, V.L. & Maguire, A. (1983). Offenders remanded for a psychiatric examination: Perceived treatability and disposition. *International Journal of Law and Psychiatry, 6* (2), 193–205.

20. Murphy, D. (2002). Risk assessment as collective clinical judgment. *Criminal Behaviour and Mental Health, 12,* 169–178.

21. Douglas, K.S. & Ogloff, J.R.P. (2003). The impact of confidence on the accuracy of structured professional and actuarial violence risk judgments in a sample of forensic psychiatric patients. *Law and Human Behavior, 27* (6), 573–587.

22. Skeem, J.L., Mulvey, E.P. & Lidz, C.W. (2000). Building mental health professionals' decisional models into tests of predictive validity: The accuracy of contextualized predictions of violence. *Law and Human Behavior, 24* (6), 607–628.

23. Hilton, N.Z. & Simmons, J.L. (2001). The influence of actuarial risk assessment in clinical judgments and tribunal decisions about mentally disordered offenders in maximum security. *Law and Human Behavior, 25* (4), 393–408.

VI TREATMENTS, SECURITY AND PROGRAM PLANNING

24. Walsh, E., Gilvarry, C., Samele, C., Harvey, K., Manley, C., Tyrer, P. et al. (2001). Reducing violence in severe mental illness: Randomised controlled trial of intensive case management compared with standard care. *BMJ, 323,* 1–5.

25. Salekin, R.T. & Rogers, R. (2001). Treating patients found not guilty by reason of insanity. In J.B. Ashford, B.D. Sales & W.H. Reid (Eds.), *Treating Adult and Juvenile Offenders with Special Needs* (pp. 171–195). Washington, DC: American Psychological Association.

26. Rice, M.E., Harris, G.T. & Cormier, C. (1992). An evaluation of a maximum security therapeutic community for psychopaths and other mentally disordered offenders. *Law and Human Behavior, 16,* 399–412.

27. Salekin, R.T. (2002). Psychopathy and therapeutic pessimism: Clinical lore or clinical reality? *Clinical Psychology Review, 22* (1), 79–112.

28. Hodgins, S. & Müller-Isberner, R. (2004). Preventing crime by people with schizophrenic disorders: The role of psychiatric services. *British Journal of Psychiatry, 185,* 245–250.

29. Kennedy, H.G. (2002). Therapeutic uses of security: Mapping forensic mental health services by stratifying risk. *Advances in Psychiatric Treatment, 8,* 433–443.

30. Collins, M. & Davies, S. (2005). The security needs assessment profile: A multi-dimensional approach to measuring security needs. *International Journal of Forensic Mental Health, 4* (1), 39–52.

31. Farkas, M., Gagne, C., Anthony, W. & Chamberlin, J. (2005). Implementing recovery oriented evidence based programs: Identifying the critical dimensions. *Community Mental Health Journal, 41* (2), 141–158.